JET-STREAM METEOROLOGY

JET-STREAM

METEOROLOGY

ELMAR R. REITER

THE UNIVERSITY OF CHICAGO PRESS
CHICAGO AND LONDON

Translated from
METEOROLOGIE DER STRAHLSTRÖME (JET STREAMS)

Standard Book Number: 226-70967-1
Library of Congress Catalog Card Number: 63-13074

The University of Chicago Press, Chicago 60637
The University of Chicago Press, Ltd., London W.C.1

Published 1963. Second Impression 1969
Printed in Great Britain by William Clowes and Sons Ltd., London and Beccles

PREFACE TO THE GERMAN EDITION

Jet-Stream Meteorology is aimed to exceed the scope of the jet-stream monographs published so far. It constitutes a new approach which proceeds from one of the most conspicuous forms of atmospheric motion—the *jet stream*—and, incorporating the most recent results of aerology and dynamic meteorology, arrives at a modern view of synoptic meteorology and of climatology. In writing this book, I was able to make extensive use of experience gained from lecturing at the University of Chicago and the University of Innsbruck.

In order to understand the text, knowledge of a few basic principles of meteorology will be necessary. The larger part of the mathematical treatment of problems associated with jet streams has been put together in the first section. In the subsequent chapters reference is made frequently to this theoretical part of the book. Whenever vector notation has been applied, the symbols customary in English and American literature have been used: vectors are denoted by bold-face letters. Explanatory parts of the text and mathematical derivations which are not essential for the understanding of subsequent sections have been printed in smaller type. They may be disregarded by the reader who wants to gain an over-all view without spending too much time.

Of the 1,845 literature references, which however are not all directly associated with the jet stream, only about 3.3 per cent are from the period prior to 1932. Between 1932 and 1946 on the average seven papers have been quoted per year. Beginning in 1947 there is a steep increase in the number of pertinent publications, reaching a maximum of 186 in 1956. Thus, one might say the field of "jet-stream meteorology" starts its development in 1947.

Springer-Verlag in Vienna has accommodated many special requests. It is the merit of the publisher that the many diagrams were reproduced clearly, and with German notations.

My thanks are due to Dr. H. Hoinkes, Innsbruck, whose great interest in the progress of this book has been very encouraging to me. Essential parts of several chapters are based upon investigations of the layer of maximum wind, which I carried out under the sponsorship of the United States Navy and under the co-ordination of Dr. H. Riehl, Fort Collins. The micro-structure of jet streams, which is also treated in detail in this book, was studied under contract with the Department of Transportation, Bonn, Germany, and with the German Lufthansa Airline, Hamburg. For the realization of this contract I am indebted to the Geophysics Research Directorate, Air Force Cambridge Research Laboratories, Bedford, Massachusetts, and to Dr. H. Flohn, Offenbach, and Dr. H.-J. Tanck, Hamburg. Last but not least the contributions of Mr. I. Vergeiner and of Mrs. G. Reiter in typing the manuscript are gratefully acknowledged.

I would hardly have dared to write this book had it not been for the experience gained over three years at the University of Chicago. My deep appreciation therefore goes to my friend, Dr. H. Riehl, and to the other faculty members of the Department of Meteorology at the University of Chicago, and to the deceased Dr. C.-G. Rossby for the influence they had—directly or indirectly—upon the writing of this book.

Fort Collins, Colorado
Summer, 1961

E. R. R.

PREFACE TO THE ENGLISH EDITION

Slightly more than a year has passed since the German edition of this book became available on the market. Since then I have received enough encouragement from reviewers and friends to venture an English translation. In a field developing and expanding as rapidly as jet-stream meteorology, the question arises whether or not a translation still can be considered "up to date." After carefully screening the literature published since the German edition went to the press, I became convinced that no revision of the text was necessary as yet.

Although this book was originally conceived mainly as a hand- and reference book, it lends itself as a textbook for a one- to two-semester graduate course in general circulation or related subjects. The great number of references should make this book particularly suitable for a combined laboratory and instruction course.

The English edition owes its existence to a number of people whose direct or indirect contributions are greatly appreciated. My thanks are due to Dr. Horace R. Byers, Chicago, whose advice and encouragement were instrumental in the preparation of the translation. The University of Chicago Press did a commendable job in putting back into English whatever Springer Verlag had painstakingly labeled in German and successfully defended the English language against all attacks from my Germanisms, which I could not help scattering throughout the text when I dictated the translation. Mrs. Gabriella Reiter and Mrs. Hedy Sargent shared in the laborious task of transcribing the manuscript.

Last but not least, I wish to thank again Dr. Herbert Riehl, Head of the Department of Atmospheric Science, Colorado State University, for his moral support while the work of translation was in progress.

Fort Collins, Colorado E. R. R.
Spring, 1963

CONTENTS

LIST OF SYMBOLS AND ABBREVIATIONS

For several parameters the same symbols had to be used in order to conform to widely used standards in meteorological literature. Since the text contains appropriate remarks, there should be no confusion.

A	Area
	Stretching deformation $= \frac{\partial u}{\partial x} - \frac{\partial v}{\partial y}$
ASJ	Arctic (Antarctic) stratospheric jet stream
B	Shearing deformation $= \frac{\partial v}{\partial x} + \frac{\partial u}{\partial y}$
C	Circulation
	Speed of a moving co-ordinate system
	Speed of sound
	Wave speed
C_E	Linear speed of a point of the earth's surface at the equator
CAT	Clear-air turbulence
CAV	Constant absolute vorticity
c_p	Specific heat of dry air at constant pressure $= 1.0046 \times 10^7$ erg g^{-1} deg^{-1}
c_v	Specific heat of dry air at constant volume $= 0.717 \times 10^7$ erg g^{-1} deg^{-1}
D	(Three-dimensional) divergence $= \frac{\partial u}{\partial x} + \frac{\partial v}{\partial y} \left(+ \frac{\partial w}{\partial z} \right)$
	Altimeter correction
	Displacement of jet maxima
E	Slant range between radar instrument and balloon
e	North-south component of the Coriolis parameter $= 2\Omega \cos \varphi$
F	Frictional force
	Froude's number
f	Vertical component of the Coriolis parameter $= 2\Omega \sin \varphi$
G^*	Reciprocal value of Froude's number $= 1/F$
GCT	Universal time (Greenwich Central Time)
g	Acceleration of gravity $= 980.6$ cm sec^{-2}
gpf	Geopotential feet
gpm	Geopotential meters
H	Geodynamic unit of length $= g \cdot z/10$
	Height of an incompressible atmosphere
	Amount of heat
h	Balloon height
	Grid distance in difference equations (e.g., in Laplace operator)
I	Momentum of inertia
I_M	Meridional index
I_Z	Zonal index
IWM	Inversion wind maximum

K	Curvature $= 1/r$
	Correction factor for gradient wind computation
	Kinetic energy
K_S	Streamline curvature
K_T	Trajectory curvature
k	Coefficient of heat conduction
k_M	Exchange coefficient for momentum
k_T	Exchange coefficient for heat
L	Wave length of planetary waves
	Length of a flight route along the great circle
L_S	Stationary wave length
LLJ	Low-Level Jet Stream
LMW	Layer of maximum wind
l	Horizontal distance of the balloon from the radar site
	Wave number (Scorer Parameter)
M	Montgomery potential $= (c_p \cdot T + g \cdot z)_\Theta$
MCD	Meridional circulation diagram
m	Scale factor
mph	Miles per hour = 0.868391 knots = 0.44704 m/sec = 1.6093 km/h
N	Number of isobaric-isosteric solenoids
n	Co-ordinate normal to the direction of flow
P	Potential energy
PFJ	Polar-front jet stream
p	Pressure force
Q	Magnitude of absolute vorticity $= q + f$
q	Magnitude of relative vorticity
q_z	Vertical component of relative vorticity
R	Radius of earth, *ca.* 6370 km
	Gas constant $= 0.287 \times 10^7$ erg g^{-1} deg^{-1}
Re^*	Reynolds' number
R_i	Richardson's number
R_i^*	Geostrophic form of Richardson's number
Ro	Rossby number
Ro_T^*	Thermal Rossby number
Ro_j^*	Rossby number in the jet core
r	Radius of curvature of flow
S	Static stability $= \dfrac{g}{\Theta}\dfrac{\partial \Theta}{\partial z}$
	Flight route
S^*	Specific virtual temperature anomaly
STJ	Subtropical jet stream
s	Co-ordinate along the direction of a streamline
	Specific humidity
	Scale factor
T	Temperature
T^*	Virtual temperature
	Taylor's number
T_p	Temperature of the standard atmosphere
TAS	True air speed
TJ	Easterly tropical jet stream

t	Time co-ordinate
u	Velocity component in x-direction
u^*	Perturbation velocity component in x-direction
V	Total speed of flow
	Volume
$\mathbf{v}$	Velocity vector
v	Velocity component in y-direction
v^*	Perturbation velocity component in y-direction
$\mathbf{v}^*$	Vector of geostrophic departure
v_λ	Zonal component of velocity in polar co-ordinates
w	Vertical velocity component in z-direction
x	Horizontal co-ordinate (positive toward east)
y	Horizontal co-ordinate (positive toward north)
Z	Geopotential unit length $= g \cdot z/9.8$
z	Vertical co-ordinate
z_p	Height of an isobaric surface in a standard atmosphere
α	Specific volume $= 1/\rho$
β	Rossby parameter $= (2\Omega \cos \varphi)/R = \frac{\partial f}{\partial y}$
	Vertical stability $= \frac{1}{\Theta} \frac{\partial \Theta}{\partial z} = S/g$
Γ	Dry adiabatic vertical temperature lapse rate of an ascending air particle $= -\frac{dT}{dz}$
γ	Angle between stream function and streamline
	Angle between trough line and meridian
	Vertical temperature lapse rate in the ambient atmosphere $= -\frac{\partial T}{\partial z}$
δ	Thickness of the liquid layer in model experiments
ε	Inclination of a boundary surface (frontal zone)
	Coefficient of cubic expansion
ζ	Vertical departure of a streamline from the undisturbed level
η	Ratio of the radius of the polar cooling cylinder to the radius of the dishpan
Θ	Potential temperature
Θ_T	Angle of wind direction (dead reckoning)
ϑ	Angle in cylinder co-ordinates
κ	Poisson's constant $= \frac{c_p - c_v}{c_p} = 0.286$
λ	Geographic longitude
μ	Dynamic viscosity
ν	Kinematic viscosity
ν_c	Thermometric conductivity
ρ	Air density
σ	Standard deviation
τ	Shearing stress
τ_i	Period of inertia oscillations
Φ	Geopotential
φ	Geographic latitude
	Elevation angle of the balloon
ψ	Angle between direction of flow and x-direction (east)
	Co-angle of geographic latitude

$\mathbf{\Omega}$	Vector of the angular velocity of the earth $= 7.292116 \times 10^{-5}$ rad. sec^{-1}
ω	Vertical velocity component, with p as vertical co-ordinate $= dp/dt$
	Angular velocity of a rotational motion relative to the earth's surface
∇	Differential operator (Nabla) $= \frac{\partial}{\partial x} + \frac{\partial}{\partial y} \left(+ \frac{\partial}{\partial z} \right)$
∇_d	Difference operator
∇^2	Laplace operator $= \frac{\partial^2}{\partial x^2} + \frac{\partial^2}{\partial y^2}$

I

INTRODUCTION

1.1. HISTORY OF JET-STREAM RESEARCH

With the development of modern aerology and aviation technology during the years since World War II, the exploration of atmospheric jet streams has made such rapid progress that it has become difficult today to gain a comprehensive view of the literature in this field—in spite of the "Meteorological Abstracts and Bibliography" (American Meteorological Society, 1950–59), excellently edited, and in spite of various summarizing monographs and reviews (Berggren, Gibbs, and Newton, 1958; Bilancini, 1950; Bracelin, 1952; Due Rojo, 1954; Dursi and Edgardo, 1954; Dzhordzhio, 1956*a*, *b*; Georgii, 1960; Malone, 1951; Pogosian, 1959*a*; Reymann, 1960; Riehl, Alaka, *et al.*, 1953, 1954; Riehl, Badner, *et al.*, 1952; Rodriguez, 1955; U.S. Air Weather Service, 1952*a*; Van der Ham, 1954; Weber, 1959). The history of jet-stream research is closely tied to the history of the conquest of space, into which science advanced so successfully during the International Geophysical Year 1957/58.

Our views of the origin and structure of jet streams are developing rapidly, and every year new facts are added to the wealth of our knowledge. In order to circumscribe the field of "jet-stream meteorology," the following *provisional definition* of jet streams has been proposed by the Commission on Aerology of the World Meteorological Organization (WMO) in a resolution (Res. 25 [EC–IX]) according to which a jet stream

"is a strong narrow current, concentrated along a quasi-horizontal axis in the upper troposphere or in the stratosphere, characterized by strong vertical and lateral wind shears and featuring one or more velocity maxima."

The following characteristic criteria are recommended in addition:

"Normally a jet stream is thousands of kilometres in length, hundreds of kilometres in width and some kilometres in depth. The vertical shear of wind is of the order 5–10 m/sec per km and the lateral shear is of the order 5 m/sec per 100 km. An arbitrary lower limit of 30 m/sec is assigned to the speed of the wind along the axis of a jet stream" [Berggren, Gibbs, and Newton, 1958].

This should merely constitute a recommendation, and not a law binding for each individual case. Weather sequences which are characteristic for the presence of a jet stream may be observed with wind speeds below the threshold value given above.

Furthermore, it seems more suitable to choose as a *lower threshold value* for *horizontal shear* the order of magnitude of the *Coriolis parameter* at the given latitude. The WMO definition has been coined mainly under the impression of the relatively narrow polar-front jet (PFJ) of the temperate latitudes. Meanwhile, reference has been made on several occasions to the importance of "jet-stream-like" high-level wind systems in the tropics and subtropics which may have relatively small horizontal shears and nevertheless give rise to characteristic weather sequences. An extension of the definition, therefore, seems to be desirable. As will be shown in more detail in Chapter 1.236, the Coriolis parameter constitutes a critical magnitude of anticyclonic shear, which determines the dynamic stability of the current. It would, therefore, seem obvious to estimate the different jet streams by the parameter f, which, after all, is also given in geophysical model experiments.

An estimate of *maximum velocities* attainable in tropospheric jet streams leaves the possibility of winds up to 740 km/h for the terrestrial atmosphere (Lettau, 1948; see also Chapter 4). Actual measurements in the PFJ are near 500 km/h (Arakawa, 1959). In the ionosphere, however, drift velocities of 500 m/sec (1800 km/h) have been observed, but the reliability of these measurements may be questioned.

The phenomenon of jet streams is by no means confined to the upper troposphere or lower stratosphere. It rather seems to appear wherever large-scale motions exist under the influence of quasi-stationary fields of forces and of the deflecting force of the earth's rotation. Thus, for example, in several studies, the importance of *low-level jet streams* (LLJ) in weather development has been stressed. *Stratospheric* jet streams have been discovered over polar and equatorial regions, and some indications from ionospheric drift measurements suggest the existence of jet-stream-like processes even there. Ocean currents, as for instance the Gulf Stream and Kuroshio, also show characteristic jet-stream features. In laboratory experiments rotating water tanks have made it possible to generate circulations, which show such striking resemblance to large-scale air motions that it seems permissible to draw conclusions from the similarity of the processes about the mechanics driving these circulations. Since the Coriolis parameter is constant with latitude in these rotating vessels, it seems that the Rossby-parameter β is only of secondary importance in the formation of jet streams.

Jet-stream research represents a relatively young area of scientific endeavor in the field of meteorology. It obtained its first impulse toward the end of World War II, when American bomber squadrons over Japan and German long-range reconnaissance planes over the Mediterranean ran into headwinds which were commensurate to the airspeed (Riehl, Alaka, *et al.*, 1954). An intensive exploration of this phenomenon, which followed at the University of Chicago, mainly under Rossby (1949, Rossby and Willett, 1948; University of Chicago, 1947), led to the discovery of the "jet stream"—a belt of great wind speed at altitudes of approximately 10 km, which surrounds the whole hemisphere in wavy "meanders."

This discovery and the subsequent systematic exploration of jet streams mark a turning point in synoptic meteorology. Whereas particular attention was devoted between the two world wars to the study of air masses and their boundary surfaces, the fronts, now the dynamical aspects of the upper flow patterns have been brought into the foreground of discussion. Thus, the old Austrian and German schools of thought, which sought the causes of weather development in the upper troposphere and lower stratosphere and which had been supplanted temporarily by the Norwegian polar-front theory, received astounding corroboration by the rapidly evolving Chicago school (Baur, 1936; Brunt, 1930; Ertel, 1939; Frankfurt, 1932; Schmiedel, 1937; Sutcliffe, 1940).

Although the reasoning of this American meteorological school went in completely new directions, certain tendencies of the development could be recognized in much earlier works, whose authors, unfortunately, did not pursue the observed facts any further.

For instance, the cloud observations taken prior to World War I provided a basis for the study of upper atmospheric currents, and in conjunction with a consideration of the temperature distribution observers arrived at the conclusion that in high levels of the temperate latitudes there were westerlies with relatively great velocities (Anonymous, 1938; Bassus, 1906–7; Dietzius, 1917; Dines, 1911; Douglas, 1922, 1925; Hesselberg, 1913; Hildebrandsson, 1898; Roth and Palmer, 1911; Shaw, 1904; Shaw and Austin, 1928; Teisserenc de Bort, 1887; Walter, 1927; cf. also Bergeron, 1959).

Several observations of balloons (Dobson, 1920; Durward, 1925) and the study of cross sections, in the twenties, already confirmed the existence of locally confined high-velocity winds in the upper troposphere (Georgi, 1950; Shaw and Austin, 1928; Willett, 1944), which appeared to have a close connection with cyclones (Goldie, 1937, 1939; Horrocks, 1942; Palmén, 1935). The wind maximum near the tropopause was also revealed in statistical summaries of balloon ascents (Carmichael and Dymond, 1939; Durward, 1921, 1936, 1937; Heywood, 1933; Lunz, 1943; Ockenden, 1939; Zistler, 1928). Seilkopf (1939) was the first to introduce the term "Strahlströme" (i.e., "jet streams") for the high tropospheric wind maxima, while Scherhag (1936) gave early mention to the importance of ageostrophic flow and the divergence resulting from it in the "delta" region of a frontal zone. It was not until World War II, however, that systematic upper wind observations gave a new view of the life cycle of upper flow patterns. Last but not least, meteorology owes this rapid development to the progress made in radio and radar technology, which helped to explore the atmospheric range up to approximately 15 km by means of radio- and rawinsondes (see Reinhard, 1951). With the advent of the rocket and satellite era the last step in this development has not yet been reached by far.

1.2. THE WIND FIELD

1.21. Co-ordinate Systems

If not stated otherwise, our considerations in the following chapters will be based on a Cartesian co-ordinate system, with its x-axis toward the east, the y-axis toward the north, and the z-axis upward, perpendicular to level, equipotential surfaces. Furthermore, we will make use of a "natural" co-ordinate system, whose s-axis points into the direction of flow, and whose n-axis is perpendicular to the current, with its positive direction pointing toward the left of the current. More details on different co-ordinate systems and their transformations may be obtained from meteorological handbooks (Godske, *et al.*, 1957; Petterssen, 1956).

1.22. The Equations of Motion

1.221. The Complete Equation of Motion

In a relative co-ordinate system which is fixed to the rotating earth, the equation of motion reads as follows:

$$\dot{\mathbf{v}} = -\alpha\nabla p - 2\mathbf{\Omega}\times\mathbf{v} - \nabla\Phi + \alpha\mathbf{F}. \qquad 1.221\ (1)$$

In this equation $\mathbf{v}$ stands for the wind vector, $\dot{\mathbf{v}}=d\mathbf{v}/dt$, $\alpha=1/\rho$ is the specific volume, $\mathbf{\Omega}$ the vector of the earth's rotation, Φ the geopotential, $\mathbf{F}$ the force of internal friction.

From reasons of mass continuity we obtain the "continuity equation"

$$\nabla\cdot(\rho\mathbf{v})=\rho\nabla\cdot\mathbf{v}+\mathbf{v}\cdot\nabla\rho=-\partial\rho/\partial t. \qquad 1.221\ (2)$$

1.222. The Geostrophic Wind

Approximately 800 m above ground the force of friction in the atmosphere normally can be neglected (Petterssen, 1956). If, furthermore, one assumes the motion to be free of acceleration, one obtains the geostrophic wind equation

$$0=-\alpha\nabla p-2\mathbf{\Omega}\times\mathbf{v}-\nabla\Phi. \qquad 1.222\ (1)$$

$\nabla\Phi$ has only one component in the vertical direction:

$$\partial\Phi/\partial z=g. \qquad 1.222\ (2)$$

g is the acceleration of gravity. Thus, 1.222 (1) also contains the *hydrostatic equation* implicitly, if one is allowed to neglect vertical components of motion:

$$g=-\alpha\ \partial p/\partial z. \qquad 1.222\ (3)$$

The "geopotential unit length" Z with the dimensions of specific work (i.e., work per unit mass), which is widely used in meteorology, is obtained from 1.222 (2) by assuming g to be 9.80. Therefore

$$Z=g\cdot z/9.8 \qquad 1.222\ (4)$$

Z is given in "geopotential meters," z in "metrical meters."

For all locations for which $g=9.80\ \mathrm{m\cdot sec^{-2}}$, $Z=z$. In all other locations on the earth's surface for meteorological purposes the differences between Z and z are negligible. The two units of measurement, therefore, may be assumed *numerically* equal.

In older textbooks one still finds the "geodynamic meter," introduced by V. Bjerknes (Koschmieder, 1951),

$$H=g\cdot z/10. \qquad 1.222\ (5)$$

Thus, the metrical meter z is shorter than the "dynamical" meter H by a factor of approximately 0.98. It has the same dimensions of a specific work as Z. Because of this numerical difference between metrical and dynamical meter, today preference is given internationally to the "geopotential" unit length (IMO Resolution No. 78, 1947; Saucier, 1955).

With the aid of the hydrostatic equation ∇z may be introduced into Eq. 1.222 (1). One obtains the geostrophic wind equation on an isobaric surface

$$\mathbf{v}_g=-(\alpha/f)\nabla p\times\mathbf{k}=-(g/f)\nabla z\times\mathbf{k}, \qquad 1.222\ (6)$$

where $f=2\Omega\sin\varphi$ is the Coriolis parameter, $\mathbf{k}$ stands for a unit vector parallel to the vertical co-ordinate, and $\mathbf{v}_g$ is the vector of the horizontal geostrophic wind.

The component equations corresponding to above expression are

$$\begin{aligned} u_g&=-(\alpha/f)\ \partial p/\partial y=-(g/f)\ \partial z/\partial y,\\ v_g&=(\alpha/f)\ \partial p/\partial x=(g/f)\ \partial z/\partial x. \end{aligned} \qquad 1.222\ (7)$$

1.223. The Gradient Wind

In case of a curved trajectory the motion is not any longer free from acceleration. Under horizontal and isobaric conditions of flow the gradient wind equation is valid in its following form:

$$-(V^2/r)\mathbf{r} = -\alpha(\partial p/\partial r)\mathbf{r} \pm f\mathbf{v}\times\mathbf{k}. \qquad 1.223\ (1)$$

The positive sign stands for cyclonic, the negative sign for anticyclonic curvature of flow. The term on the left-hand side of the equation gives the *centripetal acceleration*, which acts in the opposite direction of the unit vector $\mathbf{r}$. The first term on the right-hand side of Eq. 1.223 (1) symbolizes the gradient force—opposite to $\mathbf{r}$ in the cyclonic case ($\partial p/\partial r > 0$), parallel to $\mathbf{r}$ in the anticyclonic case ($\partial p/\partial r < 0$). $f\mathbf{v}\times\mathbf{k}$ is the Coriolis force. The roots of this quadratic equation are

$$V = \mp rf/2 \pm \sqrt{(r^2f^2/4 + r\alpha\cdot\partial p/\partial r)}. \qquad 1.223\ (2)$$

The upper sign stands for cyclonic, the lower sign for anticyclonic curvature.

With cyclonic trajectory curvature the argument of the square root is positive under all circumstances, while in anticyclonic cases the limiting condition of the argument becoming zero renders a *minimum radius of curvature*, which is given by

$$r = -(4\alpha/f^2)\cdot\partial p/\partial r. \qquad 1.223\ (3)$$

The maximum velocity, which is still able to follow a given curvature of isobars, may be expressed by

$$V_{max} = rf/2. \qquad 1.223\ (4)$$

Substituting the gradient force in Eq. 1.223 (1) by the geostrophic wind, which would prevail under straight-flow conditions with the same pressure gradient, one arrives at

$$V = (rf/2)\left[\mp 1 \pm \sqrt{1 + (4V_g/rf)}\right], \qquad 1.223\ (5)$$

and the maximum velocity of the gradient wind is given by

$$V_{max} = 2V_g. \qquad 1.223\ (6)$$

The sign convention in Eq. 1.223 (5) remains the same as in Eq. 1.223 (2). The gradient wind, therefore, is a function of the geostrophic wind, of the radius of curvature, and of geographic latitude, and may be obtained from nomographs which account for these variables.

1.224. Ageostrophic Component

Substituting the gradient force in Eq. 1.221 (1) by the geostrophic wind, as we have done above, and, furthermore, neglecting the force of friction and the acceleration of gravity (assuming horizontal flow), we obtain

$$\dot{\mathbf{v}} = f\mathbf{v}\times\mathbf{k} - f\mathbf{v}_g\times\mathbf{k} = f(\mathbf{v}-\mathbf{v}_g)\times\mathbf{k}. \qquad 1.224\ (1)$$

Defining the *geostrophic departure* as

$$\mathbf{v}^* = \mathbf{v} - \mathbf{v}_g, \qquad 1.224\ (2)$$

it arises from Eq. 1.224 (1), that the vector of acceleration is directed normal to the vector of geostrophic departure. The consequence of this is, for example, that a subgeostrophic current adapts itself to the conditions of the pressure field by departing toward lower pressures (i.e., toward lower geopotential heights on a constant-pressure surface). The flowing air particles are being accelerated by this "falling" motion. With supergeostrophic flow the contrary is the case—a departure toward higher pressure is observed. Ageostrophic components of motion are of particular importance in the entrainment and delta regions of a frontal zone or of a jet maximum.

1.225. Flow on an Isentropic Surface

From Poisson's equation which defines the potential temperature Θ

$$\Theta = T(1000/p)^{\kappa} \qquad 1.225\ (1)$$

(p given in millibars, $\kappa = (c_p - c_v)/c_p$ standing for Poisson's constant, where c_p and c_v are the specific heats at constant pressure and constant volume, respectively), after logarithmic differentiation one arrives for isentropic processes ($d\Theta = 0$) at the expression

$$(dp)_\Theta = (p \cdot c_p / T \cdot R) \cdot (dT)_\Theta = (c_p/\alpha) \cdot (dT)_\Theta. \qquad 1.225\ (2)$$

R is the specific gas constant for dry air. The index Θ indicates that the differentiation has to be performed on an isentropic surface.

On the other hand, we have

$$(dp)_\Theta = (\partial p/\partial x)(dx)_\Theta + (\partial p/\partial z)(dz)_\Theta. \qquad 1.225\ (3)$$

where z_Θ is the height of the isentropic surface. Combining Eq. 1.225 (2) and 1.225 (3) one obtains

$$-\alpha\, \partial p/\partial x = -c_p (dT/dx)_\Theta + \alpha(\partial p/\partial z) \cdot (dz/dx)_\Theta.$$

By substituting from the hydrostatic equation, 1.222 (3), we arrive at

$$-\alpha\, \partial p/\partial x = -(d/dx)(c_p T + gz)_\Theta. \qquad 1.225\ (4)$$

The expression $(c_p T + gz)_\Theta = M$ is called Montgomery potential (Montgomery, 1937). The equation of motion for adiabatic flow, which *eo ipso* has no vertical component through the isentropic surface, reads therefore as follows:

$$\dot{\mathbf{v}} = -\nabla M + f\mathbf{v} \times \mathbf{k}. \qquad 1.225\ (5)$$

1.23. Derived Quantities

1.231. Vorticity

From the velocity field we may derive several quantities, which today are of increasing importance, not only in theoretical meteorology, but also in synoptic meteorology. Above all there is the vorticity, which is defined as the "rotor of velocity."

$$\mathbf{q} = \nabla \times \mathbf{v}. \qquad 1.231\ (1)$$

For horizontal flow it is only the vertical component of 1.231 (1) which is of interest. In a Cartesian co-ordinate system it reads:

$$q_z = \partial v/\partial x - \partial u/\partial y. \qquad 1.231\ (2)$$

In a "natural" co-ordinate system the expression for the vertical component of the vorticity is

$$q_z = V/r_s - \partial V/\partial n. \qquad 1.231\ (3)$$

r_s is the radius of curvature of a *streamline*, n the direction normal to it, positive toward the left of the direction of flow. The first term on the right-hand side of 1.231 (3) is the *curvature vorticity*, the second term is called *shearing vorticity*.

The vertical vorticity component may also be obtained by the following operation:

$$q_z = \nabla \cdot (\mathbf{v} \times \mathbf{k}). \qquad 1.231\ (4)$$

The vector $\mathbf{v} \times \mathbf{k}$ has the components $(v, -u)$. If one calculates the divergence of this vector, one obtains the component q_z.

The average vorticity of an area element may furthermore be described as the circulation per unit area:

$$q_z = \Delta C/\Delta A = \frac{1}{A} \oint v_t \cdot dl. \qquad 1.231\ (5)$$

v_t is the component of the wind vector tangential to the line element dl, C is the circulation, and A the area of integration.

From the above equation one may see that cyclonic vorticity has a positive sign and anticyclonic vorticity a negative sign. Furthermore, q is equal to twice the angular velocity of the motion on a curved trajectory relative to the rotating earth and we may therefore call it *relative* vorticity. Since the vorticity is a vector, it may be added vectorially to the vorticity of the earth's rotation, $2\mathbf{\Omega}$, and one thereby obtains the *absolute vorticity* relative to an inertia system:

$$\mathbf{Q} = \mathbf{q} + 2\mathbf{\Omega} \qquad 1.231\ (6)$$

The vertical component is

$$Q_z = q_z + f. \qquad 1.231\ (7)$$

If one substitutes the geostrophic component of flow [Eq. 1.222 (7)] into 1.231 (2), one obtains the *geostrophic vorticity*

$$q_{zg} = (\partial/\partial x)\left(\frac{g}{f}\,\partial z/\partial x\right) + (\partial/\partial y)\left(\frac{g}{f}\,\partial z/\partial y\right)$$
$$= (g/f)(\partial^2 z/\partial x^2 + \partial^2 z/\partial y^2) + (1/f)(u \cdot \partial f/\partial y - v \cdot \partial f/\partial x).$$

For x and y being co-ordinates of a Cartesian co-ordinate system as described in Chapter 1.21, we may write $\partial f/\partial x = 0$ and $\partial f/\partial y = \beta$. The Rossby parameter β is defined as $\beta = (2\Omega \cos \varphi)/R$ (R = earth's radius). Thus we have

$$q_{zg} = (g/f)\nabla^2 z + u(\beta/f). \qquad 1.231\ (8)$$

∇^2 is the Laplace operator

$$\nabla^2 = \partial^2/\partial x^2 + \partial^2/\partial y^2. \qquad 1.231\ (9)$$

β/f has the order of magnitude 10^{-9}cm^{-1} and $u < 10^2$ m/sec^{-1}. The second term on the right-hand side of 1.231 (8) may therefore be neglected against the first term. One then obtains an approximation for the geostrophic vorticity:

$$Q_{zg}=(g/f)\nabla^2 z+f. \qquad 1.231\ (10)$$

By applying the operator $\nabla\times$ to the gradient wind equation, 1.223 (1), Di Benedetto (1953) obtains the following expression for the *gradient wind vorticity*:

$$\nabla\times\mathbf{v}=\frac{\mathbf{v}\times\nabla f}{f\pm 2\dfrac{V}{r}}\pm\frac{V}{r^2}\,\frac{\mathbf{v}\times\nabla r}{\left(f\pm 2\dfrac{V}{r}\right)}\pm\frac{\mathbf{v}\times\nabla\dfrac{G}{\rho}}{r\left(f\pm 2\dfrac{V}{r}\right)\left(f\pm\dfrac{V}{r}\right)}+\frac{\nabla\times\left(\dfrac{\mathbf{G}}{\rho}\times\mathbf{k}\right)}{f\pm\dfrac{V}{r}}. \qquad 1.231\ (11)$$

In this equation $\mathbf{v}$ stands for the gradient wind vector, r is the radius of curvature of the trajectory, and $\mathbf{G}$ is the horizontal pressure gradient (its scalar magnitude being G). The first term on the right-hand side of this equation gives the effect of the geographic latitude, the second term describes the influence of curvature of the trajectory. The third term decomposes into two parts whose numerators are

$$\mathbf{v}\times\nabla\frac{G}{\rho}=\frac{1}{\rho}\,\mathbf{v}\times\nabla G+G\left(\mathbf{v}\times\nabla\frac{1}{\rho}\right). \qquad 1.231\ (12)$$

The first term of this expression describes the confluence or diffluence of the gradient flow, i.e., the *streamline convergence*. The second term in 1.231 (12) contains the influence of temperature advection. The last term in 1.231 (11) finally stands for the influence of divergence and of isobaric-isosteric solenoids. From an investigation of Di Benedetto we may conclude that in cyclones all terms have the same order of magnitude; in anticyclones, however, the diffluence surpasses all other quantities by one order of magnitude.

1.232. Divergence

The divergence of a field of flow is defined as

$$D=\nabla\cdot\mathbf{v} \qquad 1.232\ (1)$$

or in its component form,

$$D=\partial u/\partial x+\partial v/\partial y+\partial w/\partial z. \qquad 1.232\ (2)$$

An expression for the divergence which is analogous to 1.231 (3) may be obtained for a natural co-ordinate system in the following way:

$$D=\partial V/\partial s+V\cdot\partial\psi/\partial n, \qquad 1.232\ (3)$$

whereby the first term on the right-hand side of the equation is the so-called *velocity divergence*, i.e., the change of velocity along a streamline, while the second term stands for the *streamline divergence*, i.e., it describes the fanning-out of the streamlines. ψ is the wind direction defined as the angle between wind vector and reference streamline of the co-ordinate system.

The horizontal divergence may also be described as the expansion per unit time of a unit area floating in a current, and bounded by the same liquid particles all the time:

$$D_h=(1/A)\,dA/dt \qquad 1.232\ (4)$$

respectively,

$$D_h=(1/A)\oint v_n\,dl. \qquad 1.232\ (5)$$

dl is a line element of a closed flat curve, v_n the component of the wind vector normal to this line element.

1.233. The Vorticity Theorem

The connection between divergence and vorticity may be seen from the vorticity theorem. For a surface of arbitrary orientation we have

$$C_a = AQ_n \qquad 1.233\ (1)$$

[see 1.231 (5)], wherein C_a is the absolute circulation of the area, and Q_n is the component of the absolute vorticity in the direction of the positive normal to this area. For cyclonic rotation the positive normal points upward into the direction of a right-handed screw. Differentiating 1.233 (1) after time, we obtain

$$\dot{C}_a = Q_n\dot{A} + A\dot{Q}_n. \qquad 1.233\ (2)$$

The circulation acceleration of the motion in an inertia system, $\dot{C}_a$, is, however, equal to the number N of the isobaric-isosteric solenoids contained inside the curve (Bjerknes, 1898; Petterssen, 1956). From this one obtains, together with 1.232 (4),

$$\dot{Q}_n = -Q_n D + N/A. \qquad 1.233\ (3)$$

Since $N = \oint \alpha\, \Delta p \cdot d\mathbf{l}$, wherein $\Delta p \cdot d\mathbf{l}$ is the pressure change along the line element $d\mathbf{l}$ of a closed curve, one obtains for an isobaric surface $N=0$, because $\Delta p = 0$. The same holds for an *isentropic* surface.

From Eq. 1.225 (1), which defines potential temperature, one obtains for isentropic motions ($d\Theta = 0$)

$$(dT)_\Theta = \kappa(T/p)\, dp = (\kappa\alpha)\, dp/R. \qquad 1.233\ (4)$$

By integration one finds

$$(\kappa/R) \oint \alpha\, dp = \oint dT. \qquad 1.233\ (5)$$

Since, however, the integral of a complete differential over a closed curve is equal to zero, 1.233 (5) renders $N=0$.

Thereby for *isobaric* and *isentropic* surfaces the vorticity equation is reduced to

$$\dot{Q} = \partial Q/\partial t + u(\partial Q/\partial x) + v(\partial Q/\partial y) = \partial Q/\partial t + \mathbf{v}\cdot\nabla Q = -QD = -Q\nabla\cdot\mathbf{v}. \qquad 1.233\ (6)$$

Q is the component of absolute vorticity normal to the respective surface (the index n has been omitted for simplicity's sake) and $\mathbf{v}$ is the "quasi-horizontal" wind vector on the respective surface.

If one allows for vertical motions penetrating the respective surface, i.e., $\mathbf{v}$ is not horizontal, one arrives at

$$\partial Q/\partial t + u(\partial Q/\partial x) + v(\partial Q/\partial y) + w(\partial Q/\partial z) = -DQ + q_x(\partial w/\partial x) + q_y(\partial w/\partial y). \qquad 1.233\ (7)$$

w stands for the vertical velocity through the surface under consideration. $w(\partial Q/\partial z)$ is the vertical vorticity advection and $[q_x(\partial w/\partial x) + q_y(\partial w/\partial y)]$ gives the transformation of the horizontal vorticity component into vertical vorticity, which is accomplished by horizontal gradients of the vertical velocity. This means that originally horizontal "vortex tubes" are tilted into a slant position. If we assume adiabatic motion on an isentropic surface, w vanishes and 1.233 (7) is reduced to the form of 1.233 (6).

1.234. Conservation of Absolute Vorticity

With the aid of 1.232 (4), 1.233 (6) can also be brought into the form

$$\dot{Q}/Q = -\dot{A}/A \tag{1.234 (1)}$$

By integration one obtains

$$A \cdot Q = A_0 \cdot Q_0 = \text{const.} \tag{1.234 (2)}$$

This means that the absolute vorticity cannot change its sign. For $A \to \infty$ it may only assume the limiting value of zero. Observations show that $Q=0$ is limited to the anticyclonic side of strongly developed jet streams. Everywhere else Q is positive. For "quasi-horizontal" motions which are free of divergence ($D=0$):

$$\dot{Q} = \partial Q/\partial t + \mathbf{v} \cdot \nabla Q = 0, \tag{1.234 (3)}$$

The absolute vorticity therefore is a *conservative quantity* for *divergence-free* motions. The local vorticity changes then are completely balanced by the vorticity advection $\mathbf{v} \cdot \nabla Q$. Vorticity will neither be generated nor destroyed. Motions completely free of divergence are hardly ever present in the atmosphere, when flow patterns are considered on level surfaces. A level of non-divergence is found in the troposphere on the average near 600 mb; this non-divergent surface, however, is generally tilted against level surfaces (Cressman, 1953). Landers (1955*b*, 1956) finds no level of non-divergence, but only a level—or under certain circumstances several levels—of minimum divergence, on which 1.234 (3) is valid only approximately. In first approximation one may neglect the divergence on the 500-mb surface and 1.234 (3) may be applied to prognostic purposes on this constant pressure surface.

For adiabatic flow on an isentropic surface 1.233 (6) may be transformed into

$$\partial Q/\partial t = -\mathbf{v} \cdot \nabla Q - Q \nabla \cdot \mathbf{v} = -\nabla \cdot (Q\mathbf{v}), \tag{1.234 (4)}$$

The divergence term in this equation has two-dimensional character. Comparing this with the equation of continuity

$$\partial \rho/\partial t = -\nabla \cdot (\rho \mathbf{v}) \tag{1.234 (5)}$$

one may interpret 1.234 (4) in the following way: the local change of vorticity per unit time and unit area on an isentropic surface is equal to the vorticity transport through the boundaries of this unit area. For frictionless adiabatic flow the isentropic vorticity is a conservative quantity, too, i.e., there are no vorticity sources or sinks. Individual air particles may, however, change their vorticity, as long as the *velocity divergence* $\nabla \cdot \mathbf{v}$ is different from zero and the form of 1.234 (3) is valid.

With the aid of 1.234 (3) one may construct CAV (constant absolute vorticity) trajectories. If the flow were indeed non-divergent, the air masses would have to follow these trajectories. CAV trajectories, therefore, are a useful tool in forecasting, because at the 500-mb level, which has only weak divergence, they may serve as an indicator of the displacement of planetary waves: If the CAV trajectories, for instance, prescribe larger wave lengths than are actually present, one may count on an eastward propagation of the long wave downstream of the point of observation. The appearance of weak divergence fields may, however, be detrimental to the quality of CAV forecasts (Hess, 1953).

In calculating CAV trajectories it is practical to choose initial conditions as simple as possible, as they prevail, for example, at the inflection point of the jet-stream axis, although a solution of the equation is also possible for more complicated flow conditions (Martin, 1955). For the inflection point we have $r=\infty$ and $\partial V/\partial n=0$, and therefore according to Eq. 1.231 (3) $Q=f_0$, where the subscript 0 should indicate conditions at this point. Because of 1.234 (3) we have

$$f_0=K_s V+f. \qquad 1.234\ (6)$$

$K_s=1/r_s$ is the curvature of the streamline in the jet axis. If the air travels much more rapidly than the wave disturbance, which is usually the case (see Chapter 4.221), one may with some approximation equalize the streamline curvature K_s and the trajectory curvature K_T. Thus we obtain from 1.234 (6):

$$K_T V=f_0-f=-\beta y. \qquad 1.234\ (7)$$

The Rossby parameter β may be taken approximately as a constant. If one further assumes with Rossby (see Rossby and Starr, 1945) that the wind speed V remains constant along the trajectory, i.e., the motion is approximately geostrophic, and making use of the equation of curvature

$$|K|=y''/(\sqrt{(1+y'^2)^3}) \qquad 1.234\ (8)$$

one obtains the differential equation for a set of CAV trajectories

$$\partial^2 y/\partial x^2=-(\beta y/V)[1+(\partial y/\partial x)^2]^{3/2}, \qquad 1.234\ (9)$$

A simplified solution of 1.234 (9) is obtained for small wave amplitudes in the following form:

$$y=A_T \sin\,(x\sqrt{(\beta/V)}). \qquad 1.234\ (10)$$

because $(\partial y/\partial x)^2 \ll 1$. The wave length of the trajectories

$$L_T=2\pi\sqrt{(V/\beta)} \qquad 1.234\ (11)$$

is identical with the wave length of stationary Rossby waves (see Chapter 3.251).

By differentiating 1.234 (10) at the inflection point ($x=0$) we obtain

$$(dy/dx)_0=A_T\sqrt{(\beta/V)}=\tan\psi_0.$$

ψ_0 is the angle between the streamline at the inflection point and the direction east. It follows that

$$A_T=\tan\psi_0\sqrt{(V/\beta)}. \qquad 1.234\ (12)$$

For larger amplitudes which do not permit one to neglect $(dy/dx)^2$ in 1.234 (9), Platzman (1947) gives the following solution:

$$y^2=(2V/\beta)(\cos\psi-\cos\psi_0). \qquad 1.234\ (13)$$

The condition $\psi=0$ for $y=A_T$ leads to

$$A_T=\sqrt{(2V/\beta)(1-\cos\psi_0)}. \qquad 1.234\ (14)$$

ψ_0, V and β may be obtained from a 500-mb topography. Considering the earth's curvature, wave lengths and amplitudes are smaller in the northern arcs of the waves than in the southern arcs. Their values may be taken from tables (Bellamy, 1945*a*; Fultz, 1945; Petterssen, 1956). Methods of constructing CAV trajectories graphically are in existence, too (Maine and Pierrehumbert, 1955).

1.235. Potential Vorticity

For adiabatic motion between two isentropic surfaces which are separated by the distance Δp, the expression

$$D_h = -(1/\Delta p)\cdot d(\Delta p)/dt. \qquad 1.235\ (1)$$

is valid. The horizontal divergence of flow is compensated by vertical stretching or shrinking of the isentropic slab by reasons of continuity. 1.235 (1), therefore, corresponds to 1.232 (4). Substituting 1.235 (1) into 1.233 (6), one obtains

$$dQ/dt - (Q/\Delta p)\cdot d(\Delta p)/dt = 0$$

or

$$(d/dt)(Q/\Delta p) = 0. \qquad 1.235\ (2)$$

The quantity $Q/\Delta p$ which has been called "potential vorticity" by Rossby is therefore a conservative quantity for adiabatic motion and for an individual parcel of air (Rossby, 1940).

Following a derivation by Ertel (1942), one obtains an expression for the potential vorticity which is particularly suitable for the study of motions on an isentropic surface. It reads as follows:

$$\frac{d}{dt}(\alpha\nabla\Theta\cdot\mathbf{Q}) = 0. \qquad 1.235\ (3)$$

Substituting from the hydrostatic equation and omitting g, which is a constant, one obtains for the vertical component

$$\frac{d}{dt}\left(\frac{\partial\Theta}{\partial p}\cdot Q_z\right) = 0. \qquad 1.235\ (4)$$

$-\partial\Theta/\partial p$ stands for the vertical stability in the respective isentropic surface or in the isentropic layer, which the flow is following (Staley, 1957, 1960). Ertel showed that instead of Q other conservative airmass properties also obey this conservation tendency, e.g., the polytropic temperature with polytropic changes of state, and the specific humidity for air motions without precipitation.

A simple derivation of this law is obtained if one transforms the continuity equation, 1.221 (2), in the following manner:

$$\nabla\cdot\mathbf{v} = -\frac{1}{\rho}\frac{\partial\rho}{\partial t} - \frac{1}{\rho}\mathbf{v}\cdot\nabla\rho = -\frac{1}{\rho}\frac{d\rho}{dt}. \qquad 1.235\ (5)$$

For the transformation of the motion from a horizontal into an isentropic surface we may write the following equation:

$$\frac{d\mathbf{v}}{dt} = \frac{\partial\mathbf{v}}{\partial t} + u\left(\frac{\partial\mathbf{v}}{\partial x}\right)_\Theta + v\left(\frac{\partial\mathbf{v}}{\partial y}\right)_\Theta + \frac{d\Theta}{dt}\left(\frac{\partial\mathbf{v}}{\partial\Theta}\right)$$

The transformation of divergence renders

$$\nabla \cdot \mathbf{v} = (\nabla \cdot \mathbf{v})_\Theta + \nabla \Theta \cdot \partial \mathbf{v} / \partial \Theta. \qquad 1.235\ (6)$$

By substituting into 1.235 (5) and by introducing the hydrostatic equation, one obtains

$$\nabla \cdot \mathbf{v}_\Theta = \frac{d}{dt} \ln \frac{\partial \Theta}{\partial p} - \frac{\partial}{\partial \Theta}\left(\frac{d\Theta}{dt}\right). \qquad 1.235\ (7)$$

For adiabatic motion the last term in this equation vanishes and by using the vorticity equation, 1.233 (6) and from 1.235 (7), one arrives at

$$\frac{d}{dt} \ln Q_z + \frac{d}{dt} \ln \frac{\partial \Theta}{\partial p} = 0$$

or

$$\frac{d}{dt}\left(Q_z \cdot \frac{\partial \Theta}{\partial p}\right) = 0,$$

which corresponds to 1.235 (4) (see Kleinschmidt, 1951). In order to make positive *absolute* vorticity agree in sign with positive *potential* vorticity, usually the latter is written $-Q_z(\partial\Theta/\partial p)$ (Staley, 1960).

1.236. Hydrodynamic Instability and Conservation of Angular Momentum

If the original state of an air particle embedded in the geostrophic basic current has been stable, the particle will describe oscillations about this state as soon as it is pushed out of its equilibrium position. Under the assumption that all motions will be adiabatic, oscillations will be possible in the vertical which are dependent on the static stability of the atmosphere. This kind of oscillations shall not be described any further. If the air particle is given a push parallel to the isentropic surface, however, normal to the direction of flow, it will undergo a change of velocity. Assuming that this impulse is directed toward the high-pressure side of the current, i.e., in the direction of ∇M, the particle is going to reduce its velocity according to Eq. 1.225 (5). Thereby, however, its motion will be subgeostrophic relative to the surrounding pressure field. Since the gradient force now is larger than the Coriolis force, an acceleration toward the low pressure side will become active, and it will drive the particle toward its original position, and even beyond this. The particle now describes oscillations around this original position which are superimposed upon the geostrophic basic current and which have a period $T = 2\pi/f = \frac{1}{2}$ pendulum day (Haltiner and Martin, 1957). The basic current in this case is hydrodynamically stable.

There may, however, be a case in which the air particle advancing toward the high-pressure side is faced with such a rapidly decreasing gradient force that even though the particle is experiencing a deceleration, the Coriolis force may still continue to be larger than the gradient force. In this case the current is hydrodynamically unstable, because a single small impulse would be enough to let the particle deviate any distance from its original position (Arakawa, 1941, 1942, 1953*a*; Kleinschmidt, 1941*a*, *b*; Meisinger, 1958; Solberg, 1939; Van Mieghem, 1944*a*, *b*, 1945, 1946, 1948, 1951).

For simplicity's sake, we will assume that the basic current is zonal, so that $\partial p/\partial x = 0$; also $\partial f/\partial t = \partial f/\partial x = 0$. The acceleration which the particle receives in the y

direction may be calculated from Eq. 1.225 (5). By differentiating this equation one obtains

$$d^2v/dt^2 = -d/dt\,(\partial M/\partial y) - d/dt\,(f\cdot u). \qquad 1.236\ (1)$$

It is assumed that the particle will adapt itself immediately to the pressure in its new surroundings. Since the motion is adiabatic, we have

$$d/dt\,(\partial M/\partial y) = v\,\partial/\partial y\,(\partial M/\partial y) = v(\partial^2 M/\partial y^2). \qquad 1.236\ (2)$$

Substitution into 1.236 (1) renders

$$d^2v/dt^2 = -v(\partial^2 M/\partial y^2) - u\cdot v(\partial f/\partial y) - f(du/dt).$$

For du/dt one may substitute from Eq. 1.225 (5). One has, however, to take into account that $\partial p/\partial x = 0$. Therefore $du/dt = fv$. Introducing finally instead of $\partial M/\partial y$ the quantity $(-fu)$, because of the geostrophic flow conditions, one obtains

$$d^2v/dt^2 = v\,\partial(fu)/\partial y - uv(\partial f/\partial y) - f^2 v$$

or

$$d^2v/dt^2 = vf(\partial u/\partial y - f). \qquad 1.236\ (3)$$

On the cyclonic side of a zonal jet stream the right-hand side of this equation always is negative. The integral of this equation constitutes a harmonic oscillation which is superimposed upon the basic current.

On the anticyclonic side, however, the limiting condition for indifferent hydrodynamic stability is given by

$$-\partial u/\partial y + f = 0. \qquad 1.236\ (4)$$

The harmonic Eq. 1.236 (3) has no periodic solution for this limiting case, and for all cases in which $\partial u/\partial y > f$. The left-hand side of 1.236 (4) stands for the absolute vorticity of the given zonal current. If the absolute vorticity becomes zero, as is the case on the anticyclonic side of strongly developed jet streams, the current is in the state of indifferent hydrodynamic stability. With negative absolute vorticity, any small initial disturbance should rapidly gain in amplitude.

With the aid of vector analysis the considerations entering 1.236 (1 to 4) may be adapted to horizontal adiabatic flow of arbitrary orientation. Equation 1.236 (1), then, assumes the form of

$$d^2\mathbf{v}/dt^2 = -(d/dt)\,\nabla M + (d/dt)(f\mathbf{v}\times\mathbf{k}). \qquad 1.236\ (5)$$

In vectorial form condition 1.236 (2) reads

$$d/dt\,\nabla M = (\mathbf{v}\cdot\nabla)\nabla M. \qquad 1.236\ (6)$$

By substituting one obtains

$$d^2\mathbf{v}/dt^2 = -(\mathbf{v}\cdot\nabla)\nabla M + (\mathbf{v}\cdot\nabla f)\mathbf{v}\times\mathbf{k} + f\,d\mathbf{v}/dt\times\mathbf{k}.$$

According to Eq. 1.231 (8) the geostrophic vorticity is

$$fq_{zg} = \nabla^2 M - [v(\partial f/\partial x) - u(\partial f/\partial y)].$$

This expression is introduced with some approximation into above equation. First, however, the term $f(d\mathbf{v}/dt\times\mathbf{k})$ needs more consideration: The retardation or acceleration $d\mathbf{v}/dt\times\mathbf{k}$

which an air particle experiences parallel to the direction of the basic current is equal to $(-f\mathbf{v})$ according to Eq. 1.225 (5), because there is no pressure gradient active in this direction due to the geostrophic condition ($\nabla M \times \mathbf{k} = 0$). The acceleration, therefore, is of a direction opposite to the geostrophic basic current. We have

$$f(d\mathbf{v}/dt \times \mathbf{k}) = -f^2\mathbf{v}.$$

Therefore the harmonic equation in the general form for any direction of flow reads

$$d^2\mathbf{v}/dt^2 = -\mathbf{v}fq_{zg} - \mathbf{v}f^2 = -\mathbf{v}f(q_{zg} + f). \qquad 1.236\ (7)$$

The condition of indifferent stability for the case of an adiabatic geostrophic current of arbitrary direction, therefore, is

$$q_{zg} + f = Q_{zg} = 0. \qquad 1.236\ (8)$$

This condition, strictly speaking, is valid only for motions along an isentropic surface. One may, however, apply it with good approximation to isobaric surfaces, if their inclination is not too different from the inclination of surfaces of constant potential temperature, and if the area for which the absolute vorticity is zero is of sufficient extent.

The angular momentum $\mathbf{G}_a$ which an air particle has in relation to an inertia system is given by the equation

$$\mathbf{G}_a = \mathbf{r}_a \times \mathbf{v}_a = \mathbf{r}_a \times (d\mathbf{r}/dt) = r_a^2\omega_a. \qquad 1.236\ (9)$$

$\mathbf{r}_a$ is the radius of curvature of the absolute trajectory; ω_a is the angular velocity of the absolute rotation. Again, the current is assumed to be adiabatic and geostrophic, and the absolute vorticity will be zero in the area under consideration when measured on an isentropic surface. The differentiation $(\partial/\partial s)$ characterizes an arbitrary direction on this isentropic surface. Thus

$$\partial\mathbf{G}_a/\partial s = 2r_a(\partial r_a/\partial s)\omega_a + r_a^2(\partial\omega_a/\partial s). \qquad 1.236\ (10)$$

From the relation $\mathbf{Q} = 2\omega_a$, the absolute vorticity may be introduced into this equation and one obtains

$$\partial\mathbf{G}_a/\partial s = (r_a\, \partial r_a/\partial s)\mathbf{Q} + (r_a^2/2)\, \partial\mathbf{Q}/\partial s. \qquad 1.236\ (11)$$

A particle which moves under conservation of angular momentum has to obey the condition

$$\frac{d\mathbf{G}_a}{dt} = \frac{\partial\mathbf{G}_a}{\partial t} + V\frac{\partial\mathbf{G}_a}{\partial s} = 0. \qquad 1.236\ (12)$$

Considering 1.236 (11), this renders

$$r_a\frac{\partial r_a}{\partial t}\mathbf{Q} + \frac{r_a^2}{2}\frac{\partial\mathbf{Q}}{\partial t} + Vr_a\frac{\partial r_a}{\partial s}\mathbf{Q} + V\frac{r_a^2}{2}\frac{\partial\mathbf{Q}}{\partial s} = 0. \qquad 1.236\ (13)$$

Under adiabatic conditions of flow, 1.233 (6) is valid on an isentropic surface and we obtain

$$Q\left(r_a\frac{\partial r_a}{\partial t} + Vr_a\frac{\partial r_a}{\partial s}\right) + \frac{r_a^2}{2}\frac{dQ}{dt} = 0.$$

This equation is valid under the assumptions made above, if $Q = 0$ in a larger area. In this case also $\partial Q/\partial t = 0$ because of 1.234 (4), since $\partial Q/\partial s = 0$. Therefore also $dQ/dt = 0$.

These conditions are usually met over several degrees of latitude on the anticyclonic side of strongly developed jet streams.

On an isentropic surface, for which an adiabatic, geostrophic motion has the absolute vorticity $Q_z = 0$, *all air particles have the same constant angular momentum* (Kleinschmidt, 1941*a*).

An air particle which moves under conservation of absolute angular momentum from its original position into a different geographic latitude, must obtain an additional angular velocity relative to the earth's surface, which we will symbolize by ω. According to 1.236 (9) we have

$$\Omega(R\cos\varphi_1)^2 = (\Omega+\omega)(R\cos\varphi_2)^2.$$

and since the zonal velocity is $v_\lambda = R\cos\varphi\cdot\omega$, the expression for the additional zonal velocity component which occurs in the geographic latitude φ_2, reads

$$\Delta v_\lambda = \frac{R\Omega(\cos^2\varphi_1 - \cos^2\varphi_2)}{\cos\varphi_2}. \qquad 1.236\ (14)$$

For a displacement from 30° N to 40° N the increase of velocity would therefore be 99 m/sec, that is approximately 192 knots. Only relatively small meridional displacement of air masses under conservation of absolute angular momentum is necessary, in order to obtain velocities as they are observed in jet streams (see Chapter 4.121).

For infinitesimally small displacements we can write 1.236 (14) in the form

$$\partial v_\lambda = -\frac{R\Omega\ \partial(\cos^2\varphi)}{\cos\varphi} \qquad 1.236\ (15)$$

or

$$\frac{1}{R}\frac{\partial v_\lambda}{\partial\varphi} = 2\Omega\sin\varphi. \qquad 1.236\ (16)$$

This, however, again conforms to the condition $Q = 0$ for a zonal current.

1.237. Deformation

The deformation of the field of flow normally is considered only in a "quasi-horizontal" plane (isobaric or level surfaces, etc.). There are two kinds of deformation, the stretching deformation,

$$A = \partial u/\partial x - \partial v/\partial y \qquad 1.237\ (1)$$

and the shearing deformation,

$$B = \partial v/\partial x + \partial u/\partial y. \qquad 1.237\ (2)$$

By a suitable choice of a co-ordinate system (letting x and y point in the direction of the main axes of deformation) the resultant from stretching and shearing deformation may be found directly. Otherwise, for an arbitrary orientation of the co-ordinates, we have

$$\operatorname{def}\mathbf{v} = (A^2 + B^2)^{1/2}. \qquad 1.237\ (3)$$

Thus, the two kinds of deformation are added vectorially.

The deformation of the wind field is of importance during frontogenetic and frontolytic processes. In conjunction with jet streams, fields of deformation have rarely been analyzed (Petterssen, 1953*b*). These few analyses show, however, that in an apparently uniform flow pattern, as it may appear in the delta region of some jet maxima, the deformation may at times reach considerable magnitude and is by no means confined to the singular or neutral points of the field of flow (Saucier, 1955).

1.238. The Decomposition of the Wind Field

If the two components u and v of a horizontal current are expanded into a MacLaurin series, one obtains for the vicinity of the point 0:

$$\begin{aligned} u &= u_0 + (\partial u/\partial x)_0 x + (\partial u/\partial y)_0 y + \cdots \\ v &= v_0 + (\partial v/\partial x)_0 x + (\partial v/\partial y)_0 y + \cdots \end{aligned} \qquad 1.238\ (1)$$

One may neglect terms of higher order under the assumption that the velocity field in the vicinity of the point under consideration is approximated to a sufficient degree of accuracy by a linear velocity gradient. By simple transformation we obtain

$$\begin{aligned} u = u_0 &+ [\tfrac{1}{2}(\partial u/\partial x + \partial v/\partial y)_0 + \tfrac{1}{2}(\partial u/\partial x - \partial v/\partial y)_0]x \\ &+ [\tfrac{1}{2}(\partial u/\partial y - \partial v/\partial x)_0 + \tfrac{1}{2}(\partial u/\partial y + \partial v/\partial x)_0]y \end{aligned}$$

$$\begin{aligned} v = v_0 &+ [\tfrac{1}{2}(\partial v/\partial x + \partial u/\partial y)_0 + \tfrac{1}{2}(\partial v/\partial x - \partial u/\partial y)_0]x \\ &+ [\tfrac{1}{2}(\partial v/\partial y - \partial u/\partial x)_0 + \tfrac{1}{2}(\partial v/\partial y + \partial u/\partial x)_0]y. \end{aligned}$$

Substituting into this expression from Eqs. 1.231 (2), 1.232 (2), 1.237 (1), and 1.237 (2) one arrives at

$$\begin{aligned} u &= u_0 + \tfrac{1}{2}(D_h + A)x + \tfrac{1}{2}(B - q_z)y \\ v &= v_0 + \tfrac{1}{2}(D_h - A)y + \tfrac{1}{2}(B + q_z)x. \end{aligned} \qquad 1.238\ (2)$$

Thereby, the velocity field in the vicinity of a certain point is composed of a pure translatory motion (u_0, v_0), of divergence (D_h), of vorticity (q_z), of stretching deformation (A) and of shearing deformation (B).

1.239. The Relation between Deformation, Vorticity, and Divergence

Starting from the equations of motion for *horizontal* flow,

$$\begin{aligned} \partial u/\partial t + u(\partial u/\partial x) + v(\partial u/\partial y) &= -\partial \Phi/\partial x + fv \\ \partial v/\partial t + u(\partial v/\partial x) + v(\partial v/\partial y) &= -\partial \Phi/\partial y - fu, \end{aligned} \qquad 1.239\ (1)$$

where Φ is given by 1.222 (2), and by considering 1.231 (2), 1.232 (2), 1.237 (1), and 1.237 (2) and the fact that in a Cartesian co-ordinate system of the kind described in Chapter 1.21, $\partial f/\partial x = 0$ and $\partial f/\partial y = \beta$, one obtains

$$\dot{A} + AD = -\partial^2\Phi/\partial x^2 + \partial^2\Phi/\partial y^2 + fB + u\beta \qquad 1.239\ (2)$$

$$\dot{B} + BD = -2\partial^2\Phi/\partial x\,\partial y - fA + v\beta \qquad 1.239\ (3)$$

$$\dot{Q} + QD = 0 \qquad 1.239\ (4)$$

$$\dot{D} + \tfrac{1}{2}DD = -\nabla^2\Phi + fq + \tfrac{1}{2}(q^2 - A^2 - B^2) - u\beta. \qquad 1.239\ (5)$$

(The subscripts h and z in divergence and vorticity have been omitted for simplicity's sake.)

According to Petterssen (1953*b*) 1.239 (2 and 3) stand for a deformation theorem,

1.239 (4) is the vorticity theorem which has already been derived in Chapter 1.233 for adiabatic, frictionless motion, and 1.239 (5) corresponds to a divergence theorem.

Since $Q=q+f$, the latter equation may also be transformed into

$$Q = (2\nabla^2\Phi+f^2+A^2+B^2+2\dot{D}+D^2+2u\beta)^{1/2}. \qquad 1.239\ (6)$$

Neglecting in this equation $2\dot{D}$, D^2 and $2u\beta$, since these quantities are much smaller, at least on the 500-mb surface, than any of the other terms contained within parentheses, we arrive at

$$Q=(2\nabla^2\Phi+f^2+A^2+B^2)^{1/2}. \qquad 1.239\ (7)$$

The usual approximation for the geostrophic vorticity [see 1.231 (10)],

$$q_g=\frac{1}{f}\nabla^2\Phi \qquad 1.239\ (8)$$

is, therefore, valid only if condition

$$q^2=A^2+B^2 \qquad 1.239\ (9)$$

is met, as may be seen from 1.239 (5), allowing for the neglect of terms mentioned above.

In those cases for which $q^2 \gg A^2+B^2$, one obtains for the absolute vorticity

$$Q=(2\nabla^2\Phi+f^2)^{1/2}. \qquad 1.239\ (10)$$

A comparison with 1.239 (8) renders

$$q+f=(2fq_g+f^2)^{1/2}$$

and from this

$$q_g/q=1+q/2f. \qquad 1.239\ (11)$$

From this equation one may see that in the cyclonic case the geostrophic vorticity is too large when compared with the actually observed vorticity; in the anticyclonic case it is too small. The deviations may be appreciable at times, the magnitude of the discrepancy, which has been introduced by the geostrophic assumption, being determined by the deformation of the wind field, according to 1.239 (9 and 5) (see Vitek, 1955, and Chapter 3.247).

2

METHODS OF UPPER-LEVEL WIND MEASUREMENT AND THEIR SOURCES OF ERROR

The analysis of atmospheric jet streams and the study of their detailed structure is by necessity linked to the accuracy of the upper-level wind measurements. It therefore seems proper to anticipate a few critical remarks on the different methods of measurement, without entering into instrumental details (see Kleinschmidt, 1935, and Middleton, 1943).

According to the methodology we may discern between *direct* and *indirect* upper-level wind measurements, depending on whether the wind vector is calculated from its immediate action upon freely movable bodies or from quantities which stand in a functional relationship with the wind vector.

2.1. DIRECT UPPER-LEVEL WIND MEASUREMENT

2.11. Pilot Balloons

2.111. General Remarks

Principle.—The ascent curve of a balloon filled with gas of a certain buoyancy is measured by visual tracking, and, from its displacement, wind direction and wind speed are calculated as functions of height.

History.—P. Schreiber may be considered the founder of pilot balloon tracking. In 1874 he measured for the first time with instruments the track of a free balloon. By 1892 a goldbeater-skin balloon by H. Hermite and G. Besançon reached a height of 7600 m and shortly afterward a somewhat larger balloon of the same kind, filled with coal-gas, reached the astounding altitude of 16,000 m. In 1901 R. Assmann for the first time used closed rubber balloons for ascent purposes (Kleinschmidt, 1935).

Balloons.—Balloons of different material and of different size, depending on their purposes, today are at the disposal of meteorological offices. In order to facilitate tracking against the background of the sky, white balloons are used with cloudless weather, red balloons with partly clouded, and dark blue or black balloons with overcast skies. During night ascents, lanterns with candles or electric battery lamps (Middleton, 1943) or red bengal lights (Iacobi, 1929) are fastened to the balloon.

The choice of material and size of balloons is primarily determined by the altitude of the ascent planned (Rand, 1951). For pilot ascents rubber balloons are available on the one hand, which are commonly used at night, because natural rubber's elastic properties rapidly deteriorate under the influence of direct solar radiation. Balloons made from neoprene, on the other hand, are better suited for daytime ascents, because they tend to become brittle, loosing their elastic properties in low temperatures. A relationship between the bursting height and the tropopause level, which has been found for rubber balloons (Schulze, 1950), lets us surmise, that the ozone content of the atmosphere, as well as the low temperature, may have an influence upon the elastic behavior of the balloons at great heights. The difference in the elastic qualities of balloons of different size makes them preferable for day or night use (U.S. Air Force, 1948). So, e.g., 1400-g balloons are better suited to day, while 500-g balloons on the average reach higher altitudes at night.

Radiosonde balloons which have been prepared in warm diesel oil, reach greater heights in the cold polar night. For ascents into a warm stratosphere, dipping baths of boiling water or a 12- to 24-hour storage time in a moist-climate chamber at temperatures of about $+55°$ C proved an advantage (Flowers, 1959).

Theodolites.—Descriptions of various registering and non-registering models and their accuracies may be obtained from handbooks pertaining to this field (Kleinschmidt, 1935; Middleton, 1943; Tanatar, 1948).

2.112. Sources of Error

The main disadvantage of the pilot balloon method lies in the fact that upper-level wind measurements are limited to fair-weather days. By this, on the one hand, the upper-level wind statistic is biased: Because of the *fair-weather bias*, preference is given to an anticyclonic streamline pattern in a time-averaged wind distribution. Since jet-stream situations frequently are connected with divergence in the upper troposphere and with bad weather, the pilot balloon is an inadequate means for synoptic studies. The decisive progress in the exploration of jet streams, therefore, runs parallel with the development of radio theodolites.

Furthermore, with strong upper-level winds the distance between observation point and balloon increases rapidly, so that visual tracking becomes difficult and the ascent must be terminated before the balloon reaches its bursting height.

Besides this decisive drawback, which is counterbalanced only by the inexpensiveness of the method, there are still other subjective and systematic errors present:

Subjective Errors:

1. The inaccuracies in tracking simulate variations in the horizontal component of the wind velocity.
2. Errors in the visual reading of angles also result in an apparent "turbulence" of upper-level winds.
3. Graphical evaluation (Kleinschmidt, 1935; Middleton, 1943) of high-level winds from the angle measurements introduces inaccuracies.

For all practical purposes, however, these errors usually are small (Väisälä, 1928).

Systematic Errors:

1. By reading azimuth and elevation angles at certain time intervals one merely obtains *mean values* of the wind velocity over vertical layers of certain thickness, and not *instantaneous values*.
2. In the so-called "single tracking," which uses only *one* theodolite for measuring the flight, we have to assume the ascent rate of the balloon to be constant. This introduces the most serious source of error in upper-level wind measurements made by this system.

The total buoyant force G of a balloon is equal to the weight of displaced air, and therefore is proportional to $\rho \cdot V$ ($\rho =$ air density, $V =$ volume of the balloon). Neglecting the small excess pressure inside the balloon, V becomes proportional to $R \cdot T/p$ and $\rho = p/R \cdot T$. Therefore, the total buoyant force G of the balloon is constant at all heights.

From B (meaning the weight of the balloon including the weight of the filling gas and of the ballast), we obtain for the free lift

$$A = G - B = \text{const.} \qquad 2.112\ (1)$$

After a rubber balloon is released, it at first rises with a velocity which is somewhat too large. Only after about 14 minutes on the average, the equilibrium between free lift A and air resistance W is reached (Meurers, 1952). From wind-tunnel measurements on spheres, one could determine, that

$$W = b_1 \cdot \rho \cdot v^2 \cdot F = A = \text{const.} \qquad 2.112\ (2)$$

(v = rate of ascent of the balloon, F = largest horizontal balloon diameter). Assuming a constant value for b_1 to begin with, the ratio between the values near the ground (indicated by the subscript 0) and at higher levels becomes

$$(v : v_0)^2 = (\rho_0 \cdot F_0) : (\rho \cdot F) = \rho_0 V_0^{2/3} : \rho V^{2/3} = (\rho_0 : \rho)^{1/3}$$

or

$$v : v_0 = \sqrt[6]{\rho_0 : \rho}\,. \qquad 2.112\ (3)$$

For temperate latitudes the following average values are valid

Height in km	0	2	4	6	8	10
$(\rho_0 : \rho)^{1/6}$	1.00	1.04	1.08	1.11	1.15	1.19.

The small theoretical increase of ascent rate with height is counterbalanced in practice in a hardly controllable manner by diffusion losses of filling gas, so that the assumption of a *constant* ascent rate seems to be justified approximately. This does not hold, however, for the traversing of strongly turbulent layers (Longley, 1956). Since F is proportional to $V^{2/3}$, and V according to 2.112 (1) is again proportional to $A + B$, it follows

$$A = b_2 \cdot v^2 (A + B)^{2/3}. \qquad 2.112\ (4)$$

The theoretical ascent rate, thereby, is

$$v = (b \cdot A^{1/2})/(A + B)^{1/3}\ \text{m/min}. \qquad 2.112\ (5)$$

Empirical laws prefer an exponent x in the numerator and an exponent y in the denominator (Kleinschmidt, 1935). In practice, the factor b is *not* constant, but dependent on the state of turbulence and on Reynolds' number.

$$R = v \cdot d \cdot \rho/\eta \qquad 2.112\ (6)$$

(d = diameter of the sphere, η = coefficient of friction of the air) (Imai, 1954; Sinha, 1959).

Only for magnitudes of Reynolds' number which are below a certain threshold value, it is necessary to take the variations of R into account. The expressions obtained in this way for the rate of ascent may be brought into good agreement with the empirical expressions (Sinha, 1958).

Since the specific drag of air on a sphere, which determines the rate of ascent after the above derivation, is a function of Reynolds' number and temperature, there may be appreciable variations in the vertical velocity of balloons, depending on the seasonally different structure of the atmosphere (Erikson, 1954; see also Prudhomme, 1949). There is a rather striking minimum of ascent rates near about 13 km height, which seems to be especially well established during summer. Double tracking of balloons executed at the observatory at Lindenberg, show somewhat different yearly variations for the troposphere; however, they, too, reveal a stratospheric minimum (Reger, 1938).

Erikson (1954) also found that marked differences may occur in different air masses. In *cold air* the balloon rises *faster* than in warm air up to approximately 8 gkm (geopotential kilometers) on the average. Above this level conditions are reversed.

Above all, the rate of ascent is influenced by vertical motions of the air, which may have different causes. Over level terrain vertical currents due to thermal convection or to roughness of the surface may be noticed up to 2.5 km. If vertical currents are strong enough above this level, to make balloon tracking drastically inaccurate, there will usually be cloud formation. Over hilly terrain, along coast lines, etc., standing lee waves in the air flow may at times disturb the rate of ascent of balloons rather markedly (Morasca, 1953).

To estimate the order of magnitude of the vertical wind component we need "double tracking" by two theodolites. Even these, however, give reliable values only in the lowest layers of the atmosphere, where reading and instrumental accuracy is still less influential.

Statistical investigations showed that the departures of the rates of ascent from those given in Hergesell-Tetens' tables are least for rubber balloons with ascent velocities $v = 180$ m/min. Larger ascent rates show tendencies for negative departures from the theoretical values; smaller ascent rates follow a reversed tendency. In the weather services ascent rates of about 1000 ft/min or approximately 300 to 350 m/min are customary.

Atmospheric turbulence may introduce strong irregularities in the rate of ascent of balloons not only through the action of vertical components of flow (Voss, 1950), which are present in the turbulence elements, but also by possible swinging motions, which reduce the ascent velocity (Raethjen, 1925). In a turbulent current itself the rate of ascent is slightly above normal, however (Wenger, 1917). Comparisons between single and double trackings showed that by assuming a constant rate of ascent, the calculation of wind directions is not subject to large errors. Measurement of wind speeds, however, may be considerably faulty, because the vertical components of the turbulent air motion are interpreted as variations in the horizontal component of wind speed (Mildner, 1933). It is easy to understand that these errors are more prominent with decreasing elevation angles.

The apparent position A' of the balloon and its apparent height h' are measured from a point T by the elevation angle φ, under the assumption of a *constant* rate of ascent. Its actual position, however, will be displaced by Δh and, therefore, will be in A, due to a non-constant ascent rate. We shall assume that the wind vector is parallel to the line between theodolite and balloon and that the error Δh was incurred only during the last minute interval of the ascent. Then Δl gives a measure of the error which has been made in the calculation of the average wind velocity for this minute interval.

$$\Delta l = \Delta h \cdot \operatorname{ctg} \varphi. \qquad 2.112\ (7)$$

From this equation it follows that the error increases rapidly with decreasing elevation angle and with a constant inaccuracy in the determination of h.

Errors in measuring the elevation angle ($\Delta\varphi$) also appear as variations in wind velocity:

$$\Delta l = h/(A \cdot \sin^2 \varphi + \tfrac{1}{2} \sin 2\varphi). \qquad 2.112\ (8)$$

In this equation $A = \text{ctg}\,\Delta\varphi$, and—not counting subjective errors in adjustment and reading—it depends on the resolution of the instrument in measuring elevation angles.

With strong upper winds, i.e., under jet-stream conditions, the elevation angle rapidly assumes small values, so that Δl according to 2.112 (7 and 8) may become very large with relatively small inaccuracies in the determination of elevation and of elevation angle (see also Rouaud, 1957). Part of the oscillations in vertical wind profiles so frequently registered—especially at or above jet-stream level—are due not so much to the magnitude of actually present turbulence but rather to the inaccuracies described above (for more details see Chapter 2.12).

Other reasons for irregularities in the ascent rate or deviations from normal values determined theoretically are: different surface characteristics of the balloons, deviations from a spherical shape, and rise in temperature of the filling gas due to the sun's radiation.

Considering all these sources of error in upper-level wind measurements in the jet-stream region, one has to take their accuracies with a grain of salt. At levels of 5 km, Middleton (1943) gives an error limit of about $\pm 4°$ and ± 2 m/sec (4 knots), while comparisons of ascent pairs over India revealed errors up to 20° and 5 knots (Ramakrishnan, Parthasarathi, and Aphale, 1957). For strong upper winds, as they occur in jet streams, the inaccuracies in wind direction may rather be sought among the values given by Middleton. The values for wind velocity, however, may be completely useless in unfavorable cases (Reiter, 1957*c*, 1958*c*).

2.12. Rawinsondes

2.121. General Remarks

Principle.—The course of a gas-filled balloon flight is followed by *radio tracking*. From its change of position the horizontal component of wind speed may be calculated as a function of altitude. Upper-level wind measurements of this kind can also be conducted with overcast skies.

History.—Kleinschmidt mentions in his *Handbook of Meteorological Instruments* (1935) as a possibility of upper-level wind measurements the radio tracking of pilot balloons equipped with a transmitter. However, at this time the method of short-wave direction finding "was generally regarded with great caution." A start toward perfecting the technique has been made with the development of *radar* (*ra*dio *d*irection *a*nd *r*ange finding) during World War II.

Balloons (see also Chapter 2.111).—Since especially with small elevation angles the errors in measurement may become large and the wind speeds computed from these elevation angles will be unreliable, balloons with a rapid ascent rate (1000 ft/min or 300 m/min) are preferred.

Principles of tracking.—We may distinguish between two basic methods:

1. *Radio direction finding* with the aid of a radio theodolite: The balloon carries a radio transmitter (as it is simultaneously used to transmit the radiosonde signals). The angle of

incidence of the radio signals is measured by a radio theodolite, and from that the position of the balloon is calculated similar to what is being done with pilot balloons (Middleton, 1943).

2. *Radio range finding* with the aid of radar: angles and the slant range to the balloon are measured simultaneously. Instead of a transmitter the balloon carries a *reflector*, which sends back the electro-magnetic waves coming from the radar set. From the time lapse between emission of the impulses and reception of the echo the distance of the balloon may be calculated.

For reflectors, one uses either a system of dipoles (usually measuring half the wave length used in the signal), which are mounted perpendicular to each other; or reflecting surfaces (tetrahedron, octahedron) of metal foil; or a hemispheric cover of metal-sprayed cloth extending over the upper half of the balloon. The quality of the reflector depends on: its size—large reflectors are used for great distances; the number of its corners and their position relative to the incoming beam (the beam is best reflected parallel to itself if it occupies the same angle with all planes which surround one corner); the accuracy of fitting the ninety-degree corners and the evenness of the reflecting surfaces; the electromagnetic albedo and the conductivity of the reflector material. Weight and air drag of the reflector should be at a minimum in order not to impair the desired rapid ascent rate of the balloon (Decca, 1957; Raftery and Plagge, 1957).

Method 1 has the advantage of less expensive equipment, while method 2 claims the advantage of greater accuracy, which is of decisive importance, especially at low elevation angles, i.e., with strong upper-level winds, as they occur in jet-stream situations.

Depending on the instrumentation, the following methods of balloon tracking are being used:

1. Assumption of a constant ascent rate of the balloon; measurement of the azimuth angles at two or more stations.

2. Calculation of the height of the balloon from the radiosonde data (pressure, temperature) reported at the same time, and from simultaneous measurements of the azimuth angles at two or more stations (British system: three stations, at the corners of a triangle with sides approximately 30 to 50 km long).

3. Assumption of a constant ascent rate of the balloon; measurement of azimuth and elevation angles at one station (U.S. radio theodolite SCR-658, operating on a frequency of 403 megacycles; it is tuned in on the "target" by hand [Kirkman and Le Bedda, 1948]). With a radiosonde run carried through at the same time, the wind evaluation may be based upon the height values obtained from the sonde. A more recent development is represented in the U.S. radio theodolite AN/GMD-1, which is equipped with an automatic tracking device that eliminates the subjective errors occurring with manual tuning. This theodolite operates at rather high frequencies (1680 mc), which increases its accuracy, especially at low elevation angles (Ference, 1951). The position of the antenna of this theodolite is automatically registered in digital form, for azimuth and elevation angles, using specified time intervals. Thus, erroneous readings are eliminated, too. The Finnish radio theodolite is based on the same principle of measuring azimuth and elevation angles with known balloon heights: two pairs of vertical antennas at the ends of the 125-m diagonals of a square measure the phase difference in the incoming signal. From this, azimuth and elevation angles may be calculated to 0.1 degree accuracy (Väisälä, 1953). The evaluation is performed graphically (Väisälä and Wilska, 1957).

4. Measurement of azimuth and elevation angle and of slant distance of the balloon (American SCR-584 radar, British GL-3 radar, Decca WF-1 [Decca, 1957]). An extremely sharp and well-defined beam is emitted at 3000 to 10,000 mc and bounced back by the

reflector. The advantage of this system becomes apparent at low elevation angles. Approximate values of wind speed may be given directly from the slant range of the balloon (Ervet, 1958). According to investigations by Robuchon and Ervet (1958), the quality of wind vectors calculated from the radial and normal component is superior to the one of vectors customarily determined from the projection of the balloon track onto a horizontal plane.

2.122. Sources of Error

For radio theodolites, which depend on the accuracy of the measurement of elevation angles, the same considerations are valid as have been made in Chapter 2.112 for pilot balloons. Experience shows that errors introduced by the operating crew are the most decisive ones (Kirkman and Le Bedda, 1948). Errors may amount to 0.3 and 0.4 in azimuth and elevation angles and may be caused on the one hand by inaccurate tuning on the oscilloscope and on the other hand by delayed observance of the sound signal at each minute interval, when angles have to be read. Instruments like the GMD-1 avoid these subjective errors caused by manual operation.

At elevation angles below 14° reflections of the signal on the earth's surface make themselves felt (cf. Anderson, 1958). They show a phase difference against the directly received signal. The error curves are by no means constant, but they vary with time, location, and azimuth angle (Kirkman and Le Bedda, 1948).

Gradual changes in the rate of ascent, as compared with the values calculated theoretically (see Chapter 2.112), may be taken into account by corrections if the pressure-height curves from radiosonde observations are available (Hering, 1955). Short-time fluctuations in the rate of ascent, caused by turbulence, are, however, difficult to deal with. Under such circumstances, radar has the advantage that it does not depend on any assumptions, but measures directly the slant range of the balloon.

A handicap in the detailed measurement of the vertical wind profiles which, unfortunately, is necessary, lies in the averaging process over discrete time intervals. This, of course, is particularly a drawback with fast-rising balloons (Shaffer, 1957). Because of the smoothing introduced by this averaging, nothing definite can as yet be said about the sharpness of crests of the vertical wind profiles at the level of maximum wind.

In view of the fluctuations, which adhere to the wind values measured at low elevation angles, such a smoothing process is definitely necessary, however. In the American weather service the position of the balloon is determined at intervals of one minute. Up to a height of 40,000 ft (12 km) overlapping two-minute averages are calculated; up to 70,000 ft (21 km) five-minute intervals, up to 100,000 ft (30 km) ten-minute intervals are averaged (Ference, 1951). Nevertheless, under unfavorable conditions large fluctuations may still be present, which, at times, may amount to 90 per cent and more of the "mean," smoothed wind speed at the particular level (Reiter, 1957*c*, 1958*c*), and which affect especially the vertical wind shears (Salmela and Sissenwine, 1959).

Figure 2.122.1 shows, as an example, the original calculation of the ascent at Washington, D.C., on 14 March, 1954, 2100 GCT (Greenwich Civil Time) (light line). The heavy line represents a graphically smoothed wind profile, which has been obtained by equalizing areas with positive and negative deviation of wind speed from the average value. It is shown in Figure 2.122.2 that the fluctuations in the measured wind speeds are not present in reality but are caused by errors in measurement and evaluation. The frequencies of the semi-periods of the speed oscillations are presented for different time intervals, in minutes, of the balloon run. The calculations

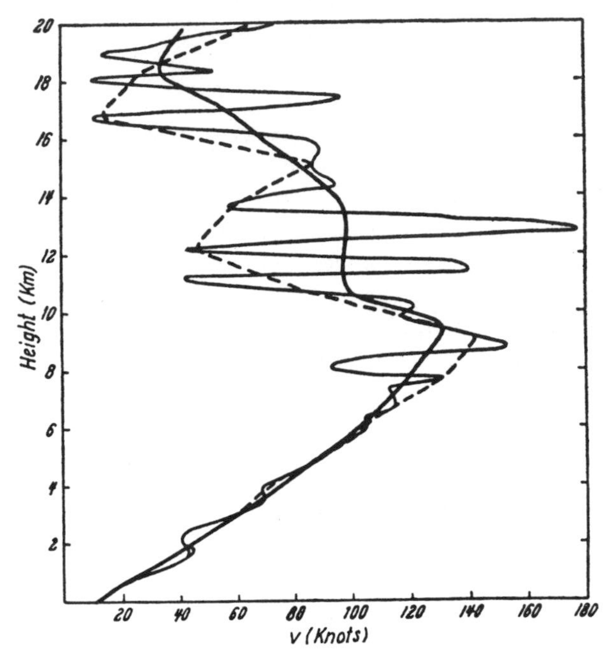

Fig. 2.122.1.—Rawin measurements, Washington, D.C., 14 March, 1954, 2100 GCT. Thin solid line, wind profile obtained from original rawin ascent; heavy solid line, smoothed profile; dashed line, wind profile obtained from teletype message.

are based on wind profiles which have been observed over Washington, D.C., at a height of 8 to 20 km, and between 11 and 15 March, 1954. The "semi-periods" are defined as the time intervals between velocity maximum and adjacent minimum in the vertical wind profile. This diagram shows that oscillations of 1 minute (interval of measurement) and 2 minutes (interval of averaging) are most frequent, while beyond that the per cent frequency of occurrence of oscillations rapidly declines.

The methodology of the measurement and evaluation processes also reveals itself clearly in an inspection of the frequency distribution of the amplitudes of oscillations with different periods. Figure 2.122.3 is based upon the same observation material as the preceding diagram. It shows that fluctuations with the semi-periods of 1 and 2 minutes have their maximum frequency at small amplitudes, as should be expected. In consequence of the smoothing process the fluctuations with one-minute periodicity completely disappear beyond approximately 35 knots. The variations with two-minute periodicity, however, are observed up to the largest amplitudes of more than 80 knots, as are the variations with all other periods. Wind-speed fluctuations at jet-stream level, therefore, do not become more plausible the larger their amplitudes. Riehl (1954*a*) instigated an experiment with the Norfolk, Virginia, rawinsonde in the course of which the balloon positions were calculated every 6 seconds. It appeared that the fluctuations, especially in elevation angles, were of the same order of magnitude as with the customary time intervals of one minute. This has to be regarded as evidence that the large disturbances in vertical wind profiles, as they appear for example, in Figure 2.122.1, may not be attributed to atmospheric turbulence, but are

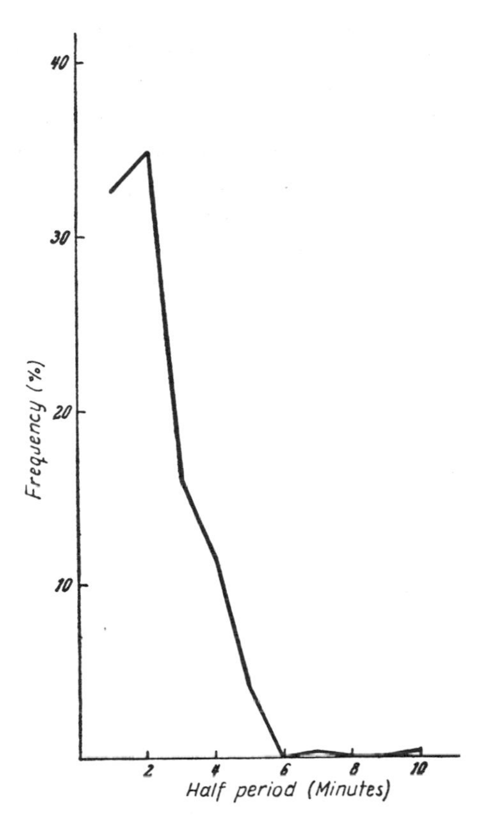

FIG. 2.122.2.—Per cent frequency distribution of half-periods (in minutes) of oscillations in the vertical wind profiles, Washington, D.C.

due to errors in measuring the position of the balloon. Instruments with automatic tracking devices are not completely exempt from these errors, because in "hunting" the target the theodolites may execute oscillations which are primarily dependent on the electronics of the regulating circuits (Kirkman and Le Bedda, 1948). Their inaccuracy of angular measurements is stated to be 0.03 to 0.05°.

Practical experience from aeronautics also corroborates the above considerations and speaks in favor of the smoothing of vertical wind profiles obtained from inadequate methods of measurement.

Teletype transmissions of such wind profiles may, at times, render a completely wrong picture of atmospheric flow patterns. This can be demonstrated with the aid of Figure 2.122.1. If by international agreement all standard levels were raised by 500 m, a completely different profile would be the result. The main wind maximum now appears split into two maxima, and there are additional maxima at the 13 and 15 km levels. It seems superfluous to state that such high-level wind information is of little value, and one should not be surprised at all if aviation-route forecasts based upon such wind reports were verified only by mere chance.

Above all, vertical shears which have been calculated from these wind reports will show large discrepancies against shears computed from the thermal wind equation (Cole and Chamberlain, 1958). Since such wind shears may be affected with large errors, it appears impractical to correlate them with clear-air turbulence (Clem, 1955).

As long as we cannot rely universally upon better methods of high-level wind measurement, drastic smoothing of the vertical profiles will be indispensable. This may be accomplished directly either by longer time intervals of averaging, or by greater ascent rates of the balloons (De Jong, 1958). With this, however, the synoptic treatment of the fine structure of atmospheric flow patterns has to be confined to the study of a few specially suited cases.

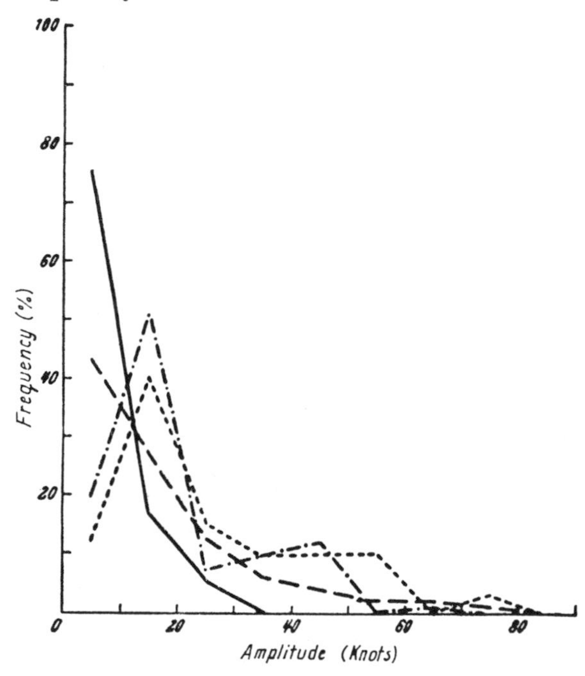

FIG. 2.122.3.—Per cent frequency distribution of the amplitudes of velocity fluctuations in the vertical wind profiles. Solid line, half-period of the oscillation = 1 min; dashed, 2 min; dashed-dotted, 3 min; shortly dashed, 4 min.

In the discussion of climatic mean values one has to realize that because of low elevation angles many wind ascents have to be terminated prematurely. Thus, in stratospheric mean values there exists a certain "slow winds" bias (Charles, 1959*c*).

Experiments with the U.S. radio theodolite SCR-658 revealed that in measuring the elevation angle, the incremental error $d(\Delta\varphi)$ from the beginning to the end of the two-minute interval used for averaging may be assumed to be 0.15° in the mean [$d(\Delta\varphi)$ is the difference between the errors $\Delta\varphi_1$ and $\Delta\varphi_2$ at the beginning and the end of this two-minute interval (Kirkman and Le Bedda, 1948)].

The standard vector deviation gives the radius of the error circle, in which the respective wind measurement lies (Brooks and Carruthers, 1953).

$$\sigma = \sqrt{(\sigma_x^2 + \sigma_y^2)} = \sqrt{(\sigma_s^2 + |V|^2 \sigma_\alpha^2)}. \qquad 2.122\ (1)$$

σ_x and σ_y are the standard deviations of the components of the wind velocity, σ_s the standard deviation of the scalar wind speed and σ_α of the wind direction. $|V|$ is the absolute magnitude of the wind velocity, which has been indicated by the rawinsonde at the respective level.

With unfavorable upper-wind conditions not showing a *reversal of wind direction* at great heights, large errors in stratospheric wind measurements will have to be expected. In temperate latitudes this is particularly the case with well-developed jet-stream situations during the winter season. Stratospheric easterlies, however, cause the balloon to drift back again toward the station, thus reducing the error in wind measurement. Such weather situations may be expected primarily during summer. For practical purposes one has to expect larger errors than in the estimate made below, because some manufacturers state the accuracy of the angle readings only with 0.1° (Decca, 1957; Ference, 1951; Meurers, 1952).

Because the smoothing of vertical wind profiles by overlapping averages over intervals of several minutes entails a systematic reduction of wind velocities at the level of maximum wind, and because on the other hand a graphical smoothing leaves too much leeway for subjective interpretations, a semi-objective smoothing method has been proposed (Reiter 1959*e*).

From 2.112 (8) one may calculate the error

$$\Delta V = \Delta l / \Delta t$$

in wind velocity, which occurs due to an error in measurements $\Delta\varphi = 0.075°$ [1] within a time interval $\Delta t = 120$ sec at different heights and different elevation angles. The result is given in Table 2.122.

TABLE 2.122. ERRORS IN HIGH-LEVEL WIND MEASUREMENTS (m/sec) AS A FUNCTION OF BALLOON HEIGHT AND ELEVATION ANGLE, FOR $\Delta t = 120$ sec AND $\Delta\varphi = 0.075°$

	HEIGHT OF BALLOON (m)					
ELEVATION ANGLE	5000	10,000	15,000	20,000	25,000	30,000
10.0°	1.8	3.5	5.3	7.1	8.9	10.7
9.5	2.0	3.9	5.9	7.9	9.8	11.8
9.0	2.2	4.4	6.5	8.7	10.9	13.1
8.5	2.4	4.9	7.3	9.8	12.2	14.7
8.0	2.8	5.5	8.3	11.0	13.8	16.5
7.5	3.1	6.2	9.3	12.3	15.4	18.5
7.0	3.6	7.2	10.8	14.4	18.0	21.6
6.5	4.2	8.3	12.5	16.6	20.8	25.0
6.0	4.9	9.8	14.6	19.5	24.4	29.2

According to the observed elevation angle the expected errors in measurements are entered at the corresponding levels along the vertical wind profiles (Fig. 2.122.4). They are graphically subtracted from the wind maxima and added to the wind minima (dotted curve in Fig. 2.122.4). If the amplitudes of the variations are less than the errors determined theoretically, the interval between the two dotted curves will have to be reduced until it corresponds to the values given in Table 2.122. The shaded area, which was

[1] This value is based on the assumption that the readings of the GMD-1A theodolite are accurate to 0.05°. The incremental error, which occurs inside of one time interval, depends on the accuracies of the angular measurements at the beginning and the end of this interval and is about $\sqrt{2} = 1.4$ larger than with a single measurement, i.e., it is approximately 0.075°. If the elevation angle changes only slowly, the error in measurement at successive points will mostly be $< 0.05°$.

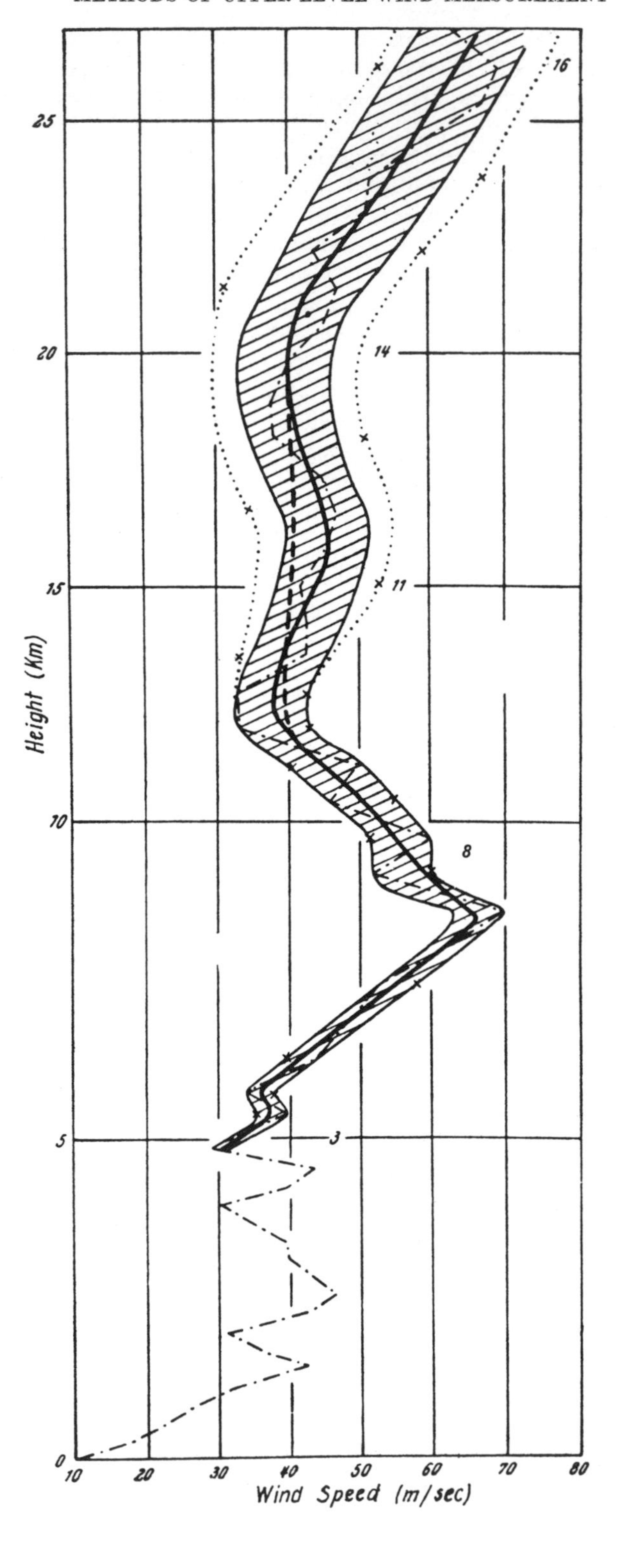

Fig. 2.122.4.—Smoothing of vertical wind profiles. The small numbers along the wind profile indicate the maximum errors according to Table 2.122. Dashed-dotted line: wind profile measured by GMD-1A, Vienna Austria, 21 February, 1959, 1200 GCT. All other lines are described in the text.

obtained in this fashion, gives the uncertainty of the wind measurements. The *most probable* vertical wind profile is obtained as center curve of this shaded area (heavy line). Thus, the vertical wind profile may be approximated by a smooth curve. The secondary wind maximum, which appears at about 16 km in Figure 2.122.4, may possibly be replaced by a straight line (dashed), which still would lie within the accuracy of measurements of the radio theodolite, given by the shaded area.

The source of errors which lies in the small elevation angles occurring with strong upper winds may be eliminated by using relay stations, lying approximately along a streamline taken at jet-stream level and equipped with radio theodolites tracking the same radiosonde. While for the first station the elevation angles assume small values, the balloon moves into a favorable range of angles with respect to the second station. This method may be applied economically, especially in areas with quasi-stationary jet streams. Successful experiments of this kind have been carried out over Japan. There, radiosonde ascents at Honjo (88 km west-north-west of Tateno) have first been tracked by the Honjo radio theodolite. After having reached a certain height, they have been tracked from Tateno (Arakawa, 1956*b*; Tateno, 1954).

Stations in flat country and in temperate latitudes, lying within the realm of strongly variable upper winds, could take advantage of this method if the balloon-launching site were equipped as a mobile unit. For this purpose a truck should be furnished with a calibrating unit for radiosondes, and with inflating implements for balloons. Connection with the permanently mounted radar station could be maintained through radio communication. Based on a 12-hour upper-wind forecast, a suitable launching site could be chosen 10 to 15 km upstream from the radar station, to which the mobile launching unit proceeds.

Such methods of measurement might improve the quality of upper-wind data effectively with relatively inexpensive means, complying with the demand for more accurate wind measurements in the stratosphere, which are necessary in the era of civil jet aviation.

The error in determining balloon positions is still present with *radar* instruments (Werner, 1952); it is much less, however, than with radio theodolites (Ewing, 1949; Mantis, 1957). For example, winds measured with the British radar system (Jones, Hooper, and Adler, 1951; Jones, 1949) do not reveal fluctuations of wind speed as large as the ones shown in Figure 2.122.1. The reason for this improved accuracy—especially with small elevation angles—lies primarily in the fact that theodolites make use of the cotangent of the elevation angle in calculating the horizontal projection of the balloon distance [see 2.112 (7)], while radar uses the cosine for the same calculations:

$$\Delta l = \Delta E \cos \varphi. \qquad 2.122\ (2)$$

ΔE is the difference in slant range from one balloon fix to the next; Δl is the horizontal projection of this distance, from which the mean wind velocity may be obtained immediately. The vertical distance Δh traveled by the balloon does not enter into this computation.

The standard deviation given by Decca-Radar for their instrument WF-1 for measurements of azimuth and elevation angle is 0.13°, and 100 m or 1 per cent of the total distance, for measurements of the slant range (Decca, 1957).

Experiments in double tracking of one balloon by two radar sets of the same type (one stationed in Bretigny, the other in Trappes, France) generally gave good agreement. On the average one has to count on inaccuracies of about 7 per cent in keeping a constant time-interval for the readings of angles and distances; this is particularly disagreeable with strong high-level winds. The instruments themselves show an error in the determination of the true wind velocity of about 5 per cent. Thus, for average conditions we have to expect a maximum total error of 10 per cent in the data of true wind velocity (Barbé, 1957). Ervet and Robuchon (1959) and Marc, Treussart, and Darmagnac (1959) report a maximum error in wind speed of about 2 m/sec, and in wind direction of about 5°.

Radar wind measurements in combination with a radiosonde offer different possibilities for determining the position of the balloon, each of which shows different sizes of errors at different distances (De Jong, 1958). For large distances, as they appear with jet-stream situations, computations of wind speed from *balloon height* and *slant range* are most suitable. The balloon height in this case may be taken from the radiosonde ascent. For balloon runs at low heights and with weak winds one should prefer computations from *height* and *elevation angle*. For average distances computations from *elevation angle* and *slant range* render the best results.

Swaying motions of the reflector may be rather disturbing, especially when the reflected signal is already weak, as it is from great distances, and reception may finally become impossible. In order to remedy this limitation in range the passive reflector on the balloon may be replaced by an active transponder (Jones, 1949; Lyons, Freeman, and Heberling, 1947), as it is used, e.g., with the Swiss "echosonde" (Lugeon, 1960), whose accuracy in the measurement of angles is given with $\pm 0.1°$ and in slant range measurements with ± 50 m. Its range of >200 km is unlimited for all practical purposes.

Correction for the curvature of the earth.—A corrective quantity, which is necessary for radar measurements as well as for radio theodolite tracking, as soon as the distance between balloon and station surpasses a certain threshold value, is brought about by the earth's curvature.

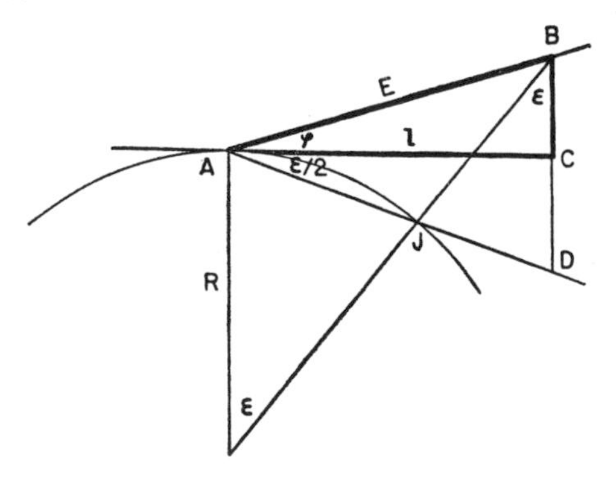

FIG. 2.122.5.—Computation of the correction in balloon heights, which becomes necessary because of the curvature of the earth's surface.

The distance $AB = E$ from radar to balloon and the elevation angle φ are being measured. Ignoring the earth's curvature, we obtain from this the distance $AC = l$ of the balloon in a horizontal projection (Fig. 2.122.5). The rate of change of this quantity renders the horizontal component of the wind vector. $BC = h$ is the apparent height of the balloon. In reality, however, the height of the balloon above ground is given by $BJ = z$. The correction to be applied reads:

$$K = z - h. \qquad 2.122\ (3)$$

Since $BJ = BD$, the relation $K = CD$ is valid, too. From trigonometric relations of Figure 2.122.5 one obtains:

$$CD = l \cdot \tan \varepsilon/2 \cong l \cdot \frac{\varepsilon}{2}$$

for small angles. On the other hand for a small angle ε one may write without making a large error

$$AC \cong AJ \cong \varepsilon \cdot R.$$

R is the earth's radius. The correction in balloon height, which becomes necessary because of the earth's curvature, thus is given by the following approximation:

$$K = l^2/2R. \qquad 2.122\ (4)$$

At a distance of the balloon in the horizontal projection of $l = 80$ km we already obtain $K = 502$ m.

This correction also has to be taken into account with double tracking of rawinsondes. The balloon heights computed from the two stations must agree with each other. For two stations (subscripts 1 and 2) the expression

$$z = h_1 + z_{01} + K_1 = h_2 + z_{02} + K_2, \qquad 2.122\ (5)$$

is valid. z_{01} and z_{02} are the elevations of the two stations above mean sea level. z, in this case, has to be understood as height above sea level. With the aid of 2.122 (5) the height calculations from both instruments may be equalized (Barbé, 1957):

$$h_1 = h_2 + (z_{02} - z_{01}) + (K_2 - K_1). \qquad 2.122\ (6)$$

The error, which is introduced by neglecting the earth's curvature may, under certain circumstances, exaggerate the maximum wind velocities by as much as 20 per cent. By the same token also the horizontal wind shear between two stations, one reporting strong, the other weak upper-level winds, is exaggerated. This may in part explain why sometimes on the anticyclonic side of a jet stream wind shears are reported between radiosonde stations which would cause appreciable dynamic instability. Vertical wind shears underneath the jet maximum will also be exaggerated.

Nomographs may be used for correcting rawinsonde observations with strong upper-level winds (Clem, Colson, and Harrison, 1954; Gustafson, 1954; Kessler, 1954).

2.123. The Representativeness of Upper-Level Wind Measurements

We finally have to ask ourselves whether the methods of measurements described in Chapters 2.11 and 2.12 render *representative* upper-level winds which are not only indicative of the instantaneous conditions at one specific point of the atmosphere but which are valid for larger regions in space and time as well. From the presently existing procedures of evaluation an average value of the wind can be calculated over a one-minute interval (and with further averaging of such intervals mean values over two or more minutes are obtained), which corresponds to a layer of 360 m in thickness (or corresponding multiples of this). The averaging process, however, extends only over the vertical co-ordinate. For the horizontal co-ordinate the balloon renders, after all, only an instantaneous value of the wind vector at one single point of the flow pattern, since it is carried away inertly by the horizontal current, not executing any relative motions to this current. Offhand we have to expect the resulting vertical wind profiles, therefore, to show features which do not correspond to the large-scale synoptic characteristics of the prevailing flow conditions, but which are coined by local and restricted influences. It would be beyond the scope of this book to enter into the theory of small- and large-scale turbulence (Kolmogorov, *et al.*, 1958). In any case, it is the spectrum of turbulent motions which determines the representativeness of the wind measurements. Depending on the size of the scale under consideration, restrictions will have to be made on the reliability of the respective measurements (see also Chapter 4.3).

Ascents of balloon pairs have been made in England (Great Britain M.O., 1940) and in the United States (Arnold, 1956) and have been released (*a*) simultaneously at different distances, and (*b*) from the same site at different time intervals. Thus, conclusions on the standard deviation of upper winds in relation to space and time scales are possible; for instance, balloons which have been released at the same time at a distance of approximately 1½ m drifted apart as much as 1 km and showed differences of up to one minute in reaching a certain level. The British measurements used station pairs which were up to 920 km distant from each other. In Table 2.123 a survey is given of the standard deviations calculated from the observed wind velocities, and of the magnitude of the horizontal and time scales.

TABLE 2.123. "STANDARD DEVIATION" OF WIND VELOCITY FOR DIFFERENT SCALES OF MEASUREMENTS

	U.S.A.		Great Britain					
Scale K (km)	0.5	5	110	180	480	600	720	920
Standard deviation (m/sec)	0.5	0.8	3.0	3.8	6.9	7.1	7.9	8.9

	U.S.A.		
Scale K (minutes)	0.5	5	90
Standard deviation (m/sec)	0.5	0.6	2.2

The "standard deviation" of the British measurements whose scale lies in the synoptic large-scale region, obey the following law:

$$\sigma = a\sqrt{K}, \qquad 2.123\ (1)$$

which is in good agreement with the statistical theory of turbulence (see Defant and Defant, 1958) (2 particles are separated with a velocity proportional to the square root of their distance). The American measurements, however, which lie in the region of small-scale turbulence show a much slower decay of "standard deviation" with decreasing scale.

Durst (1960) finds that the correlation coefficients of pairs of wind measurements *along* and *across* a certain line show a different behavior. Furthermore, in distances of $\geqq 1200$ and $\geqq 800$ nautical miles, respectively, they become negative. This reveals the influence of planetary waves and the anisotropic character of large-scale turbulence.

Measurements made by Landers (1957) on a station triangle in Florida whose sides were 1.5 km long, and at whose corner points balloons had been released simultaneously, show the existence of strong vertical gradients of horizontal divergence $[(\partial/\partial z)(\nabla_h \cdot \mathbf{v})]$, which have been calculated from changes of the positions of the balloons relative to each

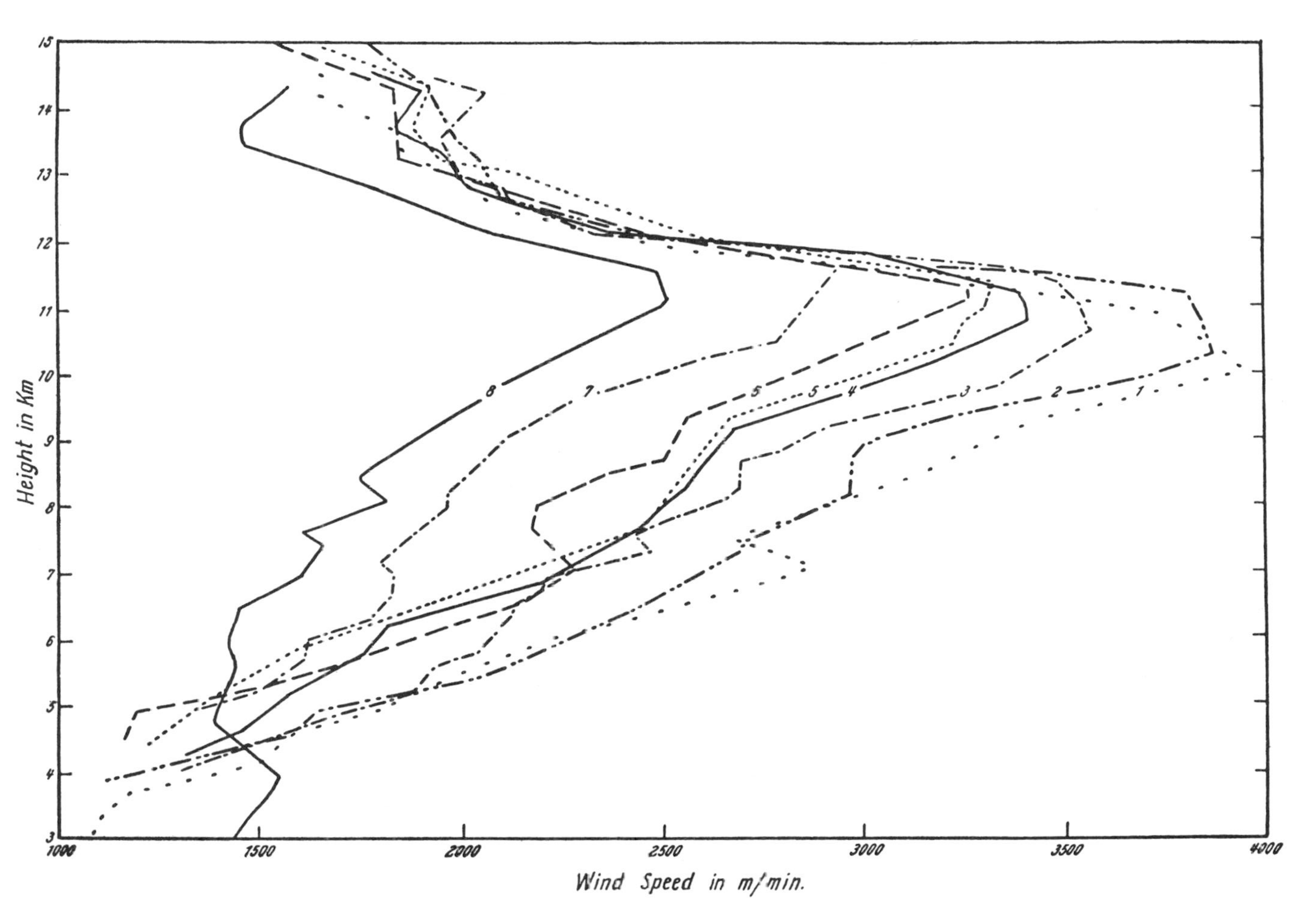

FIG. 2.123.1.—Vertical wind profiles (each averaged over 3 consecutive ascents) measured over Trappes, France, 25 and 26 January, 1956. No. 1: 0815, 0915, 1015 GCT; No. 2: 1110, 1215, 1325; No. 3: 1405, 1535, 1635; No. 4: 1715, 1803, 1900; No. 5: 1940, 2030, 2115; No. 6: 2210, 2315, 0015; No. 7: 0140, 0240, 0345 (only the ascent of 0240 went beyond the 11.5-km level); No. 8: 0450, 0550, 0830. (After Barbé, 1957.)

other. The separation of the balloons, therefore, was by no means constant over deep layers of the troposphere. The figures given in the table above, therefore, are to be taken only as average values, over a large number of observations. Some atmospheric layers may deviate widely from these values during one ascent. Studies of the meso-structure of jet streams, which will be treated extensively in Chapter 4.3, corroborate the existence of layers with stronger and weaker divergence or convergence.

From wind measurements with aircraft Brundidge (1956) draws the conclusion that local variations of wind speeds in the jet-stream region (at a height of 12 km) are correlated on the one hand with the time interval Δt under consideration, and on the other hand, however, with the wind velocity V_0 in the jet axis. The regression he found is based on too limited an observational sample to be considered reliable. It is given as follows:

$$|\Delta V| = 0.08\Delta t + 0.32 V_0 - 27.6. \qquad 2.123\ (2)$$

Δt is measured in minutes, V_0 and ΔV are given in knots.

Radiosonde ascents, which have been made in Trappes, France, with a time interval of one to two hours (Barbé, 1957, 1958) showed, that in the case of weaker upper winds the constancy in time and, thereby, the representativeness of the measurements has been worse than in well-developed jet-stream situations (see also Graf, 1940). The constancy of wind velocity is especially well maintained above the layer of maximum wind. This is the region of a height suited for operations of modern jet aviation. Upper-level wind measurements in this region should, therefore, give data which still can be used for flight briefing several hours after the termination of the ascent. Figure 2.123.1 shows this rather clearly. It contains *average* ascent profiles, each computed from three successive hourly soundings. In the region above the layer of maximum wind the wind profile may be considered approximately constant for about twenty hours in this case. Such long intervals may not always be realized—in the present case the station Trappes was situated under an anticyclonically curved upper-wind maximum on the eastern slope of a flat high-pressure ridge, which traveled eastward and slowly increased its amplitude; as a rule, however, the changes in upper flow patterns will be established well enough for all practical purposes by the ascents carried out twice daily (0000 hours and 1200 hours GCT), provided that the errors in measurements are kept within tolerable limits. The *wind direction* also changes only slightly over intervals of several hours. Corresponding to the present weather situation of the example given in Figure 2.123.1, up to 6 km a cyclonic turning of the wind prevailed. At jet-stream level the wind started turning anticyclonically with altitude, in connection with the advance of an anticyclonically curved upper-wind maximum. Above the 200-mb level, however, we again observe a cyclonic turning of the wind.

Figure 2.123.2 finally gives a time section for the station of Trappes between 24 and 26 January, 1956. In this diagram the time axis has been entered from right toward left, so that the progress in space of weather phenomena from west toward east could be expressed (see Chapter 3.23). The large-scale changes in the upper flow pattern are clearly described and they are analyzed by dashed lines. As has been mentioned already with Figure 2.123.1, above the layer of maximum wind, the flow pattern remains strikingly constant. Superimposed upon the large-scale changes in flow are small oscillations, which may be regarded as real, and not caused by instru-

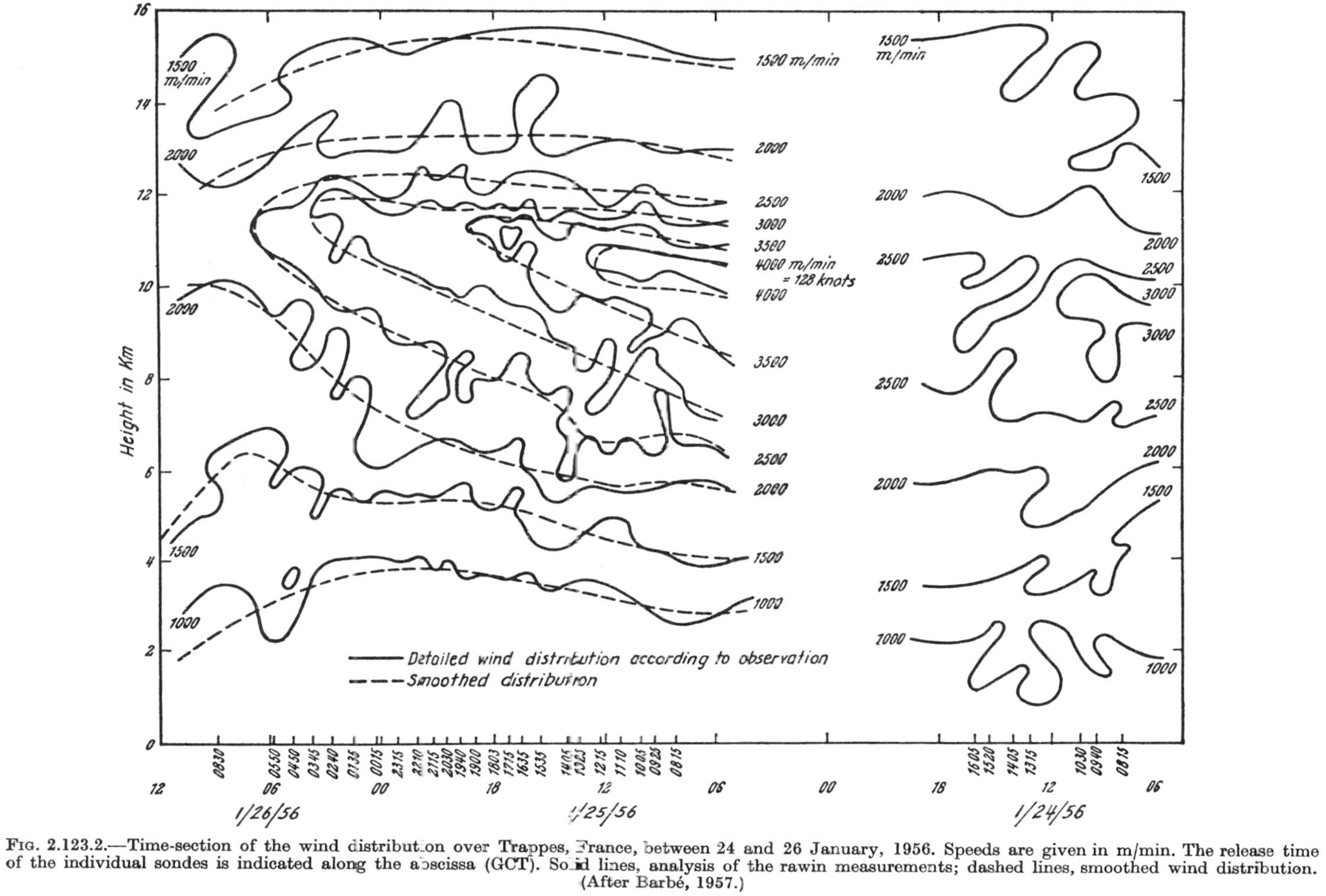

Fig. 2.123.2.—Time-section of the wind distribution over Trappes, France, between 24 and 26 January, 1956. Speeds are given in m/min. The release time of the individual sondes is indicated along the abscissa (GCT). Solid lines, analysis of the rawin measurements; dashed lines, smoothed wind distribution. (After Barbé, 1957.)

ment errors as long as they show up in successive ascents. The "standard deviation" of 2.2 m/sec for a time scale of 90 minutes, as given in Table 2.123 seems to be realized in this diagram. For larger time scales, i.e., in the order of magnitude of several hours, one should expect a further increase of the "standard deviation" for flow patterns of the middle troposphere.

2.13. Transosondes

2.131. General Remarks

Principle.—A balloon is balanced so that its flight reaches a certain pressure level and remains at that level. From the trajectory of the balloon, mean wind vectors may be calculated.

History.—Constant level balloons have been used already earlier for different purposes. Among others, with their aid successful studies of lee waves in foehn situations have been carried out (Kanitscheider, 1932–39). Arakawa (1952*a*, 1956*a*) reports on the use of such balloons as bomb carriers ("balloon bomb") from Japan to the United States during the winter of 1944–45. The most suitable levels for their drift proved to be between 10 and 12 km. In the jet stream these balloons reached the United States within 2 to 3 days. The development of the "skyhook" balloons and of the "transosondes" (transocean sondes), in the United States is based upon the experiences from these earlier applications (Anderson, 1952; Angell, 1959*b*, 1960*a*; Drouilhet, 1958; Mastenbrook and Anderson, 1953, 1954; Smith, 1958; U.S. Air Force CRC, 1956; Van Mieghem, 1959). In transosonde experiments carried out during January and February of 1956, two balloons from a total of twenty which started in Japan, after crossing the Pacific and the North American continent and the Atlantic Ocean, almost reached the European coast (Angell, 1957; Mastenbrook, 1956). One particular flight in November, 1957, reached the coast of Ireland four days after its release in Japan (Angell, 1958*a*). Another transosonde flight of 31 October, 1957, apparently traveled with a mean velocity of 81 knots in the influence region of a strong jet stream, and finally terminated north-west of Ireland, too. The favorable possibilities which this method offers for the observation of large-scale circulation systems shall be demonstrated impressively by means of Figure 2.132, which shall be discussed further.

Balloons.—In general polyethylene or neoprene (plastic) balloons are used. They expand to a certain volume, which then is kept approximately constant (Anonymous, 1950; Barford, *et al.*, 1954; Great Britain, P.O., 1955; Haig, 1954; Moore, *et al.*, 1948; Rink, 1957). From the equation of state of an ideal gas

$$p\alpha = RT \qquad 2.131\ (1)$$

one may see that p remains constant as long as the temperature of the filling gas does not undergo any changes. Constancy of the filling-gas pressure may also be maintained by a valve (Hopper and Laby, 1960*a*, 1960*b*).

Some of the balloons in use have diameters of more than 20 m, and they may carry payloads up to 40 kg (Droessler, 1950). A premature sinking of the balloon, due to loss of buoyant gas, is compensated by automatic dropping of ballast, regulated by an aneroid (Moore, Smith, and Gaalswyk, 1954; Murray, Schneider, and Smith, 1950).

Tracking.—The radio signals transmitted from the radiosonde, which is carried along, are received by several radio theodolites (Anderson, 1955*b*; Anderson and Mastenbrook, 1956; Anderson, Mastenbrook, and Cubbage, 1955). From their readings of angle the

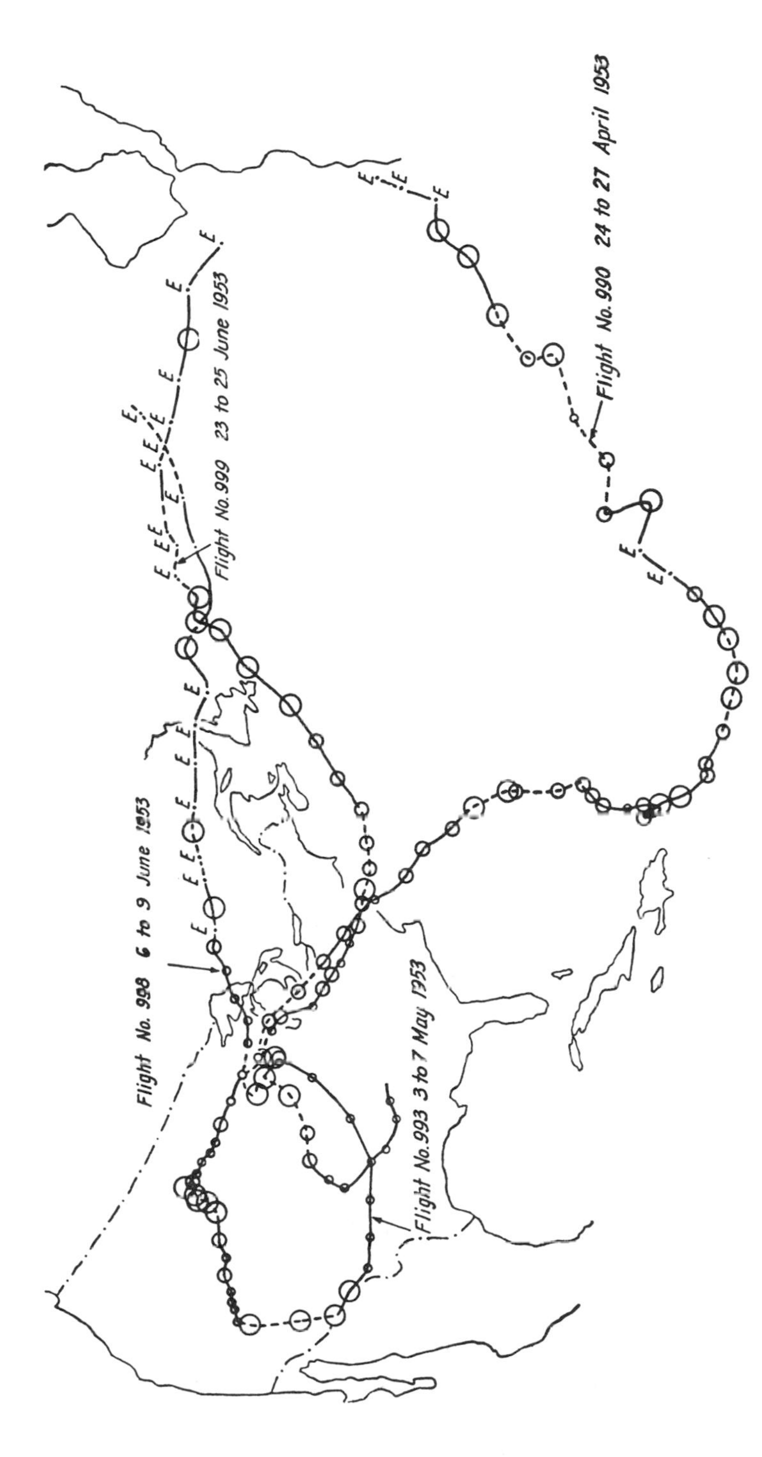

FIG. 2.132.—Two-hour transosonde positions of four flights at the 300-mb level. The circles indicate the errors made in estimating the positions (E = estimated positions). Flight legs traveled during daytime are marked by full lines, legs traveled at night have been entered with dashed lines. (After Neiburger and Angell, 1956.)

instantaneous position of the balloon may be determined. Wind vectors may be computed from the balloon positions by means of nomographs (Gaalswyk, 1958). In order to establish the trajectory of the balloons also over ocean areas with a sufficient degree of accuracy, transmitters which give a reliable signal over great distances (4500 km) are necessary. With the transosonde experiments 50-watt transmitters have been used successfully operating at frequencies of 6420 and 12,855 kilocycles (Anderson, 1955*a*; Anderson, Mastenbrook, and Cubbage, 1955).

In earlier experiments the paths of the balloons have been determined from vertical ground photography. From this the wind vectors could be calculated (Brombacher, 1936; Mastenbrook, 1956). The motions of the balloons can also be measured from accompanying aircraft (Moore, Smith, and Gaalswyk, 1954, 1955).

The essential feature of the transosonde method is the use of a Lagrangean co-ordinate system for measuring the meteorological parameters. This system moves along with the current. The streamlines of the air and the trajectories of the transosondes are, however, identical only in first approximation, because on the one hand radiation effects may lead to uncontrollable fluctuations in temperature and flight level, and on the other hand the balloon path only follows an isobaric surface under ideal conditions, while the atmospheric flow takes place along *isentropic* surfaces.

2.132. Sources of Error

Since the base line between theodolite stations may be rather long, also stratospheric winds may be determined by this method to some degree of reliability (Anonymous, 1951), especially when we deal with *mean* wind vectors over longer flight legs. This is because the determination of positions depends in essence on the accuracy of pressure height data, and on the two or more azimuth measurements. The problem of small elevation angles with strong upper winds is largely eliminated. On the other hand, we have to expect relatively large distances between balloon and tracking stations. With the present state of receiving and tracking techniques we have to expect an average error in positions over the United States of approximately 33 km (Anderson, 1955*b*).

The positioning of the balloons over the oceans is generally carried out by coastal stations. With increasing distance errors in the measurement of azimuth angles make themselves felt disagreeably (Neiburger and Angell, 1956). If, however, one evaluates the mean wind vectors (from the trajectories) over a longer period of time, these inaccuracies in the determination of positions carry less weight.

Furthermore, the determination of positions by radio direction finding shows a certain daily variation in accuracy due to the inferior reception during the night hours. This is brought out clearly by Flight No. 993 over the United States (Fig. 2.132).

In general, the positions determined by radio direction finding are less accurate than the theoretical values of instrument accuracy. Ohnsorg (1957) developed a method by which the "standard deviation" σ_e of the error e in estimating the distance may be obtained directly from the trajectory calculations.

$$\sigma_{v'(t)}{}^2 - \sigma_{v'(2t)}{}^2 = \sigma_{v(t)}{}^2 - \sigma_{v(2t)}{}^2 + 3\sigma_e{}^2/2t^2. \qquad 2.132\ (1)$$

$v_{i(t)}$ is the true velocity which is present in the ith interval while $v'_{i(t)}$ is the *measured* velocity in the same interval, to which still the error e in measuring the position is attached. t is the time interval used in tracking, and σ is the "standard deviation" of the quantity designated by the respective index. The variance of the actual velocity, in general, is rather small, so that the error in determining the position may be estimated from the following approximation:

$$\sigma_e^2 \cong \frac{2t^2}{3} (\sigma_{v'(t)}^2 - \sigma_{v'(2t)}^2) \qquad 2.132\ (2)$$

For practical purposes one proceeds by calculating the value of σ_e^2 from 2.132 (2) for the smallest possible time interval t. From the relations

$$\sigma_{v\,(\text{error})} = \frac{\sqrt{2}}{t}\sigma_e$$
$$\sigma_{a\,(\text{error})} = \frac{\sqrt{6}}{t^2}\sigma_e \qquad 2.132\ (3)$$

(σ_v = "standard deviation" of the error in the calculation of velocity, σ_a = "standard deviation" of the error in calculation of accelerations, due to erroneous positioning) one may compute the interval of measurement which is necessary in order to keep the errors below a certain limit. That is, if $\sigma_e = 30$ km and σ_v is 8 km/h, t has to be of the order of magnitude of 5 hours. Examples from actual data show that for transosondes at a flight level of 40,000 ft (12 km), whose positions have been determined by radio direction finding, σ_e is approximately 30 km. If the time interval of measurement is $t = 3$ hours, σ_a is approximately 0.06 cm/sec², a result which is of the same order of magnitude as the large-scale horizontal accelerations in the atmosphere. Radio direction finding with this magnitude of error in the time interval under consideration would therefore be unsuitable to measure directly accelerations on a synoptic scale.

2.133. The Representativeness of Transosonde Winds

In the same way as upon radiosonde balloons, meso- and micro-structure of the wind field also act upon the transosondes. We may, however, expect offhand that because of the relatively long interval between two observations the micro-structure will be of little influence upon the transosonde wind measurements. Since, however, the trajectories constitute the sum of all detailed structure, they offer an ideal possibility to study its effect. This has been done successfully by the simultaneous release of several balloons (Moore, Smith, and Gaalswyk, 1954). From the distance between the balloons, and its variation in time, one may draw conclusions as to the small scale "austausch" at flight level. One has to take into account, however, that the flight levels of the two balloons, which constitute the pair under consideration, rarely are the same. The divergence simulated by the vertical wind shear is large, only if the shear is large at flight level, and the difference in level of the two balloons is large, too. Moore found for several balloon pairs which have been tracked from aircraft and which have been flying at approximately 30,000 ft. (9.1 km) the results presented in Table 2.133.

TABLE 2.133. RESULTS OF MEASUREMENTS OF TRANSOSONDE PAIRS

DISTANCE TRAVELLED (km)	DURATION OF FLIGHT (hours)	DISTANCE BETWEEN THE TWO BALLOONS AT THE END OF TRAJECTORY (km)	DISTANCE IN PER CENT OF LENGTH OF TRAJECTORY	DISTANCE OF BALLOONS MEASURED NORMAL TO TRAJECTORY (km)
1368	14.5	32	2.3	12.9
1247	18.0	21	1.7	9.7
1930	20.2	1.6	0.08	1.6
1930	20.2	8	0.4	1.6
1930	20.2	8	0.4	1.6
2640	27.5	29	1.1	8.1

The small distances between balloons having traveled along such long trajectories prove that the high-level winds are rather regular and show relatively little fine structure. Moore calculated from the above data an exchange coefficient which had the order of magnitude of 0.035 to 20×10^7 cm^2/sec, while Miller (1948*b*) and Grimminger (1941), in applying other methods, obtained coefficients of the order of magnitude of 10^{10} cm^2/sec.

This discrepancy may be explained by the fact that the effects of small turbulence elements are integrated over the large cross section of a transosonde balloon, and thereby partly cancel each other. By observing the rate of separation of two large, closed-in volumes (balloons), one arrives at different "austausch" coefficients, as would be the case in measurements of diffusion rates of smoke clouds, which also are subject to small exchange elements in the turbulence "spectrum" and which do not cancel each other.

Angell (1958*c*) could prove the existence of tide influences from systematic oscillations of velocities. Inertia oscillations, however, are more difficult to ascertain statistically (Angell, 1958*b*).

2.134 Comparison of Transosonde Winds with Conventional Methods of Measurement

After Durst and Gilbert (1950),

$$\mathbf{v} - \mathbf{v}_g' = \frac{1}{f}\mathbf{k} \times \frac{d\mathbf{v}}{dt} \qquad 2.134\ (1)$$

[see Eq. 1.224 (1)]. In this equation $\mathbf{v}_g'$ is the geostrophic wind computed from transosonde measurements. $\mathbf{v}$ is the wind vector actually present. Furthermore, we have

$$\frac{d\mathbf{v}}{dt} = \frac{d\mathbf{v}_h}{dt} + w\frac{\partial \mathbf{v}}{\partial z} \qquad 2.134\ (2)$$

$d\mathbf{v}_h/dt$ is the horizontal acceleration of the balloon, which may be obtained from two successive wind measurements. The vertical velocity w and the wind shear $\partial\mathbf{v}/\partial z \cong \partial\mathbf{v}_g/\partial z$ may be computed to a sufficient degree of accuracy from rawinsonde measurements (computation of w, e.g., with the adiabatic method, see Chapter 3.248).

Theoretically, $\mathbf{v}_g'$ from the transosonde measurements has to agree with $\mathbf{v}_g$ from upper air maps. After investigations by Giles and Peterson (1956, 1957) this, however, proves not to be the case. The *average* of ten balloon flights showed $|\mathbf{v}_g' - \mathbf{v}_g| = 10$ knots. The reason for this apparently lies in the different methods of measurements: $\mathbf{v}_g'$ is more sensitive toward small-scale meso-structural accelerations, which do not show up yet in the distance of contour lines on an upper-level weather chart (see also Chapter 4.3).

The average deviation of angle between $\mathbf{v}$ and $\mathbf{v}_g$ was found to be 0.5° (positive, when directed toward lower pressure). The "standard deviation" σ was 10.7°. The mean difference between $\mathbf{v}_g'$ and $\mathbf{v}_g$ was −2.2° and the "standard deviation" $\sigma = 12.9°$. The average difference in angle, therefore, was still within the accuracy of measurement, so that from these numbers one cannot draw any further conclusions.

By considering the frictional influence in following equation,

$$\frac{d\mathbf{v}}{dt}+w\frac{\partial \mathbf{v}}{\partial z}=f(\mathbf{v}-\mathbf{v}_g)\times\mathbf{k}+\mathbf{F} \qquad 2.134\ (3)$$

Angell (1959) obtained for the component F_s in the direction of $\mathbf{v}-1.4$ knots/hr, and for F_n normal to the direction of $\mathbf{v}-0.2$ knots/hr. (The minus sign indicates that the frictional force is directed toward the right of the current.) Because of the different accuracies in the evaluation of the various terms in the above equation the dependability of this calculation of **F** as residual in 2.134 (3) may not be too significant.

However, if we compare the order of magnitude of **F** with the acceleration, which the transosonde experienced in the lower part of Figure 4.123.1 (approximately 6 knots/hr), we may easily see that by neglecting the frictional effects, errors may occur in the terms of the "frictionless" equation of motion, which may amount to 20 per cent or more in extreme cases.

2.14. Upper-Level Wind Measurements by Aircraft

2.141. General Remarks

In jet-stream research after World War II airplanes have become increasingly important. Especially high- and fast-flying jet aircraft have been used because they can reach, and climb beyond, the jet-stream level without any difficulties (Murgatroyd, 1956) and they still have a sufficient radius of operation even with strongest head winds. The advantage of airborne measurements lies in the fact that they render information on the horizontal wind distribution. Furthermore, by frequent determination of the position of the aircraft, meso- and micro-structure of the jet streams may be open to further investigations. An aircraft also offers more possibilities as an instrument carrier than does a balloon; finally the pilot reports obtained during flight are a valuable supplement to the registrations of the instruments. So, for instance, observations of turbulence and cloudiness are to a large extent derived from these aircraft missions.

2.142. Sources of Error

Similar to the balloon soundings the upper-level wind measurements by aircraft depend on the accuracy of the navigational methods employed. In general, the location of the aircraft is determined from the two azimuth angles from two radio beacons, as for instance with the VOR navigation system (very high frequency omnidirectional radio range operating at a frequency of 112 to 118 mc [International Civil Aviation Organization, 1956]). Errors in the determination of these angles, of course, lead to errors in positioning the aircraft. For the VOR system the accuracy of angles is given with 2°. In practice, it lies mostly between 1° and 1.5° (U.S. Bureau of Aeronautics, 1953*a*), which holds for the absolute measurement of angles. The "incremental error" between two successive determinations of position, which enters into the accuracy of upper-level wind measurements, may, however, be assumed substantially smaller. Test flights over the United States rendered an incremental error of this system of 0.3° over an arc of 10° in length (U.S. Bureau of Aeronautics, 1953*a*).

The per cent error in the calculations of velocity generally decreases with increasing wind speed (U.S. Bureau of Aeronautics, 1953*a*). The error of 2° in the accuracy of a VOR station is only felt in full when switching from one station to the next. The projection of the flight track, which is obtained from the intersections of the azimuth angles on the map may show a discontinuity at the location where the stations have been switched. Wind calculations cannot be made here, and measurements before and after the discontinuity have to be adapted to each other (Riehl and Maynard, 1954; Riehl, Berry, and Maynard, 1955; Rutherford, 1954; Saucier and Riehl, 1956).

Plotting the position of an aircraft with azimuth angles offers no major difficulties over continents with a dense station network, but it becomes very unreliable over ocean areas, so that no accurate wind calculations could be carried out there (M.A. Lee, 1955). Measurements of absolute height by radio altimetry, however, are very easy over the sea.

An additional source of error in wind calculation may arise through the measurements of air speed and of heading, from which the wind vector is calculated by vectorially subtracting the ground speed (Rutherford, 1956). Since the Pitot tube of the air speed indicator may under certain circumstances be susceptible to icing, wind measurements in clouds will have to be accepted with great caution. Some aircraft are already equipped with an automatic wind indicator which carries out the calculations of drift (Saucier, 1956*b*).

A method of measurement employed successfully by Hurst (1955) and others (Harding, 1955) consists in photographing the terrain underneath the aircraft, at constant time intervals. This, together with the air speed permits the calculation of the wind vectors. The disadvantage of the method lies in the fact that it can only be employed during fair weather situations. On the other hand, it is relatively accurate. Errors may be due to the motion of the aircraft around its longitudinal and lateral axes, which, if they are not corrected correspondingly, may simulate a change in wind vectors computed from the series of aerial photographs.

Vertical wind shears may be shown directly by photographing smoke traces emitted from a bomb. Experiments of this kind have been carried out in England (Pothecary and Murgatroyd, 1953).

Since about 1953 upper-level wind measurements have been obtained successfully in the United States from drift velocities, which have been measured with the aid of a radar bomb sight (U.S. Air Force, 1954; Tull, 1957). In the literature they have been called "K winds." The disadvantage of this system lies in the fact that it can be applied only over continents. The accuracy of measurements with this system, however, is superior to that of the VOR system.

A comparison of these wind measurements with the usual meteorological methods of measurements (balloons) reveal that the values obtained from the GMD-1A on the average have been too high by about 10 knots in comparison with the K winds, probably because the correction for the earth's curvature was neglected (see Chapter 2.122). The agreement between K winds and meteorological winds decreases in the following sequence of instruments: SCR-584, SCR-658, GMD-1A, and pilot balloons with theodolite tracking. In 80 per cent of the cases the vector difference between the winds measured by aircraft and the meteorological winds for the above instruments in the given sequence has been less than 22, 27, 30, and 37 knots. A comparison between K system and GMD-1A also revealed that only with more than two hours' difference between the measurements does the vector difference between the two types assume significant magnitude. The rawinsondes, therefore, give quite representative upper-level wind values for a time period of about two hours (see also Chapter 2.123).

Landers (1955*a*) reports that velocities measured by aircraft of the type B-29 over the United States were about 12 knots too high for wind speeds up to 60 knots. For larger wind velocities the balloon measurements gave too large values, which he also ascribed to the neglected earth's curvature. The discrepancies in the lower velocity ranges were reduced to inaccuracies of the airspeed indicator (U.S. Air Weather Service, 1954*a*).

Rutherford (1955) finds good agreement between meteorological and aircraft winds; Brundidge (1956; see also Reiter, 1961*a*) finds the same for Project Jet Stream measurements, especially when the time of arrival of the balloon at the particular flight level is taken into account. The position of the jet axis may under certain circumstances be different in balloon measurements and aircraft measurements. This may be due to the effect of the horizontal meso-structure of the wind field, which eludes the balloon measurements because of the large distance between stations, although it is clearly present in the air-borne measurements.

Upper-wind *forecasts* from balloon measurements in general give too low wind velocities (standard deviation, depending on the area, 11.5 to 13.5 knots). This may be attributed to the horizontal smoothing which underlies most of the quasi-geostrophic wind analyses from isobaric charts, be they actual or prognostic, and which appears stronger, the fewer observing stations are available (Durst, 1954).

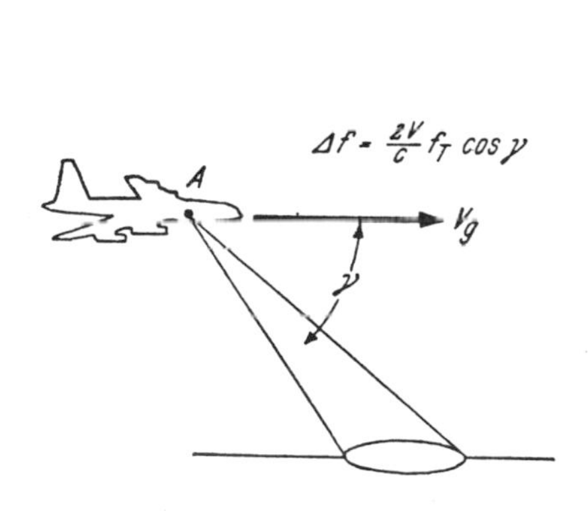

FIG. 2.142.1.—Principle of Doppler radar. (Tull, 1957.)

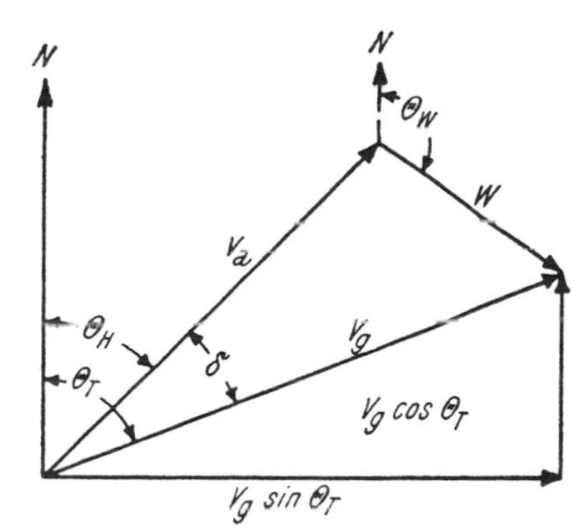

FIG. 2.142.2.—Course determination by Doppler radar. (Tull, 1957.)

A new navigational system which is completely independent of ground stations and, therefore may also make usable wind measurements over ocean areas, is based on the application of the "Doppler" effect (Tull, 1957). Figure 2.142.1 shows schematically the functioning of the principle: From a transmitter A, a signal is emitted under an angle γ against the direction of flight $\mathbf{v}_g$ and is reflected from an elliptical area at the ground. The change of frequency Δf of this beam amounts to

$$\Delta f = \frac{2V}{C} f_T \cos \gamma \qquad 2.142\ (1)$$

because of the Doppler effect. V is the air speed, f_T is the frequency of the transmitted signal and C is its rate of propagation.

If there are two transmitters operating on the aircraft, whose beams include the angle Θ in a horizontal plane, one may compute the drift caused by the upper wind W (Fig. 2.142.2) from the angle between $\mathbf{v}_a$ ("heading") and $\mathbf{v}_g$ ("ground speed"). From the angle Θ_T, which $\mathbf{v}_g$ includes with the direction of north, the east-west and the north-south components of the flight track may be determined, and from this one can carry out a complete dead reckoning.

In the United States such instruments are already in routine operation (AN/ASN-7, APA-95, APN-66). With these, calculations are carried out continuously and completely automatically.

Data on the accuracy of these Doppler instruments are available through "Project Jet Stream" (Project Jet Stream, 1959; Endlich and Rados, 1959). According to these, the absolute accuracy in determining positions is approximately 0.8 per cent of the distance from a given co-ordinate point. The wind velocity is accurate to about 3 knots (after Murgatroyd [1957] to approximately <5 knots). The reliability of the wind direction measurements depends on the wind speed: it is about 12° at 15 knots, and 1° at 200 knots. Since the incremental error is smaller than these values, measurements of gradients are considerably more accurate: in distance the error amounts to about 1.5 km, in velocity to 1 knot and in direction to 1°.

There is no doubt, therefore, that the Doppler system gives the most reliable wind values so far known, and, furthermore, with the present types of aircraft there are no limitations on flight level and air speed. Relatively large inaccuracies of measurement are, however, reported from the subtropical oceans where the smooth water surface with light surface winds offers only a rather small albedo for the slant beam. In this case, one has to resort to a steeper beam; then, however, the frequency shift according to Eq. 2.142 (1) becomes less, and with this, the reliability of the measurements decreases.

It is to be hoped that Doppler wind measurements will be adopted by commercial airlines—perhaps by using a magnetic storage unit similar to the ones in artificial satellites (National Academy of Sciences, 1958*b*), which delivers upon request an almost continuous sequence of wind data to a central weather service office. In this manner more data would be available for the high troposphere and lower stratosphere, as is the case now for the surface layers of the atmosphere.

Measurements by sailplane.—For detailed studies of the structure of jet streams, especially with respect to turbulence and lee waves over mountains, sailplanes have been used successfully (Kuettner, 1955). Experiences in this area have been gained mainly from the Rocky Mountains (Sierra Wave Project) and the Alps (Georgii, 1956*a*; Georgii, Reinhardt, and Schurer, 1957; Gerbier, 1959). In Germany (Deutsche Forschungsanstalt fuer Segelflug, Munich) there are plans to send a sailplane equipped with a jet engine up to the jet-stream level, where it could carry out measurement missions without using its engine. The problem of positioning and therefore the problem of wind calculations remains the same as with engine aircraft (Neuber, 1959).

2.15. Other Methods of Direct Upper-Level Wind Measurements

2.151. Observations of Cloud Drift

With the development of modern radiosonde techniques systematic cloud drift measurements are seldom made any more. By this, one neglects an inexpensive, but valuable, aerologic auxiliary means. The connections between jet streams and cloud formations will be discussed further in Chapter 6.3. Here we shall only point out that the drift velocity and direction of high-level clouds constitutes a dependable indicator of high-level winds (Jenkinson, 1954). Some uncertainty usually exists, however, in estimating the cloud heights, so that under these circumstances even nephoscope observations can give the wind speed only by order of magnitude.

The shape of high-level clouds sometimes may permit conclusions on the vertical structure of the wind field. So, for instance, virga from cirrus clouds often give an instructive picture of vertical wind shears. For cirri which lie below the level of maximum wind, $\partial V/\partial z$ is positive, and the virga are bending backwards under these circumstances. The wave structure of cirro-cumuli and alto-cumuli indicates discontinuities in the vertical gradients of temperature and wind speed (Schaefer, 1953*c*).

The observation of noctilucent clouds at about 70 to 90 km height (Wörner, 1935) offers the possibility of wind determination in the region of the meso- and ozonosphere. These clouds seem to form at a level of minimum temperature on the upper boundary of the ozonosphere ("mesopause") (Chapman, 1950; Nicolet, 1950; Paton, 1949, 1953; Wares, 1953). They confirm the "monsoonal" change of winds at this level with season; this matter will be discussed further in Chapter 4.415. Noctilucent clouds seem to appear only during summer (Ludlam, 1957; Spangenberg, 1949). Wind velocities in excess of 200 m/sec have been observed by these means (Chvostikov, 1952; Malzev, 1926; Störmer, 1935).

2.152. Observation of Artificial "Clouds"

Drift observations of artificial clouds usually offer the advantage of a known cloud height. Furthermore, an unambiguous target is given, which may be followed by double tracking (two nephoscopes or two theodolites). Stewart (1924) reports on smoke bombs dropped from aircraft to detect the upper-wind distribution. Durst (1948) describes a similar procedure to explore the turbulence in high-level flow. In the stratosphere wind speeds have been determined from drift velocities and diffusion of shrapnel clouds. Turbulence components of velocity of the order of magnitude of 4 to 10 cm/sec have been detected there (Johnson, 1946; Kellogg, 1952).

In this connection the possibility has to be mentioned of drawing conclusions on turbulence and fine structure of upper flow patterns from the deformation of contrails (U.S. Air Weather Service, 1956*b*).

Instead of smoke clouds, aluminum foil ("window", "chaff") has been used recently. The foil is ejected from aircraft, balloons, or rockets and is tracked by radar (Aufm Kampe, 1956, 1960; Barr, 1960; Jenkins and Webb, 1959; Rapp, 1960; Smith, 1960). This method seems to be very reliable because there are only small differences between the wind vectors computed from balloon (GMD-1A) and foil positions. (On the average the differences are less than 3.4 knots and 14.4°.) The discrepancies increase with increasing falling time, mainly because the wind field may have changed during the time between balloon ascent and descent of the foil (Anderson, 1956). Especially with strong upper winds when balloons are drifting rapidly toward low elevation angles and measurements become inaccurate, rockets and chaff releases offer decisive advantages at heights above 12 km.

Since foil "clouds" diffuse rapidly and then do not reflect the radar beam any longer, the use of small, metal-coated, automatically inflating balloons, dropped from rockets, has been suggested (Anderson, 1957*a*; Armstrong and Garrett, 1960; on dropping radio transmitters see Cline, 1957).

Photographic (Liller and Whipple, 1954) and radar measurements (Duncan, 1951; Kaiser, 1954; Robertson, Liddy, and Elford, 1953) of the drift of *meteor trails* also permits calculation of wind velocities at levels of about 90 km (Ekhart, 1940; Hughes, 1959). The movement of bright spots of "air glow," too, may give clues to the wind velocities in the upper atmosphere (Roach, 1959).

For wind speed measurements at high levels (> 50 km), clouds of metallic sodium vapor have been used successfully. They were released from rockets, and their luminescence in the 5890 Å line could be used for optical tracking (Edwards, Bedinger, and Manring, 1956).

Flashlight discharges, as used for marking a rocket trajectory, also displayed the upper-wind conditions (Woodbridge, 1959).

Ionospheric winds may be obtained from the drift velocities of electrically charged particle clouds. A comprehensive summary of such measurements has been given by Murgatroyd (1957).

2.153. Upper-Level Wind Measurement by Acoustical Methods

The speed of sound is given by (Gutenberg, 1932, 1946)

$$C = 20.1\sqrt{T}. \qquad 2.153\ (1)$$

It is dependent only on air temperature, assuming adiabatic and calm conditions. An increase of temperature in the upper stratosphere causes the sound beams to bend back toward the earth's surface (Regula, 1934, 1949). The effect of upper-level winds and vertical gradients in the wind causes an asymmetry in sound propagation. In order to separate the temperature effect from the effect of winds, and in order to draw conclusions on both quantities, azimuth and distance of the receiving station have to be varied with respect to the explosion center.

Modern procedures utilize exploding bombs (Crary, 1950*a*, *b*, 1952; Whipple, 1935). At the receiving station, a number of microphones is spread out. They permit an exact measurement of the arrival times, as well as the determination of height and azimuth angles of the incoming sound beam by comparing the different registrations. These calculations of angles put a great strain on the accuracies of the microphone registrations and especially on the synchronization, which is not always met.

The following quantities are measured: travel time (i.e., time between explosion and registration), distance from the explosion center, azimuth and apparent velocity of sound, C_a. The latter is defined as the velocity of the incoming sound wave while it traverses the horizontal terrain at the detector site. The evaluation follows a method which is also used in reflection seismics, with the exception of an additional wind velocity term appearing in each layer:

$$\frac{C_1}{\cos \alpha_1} + u_1 = \frac{C_2}{\cos \alpha_2} + u_2 = C_n + u_n = C_a. \qquad 2.153\ (2)$$

α_i is the angle between the normal to the wave front and the horizontal; u_i are the components of wind velocity in the direction of propagation of the sound wave in the ith layer. The subscript n stands for conditions in the uppermost layer. The conditions in the layers of the troposphere and lower stratosphere have been taken from radiosonde observations for the experiments conducted by Crary (1950*a*, *b*; and Bushnell, 1955). The height angle of the incoming sound beam has been calculated from the ratio of apparent speed of sound C_a to actual horizontal speed of sound. The latter could be determined from shots within the microphone network.

The conditions for measurements may be very complex, depending on the structure of the atmosphere. So, for example, during the winter of 1948 on one station in Alaska 20 to 30 arrival times have been registered from a single explosion. The apparent speeds of sound were between 320 and 400 m/sec. In such cases, a wide variation in the distances from the explosion center (mostly bomb drops) is necessary to ascertain the relationship between apparent speed of sound and altitude to some degree of reliability (Denver University, 1951; Kennedy, *et al.*, 1954*a*, *b*).

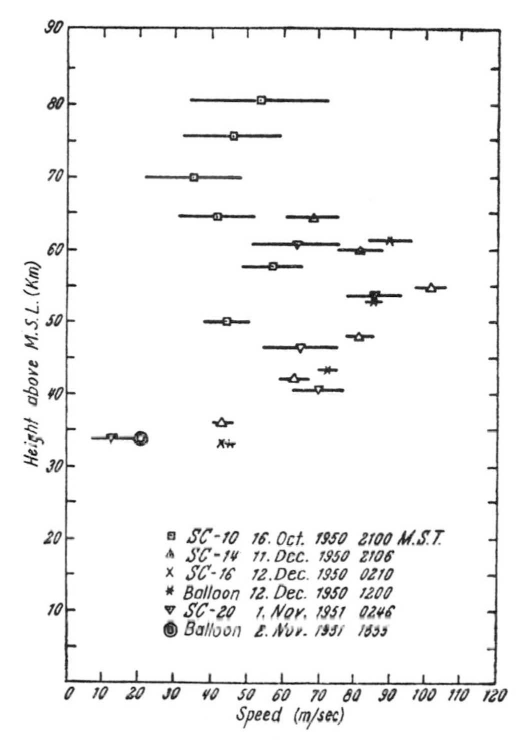

FIG. 2.153.—Acoustic upper-wind measurements with the aid of Aerobee Rockets, and comparative results from balloons over White Sands Proving Grounds, New Mexico. The lengths of the horizontal lines indicate the probable error in measurements. (After Weisner, 1956.)

The results are entered in travel-time diagrams similar to the ones used in seismology. From these one may draw conclusions on discontinuities in the vertical structure of the atmosphere. The influence of upper-level winds may be obtained from measurements at different azimuth angles made under the assumption that wind and temperature effects are additive. The following equation, then, is evaluated after the method of least squares:

$$C = C_T + u \cos (b - c). \qquad 2.153\ (3)$$

C is the speed of sound which has been read from the sound-velocity-height curves, C_T is the propagation speed caused by the temperature effect only, and u is the maximum wind speed occurring along the azimuth b. c is the geographic azimuth angle (i.e., the geographic direction of the explosion center with respect to the site of the microphones).

The wind component normal to the propagation direction of sound may be computed from the *azimuth shift*, i.e., from the difference of angle between the geographic location of the explosion and the direction from which the sound waves arrive at the site of measurement (Denver University, 1953; Kennedy, *et al.*, 1953).

If explosions are triggered in the high atmosphere, usually the determination of the wind vector is more dependable because the rising beam of sound propagation (from the ground into the stratosphere) is eliminated in the evaluation, and only the descending beam has to be taken into account. Grenades fired from rockets may serve as sources of sound ("rocket-grenade" experiment) (Hammond, 1955; Jones and Massey, 1956; Newell, 1955). For the computation of wind vectors in the different atmospheric layers, the positions of the exploding grenades, the travel time of sound between explosion and receiving station, and the angle of incidence of the sound waves has to be known. If the receiving station lies almost vertically underneath the point of explosion, the upper-wind computations become more accurate (Groves, 1956*b*). After a report by Weisner (1956) the average thickness of the layers, for which the wind values have been given, was 6.5 km. Checking of the acoustically measured winds by balloon tracking and—for daytime rocket flights—by optical positioning of the smoke clouds originating from the exploding grenades revealed good agreement. Figure 2.153 shows the results of a series of rocket ascents (Weisner, 1956). The horizontal dashes indicate the magnitude of the probable error. As can be seen from this diagram, the error increases with height. Nevertheless, from such measurements one may draw pertinent conclusions on the shape of vertical wind profiles at great heights. So, e.g., the winds measured over White Sands Proving Grounds, New Mexico, reveal a distinct maximum at approximately 55 km (peak velocities 104 m/sec $\pm$ 5 m/sec with a wind direction from $272° \pm 3°$, on 11 December).

The errors in wind measurement are mostly due to inaccuracies in measuring the time difference under which the sound waves arrive at the various microphones (Weisner, 1956). Other sources of errors, mostly of lesser importance, lie in the temperature measurements at the microphone site (at least four microphones are used), which may cause the speed of sound to be in error. Furthermore, faulty positioning of the exploding grenades, errors in determining the height and location of the different microphones, and finally the assumption of plane instead of spherical sound-wave fronts introduce inaccuracies. By a suitable distribution of the microphones, the errors may be reduced drastically (wind measurements accurate to ± 1 m/sec) (Groves, 1956*a*, *b*). Further details on upper-level wind measurements with the rocket-grenade method may be taken from Weisner's (1956) paper already cited above (see also Groves, 1956*c*; Michigan, 1955–56; Thuronyi, 1959).

2.2. INDIRECT UPPER-LEVEL WIND MEASUREMENTS

Indirect wind measurements from pressure analyses have lost importance during the last few years with the improvements in *direct* methods of measurement. Over areas where upper-level wind measurements are lacking, and where the topographies of isobaric surfaces give the only clue on flow patterns, generally the pressure analyses are largely in error, too (Murray, 1951).

Nevertheless, the indirect determination of upper-level winds carries a certain scientific importance. By a comparison with direct wind measurements it permits the computation of *ageostrophic* or *non-gradient* components of flow, which play an important role in the dynamics of jet streams.

Subsequently, a few sources of errors will be pointed out which may lead to a wrong estimate of pressure gradients and, thereby, of wind vectors.

2.21. Errors in Measurements of Radiosondes

The measurements of pressure and temperature by a radiosonde enter into the calculation of the height of an isobaric surface. Defective calibration, radiation, and lag effects may give rise to erroneous readings, which may lead to various systematic deviations with various types of radiosondes. This problem is of some importance over the European sector, with its large number of radiosonde models, and it is one of the reasons why the North American radiosonde network is preferred for detailed scientific analyses.

International radiosonde comparisons (e.g., as conducted at Payerne in 1950 and in 1956) have been made to try to determine the systematic deviations between the different radiosonde types (e.g., Beelitz, 1958; Bessemoulin, 1956; Hooper, 1957; International Meteorological Organization, 1951; Malet, 1954, 1955; Väisälä, 1957; see also Teweles and Finger, 1960). Special attention has been directed toward the different radiation errors to which the various types are subject during day-time ascents.

2.22. Accuracy of Wind Calculations

The computations of geostrophic and gradient winds usually is done with nomographs (see Chapter 3.243), which allow easy reading of wind speeds from the contour distance and streamline curvature (Amble, 1945; Dieterichs, 1952; Lamp, 1958; Matthews, 1956; Showalter, 1956; U.S. Air Weather Service, 1950*b*; Vialar, 1950).

Although in the lower troposphere there is no marked difference in accuracy between direct wind observations and gradient wind measurements (Hartmann, 1950; Matsuhashi and Furukawa, 1954)—the friction layer near the ground will be excluded here (Aubert and Winston, 1951*b*), as well as the flow conditions in low latitudes (Morley, 1953; Treloar, 1954)—the vector error of the gradient wind increases more rapidly in the upper troposphere and in the stratosphere (Godson, 1952, 1955*b*). This may be due primarily to the faulty interpolation in the analysis of non-linear and relatively large gradients at these levels, between widely separated stations.

Neiburger and his collaborators (1948) found that subjective errors in wind computations may give rise to variations up to 25 per cent (see also Primault, 1951). The gradient wind is superior to the geostrophic wind only if the *trajectory curvature* is taken into account, and not the curvature of the isohypses, i.e., if the motion of the pressure pattern enters into the calculations (see Chapter 3.243). The deviation of the gradient wind from the geostrophic wind may attain large values in cases of strong curvature (> 50 per cent [Väisänen, 1954; see Zobel, 1958]). The mean quadratic error of the geostrophic wind has been calculated by Crossley (1956*b*) to be 5 to 6 knots for an average wind velocity of 39 knots (see Kukhto, 1956). After Endlich and McLean (1960*a*, 1960*b*), in cyclonically curved jet streams the wind velocities taken from aircraft measurements are subgeostrophic by 27.5 knots on the average (= 18.4 per cent of the mean wind speed). The standard deviation of the geostrophic departure was 20 knots. The departures from the gradient wind, however, on the average were zero, and their standard deviation was 6 knots. These departures, even though they may not be very large, render *geostrophic* trajectories unreliable over short periods of time (Durst and Davis, 1957). At that, anticyclonic curvature has an even more pronounced effect; radii of curvature < 1000 km will have to be taken into account under all circumstances (Hartmann, 1950).

Next to instrument errors, errors in analysis play a dominant role in indirect upper-wind measurements. The latter are largely dependent on the density of the station network (Bessemoulin, *et al.*, 1960).

3

JET-STREAM ANALYSIS

3.1. GENERAL REMARKS

Deciding upon the "most suitable" method of analyzing jet streams is difficult because the wind field is continuous in four dimensions and an analysis must be limited to a two-dimensional surface. Therefore, we will have to chose two co-ordinates for the analysis, from the four along which the wind vector may vary. From this consideration we obtain six possible combinations. Thus, it will only depend on the purpose of the respective analysis, which of these combinations of co-ordinates should be preferred. For the thorough study of a jet-stream situation one combination will hardly ever suffice; one will have to use several combinations, in order to be able to integrate at least approximately the four-dimensional sequence in weather development.

Finally, we have to keep in mind that a two-dimensional analysis of the wind field may—by virtue of the vectorial nature of the wind—be made on the one hand after direction (isogons) and speed (isotachs), and on the other hand after the magnitude of the three velocity components parallel to the three directions of space.

As has already been described in Chapter 1.23, the derived quantities, i.e., divergence and vorticity, are particularly suited to offer an insight into the kinematics of the flow patterns. Since in graphical evaluation, a differentiation is transformed into the calculation of differences, we will have to explain practical methods for determining these derived quantities.

3.11. Common Systems of Analysis

In the co-ordinate systems described in Chapter 1.21 we have a number of pairs of co-ordinates at our command, which are suited for analyzing the wind field:

1. Analysis in the yz-plane or φz-plane (x and t remain constant): *meridional cross section*. In the nz-plane the analysis will be called a *cross section*.

2. Analysis in the xz-plane or λz-plane (y and t remain constant): *longitudinal cross section*. In the sz-plane we may call the analysis a *long section*.

3. Analysis in the tz-plane (x and y or λ and φ remain constant): *time section* for one particular station.

4. Analysis in the xy-plane (z and t remain constant): *weather map*.

5. Analysis in the yt-plane (x and z remain constant): *trend diagram*. Usually one choses the φt-plane for this presentation. An analysis in the nt-plane we may call a *space-time section*

6. Analysis in the xt-plane or λt-plane (y and z remain constant): *continuity chart*.

3.2. METHODS OF ANALYSIS

3.21. Cross Sections through the Atmosphere

3.211. General Remarks

In Figure 4.221.2 several cross sections through a jet-stream situation of 3 April, 1950, 1500 GCT are shown. In these diagrams, heavy lines indicate the boundaries of the frontal zone and the tropopause. Thin lines symbolize isotachs, and thin dashed lines represent isotherms. If the cross section is to serve for the study of a jet-stream situation, its plane should be oriented so that it lies as nearly *perpendicular* as possible to the wind direction in the jet axis (see Fig. 4.221.1). This may be done with the aid of an upper-level wind chart—preferably at the jet-stream level (300 or 250 mb). The advantage of such a choice lies in the fact that from the distance between isotachs in the final analysis one may directly obtain the maximum horizontal gradient of wind speed (wind shear), which, of course, is largest in the direction normal to the current. In general, the orientation of the cross-sectional plane is predestined by the distribution of aerological stations. It is especially important that the distance between *station* and *cross section*, measured normal to the plane of the latter, is not too large, and it should be as closely parallel to the upper current as possible. The last statement is essential for stations near the jet axis, because the horizontal gradients of the quantities describing the state and the motion of the atmosphere have a much larger magnitude in the direction *normal* to the current, than *parallel* to it. Cross sections which are drawn through strongly curved jet streams (e.g., through the tip of a low-pressure trough or through the crest of a high-pressure ridge) should utilize only stations which lie immediately on the axis of the section. Wherever this is not possible, the stations should be projected onto the cross section *not* perpendicularly to the orientation of the latter, but along streamlines of the jet stream. Now, the projection points of the aerological stations that will be used in the analysis are entered in a suitable distance scale on a cross-section diagram, which contains $\ln p$ or z as vertical co-ordinate.

If the cross section has to be drawn on a routine basis in order to gain an over-all view, it suffices to enter the significant points and standard levels of temperature, humidity, and wind into the cross-section diagram directly from the teletype messages. For more detailed analyses, however, it is recommended to plot the ascent at each station—if it is accompanied by a radiosonde—first on a thermodynamic diagram (e.g., a Stüve diagram or a tephigram). From the ascent curves thus obtained one may take the pressure values corresponding to discrete intervals of the intended analysis (e.g., at every 5° of temperature or potential temperature) and enter these points into the cross-section diagram. In analyzing the cross section, one has only to connect these points by smooth curves. By this, the accuracy of the analysis will be increased greatly, because one is relieved of an interpolation in the vertical. In order to present the structure of inversions and isothermal layers correctly, it will be necessary, nevertheless, to enter into the cross-section diagram in addition the values at significant points, or at least to consult the ascent curves in the thermodynamic diagrams while analyzing the cross section. For detailed analyses it would also be desirable to have the original ascent registrations available, because during the coding process of the ascent a certain amount of subjective smoothing is introduced, which may, at times, be rather disturbing, especially in tropopause analyses.

Another error is frequently made in cross-section analyses: If isotherms and isopleths of potential temperature are analyzed at the same time, one has to bear in mind that, according to Eq. 1.225 (1), the analysis of temperature predetermines the analysis of potential temperature *uniquely*, i.e., that isotherms and isopleths of Θ may only intersect each other at those pressure levels which satisfy Eq. 1.225 (1).

As far as they are used for the study of jet streams, *cross sections* usually are analyzed after isotachs of total wind speed. From the thermal structure of the atmosphere in the section, we may also obtain *geostrophic* wind speeds (Kaufmann, 1958). The wind direction is only rarely subject to analysis. In *meridional cross sections* usually only the velocity component normal to the plane of the section, i.e., the *zonal* component, is presented. Frequently such sections contain *average* flow conditions, as is the case in Figure 3.211, which is taken from a classical study by Palmén and Newton (1948). In this diagram the zonal component of the geostrophic wind has been analyzed, which has been averaged with respect to the position of the polar front for 12 cases in December, 1946. The cross-sectional plane runs along the meridian 80° W.

To account for the average structure of a jet stream, mean cross sections are frequently constructed which are based on a "natural" co-ordinate system with n and z as co-ordinates, moving with the speed of propagation of the jet maximum (Reiter, 1957*a*).

To present yearly mean values in a meridional cross section, the averaging is done with respect to geographic latitude (see Chapter 4.21). Because of the strongly *varying*

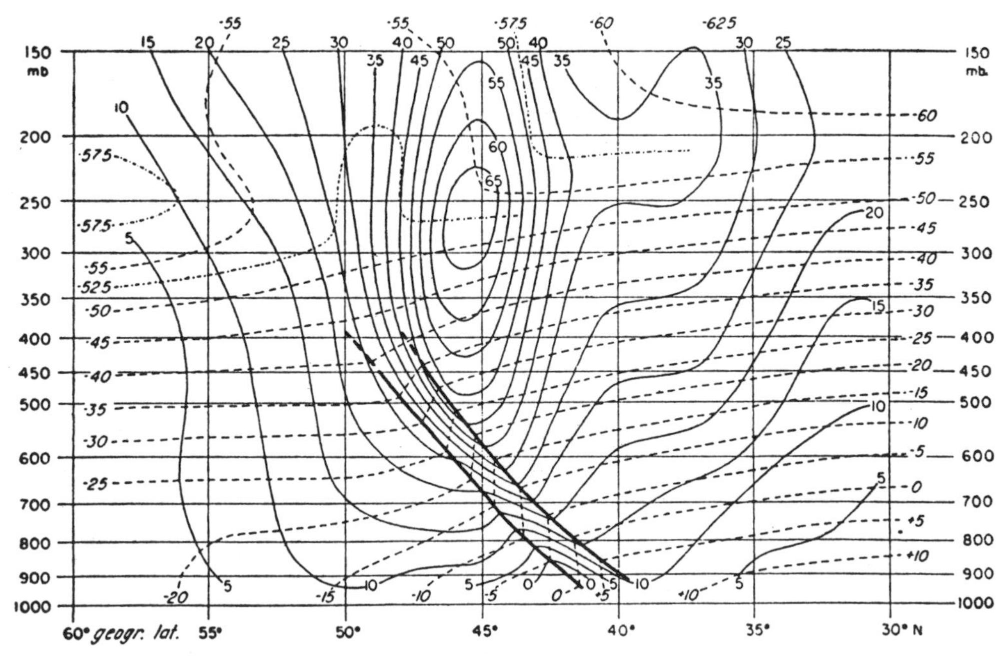

FIG. 3.211.—Mean cross section along 80° W for 12 jet-stream weather situations during December, 1946. Dashed lines, temperature (°C); solid lines, isotachs of the geostrophic wind speed (m/sec). Heavy lines indicate the frontal zone. The mean values have been computed with respect to the position of the polar front. (Palmén and Newton, 1948.)

position of jet streams, the velocity maxima appear much weaker developed in such representations, than is the case in Figure 3.211. Thus, cross sections obtained in this fashion constitute not so much a measure of the mean wind velocities present in the individual jet streams, but they reflect the more or less stationary character of these currents. The following quantities may be deduced from a carefully executed cross-section analysis:

1. The thermal wind component normal to the plane of the cross section,
2. the isopycnic level and the level of maximum wind,
3. the vertical wind shear.

3.212. The Thermal Wind Normal to the Plane of the Cross Section

From the geostrophic wind equation and the hydrostatic equation we obtain by suitable transformation

$$u = u_0(T/T_0) - (Tg/f) \cdot \int_{z_0}^{z} (1/T^2)(\partial T/\partial y)\, dz. \qquad 3.212\ (1)$$

u and u_0 are the wind components normal to the cross section at the levels z and z_0, respectively. T and T_0 are the temperatures at these two levels, measured in degrees Kelvin. In approximation we may write $T/T_0 \cong 1$. Assuming, furthermore, that $\partial T/\partial y$ is constant with height for a relatively thin layer, and symbolizing the mean temperature of the layer by $\bar{T}$, one obtains the approximate expression for the *thermal wind component* normal to the cross section:

$$u - u_0 = \Delta u = (-g/f\bar{T})(\partial T/\partial y) \cdot \Delta z. \qquad 3.212\ (2)$$

For $\partial T/\partial y = 0$ also $\Delta u = 0$, i.e., we have reached a level of extreme wind velocity. $\bar{T}$ as well as $\partial T/\partial y$ may be taken from the cross section. $\partial T/\partial y$ describes the slope of the isotherms against the horizontal direction. f is a function of geographic latitude and may be taken from tables. Thus, the vertical wind shear $\Delta u/\Delta z$ may be computed assuming geostrophic conditions (Bielinski, 1960). A graphical method of calculation from the slope of the isopleths of virtual potential temperature has been given by Matthewman (1950). A direct calculation of the geostrophic wind from the slope of isobars in a cross section cannot be recommended, because the determination of the slope angle is largely dependent upon inaccuracies in the analysis (Radok and Grant, 1951).

Diagrams for temperature cross sections in general contain $-\ln p$ as vertical co-ordinate. The thermal wind equation, therefore, should be derived for a co-ordinate system of this kind. Starting from the equation of motion 1.222 (7)

$$u_g = (-g/f)(\partial z/\partial y)$$

and from the hydrostatic equation, one obtains

$$\begin{aligned} \partial u/\partial(-\ln p) &= -\frac{g}{f}\frac{\partial}{\partial(-\ln p)}\left(\frac{\partial z}{\partial y}\right) \\ &= -(g/f) \cdot \partial/\partial y\,(\partial z/\partial(-\ln p)) \\ &= -(R/f) \cdot (\partial T/\partial y) \end{aligned} \qquad 3.212\ (3)$$

and by integration after the logarithm of pressure, assuming that $\partial T/\partial y$ is constant with height for a relatively thin layer, we arrive at

$$\Delta u = -(R/f)(\partial T/\partial y) \cdot \ln (p_0/p_1). \qquad 3.212\ (4)$$

3.213. The Isopycnic Layer

If in the representation of the cross section there appears a level in which isotherms and isobars are parallel (i.e., horizontal in this representation) we may derive for $p=\text{const.}$ also $T=\text{const.}$ and therefore according to the equation of state also $\rho=\text{const.}$ This level may be recognized over a limited area also on a constant pressure surface (e.g., the 300-mb or 250-mb surface). It appears everywhere on such a topography where the horizontal temperature gradient vanishes. In general, the isopycnic levels do not follow an equipotential surface. From analyses of the isopycnic level one may well detect wave disturbances in the jet stream (Doporto, 1951; and Morgan, 1947).

For $T=\text{const.}$, we have $\partial T/\partial y=0$, and, therefore, according to Eq. 3.212 (2) for geostrophic conditions of flow also $\partial u/\partial z=0$. The level of maximum wind, therefore, coincides with the isopycnic level as long as *geostrophic* conditions are realized (see Harsányi, 1960).

Isopycnic levels may also be found sometimes in lower atmospheric layers where they may appear in connection with low-level jet streams or levels of minimum wind velocity, in the manner described above.

3.214. The Vertical Geostrophic Wind Shear

Following the above derivation, the component normal to the plane of the cross section of the vertical geostrophic wind shear may readily be computed. Since the ageostrophic component of flow—as shall be discussed later—reaches a maximum at jet-stream level, we have to expect discrepancies between geostrophic and actually measured winds and wind shears.

3.22. Long Sections and Longitudinal Sections

Long sections through jet streams (co-ordinates s and z) are hardly ever found in meteorological literature, mainly because already small spatial differences between station location and axis of the long section may lead to large irregularities in the analysis, since $\partial/\partial s$ of the meteorological parameters is considerably smaller than $\partial/\partial n$ (Reiter, 1957*c*, 1958*c*).

Longitudinal sections, however, are used successfully for the study of meridional exchanges of angular momentum and mass (Palmén, Riehl, and Vuorela, 1958).

3.23. The Time Section

An example for a time section has already been given in Figure 2.123.2. If temperatures and potential temperatures should be analyzed together, one has to follow the directions given in Chapter 3.21 regarding the consistency between the two analyses, and also the transcriptions of the ascents from thermodynamic diagrams. Wind directions and speeds are either entered as pairs of numbers, or, if the time section is prepared routinely (e.g., for flight briefing), the usual wind arrows are plotted. For detailed analyses pairs of numbers of the observed values should be entered, because otherwise errors in drawing the wind directions may be made, and the wind speed is approximated only to the nearest 5 knots.

It is an advantage to enter the time axis from the right toward the left for temperate latitudes. In this fashion one may *qualitatively* compare the local changes in weather sequence directly with the synoptic weather pattern, which preferably follows a west-east direction of the upper current.

If the upper current were a purely advective phenomenon, i.e., if individual air particles of the current were not accelerated, one would obtain

$$\dot{\mathbf{v}} = \partial \mathbf{v}/\partial t + \mathbf{v} \cdot \nabla \mathbf{v} = 0 \qquad 3.23\ (1)$$

or

$$\partial V/\partial t = -V(\partial V/\partial s). \qquad 3.23\ (2)$$

The spatial changes of V along the streamline s, therefore, may be directly expressed by $\partial V/\partial t$, if the t- and s-axis are oriented in opposite directions. This is achieved for temperate latitudes by counting the t-axis from right toward left.

For analyses in tropical latitudes, in which the disturbances travel from east toward west one suitably lets the t-axis run from left toward right. The transformation from time into space co-ordinates thus obtained is only of *qualitative* and not of *quantitative* value because the assumption $\dot{\mathbf{v}} = 0$ which we made in Eq. 3.23 (1) is not valid in reality.

3.24. Upper-Wind Charts

3.241. General Remarks

The upper-wind charts most widely used in the daily weather service constitute analyses on constant pressure surfaces. For the representation of the jet-stream level in temperate latitudes (polar-front jet) the 300- and 250-mb surfaces are best suited. To represent the subtropical jet stream, one also has to use the 200-mb surface. The 100-mb surface is of importance in analyzing the tropical jet stream.

In order to comply with the demands of aeronavigation, Bellamy (1945*b*, 1951) proposes analyzing the anomalies of height from the standard atmosphere rather than the absolute geopotential heights.

$$D = z - z_p. \qquad 3.241\ (1)$$

D is the "altimeter correction," i.e., the amount by which the altimeter of an aircraft has to be corrected in order to avoid misreadings. z is the geopotential height of the respective isobaric surface. z_p is the height of the same surface in the N.A.C.A. (National Advisory Committee of Aeronautics) standard atmosphere. This atmosphere is also called the "U.S.-standard atmosphere." With the specific temperature anomaly S^* of virtual temperature

$$S^* = (T^* - T_p)/T_p \qquad 3.241\ (2)$$

we obtain the following relationship:

$$dD/dz_p = S^*. \qquad 3.241\ (3)$$

T^* is the observed virtual temperature at the respective level, T_p is the temperature of the standard atmosphere.

The advantage of these parameters lies in the fact that the normal vertical gradients of pressure and temperature have been eliminated so that from the anomalies the structure of wave disturbances at each synoptic map time may be studied more adequately. This becomes especially obvious in the analysis of cross sections.

From isobaric surfaces analyzed in D-isopleths, the geostrophic wind and gradient wind may be calculated in the customary fashion. For flight briefing the advantages of this method are obvious. The disadvantage of the D-analysis lies in the fact that the tropopause of the standard atmosphere (at $-55.0°$ C, at the height of 10,769 m and at a pressure of 234.53 mb) introduces a discontinuity which has to be taken into account when interpolating between points on either side of this tropopause.

The thermodynamic diagram corresponding to the D-analysis is the so-called pastagram (*p*ressure *a*ltitude *s*pecific *t*emperature *a*nomaly dia*gram*) with S^* and z_p as co-ordinates. This is an equal area diagram for energy calculations and it is especially suited for the construction of time sections.

According to the radiosonde code for combined radiosonde and wind measurements, wind directions and speeds are reported at standard pressure levels. In areas with a sparse observation network, especially in the tropics, where the geostrophic wind equation loses its validity, it may be easier to draw streamline maps from the standard levels of pilot balloons. For the surface layers a wind analysis on equipotential surfaces rather than on constant pressure surfaces is preferred also in areas with a relatively dense station network, because this gives a better means of comparison of the flow patterns in a layer of constant thickness close to the ground. Since the height of an isobaric surface undergoes large variations in time and space, the height variation of wind in the surface layer influenced by friction would appear rather disturbingly in these analyses. In the free atmosphere, however, where the equations for the geostrophic and the gradient wind are valid in good approximation, the importance of the horizontal pressure gradient predominates over the height dependency of the wind field.

Although the density of the observation network of continental areas of the northern hemisphere—especially in the jet-stream area of temperate latitudes—leaves little to be desired for large-scale aerology, the researching synoptician should strive to utilize all available observations in a thorough analysis. This should be done because the discrepancies between neighboring stations due to errors in measurements as discussed in Chapter 2 can only be detected if as many data as possible are available. In general, the analyst at a weather station will have the 500-mb chart at his dispoal. This level should be used for comparison with the jet-stream analysis. Also the surface weather map of the respective synoptic time should be consulted.

The analysis of upper-level wind maps is greatly facilitated by an easy-to-survey plotting of data (U.S. Air Weather Service, 1950*a*; U.S. Office of Naval Operations, 1952). In the weather services upper winds are marked by arrows whose points lie in the station of observation, whose direction gives the wind direction, and whose barbs indicate the wind speed: one black triangle for each 50 knots, one long dash for each 10 knots, and one short dash for each 5 knots. The wind speed, thus, is approximated to the nearest 5 knots. Since the wind values in the teletype messages are given to the nearest knot, this representation introduces an additional uncertainty of 4 knots. Experience shows that map-plotters may make errors in estimating the wind direction when entering the observation data which may amount to 20° under circumstances, discounting the rather obvious errors of 90° or 180° which may be detected easily in the analysis. The routine of data-plotting and analysis at a weather office usually is subject to great time pressure. Such weather maps, therefore, should not be used for detailed scientific studies of jet streams, although they may render a good view of the weather situation.

For scientific analyses the choice of map scale and projection is important. Weather services of the temperate latitudes make wide use of Lambert's conformal conic projection (true at latitude 30° and 60°). For hemispheric analysis, as they are frequently used for the study of jet streams and of the general circulation, stereographic projections are available. Analyses of the tropical areas are best done on cylinder projections. Also for temperate latitudes cylinder projections (Mercator projections) may be used to advantage because streamline analyses with the aid of isogons are especially simple on such maps, as will be shown below. Furthermore, the geostrophic wind in temperate latitudes shows only small variations with latitude on these maps, because the increasing Coriolis parameter is partly compensated by the distortion of a line element on the map. Because the scale of the projection increases with geographic latitude, an element $\Delta y'$ of constant length corresponds to a line element Δy on the earth's surface which decreases with increasing latitudes. (See Chapter 3.247.)

The map scale offers optimal conditions for analysis if the average distance between neighboring aerological stations is approximately 3 to 5 cm. If the map scale is too small, the detailed structure is lost; if it is too large, however, the analysis becomes difficult to examine. At weather stations, maps with a scale of 1:10,000,000 are widely used.

For more detailed analyses numerical values of wind speed and wind direction should be entered on the map which is to be analyzed in order to avoid the time-consuming search among teletype reports for dubious data. Over areas with a *dense* station network the barbs of the wind arrows are not an aid because with high wind speeds the picture rather becomes more confused than clearer. It suffices if the wind direction is given by a simple dash, for this indicates already the direction of the streamline. Isogons and isotachs may be analyzed directly from the numerical values.

If the streamlines are analyzed directly from the wind arrows without making use of the isogon analysis, one has to pay particular attention to the accuracy with which the wind directions have been plotted (Reiter, 1957*a*).

The sparser the observation network, the more resourceful the analyst will have to be in utilizing all available material. In any case, upper wind observations from pilot balloons and rawins will have to be used. On the average, the 30,000-ft level (9 km) corresponds to the polar-front jet, the 40,000-ft level (12 km) corresponds to the subtropical jet stream. Wind measurements of this kind, which have been obtained without simultaneous radiosonde ascent, should be marked on the map by giving the height in kilometers or in thousands of feet. This should be done for the following two reasons:

1. These measurements have been made with the aid of a different method, which is subject to different, usually larger (with the exception of radar) errors (see Chapter 2).

2. Since the vertical wind shear may be large in strongly baroclinic currents (as for instance in the jet stream connected with a frontal zone), the height differences between the standard height level of a pilot balloon and the respective isobaric surface may introduce a systematic error which may, however, easily be accounted for in the analysis: if the corresponding isobaric surface shows a temperature gradient indicating

an increase of wind speed with height [see thermal wind equation 3.212 (2)], the wind value given on a standard level *below* the isobaric surface will be too small. A level above this isobaric surface will report too strong a wind, unless the *isopycnic* level has been penetrated in the layer between the two wind reports (see Chapter 3.213). In order to estimate the differences between wind speeds on isobaric surfaces and adjacent level surfaces correctly, the reports 5000 ft above as well as 5000 and 10,000 ft (1500 to 3000 m) below the 30,000 ft level (9 km) should be entered.

For jet-stream analyses over areas with sparse observation network, as for instance over large parts of Asia (India) it will help to consult observations from other levels and from other map times, too. Since the wind direction varies only slightly with height in the jet-stream region, all pilot balloon ascents should be entered into the maps which reach at least the 20,000 ft level (6 km). For a streamline analysis these reports still give a rather dependable clue. An isotach analysis in the region of a baroclinic zone, however, has to be treated with great care, if it is mainly based on such observations (Reiter, 1959*a*). Taking into account the speed and direction with which disturbances in the pressure and wind fields are propagating, one may utilize to advantage reports which stem from map times 6 to 12 hours earlier.

Over the vast oceanic areas we have available only the upper wind observation of a few weather ships, which are cruising only in the regions of the temperate latitudes of the northern hemisphere preferred by traffic. In addition to this, we have several weather reconnaissance flights at the 500-mb level in the Atlantic, Pacific and north polar regions which measure the thermal structure of the lower layers of the atmosphere by drop sondes. The wind observations of these reconnaissance flights, however, usually are not very dependable because of navigational difficulties. Upper-level wind measurements over the oceans of the tropics and the southern hemisphere are extremely sparse. For wide areas we have only the measurements from expeditions available (e.g., "Meteor"-cruises and several south pole expeditions). Only in the International Geophysical Year 1957/58 have these latitudes been subject to more detailed investigations.

Since a sparse observation network allows too much leeway to the fantasy of the analyst, one uses the method of differential analysis for constructing upper-level weather maps:

Step 1: The surface pressure distribution is rather reliably given by ship and island observations. It can be converted without difficulties into the absolute topography of the 1000-mb surface (AT 1000).

Step 2: The relative topography 850 over 1000 mb (RT 850/1000) contains already less points of observation. It may, however, still be drawn by empirically considering the surface pressure and temperature distribution.

Step 3: By graphical addition to AT 1000 one obtains the AT 850, whereby certain roughnesses in the analysis may be smoothed out by utilizing the actual radiosonde measurements of coastal stations and weather ships. The AT 850 thus obtained is substantially more accurate than if the analysis had been made from the few available ascents only, because now the mean temperature of the layer 850- to 1000-mb and the surface pressure distribution has been properly considered. Analogously, one obtains the analysis of higher levels: RT 700/850 added to AT 850 renders AT 700; RT 500/700 added to AT 700 gives AT 500; etc. The analyses are facilitated by the fact that the direction of temperature gradients in the middle and upper troposphere changes only slightly until the isopycnic level is reached, and that the atmosphere is almost barotropic over wide regions, so that the configuration of contour lines in the different relative topographies is very similar.

This method of "differential analysis" may appear uneconomical and cumbersome at first sight; it counteracts, however, one error which usually is present in graphical analyses: In interpolating between neighboring stations one tends to analyze for a *linear* gradient, i.e., the existing intervals of pressure or temperature are subdivided by equidistant contour lines (isobars or isotherms). If the geostrophic wind is calculated from contour distances, the resulting wind profiles will be smoothed drastically. Above all, the peak velocities will be strongly reduced. As shall be shown in Chapter 4.122, the velocity profiles on both sides of the jet-stream axis are *not* linear. With the scanty observation network over oceans, a jet-stream analysis therefore would be impossible there. Although the analyses of the different relative topographies are subject to the same smoothing tendencies, the present gradients now will be *added*. Above all, the structure of the lower tropospheric layers, which is substantiated by more observations, is properly taken into account at higher levels.

For the significant analysis of upper level weather charts over oceanic and tropical areas, the construction of *time sections* for the existing aerological stations is indispensable (see 3.23). From these, the passage of wave disturbances and jet maxima may be pinpointed at stations located upstream, and the horizontal weather sequence may be interpreted accordingly. In doing this, the average rates of propagation of wave disturbances taken from statistics by Namias (1947*a*) may be utilized (Petterssen, 1956).

TABLE 3.241. Eastward Propagation of Troughs in the Upper Current

Season	Average geostrophic wind velocity at 700 mb in 35° to 55° N (° longitude/day)	Velocity of short waves (° longitude/day) in 40° N	Velocity of long waves (5-day average) (° longitude /day) in 40° N
Winter	12.3	11.8	1.2
Spring	9.3	10.4	2.0
Summer	7.0	8.0	1.5
Autumn	10.7	9.9	0.8

The position of long-wave troughs, therefore, may be kept constant without making too large an error, while the short-wave troughs are traveling eastward with a velocity variable with season. Continuity diagrams as described in Chapter 3.26 facilitate the determination of the position of wave disturbances.

The upper troposphere and lower stratosphere could yield more observational data than is presently the case, with the intercontinental flights of airlines. Here much better international co-operation will be necessary to initiate a synoptic observation service similar to the one making the ship observations. Statistical studies over the Pacific (Serebreny, 1951, 1955; and Wiegman, 1953; Serebreny, Wiegman, and Carlson, 1954*a*, *b*; Serebreny, Wiegman, and Hadfield, 1957) revealed that the position of the jet stream is approximately identical with the position of a zone of maximum concentration of temperature (ZOMCOT) at the 500-mb level, corresponding to the frontal zone. The region with maximum horizontal temperature gradient runs parallel to a zone with strong horizontal wind shears, whereby the higher wind velocities are found on the warm side of this frontal zone. Under the assumption that the velocity field at the 300-mb level is approximately parallel to the field at the 500-mb level, one may obtain a rough picture of the jet stream at the 300-mb level by adding the thermal wind (obtained from the relative topography of 300/500-mb) to the 500-mb isotachs (McClellan, 1954). A vectorial addition of the winds may be carried out with the aid of a nomograph, if it should prove necessary (Sieland, 1951).

3.242. Analysis of the Velocity Field

The wind *speed* shows all characteristics of a scalar field (U.S. Air Weather Service, 1951). *Maxima* and *minima* of wind speed appear as *singular points*. The line of maximum wind speed is called the *jet axis*. Lines of minimum wind speed are not marked in the analysis, unless they separate areas with opposite wind direction, as shown in Figure 3.242.1 (dashed line). Such lines are called *shear lines*; they coincide with strongly developed, elongated low-pressure troughs.

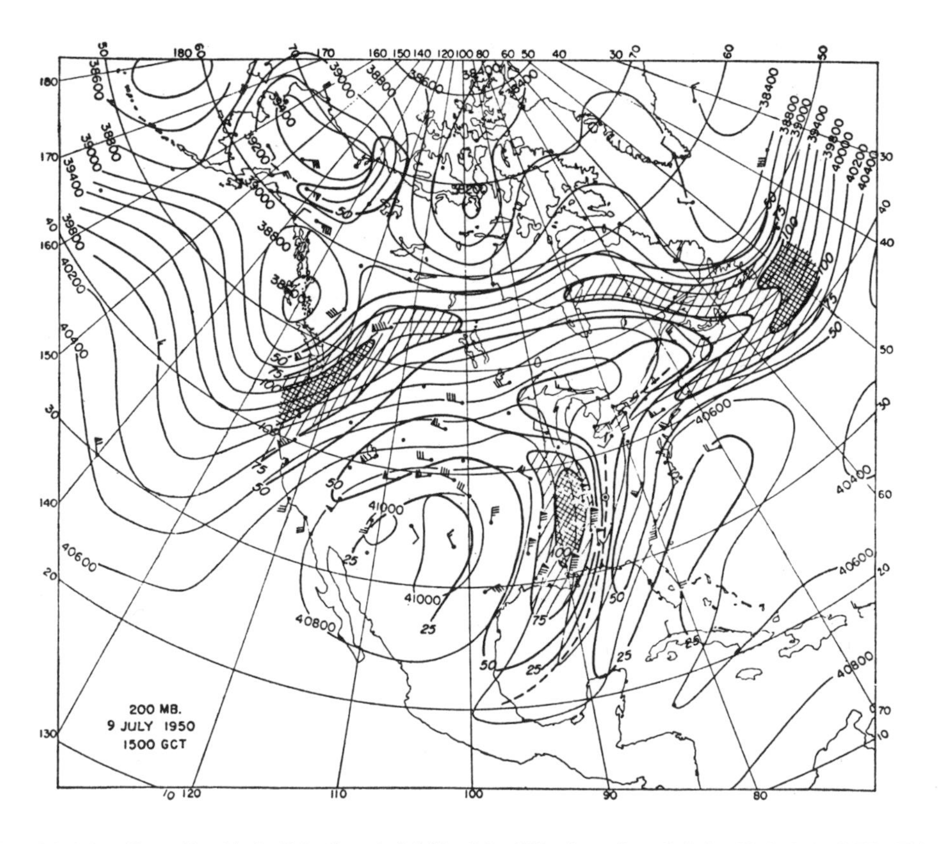

Fig. 3.242.1.—Shear line (dashed) in the wind field of the 200-mb surface (9 July, 1950, 1500 GCT). Thin lines, contours (ft); heavy lines, isotachs (knots). (From Rossby, 1951*b*, after Newton *et al.*, 1951.)

In the analysis of the wind field in terms of isotachs the following principles have to be observed:

1. Similar to isobars, isotachs can neither cross nor touch each other, because each point of the atmosphere has an unambiguous wind-speed value attached to it.

2. The closer the packing of isotachs, the larger is the wind shear $\partial V/\partial n$. In general, the shear is larger on the cyclonic side of a jet stream than on the anticyclonic side (see Chapter 4.122). As will also be shown later, the shears are not constant. In well-pronounced jet streams $\partial^2 V/\partial n^2$ is positive on the cyclonic side and negative on the anticyclonic side—except for an area in the immediate vicinity of the jet axis—i.e., the shear decreases outward from a maximum in the close vicinity to the jet axis. One should not attempt, therefore, to enforce an analysis with uniform isotach spacing.

3. Aside from small areas, the maximum possible shear on the anticyclonic side of a jet stream is given by the condition, that the vertical component of the absolute vorticity Q_z becomes zero. Stronger shears would render the current dynamically unstable (see Chapter 1.236). The distance between isotachs, therefore, is given by:

$$V/r_s - \partial V/\partial n + f = 0. \qquad 3.242\ (1)$$

This equation is most readily solved graphically. Since the area over which the absolute vorticity is zero hardly ever exceeds 5° of latitude in width, f and r_s may be assumed constant with the value that corresponds to the center of the interval Δn. Therefore,

$$\Delta V = (V/r_s + f)\Delta n = \Delta V_1 + \Delta V_2, \qquad 3.242\ (2)$$

where

$$\Delta V_1 = f \cdot \Delta n \qquad 3.242\ (3)$$

$$\Delta V_2 = (V/r_s)\,\Delta n. \qquad 3.242\ (4)$$

ΔV_1 depends on the shear, ΔV_2 on the curvature. In practical application one proceeds by computing ΔV_1 under the assumption of straight flow, and by applying ΔV_2 as a correction for curvature to this result.

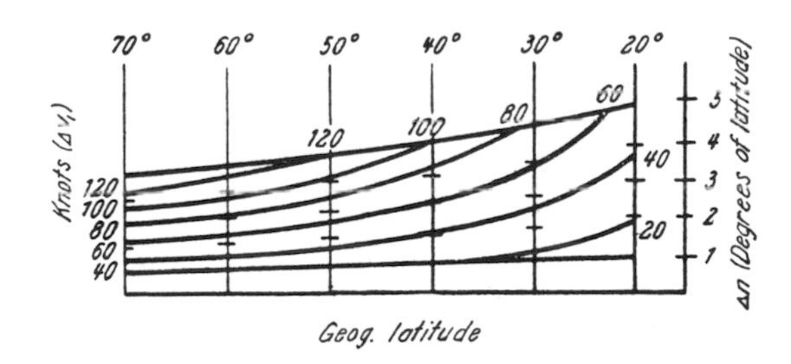

FIG. 3.242.2.—Nomograph (to be printed on a transparent foil) for computing horizontal wind shear with straight flow on the anticyclonic side of a jet stream in the area $Q = 0$ (see text). (Riehl, Alaka, *et al.*, 1953.)

Figure 3.242.2 shows a nomograph for Lambert's conformal projection (true at latitudes 30° and 60°). It is drawn on a transparent foil to the scale of the map in use. With this nomograph we may, on the one hand, estimate the distance between isotachs in the area in which $Q_z = 0$; on the other hand we may compute the wind speed in the jet axis if its position is known and one wind observation is available in the area $Q_z = 0$. The nomograph contains the distances Δn along the ordinate (marked by horizontal dashes on the right margin and along the vertical lines). The abscissa gives the relation with geographic latitude expressed in 3.242 (3), which is caused by the Coriolis parameter. To determine the distance between isotachs, the nomograph is placed at the jet axis with the point determined by *geographic latitude* and *wind speed in the jet axis*, and with the lower edge of the diagram parallel to the direction of flow. The distance between isotachs may, then, be transferred directly from the nomograph to the map.

In the determination of the wind maximum from a station report in the area $Q_z = 0$, one proceeds the other way around: The lower edge of the nomograph—again parallel to the upper current—is placed with the proper latitude line upon the station which reported the wind value. The distance Δn between station and jet axis then gives directly the wind speed difference ΔV_1 from the diagram.

The correction for curvature may be determined in per cent from 3.242 (4), if it is written in the form,

$$\Delta V_2/V = \Delta n/r_s. \qquad 3.242\ (5)$$

V is the average speed in the interval Δn and, as such, an unknown quantity. V is best computed by an iterative procedure. For cyclonic curvature the correction is positive, for anticyclonic curvature, negative. Figure 3.242.3 shows a nomograph which may be used

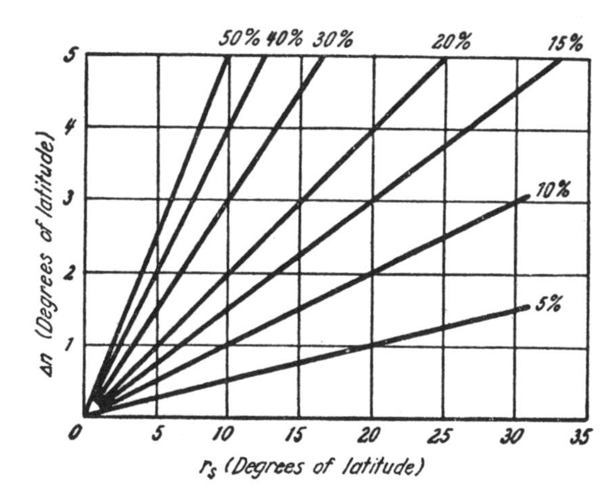

FIG. 3.242.3.—Nomograph for computing the per cent correction for curvature to be applied to maximum winds speeds calculated from Figure 3.242.2 (see text). (Riehl, Alaka, *et al.*, 1953.)

for such calculations. The abscissa of this nomograph contains the radius of curvature; Δn appears in the ordinate. Both quantities are expressed in units of 111.2 km (=1° of latitude). Interpolation between isopleths renders the per cent correction which has to be applied to ΔV_1. For cyclonically curved flow usually one approximation suffices, which is applied to the wind speed in the jet axis. For anticyclonic curvature, however, an iterative computation process is required, which has to be applied to the mean speed of the interval Δn (Riehl, Alaka, Jordan and Renard, 1954). The radius of curvature r_s is determined from the tangent circle, which also may be measured by means of a suitable transparent overlay. The following numerical example may serve to illustrate the above statements:

Let the distance Δn between station and jet axis be 3° of latitude, measured at a latitude of 40°. From Figure 3.242.2 one obtains $\Delta V_1 = 60$ knots. The distance between isotachs is given along the 40°-line in this diagram. If the station reports a wind speed of 75 knots, the wind speed in the jet axis will be 135 knots. With a *cyclonic* radius of streamline curvature of 10° of latitude (=1112 km), the correction will amount to 30 per cent of 135 knots, i.e., approximately 40 knots. The wind speed in the jet axis, therefore, will be 175 knots.

With *anticyclonic* curvature of the same amount, the mean wind speed in the interval Δn will be $(135+75)/2=105$ knots. A correction of 30 per cent amounts to roughly 30 knots, and the wind speed in the jet axis, therefore, would be in first approximation $135-30=105$ knots. For a second approximation the calculation process will be repeated: $(105+75)/2=90$ knots would be the mean wind speed in the interval Δn. Thirty per cent of this amounts to approximately 25 knots. The wind speed in the jet axis, therefore, is $135-25=$ *110 knots.*

The distance between isotachs determined from the nomograph for straight flow, of course, will have to be adjusted for the curvature conditions. For anticyclonic curvature the wind shear is less than with straight flow, for cyclonic curvature it is more.

4. Distances between isotachs on the cyclonic side of a jet stream may be obtained from our knowledge of the mean structure of jet streams (Lee, 1954). More details on this will be reported in Chapter 4.122. Since here we are dealing with statistical results, the computed values will not be as dependable as the ones obtained from the procedure with $Q_z=0$, as described above. Nevertheless, under the assumption of *average* shearing conditions, the position of the jet axis may be determined to some degree of accuracy if one wind observation is given for each, the cyclonic and the anticyclonic side of the jet stream.

3.243. Geostrophic Wind and Gradient Wind

If the direct wind observations do not suffice for an analysis of the upper wind field, the wind speed will have to be computed from the pressure distribution. For straight flow Eq. 1.222 (7) is valid, for curved flow 1.223 (2) holds. It has to be remembered, however, that the equations for geostrophic and gradient wind are fulfilled only for horizontal and isobaric motion. Currents near the entrance and exit regions of a jet maximum are not properly expressed by these equations, because in these areas the ageostrophic accelerations or retardations constitute an essential part of the wind field.

As arises from Eq. 1.223 (5), the gradient wind may be regarded as a function of the geostrophic wind. The latter, therefore, will have to be determined also in case of curved isobars.[1] One proceeds by drawing lines normal to the isobars (isohypses) at some distance from each other. From the distance between neighboring contour lines the geostrophic wind for the corresponding geographic latitude may be computed with the aid of a nomograph. The results of these computations are entered to the left of each of these normal lines. By means of a transparent overlay containing arcs of different radii (given in degrees of latitude of the corresponding map scale), one then measures the radius of curvature of the trajectories. The correction thus computed has to be applied to the geostrophic wind in order to arrive at the gradient wind. The results are marked down to the right of the normal lines on the map. The isotach analysis now may be performed, following the principles 1 through 4 of the preceding section.

[1] A nomograph for the direct calculation of the gradient wind without the aid of the geostrophic wind is given by Fortak (1960).

Geostrophic Wind Nomographs.—On a transparent overlay the contour distances for a certain interval of analysis (e.g., 200 gpf or 100 gpm) are entered along the abscissa in the *scale of the corresponding map*. The ordinate contains the geographic latitude. Lines of equal wind speed may be drawn in this nomograph by the aid of Table 3.243.

TABLE 3.243. DISTANCE BETWEEN CONTOUR LINES (IN DEGREES OF LATITUDE) ON THE MAP (CONTOUR INTERVAL 100 gpm)

GEOGRAPHIC LATITUDE	WIND SPEED IN KNOTS									
	5	10	20	30	40	60	80	100	150	200
10°	135.66	67.83	33.92	22.61	16.96	11.31	8.48	6.78	4.52	3.38
20°	68.83	34.42	17.21	11.47	8.60	5.73	4.30	3.44	2.29	1.72
30°	47.00	23.50	11.75	7.83	5.88	3.92	2.94	2.35	1.57	1.18
40°	36.60	18.30	9.15	6.10	4.58	3.05	2.29	1.83	1.22	0.92
50°	30.82	15.41	7.70	5.14	3.85	2.57	1.93	1.54	1.03	0.77
60°	27.20	13.60	6.80	4.53	3.40	2.27	1.70	1.36	0.91	0.68
70°	25.00	12.50	6.25	4.17	3.13	2.09	1.56	1.25	0.83	0.63
80°	23.88	11.94	5.97	3.98	2.99	1.99	1.50	1.19	0.80	0.60

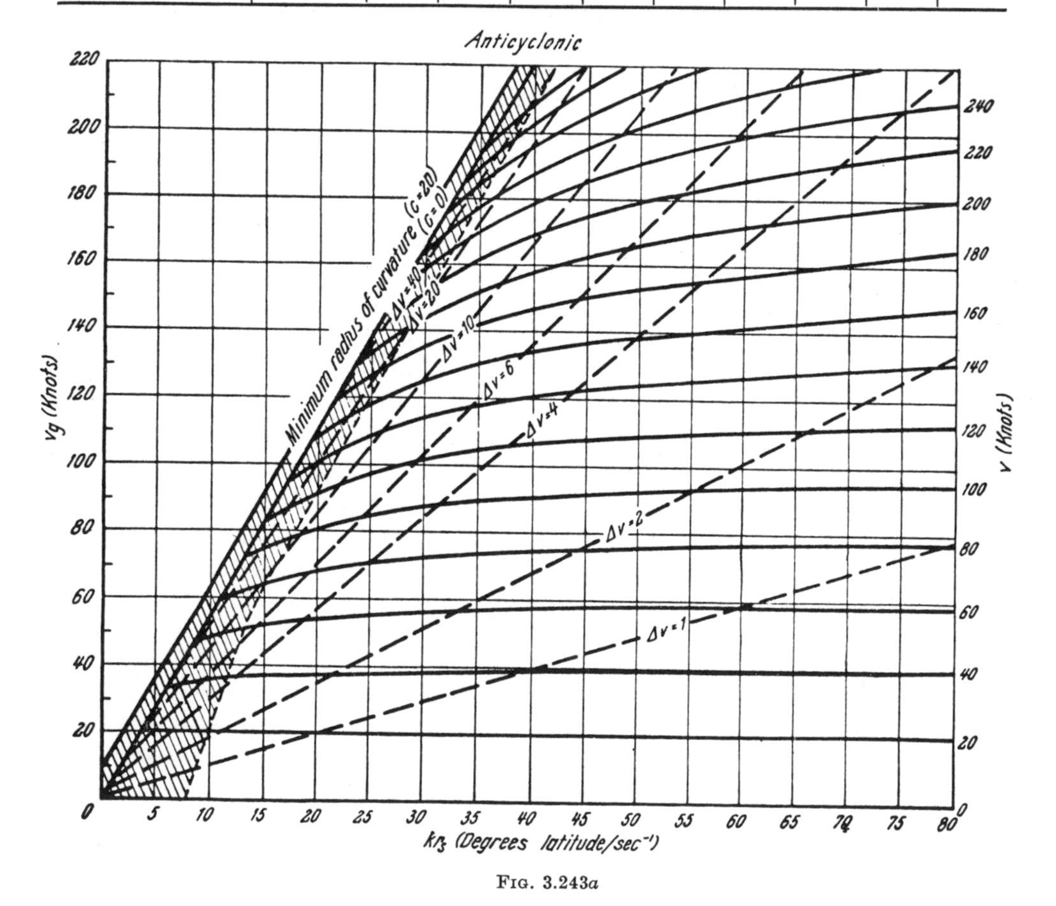

FIG. 3.243*a*

FIG. 3.243.—Gradient wind nomographs: (*a*) anticyclonic, (*b*) cyclonic flow. For explanation see text. (Riehl, Alaka, *et al.*, 1953.)

The mean geostrophic wind speed may also be determined by planimetering the area which is contained between two isohypses and two meridians. The wind speed is inversely proportional to this planimetered area (Robertson and Cameron, 1952).

The gradient wind is computed from Eq. 1.223 (5). The values of (rf) for different geographic latitudes and different radii of curvature may be taken from tables (List, 1958), as well as the gradient wind speed V as a function of the geostrophic wind speed V_g and of (rf) (see Silvester, 1955). More expediently, however, these computations are done graphically with the aid of a nomograph such as the one devised by Bellamy (1945*b*), which excels in its clearness and simplicity of handling. It does *not* take into account, however, the rate of displacement of troughs and ridges in the high-level pressure distribution. It, therefore, is based upon the assumption, that streamlines and trajectories are identical.

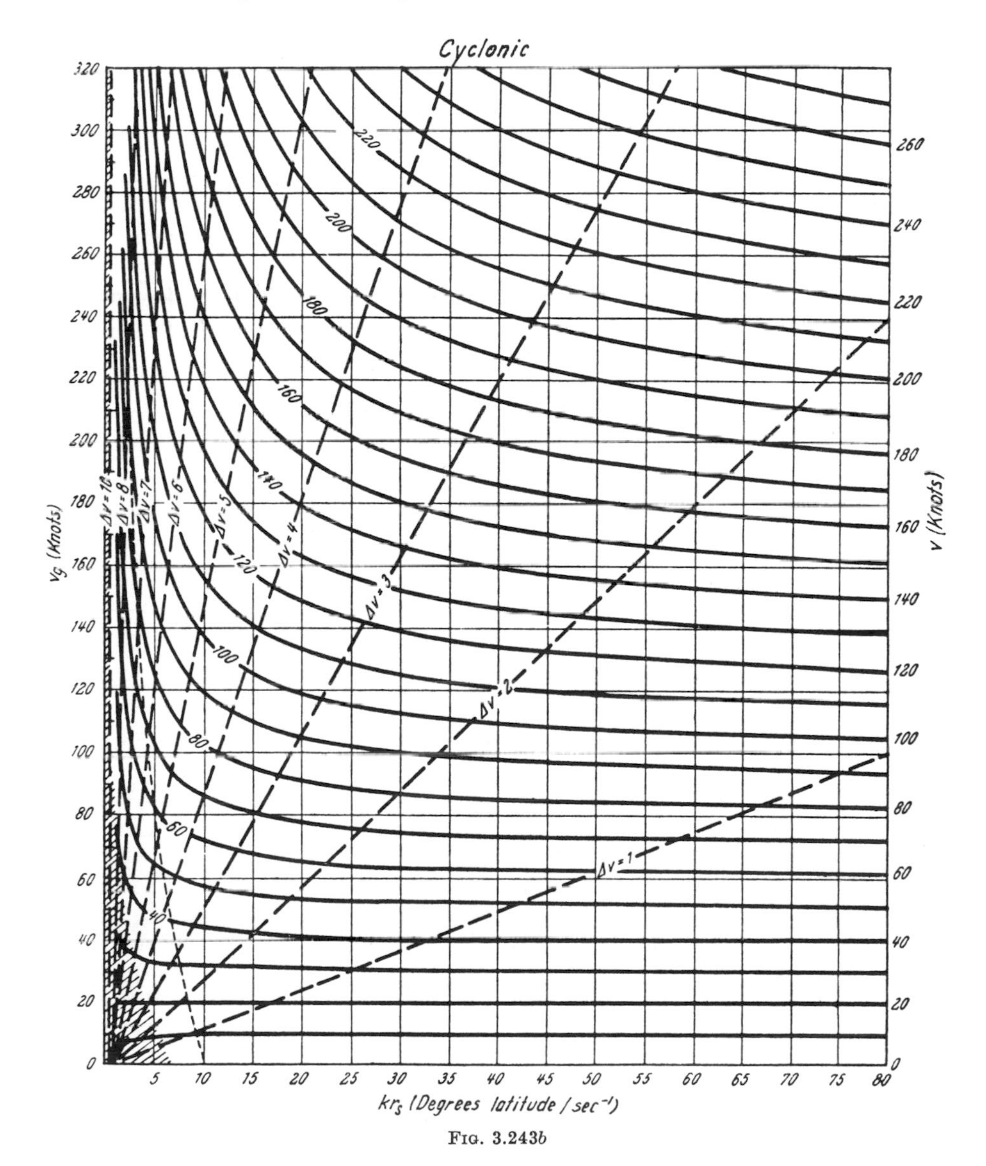

FIG. 3.243*b*

From upper-air maps only the curvature of the isohypses—equal to the streamline curvature under gradient flow conditions—can be read directly. It is, however, the curvature of the *trajectories*, that enters into the computations. From Table 3.241 we may see that short-wave troughs travel eastward at the rate of about 11° of longitude per day on the average. In temperate latitudes, this corresponds to a speed of about 20 knots, i.e., a west wind of 20 knots would follow a straight trajectory even with arbitrary streamline curvature and therefore would experience geostrophic conditions in spite of the curved streamlines.

At the University of Chicago nomographs have been devised for each, anticyclonic and cyclonic curvature (Hughes, Jordan, and Renard, 1952), which take into account the rate of propagation of the system (Figure 3.243*a* and *b*). First the radius of curvature r_s of the streamline is determined by means of an overlay. The abscissa of the diagrams is entered with the value of Kr_s. The factor of K corresponds to 10^4 times the Coriolis parameter.

Latitude	25	35	45	55	65	75°
K	0.6	0.8	1.0	1.2	1.3	1.4

The two nomographs have been constructed for an average rate of propagation of the wave disturbances of 20 knots, *parallel to the wind direction*. If this assumption holds true, which is usually the case in temperate latitudes at jet-stream level, one may directly read the gradient wind speed from the hyperbolically curved lines at the intersections of the Kr_s-lines with the horizontal lines of the geostrophic wind (labeled on the left margin of the diagrams). If the rate at which the pressure systems travel on the upper-air maps is different from the one given above, this may be taken into account by a correction. If V_c is the gradient wind corrected with respect to the actual speed C of the system. and V is the uncorrected gradient wind, we may write as an approximation,

$$V_c = V + \alpha \Delta V. \qquad 3.243\ (1)$$

The values of the correcting factor α are given in the following table:

C	−20	0	20	40	60 knots
α cyclonic	−2	−1	0	1	2
α anticyclonic	2	1	0	−1	−2

The values for ΔV are obtained by interpolation between the straight dashed lines in the two nomographs.

Example: With a radius of curvature of 8° at about 60° latitude, $Kr_s = 10$ (degrees latitude·sec^{-1}). For a geostrophic wind of 160 knots the gradient wind for the cyclonic case is 112 knots. For a stationary pressure field ($C = 0$) the factor α assumes the value −1, and $\Delta V = 5$. Thus, the gradient wind corrected for the motion of the system has a speed of 107 knots.

The equation, 3.243 (1), is only an approximation, because, strictly speaking, ΔV is not directly proportional to C, but also depends on the angle between the vectors **v** and **C**. In the non-shaded areas of the two diagrams, the error which this approximation introduces into the calculation of the gradient wind, is less than 10 per cent.

If the rate of displacement of the systems were not taken into account at all—which would correspond to using Bellamy's nomograph—the error would be less than 10 per cent to the right of the light dashed curve in the cylonic case, and to the right of the shaded area in the anticyclonic case.

3.244. Isogons, Streamlines and Trajectories

Isogons (lines of constant wind direction) are drawn as a first step in a detailed *streamline analysis*. Streamlines are curves which in each point of space are tangential to the *instantaneous* wind vector. Let $d\mathbf{s}$ be a line element of a streamline, with the components (dx, dy). The analytical expression for a streamline is obtained from the tangential condition,

$$\mathbf{v} \times d\mathbf{s} = 0 \qquad 3.244\ (1)$$

or, for a point with the co-ordinates (x,y),

$$dy/dx = v_{(x,y)}/u_{(x,y)}. \qquad 3.244\ (2)$$

In motions which are given by the geostrophic or gradient wind, the streamlines run parallel to the contour lines (isohypses or isobars). As mentioned earlier, wind speed maxima along the jet axis are, however, connected with accelerations (decelerations), which, according to Chapter 1.224, result in an ageostrophic component of flow, and which cause a departure of flow toward lower (higher) pressure. From the differences between contour pattern and streamline pattern one may, therefore, draw valuable conclusions about the existence of such accelerations. Mostly, however, the angle of deviation between these two sets of curves is rather small, hardly ever exceeding 10° in strong winds. Both analyses, therefore, will have to be carried out extremely carefully.

If the streamline analysis is made directly from the wind observations, one unintentionally is tempted to "force" the tangents through the wind arrows at various stations to join each other. In order to avoid this, an isogon analysis serves as an interpolation aid. It takes into account the continuity in the variation of upper-wind directions, and it increases the number of wind "observations."

The following will have to be considered in an isogon analysis:

1. *All* isogons are converging in *each* singular point of the wind field.

2. Depending on the sense of rotation of the labelling of isogons around a singular point, and on the orientation of the main axes, we may distinguish between (Fig. 3.244.1):

(*a*) convergence points;
(*b*) divergence points;
(*c*) centers of cyclonic rotation;
(*d*) centers of anticyclonic rotation;
(*e*) hyperbolic points.

Combinations may be obtained by turning the main axes by less than 90°. So, e.g., in Figure 3.244.1, *g* shows anticyclonic rotation and divergence; *h* shows cyclonic rotation with convergence. If the flow is only weakly divergent, i.e., almost geostrophic, the isogon patterns near the singular points correspond nearly to *c* or *d* of that figure. This is particularly true near the level of non-divergence.

3. Dense crowding of isogons marks strongly developed troughs or ridges in the upper flow pattern. Closed isogons indicate a region of maximum or minimum wind direction, synonymous with an *inflection point* in the streamline pattern. If small

dashes parallel to the corresponding wind direction are plotted along the isogons (as in Figure 3.244.1), the streamline analysis is greatly facilitated. If a larger number of isogon charts is needed, they should be analyzed on transparent paper, and the small dashes made by means of an "isogon board."

A commercially available plate of ribbed glass may serve as "isogon board." It should have rather sharp, parallel ribs about 0.5 cm apart. Markings at the margin of this plate give the orientation of the chart for different wind directions relative to the ribs. A layer of carbon paper is placed under the map on which the small dashes are to be entered, and now the isogon, for which the map has been oriented on the "isogon board," is pressed with a blunt, broad object, producing small, parallel dashes on the back of the map, which now may be used for the streamline analysis. This very simple gadget can cut the time needed for entering the small dashes by about 90 per cent.

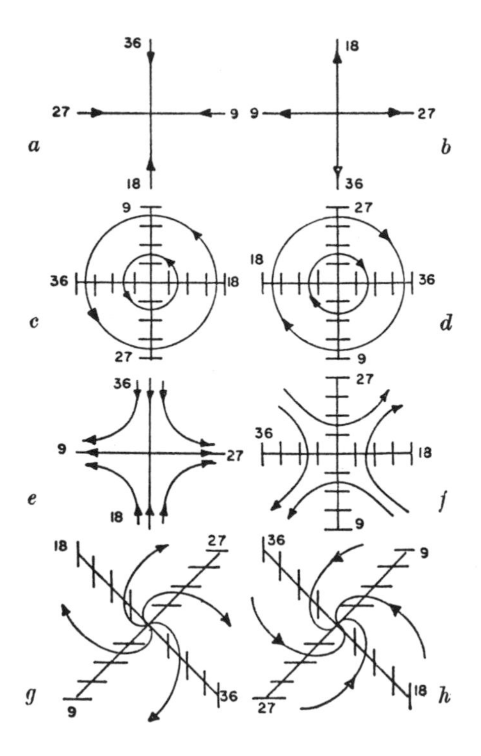

FIG. 3.244.1.—Isogon and streamline patterns: (*a*) pure convergence; (*b*) pure divergence; (*c*) pure cyclonic rotation; (*d*) pure anticyclonic rotation; (*e*) and (*f*) hyperbolic points; (*g*) anticyclonic rotation with divergence; (*h*) cyclonic rotation with convergence.

This method will be especially simple if the analysis is to be performed on a mercator map with *parallel meridians*, since constant geographic directions on this projection correspond to constant directions on the map. For other map projections one should analyze a *relative* isogon field which takes into account the turning of the meridians relative to the map co-ordinates if the additional work seems justified.

The analyses of isogons (streamlines) and isotachs completely determines the vectorial wind field. For the calculation of divergence it sometimes appears practical to break down the wind field into west-east and south-north components. An isotach analysis in each of these two components also would describe the vector field completely. Since, however, this form of analysis is more abstract and less descriptive, in jet-stream analysis preference is given to the first method.

In contrast to the *streamlines*, which characterize the *instantaneous* flow pattern, the *trajectories* describe the paths which are actually followed by the air particles, taking into account the displacement of the pressure systems. Under the assumption that the high-level flow follows adiabatic conditions, a trajectory computation is meaningful only on an isentropic surface. Trajectories on an isobaric surface are

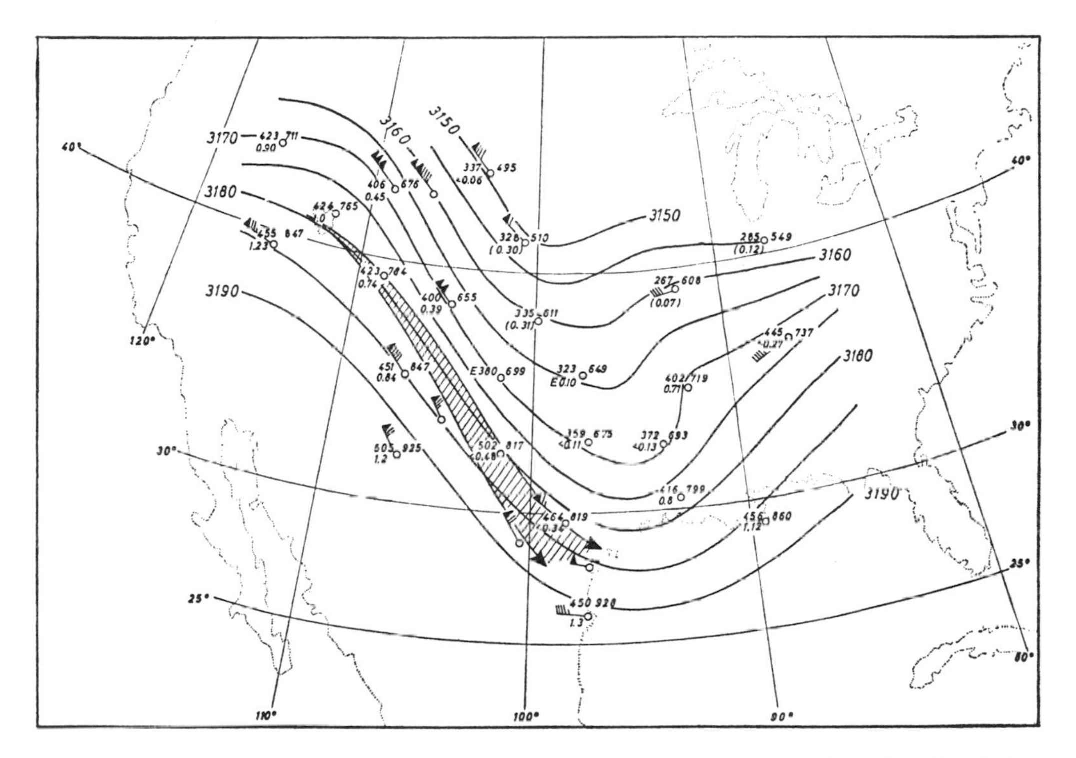

FIG. 3.244.2.—Isentropic stream function (Montgomery function) of the isentropic surface $\Theta = 45°$ C 8 January, 1953, 1500 GCT. The shaded area indicates the possible positions of the trajectory which emanates over the Great Salt Lake at 0300 GCT. At the various stations the pressure (mb) has been plotted in the upper left corner, the last three digits of the stream function in the upper right corner, and specific humidity has been entered below the station. (Numbers in parentheses indicate saturation humidity at temperatures $< -40°$ C. The symbol "<" stands before maximum humidity values corresponding to "motor boating" reports of the radiosonde, i.e., when the radiosonde signal assumes such low frequencies, due to the dryness of the atmosphere, that it resembles the sound from a motor boat.) (Reiter and Danielsen, 1960.)

based upon the assumption of isobaric flow. Since, however, large-scale vertical motions are present in cyclogenetically active jet-stream regions, we may under certain circumstances expect large differences between isobaric and isentropic trajectories.

Methods for constructing trajectories may be found in various textbooks (Petterssen, 1956; Saucier, 1955). A refined method, which is especially suited for analyses on isentropic surfaces, is shortly described in the following. The air particle which at the time $t = 0$ is located in A, is moved with the wind speed (e.g., 80 knots) that has been measured there, not along a straight line, but *along a streamline* (line of constant stream function M); this would bring the particle into point B after 6 hours. Analogously one computes from the isentropic chart $t=12$ hours the portion BC of the trajectory by starting backwards from C. If velocity changes are present along the trajectory, these will have to be considered according to Eq. 1.225 (5). We obtain

$$V = -(1/f)(\partial M/\partial n) \qquad 3.244\ (3)$$

and

$$\dot{V} = -\partial M/\partial s = \nabla M \cdot \sin \beta. \qquad 3.244\ (4)$$

β is the angle between stream function and actually observed streamline (Reiter and Danielsen, 1960). In this case, the trajectory will not follow a constant value of the stream function, but it will turn toward *higher* values in a *decelerating* current by an amount which should satisfy the above equation.

Table 3.244 gives a survey of the magnitude of wind speed changes with various deviations from the geostrophic wind direction.

TABLE 3.244. Deceleration within 6 Hours, from an Original Wind Speed of 80 Knots, at 35° Latitude (Reiter and Danielsen, 1960)

Deviation from the geostrophic wind direction (β in degrees)	10°	9°	8°	7°	6°	5°
Reduction of wind speed (knots)	24.2	22.0	19.6	17.1	14.8	12.2

Since, because of the rounding-off process in coding, the wind direction is known only to the nearest 5°, the trajectory can be given only approximately. For calculations which require greater accuracy the error limits should be stated, too, perhaps by constructing the two extreme trajectories which still would be possible. The area between these two trajectories may, then, be considered as *probable position of the trajectory*. An example of the construction of isentropic trajectories by this method is shown in Figure 3.244.2, for the isentropic surface $\Theta = 45°$ C, on 8 January, 1953, 1500 GCT. For *sinking motions* the conservation of specific humidity of an air particle may serve as a test criterion for the accuracy of the trajectory computation. Certain deviations due to errors in the humidity measurements may, however, be expected (Kleinschmidt, 1959, 1960; Reiter and Danielsen, 1960).

3.245. Isentropic Analysis

An isentropic surface is a "substantial" surface with respect to adiabatic flow, i.e., air particles which are found on this surface at a given moment remain on it as long as the flow conditions are adiabatic. This fact may be utilized for estimating vertical motions in the atmosphere (Saucier, 1955), because if one compares streamlines and isotachs on an isentropic surface with the isohypses of this surface, one may compute sinking motions directly in units of vertical velocity (cm/sec) assuming stationary conditions.

Let V be the mean (horizontal) wind speed on an isentropic surface measured along a streamline which forms the segment Δs in the horizontal projection between two neighboring isohypses (A, B). Δh is the height difference along this streamline segment, which is given by the height increment between successive isohypses in the analysis. Because $V = \Delta s/\Delta t$ and $w = \Delta h/\Delta t$, the vertical velocity is

$$w = (\Delta h/\Delta s) \cdot V. \qquad 3.245\ (1)$$

Rising air currents usually entail condensation processes which are no longer isentropic. Estimates of the vertical velocity by the above method, therefore, are of *quantitative* value only in areas with convergence at jet-stream level and with sinking motion. (Ascending motions would have to be analyzed along surfaces of constant pseudo-potential temperature [Pône, 1953]. The errors in the humidity measurements, however, would cause rather large uncertainties in the analysis.) Nevertheless, instructive *qualitative* results may be obtained by isentropic analysis even with pseudo-adiabatic changes of state: Figure 3.245.1 shows the contour pattern of the

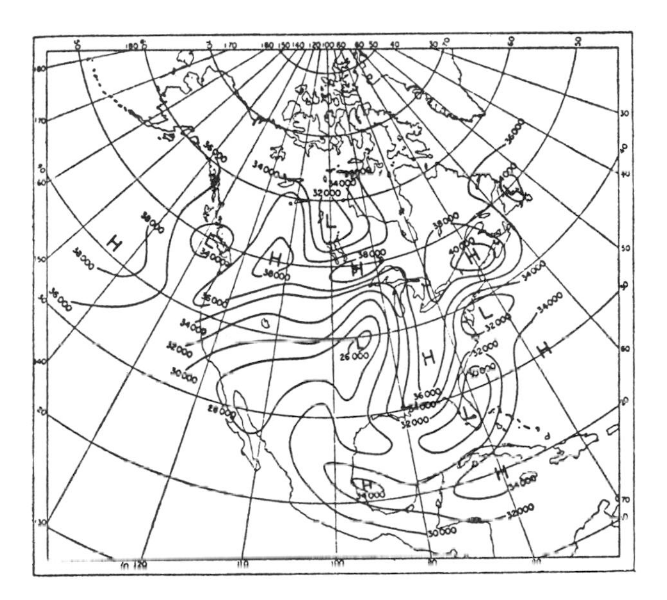

FIG. 3.245.1.—Contour pattern (ft) of the isentropic surface 340° K for the same synoptic map time as represented in Figure 3.242.1. (Newton *et al.*, 1951.)

340°-K isentropic surface for the same synoptic time as in the jet-stream analysis of Figure 3.242.1. As follows clearly from these two maps, on an isentropic surface in the jet-stream region the angle between streamlines and isohypses is relatively small. Since, however, the wind speeds are large, rather small inaccuracies in analysis may lead to large errors in estimating vertical velocities.

The height difference between two isentropic surfaces constitutes a measure of the static stability of the atmosphere.

The static stability S of an air mass may be defined as the negative vertical acceleration $-dw/dt$ which an air particle receives per unit of height:

$$S = -(1/\Delta z)(dw/dt). \qquad 3.245\ (2)$$

According to Archimedes' principle we have $dw/dt = g(\rho - \rho')/\rho'$. ρ' is the density of the air particle undergoing vertical displacement; ρ is the density in the undisturbed surroundings. Let $-\Delta T^*/\Delta z = \gamma$ be the vertical temperature gradient in the surrounding, and $-\Delta T^{*\prime}/\Delta z = \Gamma$ the adiabatic temperature gradient of the moving air particle, which will be dry or moist adiabatic, depending on the absence or presence of condensation processes during the vertical displacement. Under the assumption that everywhere $p'=p$, i.e., that the pressure of the air particle adapts itself immediately to the pressure of its surroundings, we obtain $dw/dt=(g/T^*)(\gamma-\Gamma)\cdot\Delta z$. If this expression is substituted into Eq. 3.245 (2) we arrive at the expression for static stability,

$$S=g\beta=(g/T^*)(\Gamma-\gamma). \qquad 3.245\ (3)$$

β is the stability parameter in Scorer's terminology (see Chapter 4.323).

From Eq. 1.225 (1) one obtains

$$\partial\Theta/\partial z=(\Theta/T)(\partial T/\partial z+g/c_p). \qquad 3.245\ (4)$$

Since, however, $\Gamma=g/c_p$, which results from 3.245 (4) under the adiabatic condition $\partial\Theta/\partial z=0$, the static stability may also be expressed as

$$S=g\beta=(g/\Theta)(\partial\Theta/\partial z)=g\cdot\partial(\ln\,\Theta)/\partial z. \qquad 3.245\ (5)$$

If one takes the distance between two isentropic surfaces ($\Delta\Theta=$const) as a measure of stability, it follows from 3.245 (5) that the static stability is small if Δz, the distance between the two surfaces, is large.

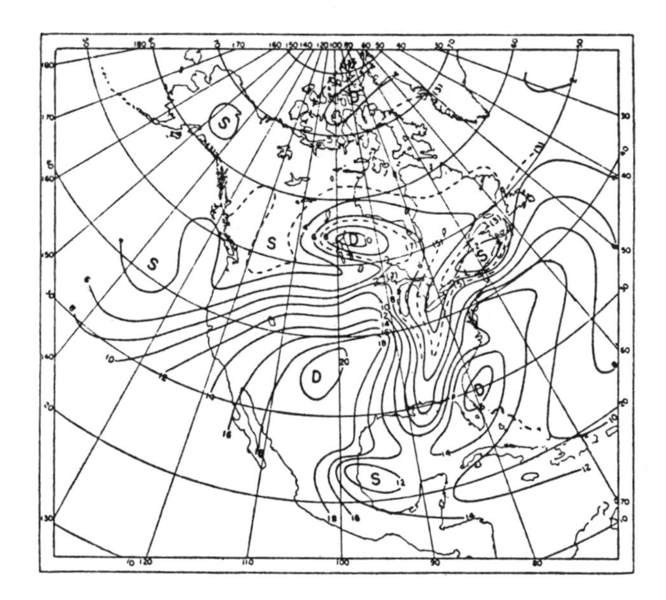

FIG. 3.245.2.—Thickness of the layer contained between the isentropic surfaces 340° and 360° K for the same synoptic map time as represented in Figures 3.242.1 and 3.245.1. S=shallow, stable: D=deep, unstable. (Newton *et al.*, 1951.)

Figure 3.245.2 shows the thickness pattern of the layer between the 340°- and 360°-K surfaces for the same map time as in the preceding chart. Relatively stable layers are marked by S, unstable layers by D.

A comparison of this diagram with Figure 3.242.1 reveals the noteworthy fact that air masses lying underneath the jet stream west of the shear line possess great stability. This is the region of predominant sinking motion, which also appears from a comparison of streamlines (Fig. 3.242.1) and isentropic contour lines (Fig. 3.245.1).

The stability conditions between two isentropic surfaces are determined by the potential vorticity as given by Ertel's equation 1.235 (4). A decrease of vorticity, i.e., an anticyclonic turning of the current, results in an increase of static stability. Increasing cyclonic vorticity leads toward decreasing stability. Last, but not least, it is this process which helps to explain the deterioration of weather in the region of upper troughs.

The importance of isentropic analysis in the United States Weather Service has waned meanwhile. Today, isentropic charts are not produced any longer in the routine weather service operations. One of the reasons for this may be that aviation —presently one of the main beneficiaries of high-altitude synoptic meteorology— is more interested in flow conditions on isobaric surfaces because the altimeters of aircraft follow the principle of a barometer. Isentropic surfaces, however, span large height differences, especially in baroclinic regions of the jet streams, so that several isentropic surfaces would have to be analyzed for only one flight plan. From the point of view of aeronavigation, therefore, isentropic analyses are impractical.

For the exploration of the three-dimensional wind structure in the free atmosphere, isentropic analyses constitute an invaluable aid, after all. This type of analysis is only impeded by the fact that potential temperatures are not obtained directly from the teletype messages in their present form and have to be taken from ascent curves in thermodynamic diagrams.

Danielsen (1959) showed that an isentropic analysis is useful only if in the calculation of the stream function

$$M = c_p T_\Theta + g z_\Theta \tag{3.245 (6)}$$

the greatest care is taken. z_Θ may be obtained in the form

$$z_\Theta = z_e + \frac{R\bar{T}}{g} \ln \frac{p_e}{p_\Theta} \tag{3.245 (7)}$$

by integrating the hydrostatic equation, 1.222 (3). z_e and p_e are height and pressure at the earth's surface.

Substituting 3.245 (7) into 3.245 (6), we obtain the following estimate of error by differentiation:

$$\Delta M = g\Delta z_e + R \ln \frac{p_e}{p_\Theta} \Delta\bar{T} + R\bar{T}\frac{\Delta p_e}{p_e} + \left[c_p \Delta T_\Theta - R\bar{T}\frac{\Delta p_\Theta}{p_\Theta}\right]. \tag{3.245 (8)}$$

The computation of the geopotential of an isobaric surface, however, is subject to the following error:

$$\Delta\Phi_p = g\Delta z_e + R \ln \frac{p_e}{p} \Delta\bar{T} + R\bar{T}\frac{\Delta p_e}{p_e}. \tag{3.245 (9)}$$

The sources of errors in calculating the Montgomery function, therefore, are greater than those made in geopotential calculations by the terms in 3.245 (8) written in brackets. In the American isentropic analyses made during the last years of World War II, T_Θ and p_Θ have been read independent of each other from aerological diagrams. These readings, however, are inaccurate and may cause errors, which show up as strong irregularities in the analysis of the stream function M. One has to consider that the stream function will have to be determined to four significant places if the resulting geostrophic winds should be dependable. (See Fig. 3.244.2.) For this purpose the temperature has to be read to the nearest tenth of a degree, and the height to the nearest ten meters. This can only be accomplished if pressure and temperature are *not* read independent of each other. One rather has to calculate T_Θ from Poisson's equation, 1.225 (1). By this, the error inside the brackets of 3.245 (8) will be reduced to only one reading:

$$\left[(T_\Theta - \bar{T})R\frac{\Delta p_\Theta}{p_\Theta}\right]. \qquad 3.245\ (10)$$

If, for example, the error in the pressure reading at 500 mb amounts to about 2 mb, the error in the stream function will be $1.15 \cdot 10^5$ cm^2 sec^{-2} with a temperature difference of 10° C. On the other hand, an inaccuracy in the temperature reading of 0.2° C, together with an inaccuracy in the determination of pressure of 2 mb will cause an error of $5 \cdot 10^6$ cm^2 sec^{-2} in the stream function. ($6 \cdot 10^6$ cm^2 sec^{-2} corresponds to a height difference on an isobaric surface of about 200 ft = 61 m.)

The errors which arise from computing expression (10) are by all means tolerable and do not impair the dependability of the analysis. This short numerical example illustrates clearly why the routine isentropic analyses made during World War II have failed.

Furthermore, one will have to be careful not to use approximate values for g or c_p, but only the values upon which the aerological diagram in use has been based. (In general these are $g = 980.6$ cm sec^{-2} and $c_p = 1.0046 \cdot 10^7$ erg g^{-1} deg^{-1}.)

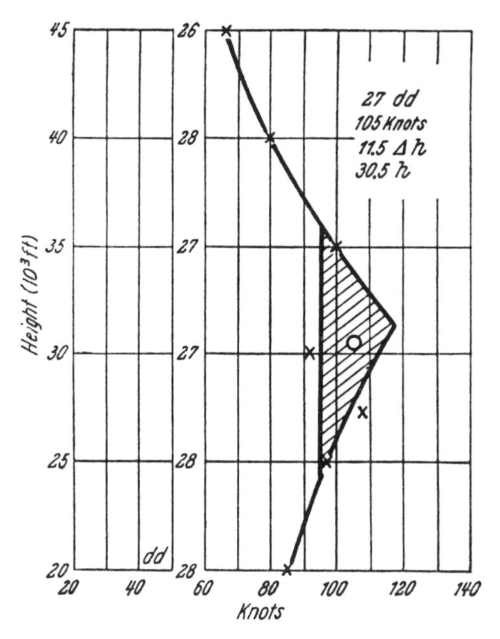

Fig. 3.246.1.—Computation of the parameters of the LMW: wind direction dd in tens of degrees. Speeds are marked by crosses; they are indicated to the nearest 5 knots. The heavy solid line gives the smoothed wind profile. The LMW is shown by hatching. Δh = thickness of the layer, h = height of the LMW.

3.246. The Layer of Maximum Wind

In the practical routine of the air weather service one has to strive for analyses and forecasts of the wind field in the jet-stream region as free as possible from errors in measurement and of unrepresentative fluctuations (see Chapter 2.123). It is proposed, therefore, that *vertically integrated parameters* be used for the analysis instead of topographies of individual surfaces. The *necessary smoothing* of the data is not carried out while analyzing the chart, but already in the vertical wind profile at each station.

Experiments (Reiter, Riehl, and Hinkelman, 1957; Reiter, 1957*c*, 1958*c*; U.S. Navy, 1959*a*) showed that the layer of maximum wind (LMW) meets these practical requirements. Since the end of 1958 such analyses are transmitted daily by the U.S. Navy weather service on facsimile (Riehl, personal communication).

Definition of the layer of maximum wind.—The *mean wind* of the LMW is defined as 90 per cent of the maximum wind speed of the vertical profile.

The *layer of maximum wind* is the layer of the atmosphere in which the wind speed differs by less than 10 per cent from the mean wind (or by about 20 per cent from the maximum wind).

It has been pointed out earlier (Chapter 2.123) that the upper-level wind measurements render only an instantaneous value of the wind vector. Aside from errors in measurement, therefore, one has to expect turbulent fluctuations of the upper-level currents, which—as may be seen from Table 2.123—let the measured values appear representative for the large-scale flow patterns only by about 90 per cent (Endlich, Harney, *et al.*, 1954). After the above definition the LMW includes a safety factor which permits a comparison of the instantaneous measurements with the conditions integrated over space and time as they may be encountered, e.g., along a flight route.

For the investigations of jet streams over North America, which shall be described shortly in the following, as upper limit of the thickness of the LMW, 5 km (15,000 ft) have been chosen, and a lower limit of 60 knots has been set arbitrarily for the mean wind speed. Thicknesses of layers and wind speeds which lie beyond these limits have been marked as "quasi-barotropic" regions on both sides of the jet stream. In these regions the vertical wind shears are of no particular concern to aeronavigation. These limiting values, of course, should not be taken as fixed rules, but they have been chosen only to apply best to local conditions. In the analyses of subtropical jet streams the limiting value for the thickness of the layer probably will have to be increased somewhat.

The following parameters have to be considered in an LMW analysis:

1. Mean wind speed of the layer;
2. Thickness of the layer;
3. Height of the center point of the layer;
4. Mean wind direction of the layer.

Preparatory analysis.—First we have to evaluate the four parameters determining the LMW for each station with upper wind measurements. This is best done by entering the ascent into a small diagram (Fig. 3.246.1). As ordinate we use the height between 20,000 and 45,000 ft. In the European weather services the height interval between 6 and 14 km may be used. For the tropics the interval between 30,000 to 60,000 ft is recommended. The abscissa gives the wind speed between 20 and 140 knots (in Fig. 3.246.2 between 20 and 180 knots). For greater wind speeds the scale may be shifted accordingly.

The crosses in Figure 3.246.1 indicate the wind speed values from the teletype data. The corresponding wind directions have been marked to the left of the ascent. As the next step, a *smoothed* wind profile is drawn (heavy line) under the assumption that irregular fluctuations of wind speed are caused by errors in measurements or by small-scale structure (see Chapters 2.12 and 4.3). In the new weather code as of

January, 1955, height and speed of the maximum wind along the profile are reported. These data may be utilized for the construction of the smoothed profile. These values, however, are subject to the errors discussed in Chapter 2.122 (Reiter, 1959*e*), since they have been taken from the unsmoothed ascent curves.

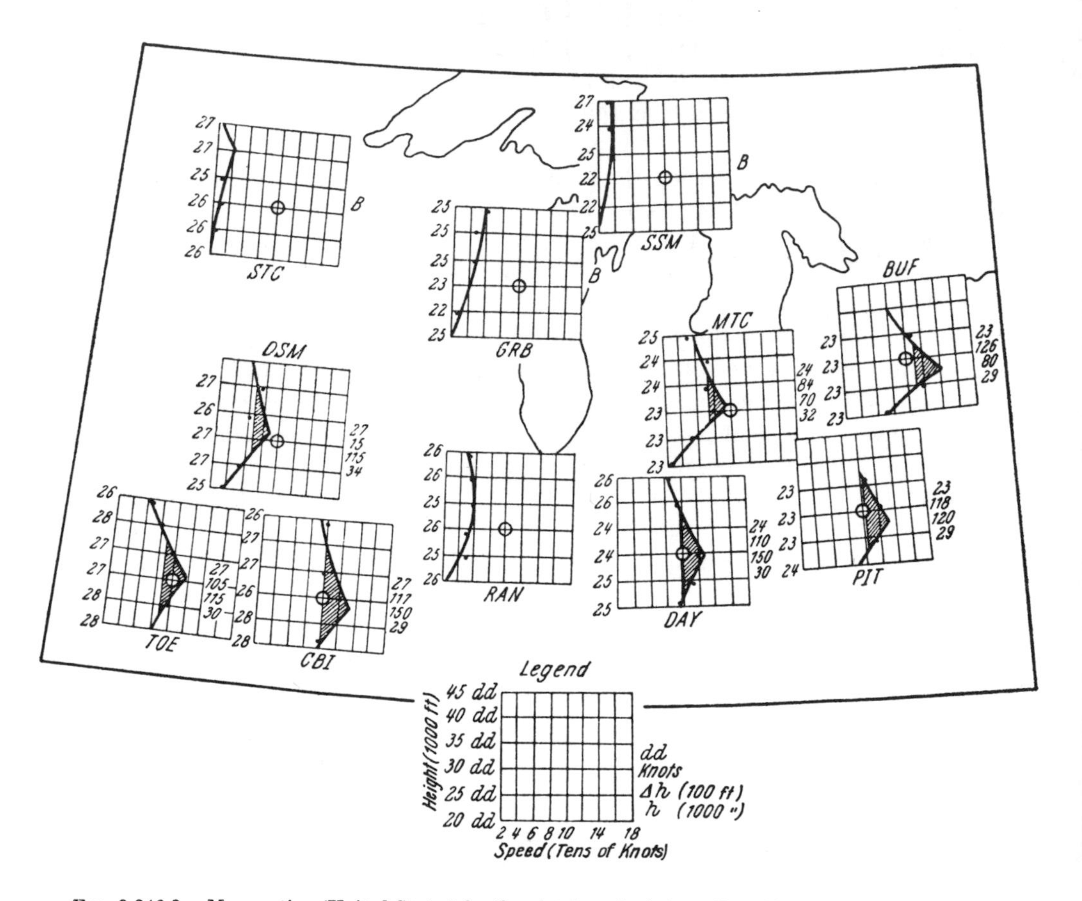

FIG. 3.246.2.—Map section (United States) for the plotting of wind profiles. (The station model is given in Figure 3.246.1.) Numbers on the left margins of the diagrams give the wind directions. B = "quasi-barotropic" areas. The small circles indicate the positions of the stations.

It is recommended to draw sharply peaked profiles as shown in Figures 3.246.1 and .2 wherever possible because in this fashion some continuity of the method is warranted for the relatively few data points that are obtained from the teletype messages.

Figure 3.246.2 shows a section of a map of the United States which has been constructed for the purpose of such analyses and which proved to be very useful. Each station with rawinsonde data has a small diagram of the kind shown in Figure 3.246.1. In the analysis of the smoothed wind profiles one may already consider space and time continuity when such a map is used.

During the next step the *mean speed* of the layer is determined by subtracting 10 per cent from the maximum wind. The thickness of the layer is obtained from the height difference between the intersection points of the wind profile with a vertical line that is drawn at a distance of 20 per cent from the maximum wind (Fig. 3.246.1 and .2). It facilitates the reading of the map if the LMW thus obtained is entered with red pencil (shaded area in Fig. 3.246.1, dotted in .2). The *mean height* of the LMW constitutes the arithmetic mean of the heights of the two intersection points mentioned above. The *mean wind direction* of the layer can easily be estimated from the numerical values of direction entered into the diagram.

The quantities obtained in this fashion are entered into the diagrams as shown in Figure 3.246.1 and .2. "Quasi-barotropic" wind profiles are marked with the letter *B*. A chart as shown in Figure 3.246.2 may be used for practical purposes of flight briefing even without any additional analysis. The accuracy of the winds which may be read off for various levels is superior to that of geostrophic winds and gradient winds, because the actually measured wind vectors on the one hand contain the ageostrophic components, which are especially present in the jet-stream region; and on the other hand the smoothing, which is involved in the analysis of a topography, is avoided.

In order to obtain good space and time continuity of the analyses, one should analyze LMW charts twice a day (0000 hours and 1200 hours GCT). Stations which conduct the ascents 6 hours before these map times will also be considered with special notation.

The different parameters may be analyzed directly from Figure 3.246.2 on a paper overlay. The numerical values of these parameters entered on a map of smaller scale will allow a clearer view. The following "station model" may be used: above the station circle, the wind direction is entered in tens of degrees. It is furthermore indicated by the direction of the "wind arrow." Below the station circle, the mean wind speed of the LMW is written, to the right of the circle the height, and to the left

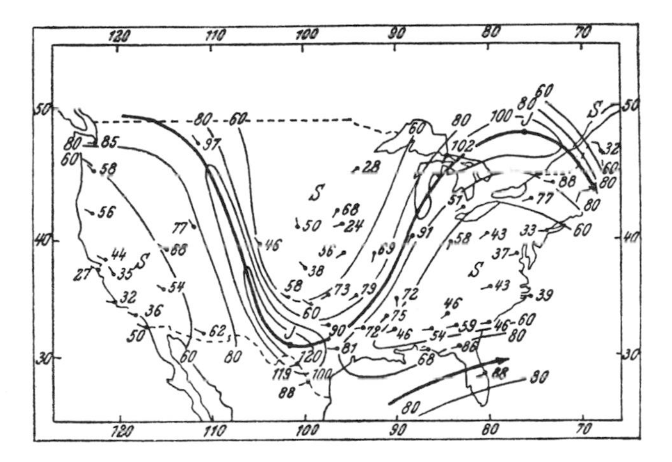

FIG. 3.246.3.—Isotachs of the LMW (knots), 28 February, 1954, 0300 GCT. *J* = jet maximum. The heavy line indicates the position of the jet axis. *S* = areas of slow air motion.

of the circle, the thickness (in units of 1000's of feet) is entered. The wind direction at the height of the wind maximum is also given for stations with "quasi-barotropic" wind profiles, in order to warrant a better space continuity for streamline analyses.

The following diagrams may serve as examples of an LMW analysis: Figure 3.246.3 shows the wind-speed analysis of the LMW over the United States on 28 February, 1954, at 0300 GCT. The speeds at the various stations are given in knots. Figure 3.246.4 gives a height analysis in kilometers for the same synoptic time and Figure 3.246.5 contains the thickness of the layer in kilometers. Characteristic details of the analysis will be discussed further in Chapter 4.13. Here it will only be pointed out that

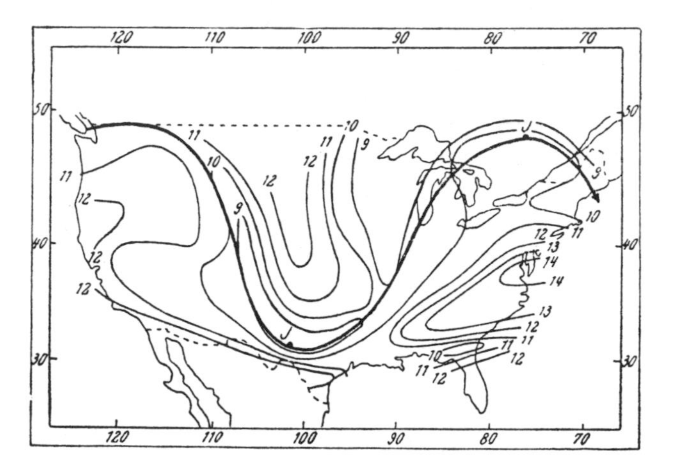

FIG. 3.246.4.—Mean height of the LMW (km), 28 February, 1954, 0300 GCT

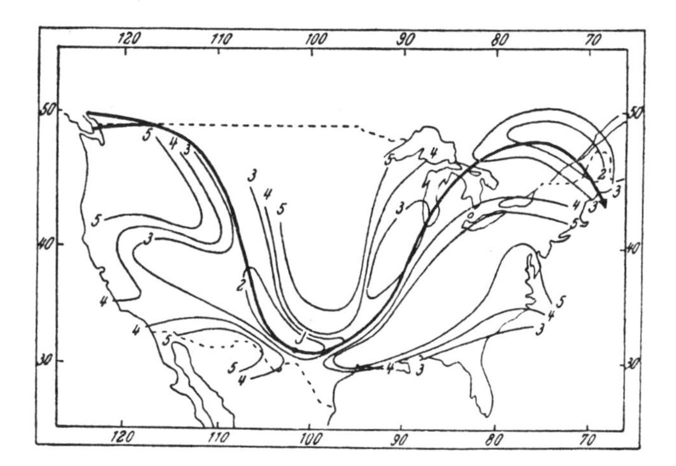

FIG. 3.246.5.—Thickness of the LMW (km), 28 February, 1954, 0300 GCT.

the jet maximum carries a "trough" of minimum height and minimum thickness of the LMW along on its cyclonic side. This fact has been found empirically, and it facilitates the construction of isopleths of height and thickness of the LMW.

An analysis of the maximum wind speeds alone is used by Lee (Lee *et al.*, 1958) for forecasting squall lines and tornadoes. In the United States Air Weather Service (1956*d*), on the other hand, the *level* of maximum wind is analyzed together with the vertical shears above and below this level. This method also describes the three-dimensional upper wind field by four parameters (maximum wind speed, height of the maximum wind level, shear above and below this level) as does the LMW. A smoothing of the data, however, is not accomplished by this (see Cole and Chamberlain, 1958; Johannessen, 1956*b*).

3.247. Analysis of Vorticity and Deformation

Geostrophic vorticity.—The field distribution of geostrophic vorticity is most easily calculated by means of Eq. 1.231 (10). For this purpose one subdivides the map area into a grid of squares whose sides should not be too long, since the averaging over a wide area smooths out the detailed structure of the vorticity pattern. On the other hand too small a grid distance would give too much weight to errors in analysis and in data-reading. In general a grid distance of about 300 km will suffice, as it is used in certain grids of numerical weather prediction. It shall be anticipated here, however, that near the jet axis, where large vorticity gradients are present, other methods, which incorporate less smoothing, of vorticity calculation will have to be used.

Statistical investigations (Peterson, 1956, 1957) revealed that the grid distance is not without influence on the vorticity calculation. The geostrophic vorticities calculated from a grid of 600 km in length (q_g) and 300 km length (q_g') computed for a number of cases (n) over the United States in the region between Wyoming and Missouri have been compared with each other. σ_g and σ_g' are the standard deviations of the two sets of data, r is the linear correlation coefficient, S_g^* is the standard error made in estimating q_g from q_g', and S_g' is the analogous standard error in estimating q_g' from q_g.

TABLE 3.247.1

	n	q_g	q_g'	σ_g	σ_g'	r	S_g^*	S_g'
Winter	141	0.97	5.52	3.55	7.16	0.726	2.43	4.93
Summer	244	1.16	7.44	2.69	7.44	0.740	1.81	5.01
Year	385	1.09	6.74	3.03	7.39	0.723	2.09	5.11

The smaller grid, therefore, renders larger mean values of vorticity but also larger fluctuations which are expressed in the standard deviation. The reason for this lies in the fact that smaller irregularities in the topography, which are reflected in non-linear gradients, are brought out much clearer in the smaller grid. The error which is made in estimating the vorticity of the large grid from the vorticity of the small grid is smaller than when carrying the estimate in the opposite direction.

The method for calculating the geostrophic vorticity is essentially based upon the replacement of the differential operator ∇^2 of Eq. 1.231 (10) by the difference operator ∇_d^2. Let $z_1 \ldots z_4$ be the height values of an isobaric surface. z_0 will be the height value at the center point of the area for which the calculations are to be made. h is the grid distance (Fig. 3.247.1). The differential $\partial^2 z/\partial x^2$ may be resolved into $(1/h^2)(z_1 - z_0) - (1/h^2)(z_0 - z_3) = (1/h^2)(z_1 + z_3 - 2z_0)$. Analogously one obtains for $\partial^2 z/\partial y^2$ the difference expression $(1/h^2)(z_2 + z_4 - 2z_0)$. The expression for the geostrophic vorticity therefore, reads:

$$Q_g = (g/f)(\nabla_d^2 z) + f = (g/f \cdot h^2)(z_1 + z_2 + z_3 + z_4 - 4z_0) + f \qquad 3.247\ (1)$$

In 3.247 (1) the difference operator ∇_d^2 is defined for a Cartesian co-ordinate system of the kind which has been described in Chapter 1.21. But since the earth's curvature already plays an important role in the calculations over larger areas, one should rather use a spherical co-ordinate system. For this, however, the calculations become very complicated. The use of conformal map projections offers a simple remedy: since the

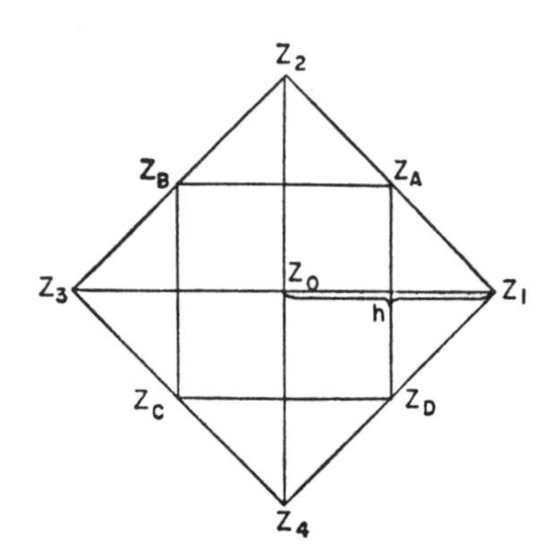

FIG. 3.247.1.—Grid with grid distance h for the computation of the Laplacian and of deformation (see text).

scale of these maps is a function m of geographic latitude only, each unit length taken from the map may be transformed into a corresponding unit length of the earth. x' and y' are Cartesian co-ordinates on a conformal map of the earth. Since the *angles* are conserved in such a projection (condition of conformity), a closed curve K' will have the same shape on the map as it has on the earth; it will appear, however, reduced by a dimensionless scale factor m. The line element dl' of this curve, therefore, has the length

$$dl' = m \cdot dl. \qquad 3.247\ (2)$$

dl is the corresponding line element on the earth. For an element of area we obtain

$$dA' = dx' \cdot dy' = m^2\, dx \cdot dy = m^2\, dA, \qquad 3.247\ (3)$$

for a velocity

$$u_g' = -(g/f)(\partial z/\partial y') = -(g/mf)(\partial z/\partial y) = (1/m) \cdot u_g \qquad 3.247\ (4)$$

and for the operator $\nabla'^2 = \partial^2/\partial x'^2 + \partial^2/\partial y'^2$

$$= (1/m^2)(\partial^2/\partial x^2 + \partial^2/\partial y^2) = (1/m^2)\nabla^2. \qquad 3.247\ (5)$$

The relationship between the vorticity on the plane of the map and on the earth is given by

$$\begin{aligned} Q_g &= (gm^2/f)(\nabla'^2 z) + f = (gm^2/f)(\partial^2 z/\partial x'^2 + \partial^2 z/\partial y'^2) + f \\ &\simeq (gm^2/f)(\nabla'^2_d z) + f = (gm^2/fh'^2)(z_1 + z_2 + z_3 + z_4 - 4z_0) + f \end{aligned} \qquad 3.247\ (6)$$

under consideration of 3.247 (1 to 5), or—since the analyses are made in geopotential meters—one may use Eq. 1.222 (4), and one arrives at

$$Q_g = (9.80\ m^2/fh'^2)(Z_1 + Z_2 + Z_3 + Z_4 - 4Z_0) + f. \qquad 3.247\ (7)$$

h' is the grid distance used on the map projection.

Let φ_1 and φ_2 be the geographic latitudes for which the corresponding projection is true. ψ_1 and ψ_2 are the complementary angles of these latitudes, and s is the *reduction factor*, which is given for the respective map (e.g., 1:10,000,000). Conic and cylinder projections (Mercator) are made from the center of the earth. Polar stereographic projections, however, are made from the opposite pole. For *Lambert's conformal conic projection* one obtains (Saucier, 1955)

$$m = s(\sin\psi_1/\sin\psi)\left[\left(\tan\frac{\psi}{2}\right)\Big/\left(\tan\frac{\psi_1}{2}\right)\right]^n$$
$$= s(\sin\psi_2/\sin\psi)\left[\left(\tan\frac{\psi}{2}\right)\Big/\left(\tan\frac{\psi_2}{2}\right)\right]^n. \qquad 3.247\ (8)$$

n is the constant which describes the position of the projection cone,

$$n = (\log\sin\psi_1 - \log\sin\psi_2)\Big/\left(\log\tan\frac{\psi_1}{2} - \log\tan\frac{\psi_2}{2}\right).$$

For a projection which is true at the standard latitudes of 30° and 60°, $n = 0.716$.

For a *Mercator projection* with two standard latitudes equidistant from the equator, $n = 0$ and

$$m = s(\sin\psi_1/\sin\psi). \qquad 3.247\ (9)$$

In a *polar stereographic projection* with the standard latitude φ_0, $n = 1$ and

$$m = s(1+\sin\varphi_0)/(1+\sin\varphi). \qquad 3.247\ (10)$$

From 3.247 (8, 9, and 10) it is obvious that at standard latitudes $m = s$.

With the aid of 3.247 (6) and with the grid described above the following simple evaluation scheme may be devised: the factor gm^2/fh'^2 depends on geographic latitude only, and it can be determined for the map projection in use and for the respective grid once and forever. For each grid point—with the exception of the ones at the margin of the map—the quantity $(z_1+z_2+z_3+z_4-4z_0)$ is evaluated and this field is analyzed. Graphical multiplication with the isopleths of the expression gm^2/fh'^2 renders the relative geostrophic vorticity. One should be careful to choose the iso lines so that the vorticity is available immediately in units 10^{-5} sec^{-1}.

For a polar stereographic projection with the scale $s = 10^{-7}$, which is true at latitude 60°, one obtains from 3.247 (10) and 3.247 (7), and with a grid distance $h' = 3$ cm

$$q_z = A\cdot B_{(\varphi)}\cdot C. \qquad 3.247\ (11)$$

In this equation,

$$A = (gs^2/2\Omega h'^2)(1+\sin\varphi_0)^2 = 0.2601\cdot 10^{-5}\ (\mathrm{m}^{-1}\ \mathrm{sec}^{-1}),$$
$$B_{(\varphi)} = (1/\sin\varphi)(1+\sin\varphi)^{-2},$$
$$C = (z_1+z_2+z_3+z_4-4z_0)\quad (\text{Meter}).$$

TABLE 3.247.2

GEOGR. LATITUDE (degrees)	B	$A\cdot B\cdot 10^{-5}$ (m^{-1} sec^{-1})	$A\cdot B\cdot 10^{-5}$ (m^{-1} sec^{-1})	GEOGR. LATITUDE
10	4.181	1.088	1.0	10.2
20	1.623	0.422	0.9	11.0
30	0.889	0.231	0.8	12.1
40	0.576	0.150	0.7	13.5
50	0.419	0.109	0.6	15.3
60	0.331	0.086	0.5	17.6
70	0.283	0.074	0.4	20.8
80	0.258	0.067	0.3	25.4
90	0.250	0.065	0.2	33.0
			0.1	53.3

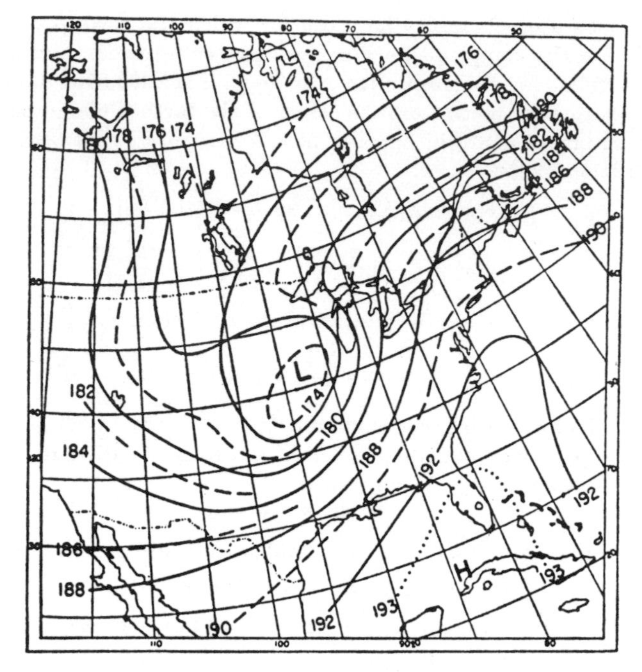

FIG. 3.247.2.—Absolute topography (10^2 gpf) of the 500-mb surface, 26 November, 1952, 0300 GCT. (Petterssen, 1953b.)

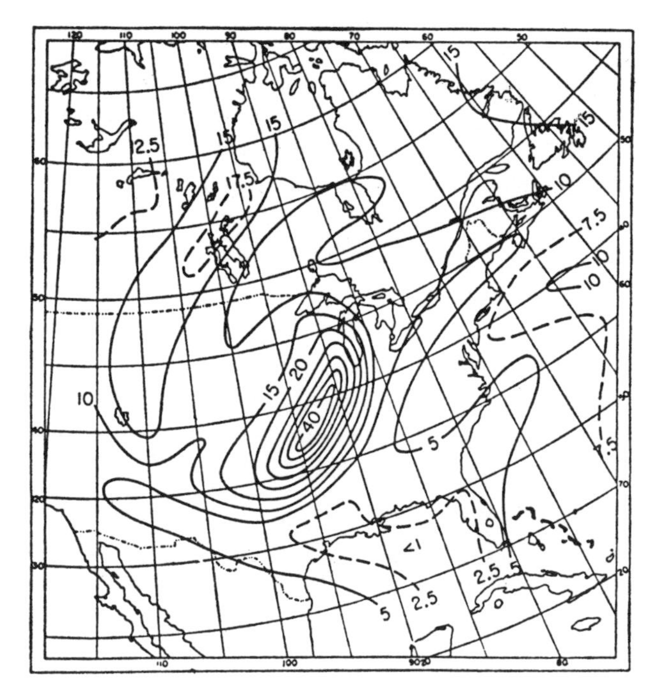

FIG. 3.247.3.—Absolute geostrophic vorticity (in units of 10^{-5} sec^{-1}) of the topography represented in Figure 3.247.2. (Petterssen, 1953b.)

From Table 3.247.2 it appears that geostrophic vorticity analyses are unreliable toward the equator from about 20°, because the factor $A \cdot B$ varies too much with geographic latitude.

The reason for this lies in the fact that near the equator the geostrophic wind equation 1.222 (7) loses its validity, because f approaches the value of 0. For equatorial latitudes, therefore, the vorticity has to be evaluated by other methods, using direct wind observations. If C is analyzed in intervals of 10 gpm, the vorticity may be computed in units 10^{-4} at the intersections with the set of curves $A \cdot B$, which are parallel to latitude circles.

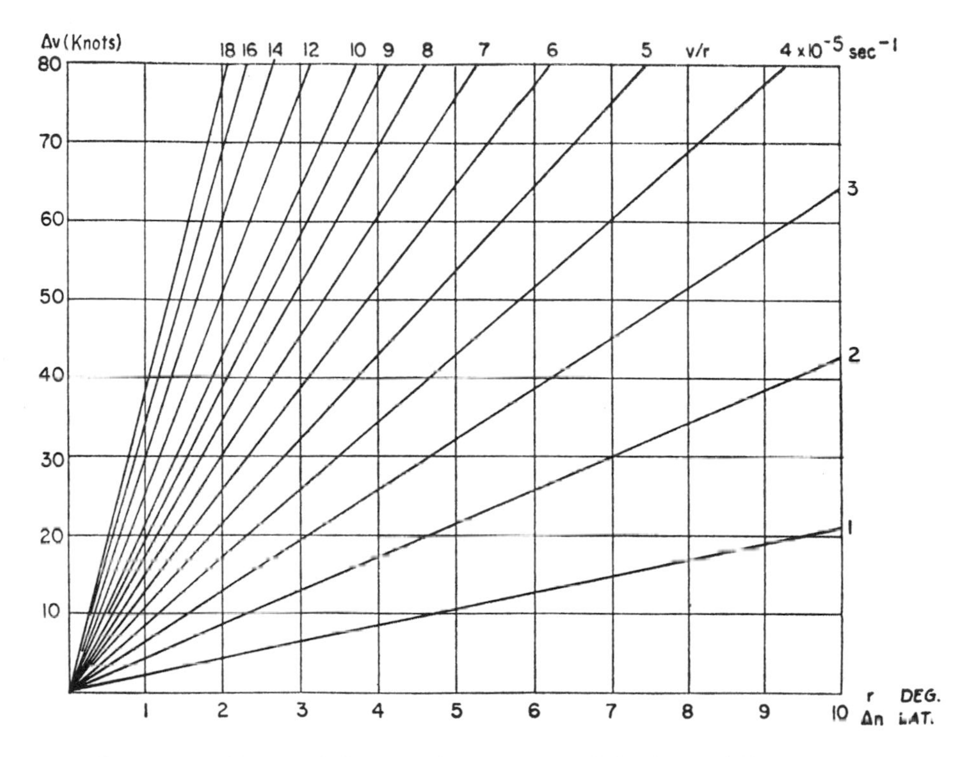

Fig. 3.247.4.—Nomograph for computing curvature and shearing vorticities (see text).

Graphical addition of the field of q_z to the field of f, which consists of a set of latitude-parallel circles, renders the distribution of absolute vorticity Q_z. In Figure 3.247.2 the topography of the 500-mb surface of 26 November, 1952, 0300 GCT, is given. Figure 3.247.3 shows the absolute geostrophic vorticity computed from this topography by the method described above (Petterssen, 1953b).

Calculation of vorticity from wind observations.—For the calculation of the vorticity from actually observed winds we have a number of methods at our command. Let $\bar{u}$, $\bar{v}$, $(\bar{u}+\Delta\bar{u})$, and $(\bar{v}+\Delta\bar{v})$ be the mean velocity components along the sides of a quadratic area on the upper-wind chart. If the side length is not chosen too large, one may write in approximation (see Fig. 3.247.1):

$$\bar{u}=(u_C+u_D)/2.$$

For the other mean values of velocity we have similar expressions. Equation 1.231 (2), then, reads in difference form:

$$\bar{q}_z = \Delta\bar{v}/\Delta x - \Delta\bar{u}/\Delta y. \qquad 3.247\ (12)$$

$\bar{q}_z$ is the mean vertical component of the vorticity of this area.

A practical approach for these calculations is to analyze the fields of u and v and to evaluate from these analyses the gradients of u and v along the sides of the grid in use. The fields $\partial v/\partial x$ and $\partial u/\partial y$ now are analyzed again and are subtracted graphically from each other. The resulting field is the vorticity in units, which are determined by the grid distance and the unit in which the speeds are given.

If meridians and latitude circles are chosen for y and x axes one has to add a corrective term which accounts for the convergence of the meridians, which, however, is of importance only near the poles. The equation then reads:

$$q_z = \partial v/\partial x - \partial u/\partial y + (u/R)\cdot\tan\varphi. \qquad 3.247\ (13)$$

R is the earth's radius. This equation is obtained from a transformation of Cartesian into spherical co-ordinates and may also be transcribed into a difference expression as has been done with 3.247 (12) (Saucier, 1955).

For vorticity calculations near the jet axis Eq. 1.231 (3) is used to advantage. Both terms may be taken from a nomograph.

The radius of curvature is determined in units of degrees of latitude by means of a transparent overlay. If V is given in knots, V/r ($\sec^{-1}$) may be read from Figure 3.247.4. The same diagram can be used for calculations of the quotient $\Delta V/\Delta n$, if Δn is also measured in degrees of latitude. By simple relabeling of the co-ordinates the range of this diagram may be increased to fit any need.

One has to consider that the first term has to be evaluated for the center point of the distance Δn. If V/r varies strongly, an average value over the distance Δn has to be used.

If a streamline and an isotach analysis are available, the vorticity may be obtained by means of Eq. 1.231 (5): let n_1 and n_2 be normals to the streamline s. The line integral then reduces to $\bar{V}_1\cdot\Delta s_1 - \bar{V}_2\cdot\Delta s_2$. The area A may be obtained by planimetering. If ψ is the angle between the tangent to the streamline at the point P and the streamline itself, measured clockwise, the following expression is valid:

$$q_z = \partial V/\partial n - V(\partial\psi/\partial s). \qquad 3.247\ (14)$$

From Eq. 1.231 (4) one may see that all methods of divergence calculation may also be applied for vorticity computations if the field of the horizontal wind vector is turned toward the right by 90°.

Comparison between observed and geostrophic vorticity.—A comparison between the geostrophic vorticity q_g, and the relative vorticity which has been computed from the actually observed winds shows that the former renders too large values for cyclonic cases, and too small values for anticyclonic cases. The differences may be considerable if the orders of magnitude of Q and Q_g exceed the one of the Coriolis parameter (see Chapter 1.239) (Petterssen, 1953*b*). Figure 3.247.5 contains the absolute vorticity for the 500-mb topography reproduced in Figure 3.247.2. Graphical subtraction of this

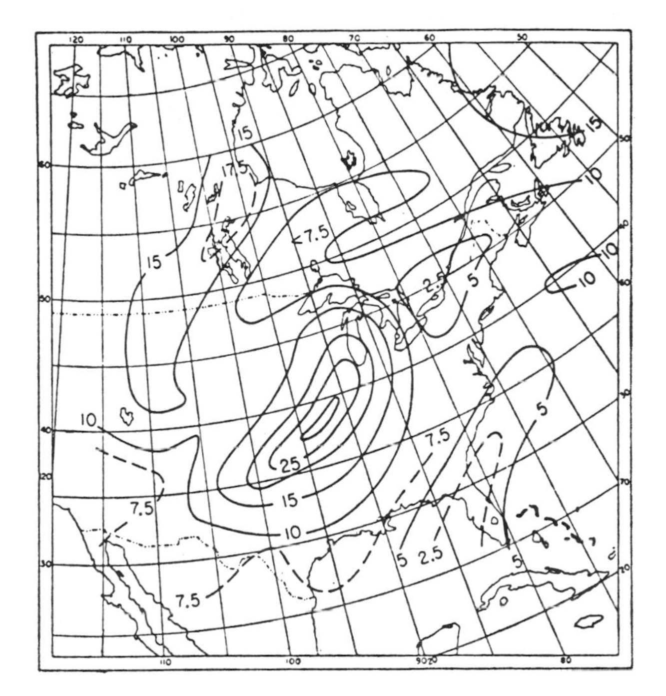

FIG. 3.247.5.—Absolute vorticity (10^{-5} sec^{-1}) of the topography represented in Figure 3.247.2, computed with the aid of Eq. 1.239 (7). (Petterssen, 1953*b*.)

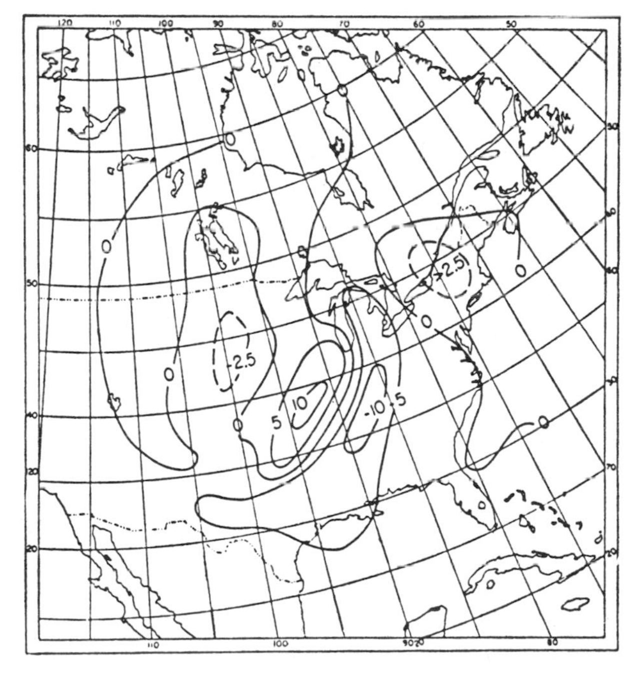

FIG. 3.247.6.—Difference between Figures 3.247.3 and 3.247.5. (Petterssen, 1953*b*.)

diagram from Figure 3.247.3 results in the difference $Q_g - Q$. This difference is shown in Figure 3.247.6. In this connection the question arises whether the methods of numerical weather prediction, which are based upon the *geostrophic* vorticity, should not be revised in view of these discrepancies (Landers, 1956).

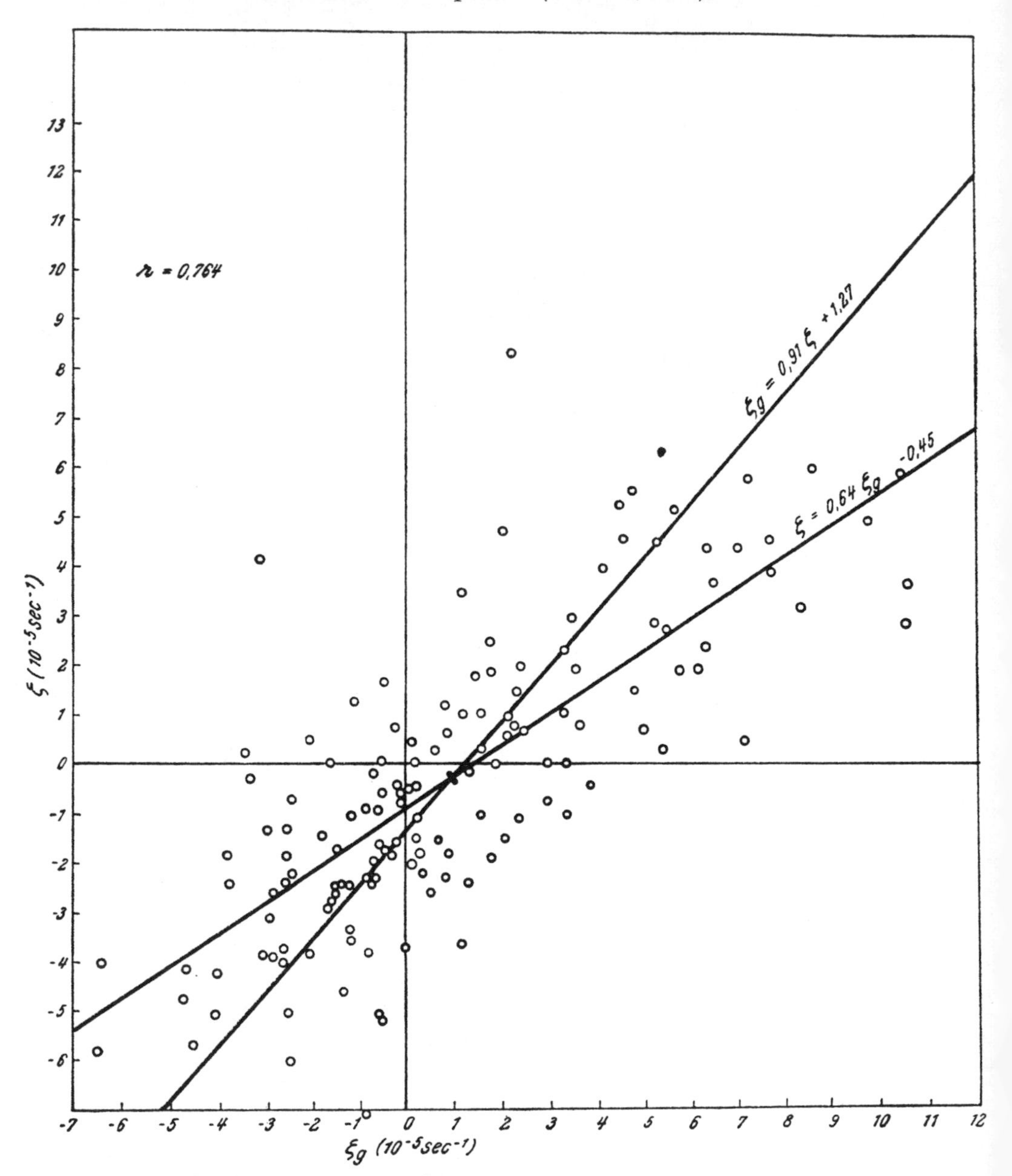

FIG. 3.247.7 —Correlation between actual (ζ) and geostrophic vorticity (ζ_g) for winter data. (Peterson, 1957.)

Statistical investigations of the 500-mb level over the United States, using a grid distance of 600 km, show similar results (Peterson, 1956, 1957). Figure 3.247.7 contains a scatter diagram, comparing the relative geostrophic vorticity q_g with the vorticity q obtained from wind observations (units 10^{-5} sec^{-1}). (For the relative vorticity the symbol ζ has been used in this diagram.) The results of the measurements are presented in the following table. n is the number of observations, σ_g and σ the standard deviations of the respective vorticities, r is the linear correlation coefficient, S_g the "standard error" for an estimate of q_g from q, and S the standard error for an estimate of q from q_g. R is the root mean squared difference between the two kinds of vorticity:

$$R = \sqrt{\left(\frac{1}{n}\sum_{1}^{n}|q_{gi}-q_i|^2\right)}$$

TABLE 3.274.3

	n	q_g	q	σ_g	σ	r	S_g	S	R
Winter	141	0.97	−0.33	3.55	2.98	0.764	2.28	1.92	2.65
Summer	244	1.16	−1.25	2.69	2.60	0.653	2.04	1.97	3.26
Year	385	1.09	−0.91	3.03	2.78	0.689	2.20	2.02	3.05

According to this, the correlation between geostrophic and actually observed vorticity, seems to be better in winter than in summer. On the average of the observed cases, larger values are obtained for the geostrophic vorticity than for the observed one. Fluctuations in the wind field and inaccuracies in the wind observations, of course, have their effect upon the calculation of the observed vorticity. Part of the fluctuations of the geostrophic vorticity, however, are due to inaccurate analyses, too. It may be assumed that the inaccuracies in the calculation of the geostrophic vorticity exceed the ones of the observed vorticity the more, the smaller the grid distance of the station network in use.

Deformation analysis.—The total deformation is obtained by vectorial addition of the stretching deformation and the shearing deformation [1.237 (1) and (2)]. It is independent of the orientation of the co-ordinate system. For the evaluation from analyses of the u and v components of the observed wind field we have similar procedures as with vorticity and divergence.

Assuming geostrophic conditions of flow and neglecting the variation of the Coriolis parameter with geographic latitude, one obtains—similar to the computation of the geostrophic vorticity—the two components of deformation:

$$A_g = -(2g/f)(\partial^2 z/\partial x\,\partial y) \qquad 3.247\ (15)$$

$$B_g = (g/f)(\partial^2 z/\partial x^2 - \partial^2 z/\partial y^2). \qquad 3.247\ (16)$$

For a grid as shown in Figure 3.247.1 one arrives at

$$\partial^2 z/\partial x\,\partial y = (1/h^2)(z_A - z_B + z_C - z_D) \qquad 3.247\ (17)$$

$$\partial^2 z/\partial x^2 - \partial^2 z/\partial y^2 = (1/h^2)(z_1 + z_3 - z_2 - z_4). \qquad 3.247\ (18)$$

Considering the scale factor m, which appears when taking the values z_i from a Cartesian co-ordinate system on a plane map, one obtains

$$A = -(2gm^2/fh'^2)(z_A - z_B + z_C - z_D) \qquad 3.247\ (19)$$

$$B = (gm^2/fh'^2)(z_1 + z_3 - z_2 - z_4). \qquad 3.247\ (20)$$

In Figure 3.247.8 an analysis of the geostrophic deformation on the 500-mb surface is given, corresponding to the synoptic map time of Figures 3.247.2, .3, .5, and .6. A comparison with Figure 3.247.5 shows that the deformation is of the same order of magnitude as the vorticity computed from the wind observations. The geostrophic vorticity (Fig. 3.247.3) correspondingly shows strong deviations (Fig. 3.247.6), which agree well with the theoretical considerations in Chapter 1.239.

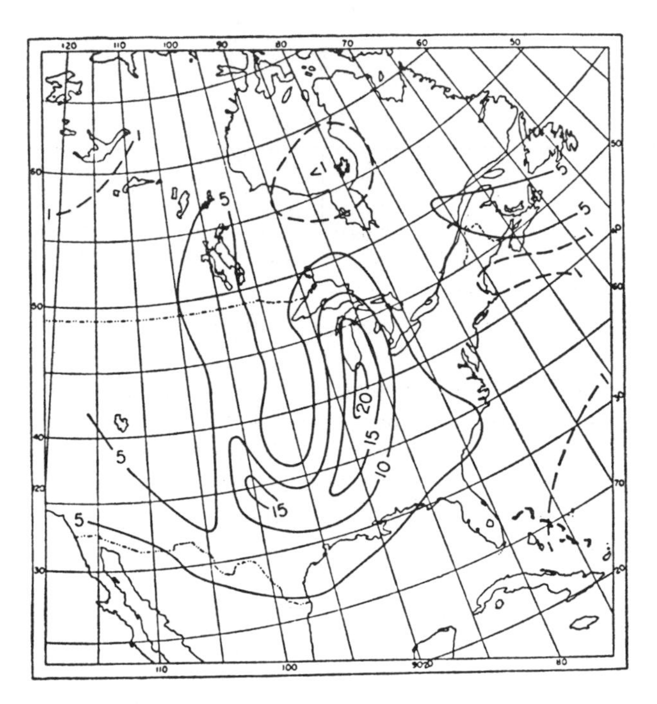

FIG. 3.247.8.—Geostrophic deformation $(A^2+B^2)^{1/2}$ in units 10^{-5} sec^{-1} of the topography represented in Figure 3.247.2. (Petterssen, 1953b.)

3.248. Analysis of Divergence and Vertical Motion

The divergence of the upper flow may be computed from an analysis of the actually observed wind field. The divergence of the geostrophic wind consists only of one term, which results from the variation of the Coriolis parameter with geographic latitude. By partial differentiation of Eq. 1.222 (7) after x and y and subsequent addition, one obtains

$$\nabla \cdot \mathbf{v}_g = -(g\beta/f^2)(\partial z/\partial x) = -(v_g/R)\cdot \cot \varphi. \qquad 3.248\ (1)$$

At 45° latitudes g has the order of magnitude 10^3 cm·sec^{-2}. β is approximately 10^{-13} cm^{-1}·sec^{-1}, f^2 is about 10^{-8} sec^{-2} and $\partial z/\partial x$ amounts to about 10^{-3} for 170 knots. Therefore, the divergence of the geostrophic wind has the maximum order of magnitude of 10^{-5}·sec^{-1}, which, however, is realized only with extremely strong meridional components of the upper current, which in reality hardly ever occur. Zonal geostrophic currents are completely non-divergent. In atmospheric jet streams usually the zonal component predominates, so that the geostrophic divergence in most cases may be neglected.

With the equations quoted in Chapter 1.232 the divergence may be obtained in different ways from the wind observations. From a comparison of Eq. 3.247 (3) with 1.232 (4) it appears that in divergence calculations the map scale is of no importance:

$$D_h' = (1/A')(dA'/dt) = (1/A)(dA/dt)(m^2/m^2) = D_h,$$

because $dm/dt = 0$ for not too long trajectories on the map. The divergence determined on the map, therefore, corresponds to the divergence on the spherical earth.[2]

If the field distribution of the divergence has to be determined Eq. 1.232 (2) is most suitably used. The term $\partial w/\partial z$ in this equation vanishes with *horizontal* flow.

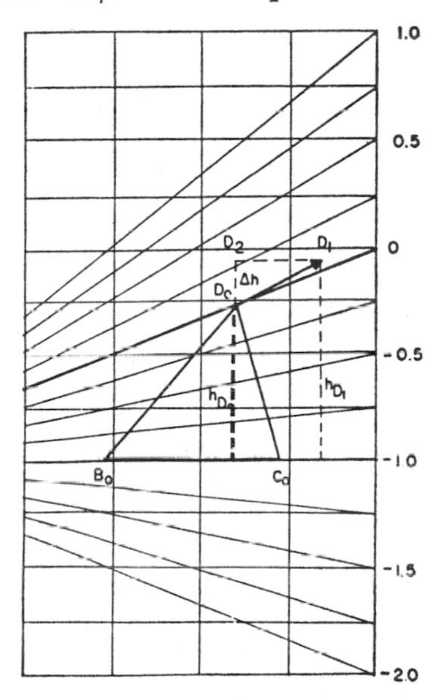

FIG. 3.248.—Computation of divergence from upper-wind observations at 3 stations B_0, C_0, and D_0 (see text). (After Bellamy, 1949.)

In the form of differences the expression for the mean divergence over a square with the sides Δx and Δy reads,

$$D_h = \Delta\bar{u}/\Delta x + \Delta\bar{v}/\Delta y. \qquad 3.248\ (2)$$

If the sides are not too long, we have approximately $\bar{u} = (u_B + u_C)/2$ (see Fig. 3.247.1). For the other mean speeds, analogous expressions are valid. For practical purposes one adopts graphical schemes for analysis and addition similar to the ones described for the vorticity.

If y and x axes are chosen identical to meridians and latitude circles, the expression

$$D_h = \partial u/\partial x + \partial v/\partial y - (v/R)\cdot \tan\varphi. \qquad 3.248\ (3)$$

is valid because of the convergence of the meridians (Godske *et al.*, 1957; Saucier, 1955). The corrective term is of importance only near the poles.

[2] A slight dependency of the divergence on the scale factor m (Hollmann, 1958) usually is suppressed in the models used in numerical weather prediction.

In a natural co-ordinate system the line integral in Eq. 1.232 (5) reduces to $\bar{V}_2 n_2 - \bar{V}_1 n_1$. n_1 and n_2 are normals to the streamlines, $\bar{V}_1$ and $\bar{V}_2$ are the mean speeds across these normals. The area A may be measured by planimeter. Let ψ be the angle between the direction of the two streamlines enclosing the area. The divergence may then be determined as

$$D_h = \partial V/\partial s + V(\partial\psi/\partial n)$$

[see 1.232 (3)].

From the wind observations at three stations the divergence may be calculated from the change of area per unit time [1.232 (4)]. A_0 is the area of the triangle $B_0C_0D_0$; the end points of the wind vectors in these three corners make up the new triangle $B_1C_1D_1$, whose area shall be called A_1. (In Fig. 3.248 only the point D_1 of triangle A_1 has been plotted.) Under the assumption that the wind variation between the stations shall be linear and that the length of the vectors is $\Delta\mathbf{s} = \mathbf{v}\cdot\Delta t$, one obtains for the mean divergence of the area of the original triangle

$$D_h = (A_1 - A_0)/A_0 \cdot \Delta t. \qquad 3.248\ (4)$$

The areas A_0 and A_1 may be measured with a planimeter. A graphical method is reported by Bellamy (1949).

D_h is broken down into contributions, which are made from the wind vectors at the different stations, i.e.,

$$D_h = D_B + D_C + D_D.$$

The area of the original triangle is $(\overline{B_0C_0}/2)\cdot h_{D_0}$; the area of the triangle which is obtained by considering the wind vector in D_0 is $(\overline{B_0C_0}/2)\cdot h_{D_1}$. Therefore,

$$D_D = (1/\Delta t)(\Delta h_D/h_{D_0}).$$

In this equation $\Delta h_D = h_{D_1} - h_{D_0}$ (Fig. 3.248).

Analogous expressions may be derived for the other points. In a nomograph containing the isopleths of $\Delta h/h$ (slanting lines in Fig. 3.248) D_D may be determined as follows:

The nomograph is placed on the station triangle so that the base of the triangle coincides with the straight line (-1.0), and that the corner D of the triangle lies on the straight line 0. $\Delta h/h$ may be read immediately from the slanting lines as the distance $\overline{D_2D_0}$. The point D_2 is obtained as the intersection of a horizontal line through D_1 and a vertical through D_0, as indicated in Figure 3.248.

The *order of magnitude* of divergence depends on the length of the time interval which has been used for averaging, and therefore depends on the weather sequence which characterizes the formation of the divergence. Petterssen (1956) gives the following values to be characteristic for divergence:

D (sec^{-1})	Δt	Scale of the flow pattern
1.9×10^{-4}	1 hour	*subsynoptic* convective processes, tornadoes, hurricanes, etc.
3.2×10^{-5}	6 hours	*intense synoptic:* strongly developed upper troughs, cyclogenesis at sea-level
0.8×10^{-5}	1 day	*medium* synoptic
0.4×10^{-5}	2 days	*feeble* synoptic
1.1×10^{-6}	1 week	*planetary waves*

For the development and maintenance of jet streams, therefore, divergence values of the order of magnitude of 1 to $4\cdot10^{-5}$ are necessary. Even these small divergences would cause enormous pressure changes at the surface, if they were uniformly present throughout the whole depth of the atmosphere.

From the hydrostatic equation, 1.222 (3), and in consideration of Eq. 1.222 (2) one obtains the following relation for pressure changes at the surface:

$$(\partial p/\partial t)_0 = \int_0^\infty (\partial \rho/\partial t)\, d\Phi. \qquad 3.248\ (5)$$

Substituting from the equation of continuity, 1.221 (2), we arrive at

$$(\partial p/\partial t)_0 = -\int_0^\infty \nabla_h \cdot (\rho \mathbf{v})\, d\Phi + (g\rho w)_0. \qquad 3.248\ (6)$$

$\nabla_h \cdot (\rho \mathbf{v})$ is the horizontal mass divergence. For a horizontal earth's surface $w=0$. Since, furthermore, $\rho(\nabla \cdot \mathbf{v})$ usually exceeds the expression $\mathbf{v} \cdot \nabla \rho$ by one order of magnitude, one may write in approximation:

$$(\partial p/\partial t)_0 = -\int_0^\infty \rho(\nabla_h \cdot \mathbf{v})\, d\Phi. \qquad 3.248\ (7)$$

Introducing from the hydrostatic equation the vertical co-ordinate in the form of pressure, we obtain

$$(\partial p/\partial t)_0 = +\int_{p_0}^0 (\nabla_h \cdot \mathbf{v})\, dp. \qquad 3.248\ (8)$$

A mean divergence of $2 \cdot 10^{-5}$ sec^{-1} throughout the total air column would, therefore, for $\int_{p_0}^0 dp = -1000$ mb result in a pressure change at the surface of about $2 \cdot 10^{-2}$ mb$\cdot$sec^{-1}. This corresponds to a pressure tendency of about 72 mb per hour. The actually observed pressure tendencies at sea level are, however, smaller by almost two orders of magnitude. In the atmosphere there are, therefore, *at least* two layers on top of each other, in which the divergence reverses its sign. This is already evident from investigations by Schedler (1917), Dines (1912, 1919, 1925), and more recently from papers by Sutcliffe (1939, 1947).

Reuter and Huber (1956) are considering the contribution of various pressure levels in the development of surface pressure changes by taking the local changes and the advection of the reciprocal values of absolute vorticity instead of the divergence $\nabla_h \cdot \mathbf{v}$ in Eq. 3.248 (8). Strong pressure falls build up when both terms have the same sign.

The jet-stream level is characterized by a maximum of divergence or convergence (see also Faust, 1953, 1954*a*, *b*, 1955*a*, *b*). The vertical component of velocity $\omega = dp/dt$, however, shows a maximum at the level of non-divergence. The surface-pressure changes are composed of the effects of positive and negative divergences above and below the level of non-divergence p_D. They constitute, therefore, a small residual between two larger quantities of opposite sign.

$$(\partial p/\partial t)_0 = \int_{p_0}^{p_D} (\nabla_h \cdot \mathbf{v})\, dp + \int_{p_D}^0 (\nabla_h \cdot \mathbf{v})\, dp. \qquad 3.248\ (9)$$

The connection between vertical velocity $\omega = dp/dt$ and divergence is established from Eq. 1.235 (1) for $\lim \Delta p \to 0$

$$\partial \omega/\partial p = -D. \qquad 3.248\ (10)$$

Equation 3.248 (10) contains the fact that ω reaches an extreme value for $D=0$. Its characteristic is determined by the sign of

$$\partial D/\partial p = -\partial^2 \omega/\partial p^2.$$

For divergence increasing downward toward the ground ($\partial D/\partial p > 0$) we have $\partial^2\omega/\partial p^2 < 0$. The vertical velocity dp/dt, therefore, assumes a maximum value here and indicates *sinking* motion. *Convergence* near the surface, which decreases upward, causes a minimum of vertical velocity component at the level of non-divergence, and therefore indicates ascending motion.

For the extreme value of divergence at about 300 mb we have $\partial D/\partial p = -\partial^2\omega/\partial p^2 = 0$, i.e., the second derivative of the vertical velocity with respect to the vertical co-ordinate has to be zero. At the same level, however, $D = -\partial\omega/\partial p \neq 0$, i.e., the profiles of vertical velocity show an *inflection point* at about 300 mb, which approximately corresponds to the jet-stream level. The vertical component of velocity itself, however, does *not* necessarily have to vanish here (Reiter, 1959*f*).

The *vertical velocity* may be computed by various methods (Panofsky, 1951). By stepwise integration of the equation of continuity in the form of 3.248 (10), and with the aid of the boundary condition $\omega = 0$ for sea level, the vertical velocity may be computed directly from the analyses of divergence, without making any assumptions on the mechanism of flow. By means of Bellamy's (1949) "triangle method" for estimating the divergence, the vertical velocity may be determined from the relation

$$w_2 = \frac{\rho_1}{\rho_2} w_1 + \tfrac{1}{2}\left(\frac{\rho_1}{\rho_2} D_1 + D_2\right) h. \qquad 3.248\ (11)$$

w_2 and w_1 are the components of vertical velocity at the upper and lower boundary of a layer whose thickness is h. ρ_2 and ρ_1 are the corresponding densities, and D_2 and D_1 the divergences in the two boundary surfaces. Since, however, the wind observations and analyses have to be very accurate, this method has only limited practical application. Especially in the jet-stream region one will have to expect errors.

Under the assumption that the flow is adiabatic, i.e., $d\Theta/dt = 0$, one obtains

$$\partial\Theta/\partial t + \mathbf{v}_h \cdot \nabla_h \Theta + \omega(\partial\Theta/\partial p) = 0$$

or

$$\omega = -\big(1/(\partial\Theta/\partial p)\big) \cdot [\partial\Theta/\partial t + V(\partial\Theta/\partial s)]. \qquad 3.248\ (12)$$

V is the magnitude of the horizontal wind velocity, $\partial\Theta/\partial t$ is the local change of potential temperature per unit of time, and $\partial\Theta/\partial s$ is the change of potential temperature per unit of length along the streamline (see also Arizumi, 1950). From Eq. 1.225 (1) and from the hydrostatic equation one may substitute into 3.248 (12) and one obtains for the vertical velocity, with z as vertical co-ordinate,

$$w = -\big(1/(\Gamma - \gamma)\big) \cdot [\partial T/\partial t + V(\partial T/\partial s)]. \qquad 3.248\ (13)$$

Γ is the dry adiabatic vertical lapse rate of temperature.

$$\Gamma = \kappa_d / R_d = 1/c_{pd} = 0.00996°\ \mathrm{C/gpm} \qquad 3.248\ (14)$$

and γ the actually present vertical lapse rate. Equation 3.248 (13) may also be evaluated from the ascent curves and hodographs of single stations. The dependability of the calculation suffers, however, from the assumption of geostrophic flow conditions.

Equation 3.248 (13) may be transformed by taking horizontal and vertical components of flow into account separately.

$$w=-\frac{1}{\Gamma-\gamma}\left(\frac{\partial T}{\partial t}+V_h\left(\frac{\partial T}{\partial s}\right)_h+\frac{dz}{dt}\cdot\frac{\partial T}{\partial z}\right)$$

or

$$w=-\frac{1}{\Gamma-\gamma}\left[\frac{\partial T}{\partial t}+V_h\left(\frac{\partial T}{\partial s}\right)_h-\gamma\frac{\partial z}{\partial t}-\gamma V_h\left(\frac{\partial z}{\partial s}\right)_h\right].$$

For moist adiabatic processes, Γ in 3.248 (13) must be replaced by the moist adiabatic vertical temperature lapse rate (Petterssen, 1956).

Let C be the speed with which an isotherm moves along a streamline. We then have

$$\partial T/\partial t=-C(\partial T/\partial s) \qquad 3.248\ (15)$$

and

$$w=-(1/(\Gamma-\gamma))\cdot(V-C)\cdot(\partial T/\partial s). \qquad 3.248\ (16)$$

The disadvantage of this method lies in the fact that because the streamlines are nearly parallel to the isotherms, points of intersections between the two sets of curves are difficult to pinpoint, especially if the wind analysis is based on gradient wind conditions, which make the streamlines identical with the isohypses. The determination of w, therefore, depends strongly on the accuracy of the analyses. Furthermore, moist adiabatic and non-adiabatic processes complicate the calculations, because a simple value for Γ does not suffice any longer.

Another method for the calculation of vertical velocities is given by Eq. 1.233 (7). The two last terms on the right-hand side of this equation usually may be neglected (they indicate the raising of horizontal vortex tubes), except for areas with a strongly marked horizontal gradient of vertical wind speed. By introducing p as vertical co-ordinate, one obtains

$$\partial Q/\partial t+V(\partial Q/\partial s)+\omega(\partial Q/\partial p)=(\partial\omega/\partial p)Q \qquad 3.248\ (17)$$

or by simple transformation,

$$\partial Q/\partial t+V(\partial Q/\partial s)-Q^2\cdot\partial/\partial p(\omega/Q).$$

Integration of this equation yields

$$\omega_1/Q_1-\omega_0/Q_0=\int_0^1(1/Q^2)\cdot[\partial Q/\partial t+V(\partial Q/\partial s)]\cdot dp.$$

Since ω_0 is 0 at the horizontal surface of the earth, one may obtain the vertical velocity at an arbitrary level by stepwise integration:

$$\omega_1=Q_1\int_0^1(1/Q^2)\cdot[\partial Q/\partial t+V(\partial Q/\partial s)]\,dp. \qquad 3.248\ (18)$$

For vorticity values smaller than $0.4\cdot10^{-4}$ Petterssen (1956) recommends neglecting the right-hand side of 3.248 (17). In this case one arrives at the approximate expression for the vertical velocity:

$$\omega=-[\partial Q/\partial t+V(\partial Q/\partial s)]/(\partial Q/\partial p). \qquad 3.248\ (19)$$

The evaluation of the term $\partial Q/\partial s$ usually offers no difficulties because the isopleths of Q render well-defined intersections with isohypses and streamlines (see Figs. 3.247.2 and .3). $\partial Q/\partial t$ is more difficult to evaluate, since upper-level wind charts are available for only 12-hour intervals. Petterssen recommends computing the vorticity change $\delta Q/\delta t$ relative to a co-ordinate system which moves with the center of the disturbance at the ground, and whose speed is C. We, then, have

$$\partial Q/\partial t = \delta Q/\delta t - C(\partial Q/\partial S), \qquad 3.248\ (20)$$

where **S** gives the direction of propagation of the disturbance.

In the jet-stream region, where air masses are moving through the field of isohypses with great velocity, we find $\partial Q/\partial t \ll \partial Q/\partial s$, so that the vorticity equation may be approximated by

$$V(\partial Q/\partial s) = -Q \cdot D. \qquad 3.248\ (21)$$

In the region of strong *advection of positive vorticity* ($\partial Q/\partial s < 0$) we may, therefore, count on marked *high-level divergence* associated with *rising* air motions in the part of the troposphere immediately underneath. If there is a possibility for convergence near the ground, this may, under certain circumstances, lead to cyclogenesis.

Considering that pronounced upward motions in the atmosphere usually lead to a state of saturation and, from there on, proceed moist adiabatically, and that descending motions on the other hand follow a dry adiabate, which leads away from the state of saturation, one may obtain a *qualitative* picture of the vertical motions by considering the difference between dew-point temperature (T_d) and dry-air temperature (T). This difference constitutes a measure for the degree of saturation. This very simple method is especially suited for analyses of cross sections and time sections (see Fig. 6.2.3, Reiter and Heuberger, 1961; Vuorela, 1953, 1954, 1957*a*). Areas with small differences $T - T_d$ indicate ascending motion. If $T - T_d$ is large, descending motion is to be expected in this region. The disadvantage of this method is that humidity measurements at low temperatures ($< -40°$ C) and with small concentrations of water vapor become unreliable, so that usable measurements from the jet-stream level are not very frequent.

Hollmann and Wegner (1958) give an approximation formula which allows one to compute vertical velocities through the 700-mb level at a center grid point, from values of the relative topography 500/850-mb at surrounding grid points, using a scheme similar to the one shown in Figure 3.247.1.

$$w_7 = \frac{p_{10} - p_7}{g f^2 p_7} R T_7 \left\{ \frac{\partial}{\partial y} (\Phi_5 - \Phi_{8.5}) \frac{\partial Q_{8.5}}{\partial x} - \frac{\partial}{\partial x} (\Phi_5 - \Phi_{8.5}) \frac{\partial Q_{8.5}}{\partial y} \right\}. \qquad 3.248\ (22)$$

w_7 is the vertical velocity at the 700-mb level, $p_{10} = 1000$ mb, $p_7 = 700$ mb, T_7 is the absolute temperature at the 700-mb level, $Q_{8.5}$ is the absolute vorticity at the 850-mb level, and $(\Phi_5 - \Phi_{8.5})$ is the relative topography of the geopotential between 850 and 500 mb. In the form of differences this equation may be written:

$$w_0 = 2.02 \frac{1 - 0.0037 t_0}{f_0^2} \{(D_2 - D_4)(Q_1 - Q_3) - (D_1 - D_3)(Q_2 - Q_4)\}. \qquad 3.248\ (23)$$

for a grid distance of 300 km in 60° latitude, and on a stereographic projection. The subscripts refer to the grid points shown in Figure 3.247.1. t_0 is the temperature at the point 0, measured in degrees centigrade. D_i are the thicknesses of the relative topography 500/850 mb, and Q_i are the values of the absolute *geostrophic* vorticity at the 850-mb level. Q and f are to be taken in units (6 hours)$^{-1}$. w, then, is obtained in cm/sec.

Wiin-Nielsen (1959*a*) offers a graphical approximation method for calculating the ω-field, which is similar to the Fjørtoft (1952) method of graphical integration of the prognostic equations, and which, in essence, uses the temperature advection in the (isobaric) field of relative vorticity.

The choice of the calculation method for divergence and vertical motion in a particular case will have to depend on the quality and number of available data, and also on the purpose, for which these calculations are to be carried out. The reliability of the computations will increase if several methods are used simultaneously, and if the results are compared.

3.249. Tropopause and Frontal Analyses

There is a marked correlation between height and temperature of the tropopause on the one hand, and the position of the polar-front jet (PFJ) and subtropical jet (STJ) on the other hand, which may be utilized to identify the jet-stream axis by means of a tropopause analysis. While the polar tropopause may be found in the vicinity of the 300-mb level—sometimes also below this—the tropical tropopause is near the 100-mb level (Fig. 4.412.1). Between these two extreme tropopause positions there is a zone in which a tropopause may be found at about 200 mb (see Raethjen, 1951).

The transition between the different tropopause positions is not continuous, but shows "break zones," in which the ascent curves contain no well-defined tropopause. It is in these break zones that the two jet streams, the PFJ and STJ, are located (Nagai and Matuoka, 1949). The position of jet streams, therefore, may be determined from a topography of a tropopause surface, or—from what is more easily obtained from aerological diagrams—an isobar or isotherm analysis of the tropopause surface. The jet streams usually coincide with strong temperature and pressure gradients of the tropopause as they are clearly shown in Figure 4.141.

F. Defant (1958; see also Defant and Taba, 1958*c*) introduces a secondary break zone within the subtropical tropopause, in which the tropopause changes from about 250 mb to about 200 mb, and which, in his point of view, is accompanied by a branch of the STJ. This detailed subdivision, however, carries no significance, if one considers the inadequacies the definition of the tropopause is subject to.

According to the international weather code, the tropopause is defined as the lower boundary of a layer, in which the temperature lapse rate is $\leqq 0.2°$ C/100 m. This layer has to be at least 2 km thick. Studies by Endlich (1954), and by others (F. Defant, 1958; Havens and Baum, 1956) show that tropopause heights taken from coded weather messages show very pronounced frequency maxima at 300, 200, 150, and 100 mb. Weaker maxima are interspersed at levels with multiples of 10 mb. Figure 3.249.1 shows such a frequency distribution for 2500 radiosonde ascents of the northern hemisphere (January, 1956). Pronounced frequency maxima appear at 300 and 200 mb. In between there is another maximum at 250 mb. Since, according to the new radiosonde code (as of January, 1955), the latter also lies on a standard

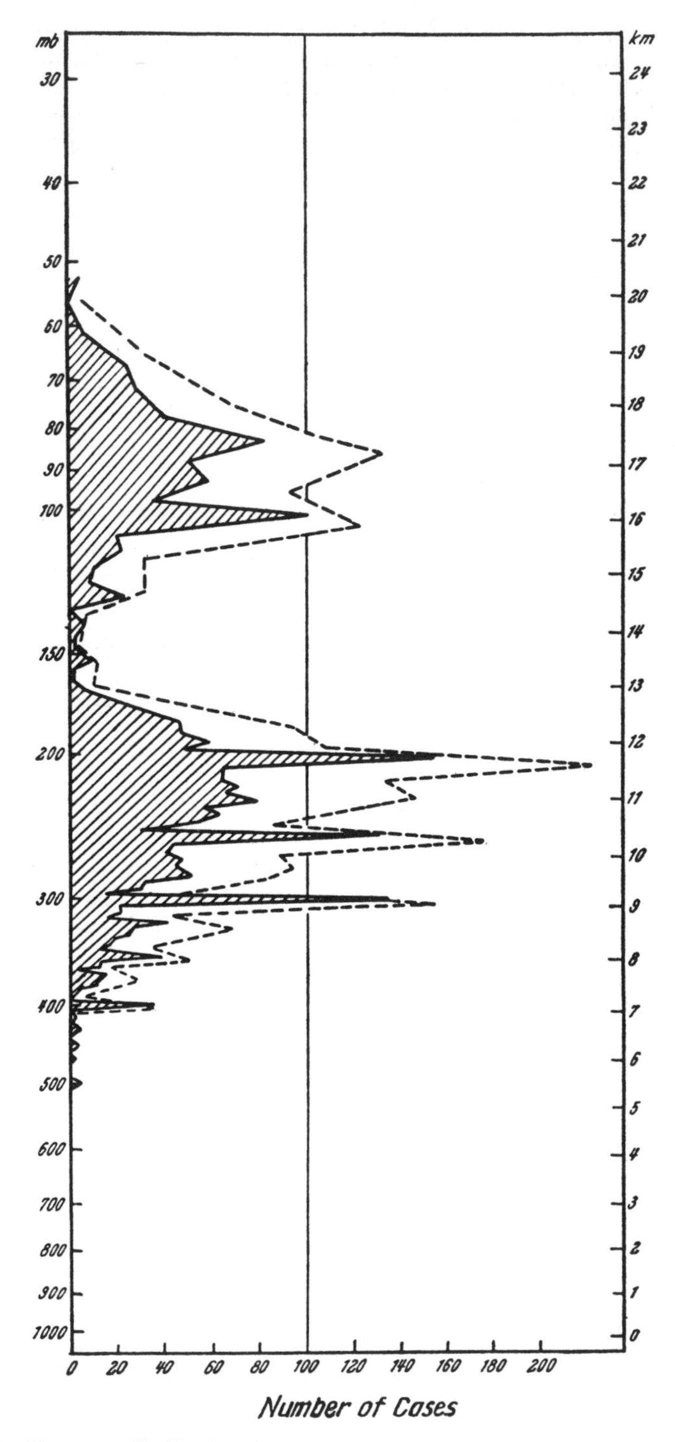

FIG. 3.249.1.—Frequency distribution of tropopause pressures, January, 1956, for 2500 radiosonde ascents over the northern hemisphere. Shaded, frequency distribution for 5-mb intervals; dashed, frequency distribution for 10-mb intervals. (After Defant, 1958.)

level, the deduction of the existence of a secondary "tropopause break" between 250 and 200 mb is not very conclusive. The frequency minimum at 150 mb and another maximum between 100 and 80 mb are very pronounced.

Preference of standard isobaric levels certainly is not a whim of the tropopause but is due to the method of coding. Significant points are reported in the ascent curve above 500 mb only, if a straight connection between temperature values on standard isobaric surfaces would lead to an error of more than 2° C as compared with the actually measured temperature (Endlich, 1954). According to these instructions, the observers try to place significant changes in the vertical temperature lapse rate into standard isobaric levels, if the error does not exceed 2° C.

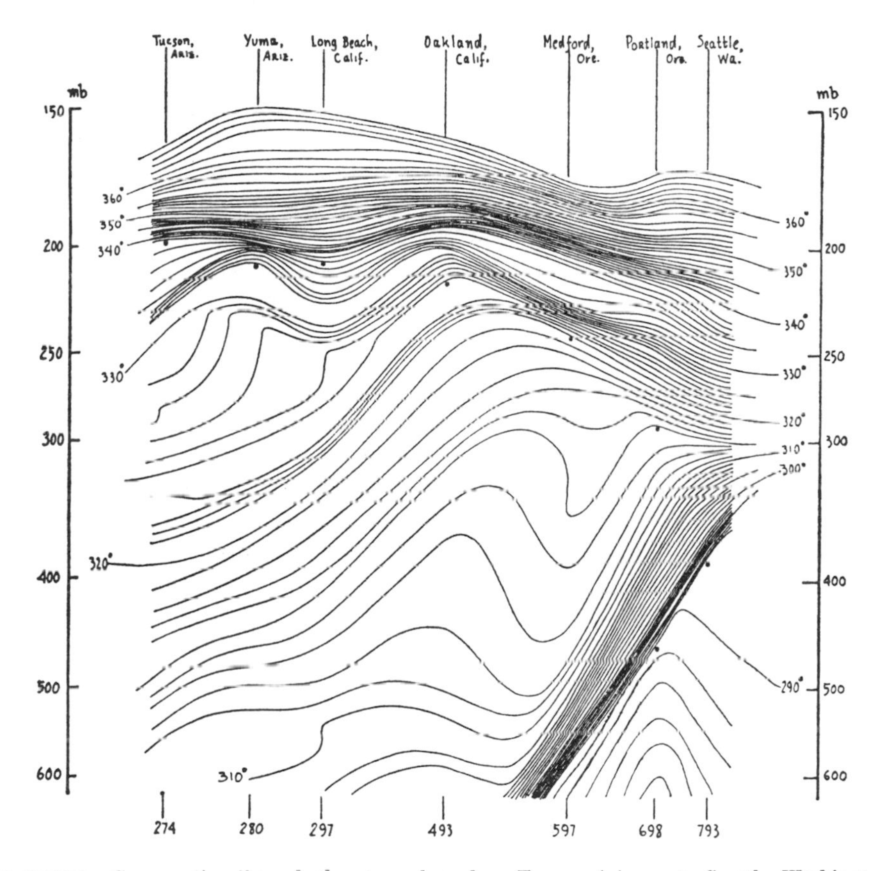

FIG. 3.249.2.—Cross section through the atmosphere from Tucson, Arizona, to Seattle, Washington, 27 March, 1956, 0300 GCT. The dots indicate the tropopause position as obtained from the teletype messages. (Danielsen, 1959.)

Another difficulty in the analysis of tropopauses arises through the fact that parts of stable layers, which in some stations are coded as tropopauses, may drift into the upper and middle troposphere by sinking motions and are then coded as stable layers, inversions, or frontal surfaces, while a new tropopause is reported at a higher level. If this new level lies significantly higher than the old one, this discrepancy in height will be interpreted as "tropopause break." In reality, however, shallow stable layers are sloping downward into the troposphere inside this "break," and are lost during the coding process, if the temperature change within these layers is less than 2° C. At the most, they may still show up as a somewhat more stable vertical temperature lapse rate between the two neighboring isobaric surfaces. This is also the reason why smaller inversions or stable layers are very difficult to analyze in cross sections, because at some stations they were abandoned during the coding process, although in the original temperature registrations of the radiosondes they are still present (Danielsen, 1959).

Figure 3.249.2 shows a detailed cross section from Tucson, Arizona, to Seattle, Washington, of 27 March, 1956, 0300 GCT. From the crowding of isentropes the stable layers are clearly visible. The dots indicate the tropopause position as obtained from the coded weather messages. The position of the PFJ would have to be sought above the frontal zone in the right portion of the diagram, where the tropopause indicates the presence of a break zone by its marked change in height. As may be seen clearly from this diagram, in those areas of the tropopause on the anticyclonic side of the jet stream which are characterized by small height differences in the positions of the significant points obtained from the coded messages, numerous stable layers slope down into the troposphere. One, therefore, should rather call this area a "break zone," or speak of a "leaflike" structure of the tropopause when a tropopause analysis of the kind shown in Fig. 4.141 leads us to expect this least. It may be easily seen from this representation that by virtue of this leaflike structure stratospheric air may penetrate into the troposphere and vice versa, without the tropopause changing its position. The tropopause, therefore, is *not a substantial surface* (see Ertel, 1936; Lowell, 1951).

The tropopause has advective characteristics (Sawyer, 1951*b*) because it follows one and the same isentropic surface over large regions, even with the coding method presently in use. The leaflike structure becomes evident only in seemingly non-isentropic tropopause shifts, as they frequently occur in the neighborhood of jet streams (formations of "tropopause funnels," etc.).

Even during the intrusion of stratospheric air into the troposphere, which will be discussed further in Chapter 6, the horizontal component of flow outweighs the vertical component by orders of magnitude. For all practical purposes of aviation meteorology the flow, therefore, may be regarded as quasi-horizontal, even though the vertical motions are of significance in other respects.

For vertical exchange processes the tropopause constitutes a lid because of the stable structure of the stratosphere. In flights at great altitude it may, therefore, be recognized under certain circumstances as a haze layer (Stevens, 1936).

In order to remedy the deficiencies due to the arbitrary coding process, Danielsen proposes placing the tropopause into *those* points in which the isentropic surfaces reach their maximum height, and at the same time separating an area of large stability from an area of lesser stability. At this newly defined tropopause surface, therefore, the baroclinicity reverses its sign. If this definition of the tropopause is applied in Figure 3.249.2, one should connect the upper surface of the stable frontal zone with the tropopause of the anticyclonic side of the jet stream by a continuous line. The lower surface of the frontal zone, however, may be connected with the tropopause above the cold air (see Fig. 6.123). This "water-spout model" (Reed and Danielsen, 1959) of the tropopause above a frontal zone, and the associated jet stream avoid, therefore, the indication of a "break," which has become a misleading term in view of the leaflike structure of the atmosphere mentioned above.

Aircraft measurements of Project Jet Stream revealed that especially in the "break zone" between polar and subtropical tropopause the separation between stratosphere and troposphere is very clearly marked by a stable and baroclinic zone—the "upper jet stream front." This upper frontal zone becomes conspicuous only by measurements in a horizontal plane. One radiosonde ascent at a single station alone, however, cannot determine the character of a stable layer in the ascent curve.

These flight measurements, furthermore, revealed that in most cases south of the jet-stream axis there is a marked upward bulge in the isentropic surfaces—the so-called isentrope hump (Partl and Tanck, 1960; Reiter, 1960*d*, *e*, 1961*e*). If one identified the tropopause with the axis of this isentrope hump, following Danielsen's proposal, the maximum wind speed according to this definition would fall into the stratosphere in most cases. In this case the statistical findings stated below would be considerably changed.

If the inadequacies of the present definition and labeling of the tropopause are considered properly (Janz, 1954), an analysis of the tropopause "surface" offers a valuable aid for jet-stream and surface weather diagnosis and prognosis (Badner and Johnson, 1957; Culkowski, 1956; Hughes and Foster, 1954; James and Holzworth, 1954; Sawyer, 1951*a*, 1954; U.S. Air Weather Service, 1952*b*).

The correlation between the layer of maximum wind (LMW) and the height of the tropopause is not very distinct. On the average the LMW lies about 1 km (40 mb) above the tropopause (Bannon and Jackson, 1953; Faust, 1953; Gold, 1953). This distance, however, is subject to large, partly systematic, fluctuations (Austin and Bannon, 1952; Reiter, 1958*a*).

From upper wind statistics obtained over Brest and Trappes (France), Coudron (1952) found that the wind maximum in the jet-stream region may lie anywhere between 1 km above and 4 km below the tropopause.

On the anticyclonic side of the jet stream the tropopause usually lies above the level of maximum wind, while on the cyclonic side in the immediate vicinity of the jet stream the largest wind velocities usually are found in the stratosphere, a fact which was already pointed out by Peppler (1914).

Similar to the location of the tropopause in space, the position of *fronts* may be represented as their intersection lines with various isobaric or level surfaces This kind of analysis has been used by Palmén (1951*a*; Bjerknes and Palmén, 1937) successfully for the study of cut-off lows (see Fig. 6.124.2). It also has been used in the Canadian weather service (R. Anderson, Boville, and McClellan, 1955; Crocker, 1949, and Godson and Penner, 1947; Galloway, 1958; Godson, 1950*a*). According to Margules's equation, 6.11 (1), the slope of a boundary surface is given by the horizontal wind shear between the two adjacent air masses and therefore constitutes a measure of the intensity of the PFJ which flows in the warm air.

The STJ is characterized by the absence of a pronounced frontal zone in the middle and lower troposphere, as will be shown later. The baroclinic zone with which it is associated extends only through the upper troposphere. A frontal analysis, therefore, is not possible in this case.

3.25. Trend Diagrams and Space Time Sections

3.251. Zonal Index and Trend Diagrams

In order to express by a simple measure the intensity of the zonal current and its time variations, averaged over the total hemisphere, one uses the *zonal index* (Kats, 1955). This is nothing else than the difference of the mean geopotential heights of an isobaric surface averaged along two latitude circles. Therefore, it is a measure of the mean zonal geostrophic wind in this latitude belt. In calculating the zonal index, one commonly uses the geopotential heights of the respective isobaric surfaces tabulated over discrete intervals of geographic longitude (e.g., every 5°).

$$I_z = (1/n) \cdot \sum_{i=1}^{n} (z_{\varphi_1}^{(i)} - z_{\varphi_2}^{(i)}). \qquad 3.251\ (1)$$

I_z is the zonal index, n is the number of pairs of grid points used and $z_{\varphi_1}^{(i)}$ and $z_{\varphi_2}^{(i)}$ are the height values at these grid points read off at the geographic latitude φ_1 and φ_2.

In many cases the zonal index is also given as the mean speed of the zonal current, which may be obtained from 3.251 (1) in the following way:

$$I_z' = u = -\frac{1}{R \cdot \Delta\varphi} (g/\bar{f}) \cdot (1/n) \cdot \sum_{i=1}^{n} (z_{\varphi_1}^{(i)} - z_{\varphi_2}^{(i)}). \qquad 3.251\ (2)$$

$\bar{f}$ is the mean Coriolis parameter of the latitude zone $(\varphi_1 - \varphi_2)$. For tropical areas I_z has to be preferred instead of u because of the vanishing Coriolis parameter which renders the geostrophic wind equation meaningless.

Rudloff (1951) proposes characterizing the zonal index by the angular momentum d of an air particle with respect to the earth's axis.

$$d = \rho \cdot u \cdot R \cdot \cos\varphi.$$

From this he derives the "drift number" D, which, in essence, corresponds to the zonal average of the angular momentum for the respective latitude zones.

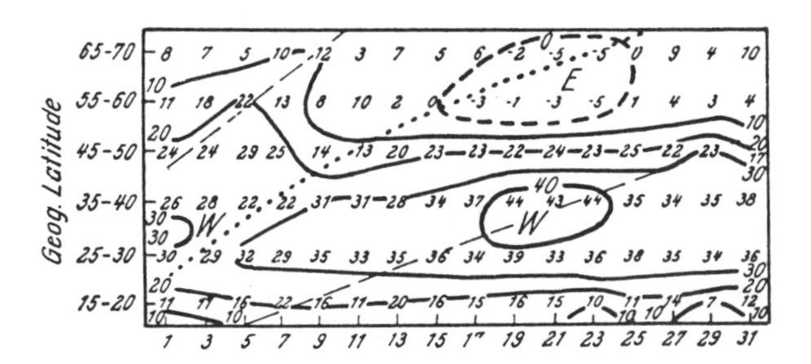

Fig. 3.251.1.—Trend diagram of the northern hemisphere between 20° and 110° E (without Asia), for the 300-mb surface, December, 1945. Numbers have been entered only for every second grid point. They give the zonal wind speeds in m/sec. Dashed lines indicate the trends of relative wind-speed maxima, dotted lines stand for the trends of the minima. (After Riehl, La Seur, *et al.*, 1952.)

One obtains the so-called trend diagrams by carrying out the calculations according to 3.251 (1 or 2) on a daily basis. An example for this is given in Figure 3.251.1 (Namias, 1947*a*; Riehl, Badner, *et al.*, 1952). The ordinate contains the geographic latitude, the abscissa gives the time. In this diagram isopleths of the zonal wind may be analyzed. If I_z' assumes large values which are concentrated in one maximum at temperate latitudes, one speaks of a "high-index" situation (see Fig. 3.251.4). If the average maximum of the zonal wind speed is weak and diffuse, and perhaps even split into two small maxima—one in the north and one in the south—this situation characterizes a "low-index" circulation. In this case the planetary waves have great amplitudes. The zonal wind components present in the vertices of the waves (high-pressure ridges and low-pressure troughs) contribute in the averaging process over the whole hemisphere to the appearance of the two maxima in the trend diagram.

The transition from a high-index to a low-index situation and back again to high-index is called an *index cycle*. It is noteworthy that the magnitude of angular momentum of the zonal current remains constant during one index cycle (Namias, 1950). If one plots the geographic latitude corresponding to the area which is contained between two latitude circles (i.e., sin φ as ordinate), the areas with velocity increase and decrease should be approximately equal to each other.

Figure 3.251.2 shows schematically the circulation types which correspond to an index cycle (Namias and Clapp, 1951). During Stage 1 (low index) troughs and ridges have strongly tilted axes. The jet stream is split into two belts, one of which runs far in the north, the other in subtropical latitudes. Subsequent to a shift in the long wave pattern

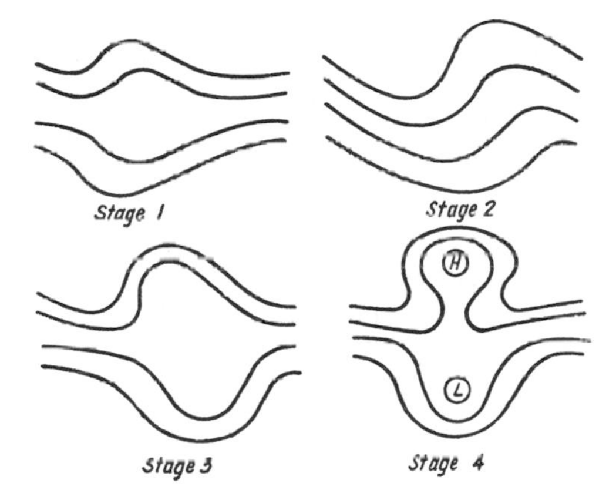

Fig. 3.251.2.—Schematic representation of the upper flow pattern during an index cycle. Time interval from Stage 1 through Stage 4: approximately 2 weeks. (After Namias and Clapp, 1951.)

(see below) warm and cold air masses are brought together on the east side of this strongly sloping trough axis. By virtue of this confluence the meridional temperature gradient is strongly increased, and the zonal wind speed picks up (see Chapter 4.142). In Stage 2, the high index situation is reached. A deepening of troughs finally leads to a re-orientation of the trough axes, and to their breakdown (Stage 3). Again, two separate jet-stream bands are formed in high and low latitudes. The low-index stage reaches its climax (Stage 4) during the formation of blocking anticyclones and cut-off lows.

In some instances excessive hopes have been placed upon the prognostic applicability of the trend diagrams. As may be seen from Figure 3.251.2 a *uniform trend of displacement* of the mean zonal maxima over a longer period can seldom be expected because of the splitting and the confluence of jet-stream bands. Shapiro and Ward (1960) could not recognize any significant and uninterrupted "index cycles" from a Fourier analysis of the meridional component of the kinetic energy at the 500-mb level. Nevertheless, valuable hints may be gained from these diagrams, if they are interpreted correctly. Even the recognition of a low- or high-index stage in itself allows conclusions about the weather types to be expected (see Fig. 3.251.2, and investigations by Willett, 1950).

Because of the correlation between jet stream, frontal zone, cyclone tracks, and weather sequence, which will be discussed further in Chapter 6, indications of the hemispheric weather character may be taken from trend diagrams (Riehl, La Seur, *et al.*, 1952). Northward trends usually indicate warm air advances from the subtropics, which reach their largest extent during the low-index stage. Inversely, southward trends are usually accompanied by intrusions of Arctic cold air into lower latitudes.

Contrary to original expectations, these trends may seldom be followed for a longer period, mainly because cold air and warm air intrusions take place simultaneously at different places around the hemisphere. Preferred areas for cold outbreaks are found in the lee of the Rocky Mountains and of the Himalayas, while farther to the east—on the western slopes of the subtropical high pressure centers—the warm air intrusions usually originate.

The typical weather sequences for high and low index are somewhat better established. A high-index situation is usually accompanied by a rapid sequence of surface cyclones which travel from west to east and which cause changeable weather in temperate latitudes. During low-index stages, however, the activity of disturbances in temperate latitudes is greatly reduced. With this kind of index a blocking high usually may be found over the European sector, as has been pointed out schematically in Figure 3.251.2. The low pressure activity is displaced into the Arctic Sea on the one hand and into the Mediterranean on the other hand. Depending on the position of the long wave troughs, low-index situations may give rise to Vb-cyclones over eastern Central Europe. These cyclones are dreaded because of long-lasting precipitation and resulting inundations in the Danube area.

Transition periods during an index cycle, when the general circulation experiences large re-adjustments, usually are well recognizable on a trend diagram, although one has to be careful about two facts, which, eventually, might lead to gross misinterpretations:

1. If one does not take into account the eccentricity of the circum-polar vortex (La Seur, 1954), the zonal wind maxima may be rather diffusely expressed in the trend diagram, because of the hemispheric averaging.

2. In different parts of the hemisphere warm- and cold-air intrusions, which cause the displacement tendencies of the wind maxima, may have matured to different degrees. Taking a hemispheric average, again, one obtains a rather inadequate picture of the actually present zonal index.

In order to remedy the first drawback, one would have to determine first the phase and amplitude of wave number 1. Thus, a Fourier analysis of the average high-level pressure distribution in a latitude belt would give a measure of the eccentricity of the circum-polar vortex (Graham, 1955). Subsequently, a new spherical co-ordinate system would have to be designed, which is centered in the rotation pole of this vortex, and with respect to which the mean quasi-zonal wind speed has to be calculated. One would have to consider that in this co-ordinate system the Coriolis parameter is a function of geographic longitude, too. Since such calculations mean quite an expense in labor, they hardly ever can be carried out in routine operations, unless an electronic computer is available. It becomes evident, though, that when taking into account strong eccentricities of the circum-polar vortex, a completely different picture of the index stage may result. Figure 3.251.3 shows a mean profile of the zonal component of 12 October (*a*), 18 October (*b*), and 24 October (*c*), 1951, in a co-ordinate system centered on the *earth's pole*. Figure 3.251.4 contains the same wind profiles in an eccentric co-ordinate system. While profile *b*, without considering the eccentricity simulates a low-index stage, Figure 4 shows that, in reality, it characterizes a well-defined high-index situation.

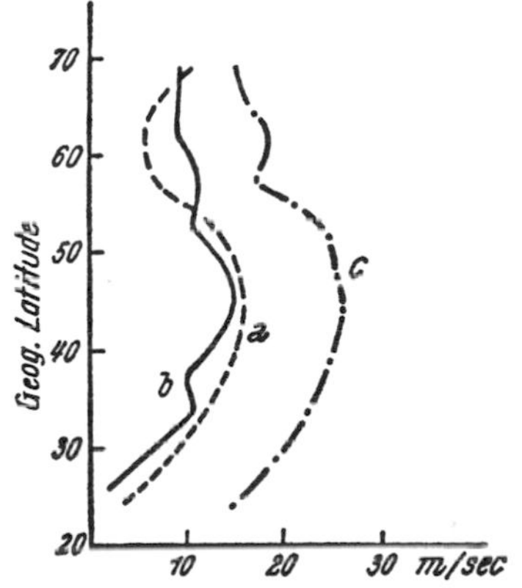

Fig. 3.251.3.—Zonal wind profiles, 500 mb. (*a*) 12 October, 1951, (*b*) 18 October, (*c*) 24 October. (After Riehl, La Seur, *et al.*, 1952.)

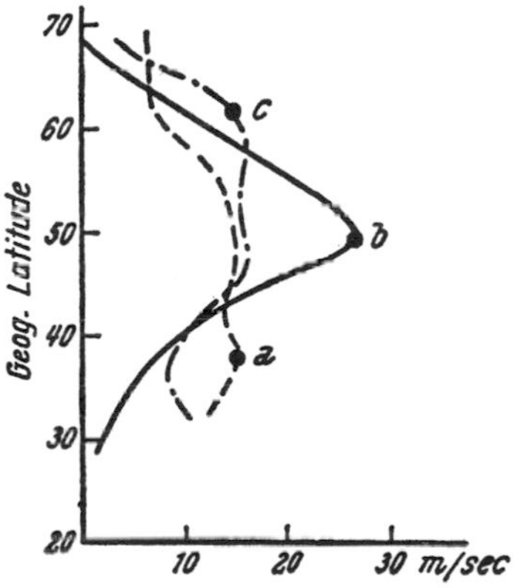

Fig. 3.251.4.—Zonal wind profiles, 500 mb, for the same days as in Figure 3.251.3, however under consideration of the eccentricity of the circum-polar vortex. (After Riehl, La Seur, *et al.*, 1952.)

The second drawback can be handled by computing zonal indices for hemispheric *sectors* (Berry, Haggard, and Wolff, 1954; F. Defant, 1954; University of Chicago, 1947). These sectors should not be too small, however, because the displacement tendencies, then, would give nothing else than an image of the planetary long waves traveling through these sectors. For the European region usually the sector from the American West Coast to the Ural Mountains will suffice, while for the North American forecasting region the Pacific area, including East Asia, should bear significance.

Detailed studies of the mechanism which governs the displacement tendencies of zonal wind maxima show that the transition from low to high index and vice versa does *not* occur simultaneously over the whole hemisphere. The breakdown of circulation periods seems to occur in *preferred areas*, from which the change of index propagates downstream (F. Defant, 1954, 1956*b*; Hoinkes, 1940; Sanders and Kessler, 1955). So, e.g., pressure-rise centers, which are connected with warm-air intrusions, and which initiate a northward trend, seem to have their preferred origin in the subtropical West Atlantic and West Pacific. The transition from low to high index is related to a simultaneous contraction of the circum-polar vortex, i.e., a decrease in the area circumscribed by the hemispheric jet-stream belt. Cold-air outbreaks leading to a renewed increase in amplitude of the planetary waves occur more often in the lee of the Rocky Mountains and over the Asiatic East Coast, as has been mentioned earlier (Hoinkes, 1940). The orographic cause for the outbreaks in these areas will be discussed in detail in Chapter 7.3.

Although clear-cut trends may not always be easy to determine, the trend diagram yields a number of valuable parameters, so, e.g., from the strength of the zonal current one may immediately draw conclusions about the wave length of the planetary waves under stationary conditions (Forsdyke, 1951).

The basic derivations have been made by Rossby (1940, 1945*a*, *et al.*, 1939). For a uniform zonal current without horizontal wind shear he derived the following expression:

$$A_T/A_S = u/(u-C). \qquad 3.251\ (3)$$

A_T is the amplitude of the isotherms, A_S is the amplitude of the streamlines, u is the zonal wind speed, and C is the phase velocity of the Rossby waves. From 3.251 (3) one may see immediately that these long waves are progressive ($C > 0$), as long as the amplitude of the isotherm exceeds that of the streamlines ($A_T > A_S$). If the reverse is true, the waves will be retrograde. If $A_T = A_S$ the waves will be stationary (see also Palmén, 1948*a*).

For a current with *constant absolute vorticity* one may also obtain the wave velocity in the form

$$C = u - (\beta L^2/4\pi^2). \qquad 3.251\ (4)$$

β is the Rossby parameter and L stands for the wave length of long waves. The length of stationary waves is obtained for $C = 0$

$$L_S{}^2 = (4\pi^2/\beta)\cdot u. \qquad 3.251\ (5)$$

L_S is a function of zonal wind speed and of geographic latitude (because of β) only. One obtains for the wave speed

$$C = (\beta/4\pi^2)(L_S{}^2 - L^2). \qquad 3.251\ (6)$$

In a nomograph designed by Byers (Fig. 3.251.5), which represents a graphical solution of 3.251 (4 and 6), the abscissa gives the wave length (in degrees of longitude), while the ordinate contains geographic latitude (Byers, 1959). The set of curves gives the zonal wind speed in degrees of longitude per day. From the trend diagram the value for u_{max} and its geographic latitude may be taken. Let us assume that point A in the nomograph of Figure 3.251.5 is the result of this pair of values for a stationary wave length. Let the point B correspond to the actually present wave length as taken from upper-level maps. If the actual wave length is too short as compared with the stationary wave length (as is the case in the above example), the long wave will have a tendency for progression, at a rate given by the difference of the u isopleths in the points B and A. One may assume that the trough in the lee of the Himalayas because of its orographic position may be stationary ("anchored"). Only the ridges and troughs downstream of this position will be displaced corresponding to 3.251 (6). Analogous conditions hold for retrogression. Discontinuous retrogression is much more frequently observed than continuous retrogression (Cressman, 1948; Namias and Clapp, 1944). The former occurs if a new trough forms upstream and becomes stationary (see Petterssen, 1956). In the case of a stable stationary wave pattern the wave length (in degrees of longitude) from 3.251 (5) times the number of planetary waves should yield 360°. This condition is hardly ever realized. Nevertheless, this equation allows valuable conclusions: e.g., if the actually present wave number is

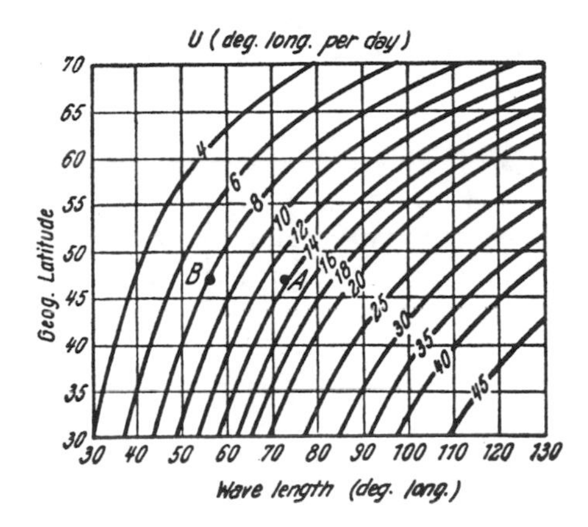

FIG. 3.251.5.—Nomograph for computing the displacement of planetary long waves. (After Byers, 1959.)

too small with respect to the zonal speed u, i.e., the mean wave length L is too large, one may expect a breakdown of the circulation pattern, leading to a rearrangement of the waves. One, therefore, would have an indication in advance of a transition from high to low index. The contrary holds if the zonal component u should call for a smaller wave number. We then have to expect a tendency for the rearrangement of long waves, and a reduction in wave number, which often occurs via a "cutting-off" process, leading to the formation of a cut-off low.

Since Rossby's wave equation, strictly speaking, is valid only at the level of non-divergence near the 600-mb surface, an empirically determined negative correction will have to be applied to the calculation of the zonal index at the 500-mb surface.

Petterssen (1952, 1956) gives the following wave equation for quasi-horizontal flow, which takes into account the horizontal wind shear and the divergence D:

$$C = u - \frac{\beta \cos \gamma + u/B^2 + (1 + f/uK_s)(\partial D/\partial x)}{(2\pi/L)^2 + 1/B^2 - (3/u)(\partial D/\partial x)}. \qquad 3.251\ (7)$$

In this equation B is the half-width of the jet stream (lateral distance within which the wind speed decreases to half of the maximum value), which gives a measure of the wind shear. γ is the angle between trough and ridge lines and the direction north (meridian), and K_s is the curvature of streamlines in the trough or ridge.

Neglecting the divergence, one obtains

$$C = \frac{u - \beta \cos \gamma (L/2\pi)^2}{1 + (L/2\pi B)^2}. \qquad 3.251\ (8)$$

For well-defined wind maxima as they may appear in the trend diagrams of different sectors of the hemisphere, or in considering single waves in the jet stream, Petterssen's wave equation, 3.251 (8), is superior to Rossby's equation, 3.251 (4). The main difference between these two equations is the introduction of the wind shear in 3.251 (8), whose influence upon the wave speed may be considerable under certain conditions, as shown in Table 3.251 (Petterssen, 1956). The angle γ usually is small and has little influence.

TABLE 3.251

L/B	2	4	6	8	10	12	14	16
$1+(L/2\pi B)^2$	1.1	1.4	1.9	2.6	3.5	4.6	5.9	7.4

A wave which is 16 times longer than its half-width, therefore, progresses only by one-seventh of the speed of a Rossby wave as obtained from Figure 3.251.5, if one enters the *peak* zonal speed of the mean profile of the westerlies into this diagram instead of taking the *mean* zonal speed for which Rossby's equation was originally designed. The use of the latter would drastically reduce the discrepancies between Petterssen's and Rossby's formulations.

The stationary wave length is independent of the width of the current

$$L_s = 2\pi\sqrt{(u/\beta\cos\gamma)}. \qquad 3.251\ (9)$$

Therefore,

$$C = \frac{(\beta\cos\gamma/4\pi^2)(L_s^2 - L^2)}{1+(L/2\pi)B^2}. \qquad 3.251\ (10)$$

Introducing the speed of Rossby waves, C_R, from 3.251 (6), with u again being the *peak* zonal speed, we obtain

$$C = \frac{\cos\gamma C_R}{1+(L/2\pi B)^2}. \qquad 3.251\ (11)$$

The speed of progression or retrogression of long waves, as determined from the nomograph of Figure 3.251.5, has to be reduced by the corresponding factors given in the above table whenever the wind maxima are well pronounced. The movement of strongly baroclinic long waves, therefore, is considerably slower than of waves in a barotropic current whose speed equals the peak speed of the baroclinic flow.

Rossby's equation does not give any useful values in the tropics, whereas Petterssen's equation may still be applied. There, a co-ordinate system is suited best, whose positive x-axis points toward west. In this system $\beta < 0$.

For a horizontal, non-divergent flow in an *autobarotropic* atmosphere Kao (1958) computed jet-stream waves whose phase velocities increased with decreasing jet-stream width.

3.252. Meridional Index

The meridional index is defined, in analogy to the zonal index, as the mean magnitude of the geostrophic meridional current around a latitude circle. One has to consider, however, that the geostrophic mass transport per vertical unit area becomes zero when integrated around a latitude circle,

$$\oint \rho v_g\, d\lambda = (1/f)\cdot\oint (\partial p/\partial x)\, d\lambda$$

because $dx = R\cdot\cos\varphi\, d\lambda$ (λ=geographic longitude, R=radius of the earth). The equation for the geostrophic mass transport then reads

$$\oint \rho v_g\, d\lambda = (1/fR\cdot\cos\varphi)\cdot\oint dp = 0. \qquad 3.252\ (1)$$

Fluctuations of mass poleward of a given latitude circle, therefore, may only be brought about by ageostrophic components of flow.

In order to obtain usable values for the meridional index one has to average the *absolute magnitude* of the pressure differences of neighboring grid points on a latitude circle, irrespective of sign,

$$I_M = (1/n) \sum_{i=0}^{n-1} |z_\varphi^{(\lambda_{i+1})} - z_\varphi^{(\lambda_i)}| \qquad 3.252\ (2)$$

or

$$I_M' = (g/f)(1/n) \sum_{i=0}^{n-1} |z_\varphi^{(\lambda_{i+1})} - z_\varphi^{(\lambda_i)}|. \qquad 3.252\ (3)$$

Because of the existence of ageostrophic components of flow for one specific level we may have $\oint \rho v\, d\lambda \neq 0$, because

$$\oint \rho v\, d\lambda = \oint \rho(v_g + v_a)\, d\lambda = \oint \rho v_a\, d\lambda.$$

If one postulates, however, that the total mass of air of a hemisphere shall be constant with time, we arrive at

$$\int_{z=0}^{\infty} \oint \rho v_a\, d\lambda\, dz = 0, \qquad 3.252\ (4)$$

i.e., the mass transport caused by the ageostrophic components of flow has different direction at different levels. The compensating transport of mass occurs through large-scale vertical motions (Vuorela, 1957*b*).

In the atmosphere even 3.252 (4) is not strictly valid, because there are seasonal mass transports between the two hemispheres.

In routine operations the meridional index hardly ever is determined, probably because its calculation calls for a much larger expense in work than is the case with the zonal index. Nevertheless, trend diagrams of both indices may give valuable hints on the average momentum of the atmosphere and its variation with time at the respective pressure level. The decrease of zonal index is coupled with an increase of meridional index, i.e., the amplitudes of planetary waves increase simultaneously with the increase of the meridional component of wind velocity. Since the breakdown and reformation of an index stage does *not* occur simultaneously over the whole hemisphere, as has been mentioned earlier, but originates in preferred areas and then propagates downstream, a consideration by sector of the zonal and meridional indices could give valuable prognostic clues.

3.253. Space-Time Sections

In order to represent the change of a quantity relative to a moving co-ordinate system, one uses space-time sections. Figure 5.33 shows such a space-time section for the mean wind speed of the layer of maximum wind of 26 February to 2 March, 1954. This section has been constructed in the following manner: at each synoptic map time a line perpendicular to the jet axis has been drawn through the wind maximum on each map, as shown in Figure 3.246.3. (The wind maxima have been marked by the letter "*J*" and a heavy dot in the analysis.) These perpendicular lines have been transferred, together with the intersection points of the isotachs to Figure 5.33, and these points, then, have been connected by isolines. From such an analysis it is immediately evident by how much the wind speed changes in the jet maximum as the latter shifts its position, and which fluctuations the horizontal wind shear $\partial V/\partial n$ is subject to. Analogous analyses may be performed for the other parameters which characterize the layer of maximum wind.

3.26. Continuity Diagrams

In order to obtain a clear representation of the changes with time of structure and position of the planetary waves along a latitude circle or a latitude band, one uses the so-called continuity diagrams. In their simplified form the geographic longitude is entered along the abscissa, and the ordinate contains the height of the 500- or 300-mb surface in gpm or gpf. For a clear recognition of the wave structure one usually prefers the 500-mb surface because the short waves, which carry the weather sequence, are clearly expressed on this surface (California Institute of Technology, 1948). Figure 3.26.1 shows such a continuity diagram (see also Cressman, 1948). The analyses for individual days are joined together in the given fashion, and the position of the wave ridges and troughs are connected by lines. In doing this, one has to consider that ridge as well as trough positions have to be projected upon the *base line* of each diagram and only these projection points will have to be joined by lines. In order to filter out small fluctuations one usually enters into the diagram the *mean height* of the 500- or 300-mb surface taken over a *latitude belt* (e.g., between 45° and 60° N). This average height is calculated by forming the arithmetic mean from the contour values along a meridian at intervals of 5° of latitude.

As is shown in Figure 3.26.1, the superposition of short and long waves makes it difficult to determine the position of the latter accurately. This hampers the calculation of wave speeds from any of the equations given in Chapter 3.251. Several methods have been proposed, therefore, to filter out the long waves. A smoothing in time by computing five-day means (Namias, 1947*a*, Willett *et al.*, 1940) has the disadvantage that the wave positions determined by this method are already two and a half days old. Wolff (1955) proposes the calculation from area-mean values. Experiments showed that especially overlapping rectangles with 20° of longitude and latitude as diagonals render satisfactory results.

A somewhat simpler and less time-consuming scheme may be devised by using the *geographic latitude* as ordinate instead of the geopotential height, and by projecting a certain contour line which is closest to the jet axis onto this diagram. This kind of representation may be ambiguous in the case of blocking anticyclones or cut-off lows, when one and the same contour value appears several times along one meridian. Such cases may be treated satisfactorily, however, even with limited experience. Under certain circumstances the plotting of high-pressure and low-pressure vortices, which have separated from the belt of maximum westerlies, may even add to a clearer understanding of weather development.

A somewhat better-designed diagram is offered by Hovmöller (1949; see also Riehl, Yeh, and La Seur, 1950). This "*trough-ridge diagram*" contains the geographic longitude along the abscissa, and time along the ordinate. The values of the mean heights of the 500- or 300-mb surface over a latitude belt of 15° to 20° width are entered at the corresponding geographic longitude, and subsequently contour lines are analyzed (Fig. 3.26.2). From such a diagram the eastward propagating short waves and the quasi-stationary or only slowly progressive long waves, which, at times, may also be discontinually retrograde, are clearly evident. Extrapolation can be facilitated by entering lines for average wave and group velocities into this diagram (Reiter, 1958*a*).

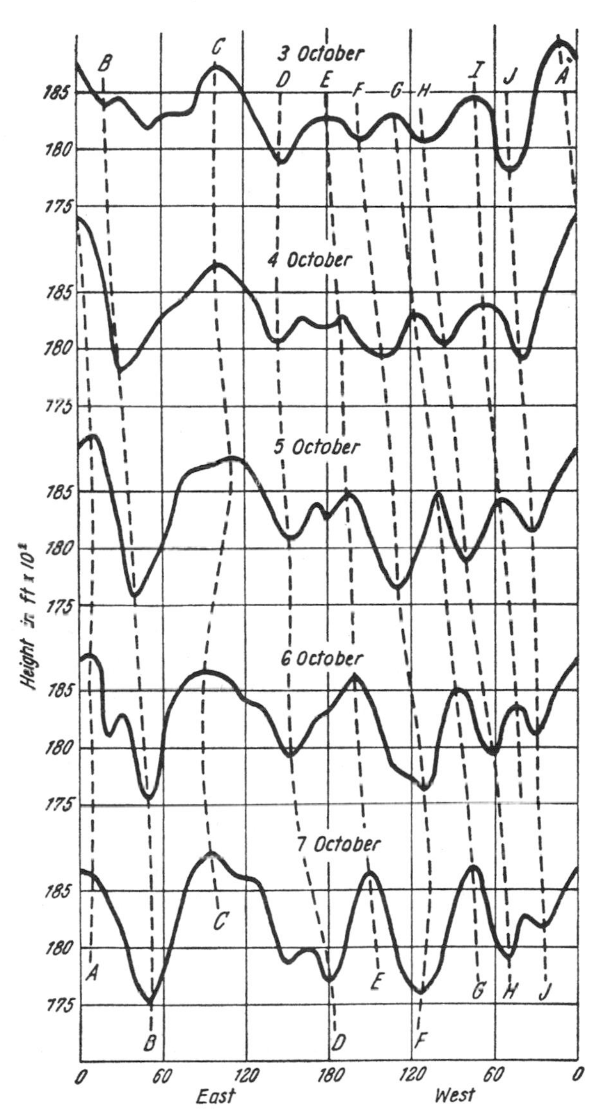

FIG. 3.26.1.—Continuity diagram of the 500-mb surface (3 through 7 October, 1949, averages taken between 45° and 60° N). (After Petterssen, 1950.)

The speed of Rossby waves is given by 3.251 (4). Rossby (1945*b*) was able to show that a sequence of such waves, which are embedded in a zonal current of constant velocity u and whose wave speed, according to 3.251 (4), is a function of wave length only, may exhibit the same group velocity as other interference processes, which is given by

$$C_g = C - L(dC/dL). \qquad 3.26\ (1)$$

From 3.251 (4) it results that

$$L(dC/dL) = -2\beta(L/2\pi)^2.$$

Therefore, the group velocity of a series of Rossby waves is

$$C_g = C + 2\beta(L/2\pi)^2 = u + \beta(L/2\pi)^2. \qquad 3.26\ (2)$$

Assuming a speed of $C = 12°$ longitude per day for short waves (see Table 3.241), we obtain an average wave length of 50° longitude and a frequency of one wave per 4 days. From 3.26 (2) one arrives at a group velocity of about 28° longitude per day. The group velocity, therefore, is considerably larger than the wave speed. It may surpass even the zonal wind speed. This may explain the fact that some disturbances propagate downstream too rapidly to be explained by mere advection (Carlin, 1953; Gambo, 1951; Yeh, 1949).

The transition of short wave disturbances through the system of long waves may be easily followed in a continuity diagram. The mean wave speed of 12° longitude per day corresponds well to average conditions. The intensification of wave amplitudes, however, proceeds with group velocity (about 30° longitude per day).

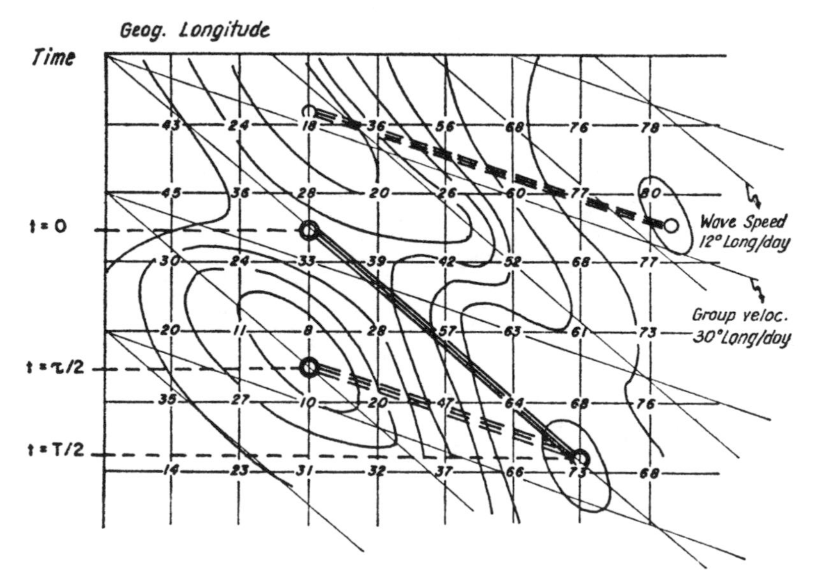

FIG. 3.26.2.—Design of a trough-ridge diagram (continuity diagram). The triple-dashed lines indicate displacements with group velocity, the triple-solid lines give displacements with wave speed.

For an estimate of the meridional component of flow the "meridional circulation diagram" (MCD) offers good services (Reiter, 1958*a*). It is obtained by analyzing isopleths for height differences Δh along overlapping intervals of 20° longitude on the 500-mb surface, and at 45° N, similar to what has been done in continuity diagrams. The transition of short waves troughs and ridges may be followed just as in the

Hovmöller diagram described above. It is much clearer, evident from the MCD, however, that *intensification tendencies* propagate with group velocity. According to this, a jet maximum which, e.g., approaches a long wave trough on its west side makes itself felt in the downstream region of the ridge by an increase in the southerly wind component. This effect propagates at a rate of about 30° longitude per day, a fact which will have to be considered in jet-stream forecasting.

4

THE STRUCTURE OF JET STREAMS

It has already been pointed out in Chapter 2 that the accuracy of upper wind measurements leaves much to be desired when strong upper-level winds are present. In jet-stream weather situations we have to expect, therefore, that the quality as well as the number of observations will be reduced. Some knowledge of the average structure of the jet stream will enable the analyst to derive the best possible results in consistency and dependability of the analysis, even from few observations. On the other hand, air navigation is also interested in dependable jet-stream "models," for flight planning as well as for air traffic control. It should be no surprise, therefore, that large amounts of money and material are used every year in detailed studies of the jet stream.

The techniques of meteorological analysis (see Chapter 3) on superficial inspection leave the impression that the wind shears in the horizontal and vertical dimensions were approximately equal to each other, due to the exaggeration of the vertical scale. In reality, however, the wind speed drops to half the value of the speed in the jet center at about 200 to 300 km of horizontal distance from the jet axis (depending on the cyclonic or anticyclonic side); in the vertical, however, the half value of speed appears on the average about 5 km above or below the level of maximum wind. Jet streams, therefore, are extremely *shallow* layers of high wind speed which are embedded in the atmosphere and whose horizontal dimensions—measured normal to the jet axis—exceed the vertical dimensions by almost two orders of magnitude (Raethjen, 1960).

Correspondingly, the vertical gradients are considerably larger than the horizontal ones (Sasaki, 1958). According to Kochanski (1956) we may assume a horizontal temperature gradient of 7° C per degree latitude within a frontal zone, which would correspond to about $6.3 \cdot 10^{-5}$° C/m. Against this, the adiabatic temperature lapse rate in the vertical amounts to $dT/dz = -1 \cdot 10^{-2}$° C/m, and the ratio between these two gradients is $6.3 \cdot 10^{-3}$.

The horizontal wind shears $\nabla_h V$ have the magnitude of the Coriolis parameter in the vicinity of the jet stream. This corresponds to about 10^{-4} sec^{-1} or 21 knots per degree of latitude in temperate latitudes. The vertical shear $\partial V/\partial z$ however amounts to about $5 \cdot 10^{-3}$ sec^{-1} with a jet-stream speed of 100 knots at the 10-km level, assuming a linear wind profile.

It will be rather obvious that turbulence elements are superimposed in the vertical as well as in the horizontal upon a basic current, which changes only gradually with time. These turbulence elements will cause departures of the instantaneously measured flow conditions from the mean value of the basic current. The magnitude of these departures will depend on the space and time scale of the measurements. This turbulence spectrum has already been referred to in Chapter 2.123.

The classification of the structure of jet streams with respect to different magnitudes of scale may be made rather arbitrarily (Flohn, 1959*a*). Most suitably one will consider orders of magnitude which are predetermined either by the conditions of flow, or by measuring techniques.

In general, it will suffice to consider three ranges, which we will call (Reiter, 1960*b*) macro-structure, meso-structure, and micro-structure. The "structure" is the perturbation component of the meteorological parameter under consideration, which is superimposed upon a quasi-stationary basic state. Since the vertical extent of jet streams is smaller by almost two orders of magnitude than the horizontal extent, the threshold values given in the following have to be reduced accordingly.

The macro-structure.—Perturbations of the order of magnitude $>10^6$ horizontal meters will be classified among the macro-structure. These are the hemispheric long waves and the wave disturbances associated with cyclones, as well as individual jet maxima. The hemispheric zonal circulation will have to be regarded as the basic current for this macro-meteorological range. In comparison to the air masses flowing through the disturbances, the latter may be regarded as stationary. With the wind speed in the jet stream having an order of magnitude of 10^2 m/sec, these waves will be traveled through in about $\geqq 10^4$ sec. This, therefore, would be the corresponding time scale for *individual* changes (d/dt). It lies near the lower limit of the changes, which still can be obtained from synoptic observations. Assuming a propagation speed of the waves of about 12° longitude per day or 10 m/sec in temperate latitudes (Namias, 1947*a*) (see Table 3.241), we arrive at a time scale of $\geqq 10^5$ sec for *local* changes ($\partial/\partial t$). This corresponds to the time interval of interdiurnal variations of the upper wind field.

Within this range of space and time variations changes of the wind speed from calm to jet-stream velocities are possible, i.e., the disturbance components have the same order of magnitude as the basic current. The variations, however, usually proceed so slowly that *geostrophic* conditions may be assumed as a first approximation.

The vertical space scale has the order of magnitude of $>10^4$ m and comprises the mean vertical wind profiles.

The meso-structure.—The "meso" realm contains disturbances of the order of magnitude 10^4 to 10^5 horizontal meters. The basic current for this scale is the jet stream in the region of a planetary long wave or a jet maximum with its entrance and exit region. As a directive, the range of variation of the disturbance will be about 20 per cent of the basic current.

The time scale (in sec) seems to be reduced in comparison to the space scale (in m) by about two orders of magnitude, as was the case with the macro-structure. This is advocated by the assumption that gravity and inertia waves traveling approximately with the speed of wind belong to this type of disturbance. Assuming, again, the wind speed in the jet stream to be about 10^2 m/sec, we obtain as lower limit for local changes 10^2 sec, as upper limit, however, about 10^4 sec. In this scale range of atmospheric structure the "jet fingers" and extended cloud fields will be found. The flow conditions are ageostrophic.

In the vertical this scale range corresponds to 10^2 to 10^3 m, and it describes wind shifts at the tropopause, at inversions and fronts, and the detailed structure of the jet-stream core.

The micro-structure.—If we count all variations below 10^4 horizontal meters, and 10^2 sec to the meso-structure, we arrive at a range which contains shearing waves, lee waves, billow clouds, and, finally, clear-air turbulence. Especially from the study of turbulence it becomes apparent that considerable fluctuations of wind speed may be possible within short distances (Reiter, 1960*a*, *b*). In extreme cases the range of fluctuations of micro-structural disturbances will have the same order of magnitude as in the meso range. In general, however, one usually may take less than 10 per cent of the basic current as amplitude of the disturbances, if we take the basic current, again, to be the region of a jet-stream maximum with its entrainment and delta area, including also its meso-structure. The velocity components of these disturbances are strongly ageostrophic.

The micro-structure will become apparent—as far as it is measurable at all (Saucier, 1956*a*)—especially in clear-air turbulence and cloud formations.

If we accept this scale classification of jet streams, the available methods of observations and measurements will give very distinct limitations to meteorological research. The world-wide radiosonde network with its twelve-hourly sequence of observations will disclose only the horizontal macro-structure (Eliassen, Sawyer, and Smagorinsky, 1960). The distance between neighboring stations in densely populated areas (the United States, Europe) is about $5 \cdot 10^5$ m, i.e., it lies at the border between meso- and macro-structure. Correspondingly, one may take characteristics from a detailed jet-stream analysis of the 300- or 250-mb surface, which actually would belong to the meso-structure, e.g., the existence of so-called jet fingers. These are the closely adjacent branches into which one main jet maximum may split at times (Dickson, 1955*a*, Reiter, 1961*a*). (Such jet fingers are frequently observed in the entrance and exit region of a well-pronounced jet-stream maximum.) Great care is needed in the judgment of data and in the analysis, if such details should be recognized. This can hardly be demanded from a routine weather service operation. With the present state of the observation network over ocean areas not even the macro-structure of the jet stream may be determined with certainty.

In the vertical, the conditions are much better. Especially the temperature measurements allow a study of the meso-structure if the original registrations of the radiosonde run are considered. These significant details of the ascent are, however, largely eliminated during the coding process (Danielsen, 1959).

The wind measurements are subject to larger errors, especially in the jet-stream region (Reiter, 1958*c*, 1959*e*), because of the small elevation angles under which the balloons are viewed. Conclusions about the meso-structure from these measurements, therefore, should not be accepted unquestioningly. A rapid sequence of balloon ascents, e.g., at hourly intervals (Barbé, 1957), may contribute only little to the exploration of the meso-structure, first, because of the uncertainties in the measurements already mentioned, and second, because of the fact that the data characterize only an isolated point in time and space (or rather a mean value over a two-minute interval, or over 600 vertical meters), which in itself is influenced by the meso- and micro-structure. Thus, the structural details may not be determined unambiguously. Rapid sequences of ascents are valuable, however, for statistical purposes because the average variability of meteorological parameters may be determined at different levels, thus making short-range forecasting feasible (U.S. Air Weather Service, 1956*c*).

The situation is completely different with aircraft measurements, as for instance those of Project Jet Stream (Brundidge, 1956, 1958; Endlich *et al.*, 1954; *et al.*, 1959; Landers, 1955*a*; Reiter, 1960*c*, *d*, *e*, 1961*a*, *b*, *d*, *e*; Saucier, 1956*b*, 1958*b*). The instrument panel has been photographed at time intervals of about 25 to 30 sec. With a true airspeed of about 400 knots (740 km/h), this amounts to a space distance of the points of measurement of about 5 km. If we allow for certain inaccuracies of the measurements, which are estimated to be about 3 knots and 1° C in the absolute values, or 1 knot and 0.1° C in the gradients, one may consider real those fluctuations in speed and temperature which follow the same trend over at least three successive points of measurement. Therefore, from these data the variability of wind and temperature in the horizontal may be determined to a scale of about 15 km. The meso range, therefore, is still covered by these measurements (Kasahara, 1956). It will be shown in Chapter 4.3 that in the analysis of this meso-structure consideration has to be given to the order of magnitude of the time and space scale. One should avoid combining macro- and meso-structure or meso- and micro-structure into one analysis (Reiter, 1960*b*, 1961*a*).

4.1. THE HORIZONTAL STRUCTURE

4.11. THE TEMPERATURE FIELD

4.111. Geographic and Seasonal Distribution

The seasonal variations in the mean position and strength of the jet streams, especially of the PFJ, are closely related to changes in the position and strength of the frontal zone in the troposphere. During summer the baroclinic zone is less developed and located farther to the north than it is in winter (Scherhag, 1948*b*). This is mainly due to the fact that during summer the meridional temperature gradient is reduced because of the irradiation of the polar cap. That the average strength and position of the jet stream reacts upon seasonal fluctuations in the heat budget of the hemisphere proves that the tropospheric jet stream is a phenomenon based upon the thermal differences between pole and equator—a rather trivial conclusion, if one considers the thermal wind equation. It is noteworthy, however, that the temperature gradient is not distributed evenly over all latitudes between thermal equator and pole, but it is concentrated in a narrow frontal zone. This fact would speak in favor of the mixing theory of jet-stream formation (see Chapter 4.121). We, therefore, do not have a broad zone of uniform westerlies as it is postulated in the theory of Rossby waves; we find instead a belt of high wind velocities—the jet stream.

The existence of jet streams in the atmosphere is based upon two necessary and sufficient conditions:

1. A meridional temperature gradient causes a pressure gradient force which brings the air masses into motion.
2. Angular momentum is imparted by the rotation of the underlying surface.

The proof of these statements is given by geophysical model experiments: in a rotating dishpan, in which a temperature gradient is maintained from the rim toward the center, atmospheric jet-stream situations may be simulated under certain conditions given by the rate of rotation and the temperature difference between "pole" and "equator" (see Chapter 4.43).

The relation between temperature gradient and jet-stream position is brought out clearly by means of meridional cross sections (Palmén, 1948*b*; and Nagler, 1948; and Newton, 1948). The mean horizontal temperature gradient on various isobaric surfaces along the longitude of 80° W may be taken from Figure 3.211 for twelve weather situations during December, 1946. According to this, the strongest gradient may be found at about 800 mb. The isopycnic level is located between 300 and 250 mb, while the meridional temperature gradient in the jet-stream region is already reversed at the 200-mb level. A band of somewhat colder air appears at 250 mb south of the jet stream, and north of it there is a marked area of warmer air (Bessemoulin and Viaut,

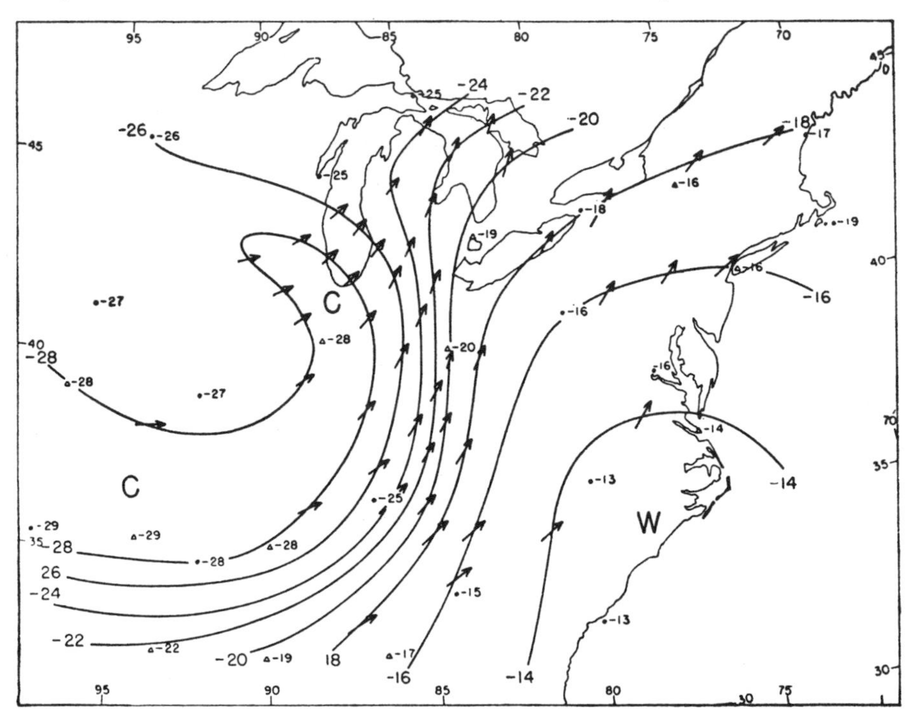

Fig. 4.112.1.—500-mb isotherms (° C) of 24 March, 1953, 0300 GCT. The arrows indicate the intersections of the isotherms with the contour lines of the 500-mb topography. (Riehl, 1954*b*.)

1958; Reiter, 1960*d*, *e*). South of the area of cold air there follows another zone with the temperature gradient directed toward the north, in a "normal" fashion. Above this area, therefore, the level of maximum wind lies higher, as is also apparent from the wind speed distribution in Figure 3.211. The frontal zone is an area of strong horizontal wind shear whereby the largest wind speeds are found on the "warm" side of the zone. The jet-stream level at 300 mb lies approximately above the anticyclonic boundary surface of the frontal zone at the 500-mb level. A weakly developed offshoot of the jet stream appears at the 200-mb level in about 38° latitude. This offshoot will be discussed in more detail later.

4.112. The Temperature Distribution in Individual Synoptic Cases

The temperature distribution in the troposphere and in the lower stratosphere is characterized by the example of 23 March, 1953, which shows a fully developed jet stream. The 500-mb isotherms (Fig. 4.112.1) show a marked concentration underneath the jet axis (see Fig. 4.122.4). (The synoptic map time of this chart—24 March, 1953, 0300 GCT—lies about 4 hours before the execution of a research flight. This time difference, therefore, has to be taken into account in the evaluation of the flight data.)

Bradbury and Palmén (1953) find from statistical investigations that on the average in winter the $-28°$ or $-29°$ isotherm at the 500-mb level corresponds to the position of the frontal zone. A secondary concentration of the horizontal temperature gradient may be found at about $-13°$ and indicates the average position of the STJ.

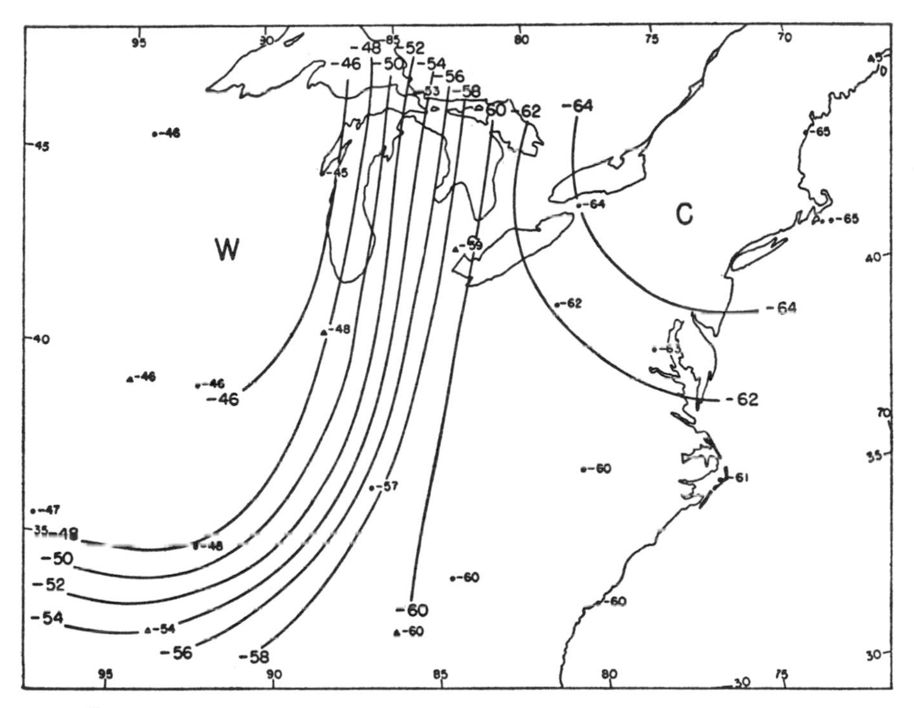

FIG. 4.112.2. 200-mb isotherms (° C), 23 March, 1953, 2100 GCT. (Riehl, 1954*b*.)

In general, however, the value of such statistical considerations of the relationship between frontal zone and isotherms or isohypses has to be treated carefully when the purposes are analytic or prognostic. Such relationships express only that in a given season the meridional air mass contrasts assume a certain preferred magnitude and they form the jet stream in this particular baroclinic transition zone. If the statistics are too detailed (Clodman, 1954), as is apparently the case with the Canadian three-front model (Anonymous, 1956), we run the risk of influencing the analysis in favor of the preconceived model.

The fact that the position of the frontal zone at the 500-mb level on the average coincides well with the jet-stream location agrees with the results of extensive investigations over the Pacific area (Beamer and Serebreny, 1953; Serebreny, 1951, 1955; and Wiegman, 1953, 1954; and Wiegman and Carlson, 1954*a*, *b*; and Wiegman and Hadfield, 1957). The frontal zone at the 500-mb level, therefore, constitutes a useful indicator for the position of the jet stream. For intercontinental flights the rule of thumb has been that in the middle troposphere the strongest winds blow on the anticyclonic side, the weakest winds on the cyclonic side of the frontal zone. Continuous thermometer readings, therefore, may give valuable clues on the wind conditions that are to be expected at flight level. In this way Pan American World Airways and other airlines established several speed records in crossing the oceans.

The small arrows in Figure 4.112.1 indicate the intersections of the 500-mb isobars with the isotherms. The frontal zone seems to have a tendency toward intensification on its eastern boundary, and a tendency for weakening on its western edge (see Reed and Sanders, 1953). Therefore, it seems to be moving slowly toward the northeast. As is the case here, the region with strong isotherm advection frequently coincides

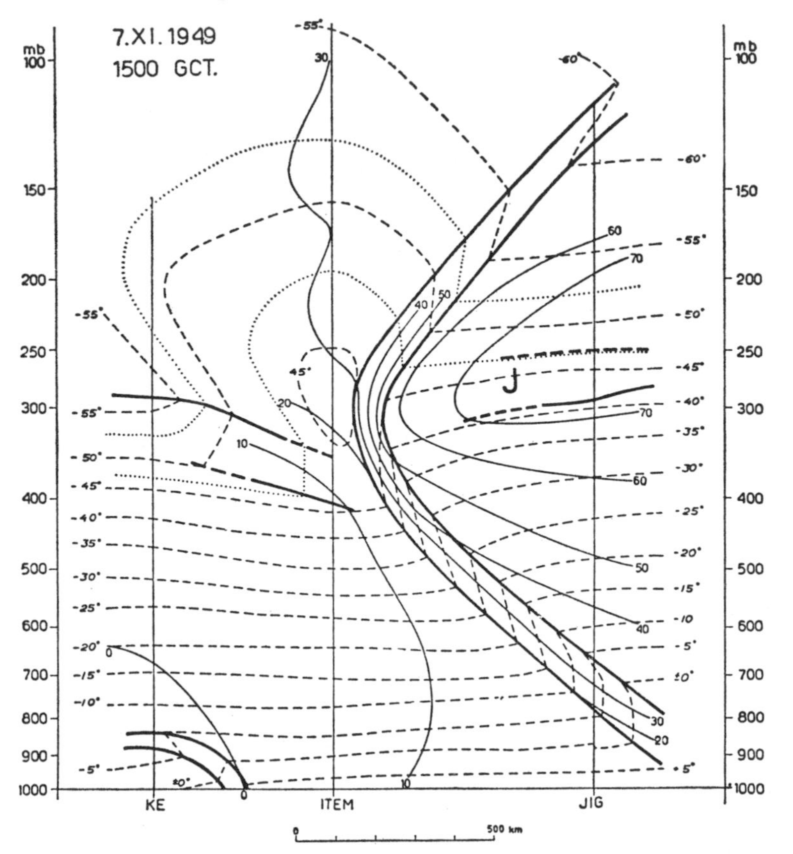

FIG. 4.112.3.—Cross section through the atmosphere, 7 November, 1949, 1500 GCT. Dashed and dotted, isotherms (° C); solid lines, isotachs (m/sec) of *observed* wind speed component normal to cross section; heavy lines, frontal zone and tropopause. (Berggren, 1953*a*.)

with sinking motion and fair weather, whereby the isotherm motion is slowed down (see Fig. 4.122.5). The tonguelike shape of the cold-air reservoir in Figure 4.112.1, in which the cyclone is attached, may frequently be found in North American storms which travel northeastward on the east side of a long wave trough. They usually carry in their wake a severe cold outbreak into the midwestern states. Generally, however, the opening of the frontal zone delta is directed eastward. The frontal zones in the European region which are connected with violent cyclones over the Atlantic or the North Sea frequently are oriented from northwest toward southeast.

The temperatures of the 200-mb surface (Fig. 4.112.2) are also characteristic of a well-developed jet stream. The level of maximum wind is located already below this isobaric surface because the temperature gradient normal to the direction of flow is opposite to the one in the middle troposphere. The maximum gradient, again, coincides approximately with the position of the jet axis and may at times attain considerable magnitude (Kochanski [1956] measured 7° C per degree of latitude). The wind speed, therefore, decreases more rapidly with height in the jet-stream region than in the surrounding areas. At the 200-mb level, too, there is a strongly baroclinic zone (Zubian, 1956, 1957). The solenoids in this zone, however, exert a braking action upon the circulation (see Arakawa, 1953*h*). The proposal by Berggren (1952, 1953*a*, *b*) to extend the frontal analysis into the stratosphere therefore seems to be justified (see Fig. 4.112.3).

In this diagram the isotherm pattern in the stratosphere above the cold air mass indicates that a regional warming occurs here, because of sinking motion. This sinking seems to take place mainly in the region of a warm air tongue ("isentrope trough") on the cyclonic side of the jet axis (Reiter, 1961*e*). The temperature contrast across the "frontal zone" at the 200-mb level, therefore, is decisively influenced by *dynamic* processes. A frontal analysis in the form proposed by Berggren would, however, lead us to accept an analogy with the lower troposphere, where *advective* processes are predominant. Furthermore, a continuous frontal zone reaching from the ground into the stratosphere may not always be found. The lower part of the front, which is brought about by air mass contrasts, may, at times, be separated from the upper baroclinic zone, which is connected with the jet stream. As has been shown by Reed and Danielsen (1959), this "jet-stream front" does not constitute an air mass boundary which has become diffuse by mixing processes, but it consists of sinking stratospheric air—at least in the entrainment region of the jet maximum. In the stratosphere the frontal zone spreads out with increasing height (see Fig. 6.123). This will be discussed further in Chapter 6. The aforementioned, however, should suffice to let Berggren's way of analyzing a frontal zone appear valid only with reservations.

On the anticyclonic side of the jet stream a tongue of cold air ("isentrope hump") appears above the maximum wind level. This hump sometimes is very narrow, especially when the subtropical jet stream, located at higher levels, runs in the vicinity of the polar-front jet (Foster and Robinson, 1953; Reiter, 1960*d*, *e*, 1961*e*; Riehl, 1948*a*). In Figure 4.112.2 a normalizing of the temperature gradient in the sense of a continued increase of wind speed with height is indicated over the northeast coast of the United States. In this area, therefore, the level of maximum wind should lie above the 200-mb level. The isotherm pattern in this diagram indicates a diffluence between the polar-front jet and a weaker subtropical jet stream which occurs above 200-mb.

4.12. Wind Field and Vorticity

4.121. Geographical and Seasonal Distribution. The "Mixing Theory" of Jet-Stream Formation

Parallel to the seasonal shift of the horizontal temperature gradient in the troposphere and its increase or decrease, the jet streams, too, undergo a yearly cycle in intensity and position (see Pogosian, 1957*c*). In Figure 4.121.1 and 4.121.2 the average

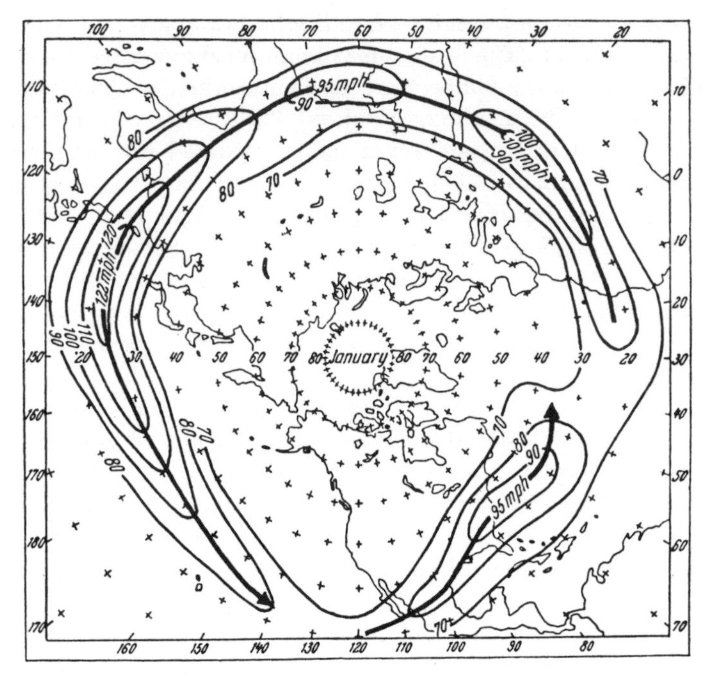

FIG. 4.121.1.—Mean position and intensity (geostrophic wind speeds in mph at the level of maximum wind) of the jet stream in January. (Namias and Clapp, 1949.)

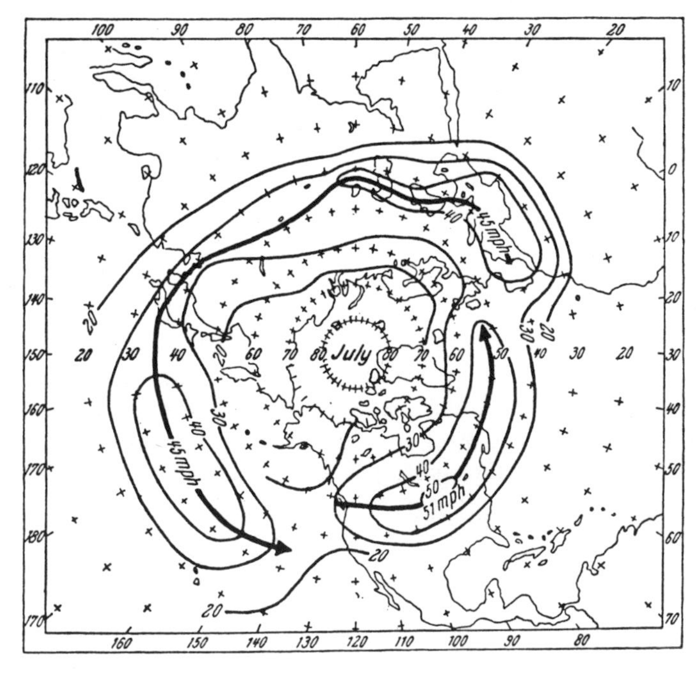

FIG. 4.121.2.—Mean position and intensity (geostrophic wind speeds in mph at the level of maximum wind) of the jet stream in July. (Namias and Clapp, 1949.)

jet-stream conditions are shown for January and July (Namias and Clapp, 1949). Irrespective of the different intensities of the mean jet maxima in winter and summer (e.g., over the Pacific 45 mph in summer, 122 mph in winter), the most pronounced changes appear in the Asiatic sector. While during summer the axis of a relatively weak jet stream crosses the Mediterranean, and, after traversing Mongolia, reaches Japan from a northwesterly direction, during winter its position is shifted over the Sahara Desert. Over northern India a distinct jet maximum appears south of the Himalayas; the largest mean wind speeds are measured over Eastern Asia and Formosa, coming from a southwesterly direction. Since in individual weather situations the maximum wind velocities in a jet stream of this main high-speed zone may show interdiurnal variations, but no large geographical shifts, the conclusion may be drawn from this diagram that the winter jet stream over Southeastern Asia is one of the most stable elements of the general circulation. The significance of this for the monsoon will be considered later (see Chapter 7.413). Because Figures 4.121.1 and .2 give only mean values of wind speed, no differentiation can be made between polar and subtropical jet streams because of the variable position of the jet-stream axes (see Chapter 4.14).

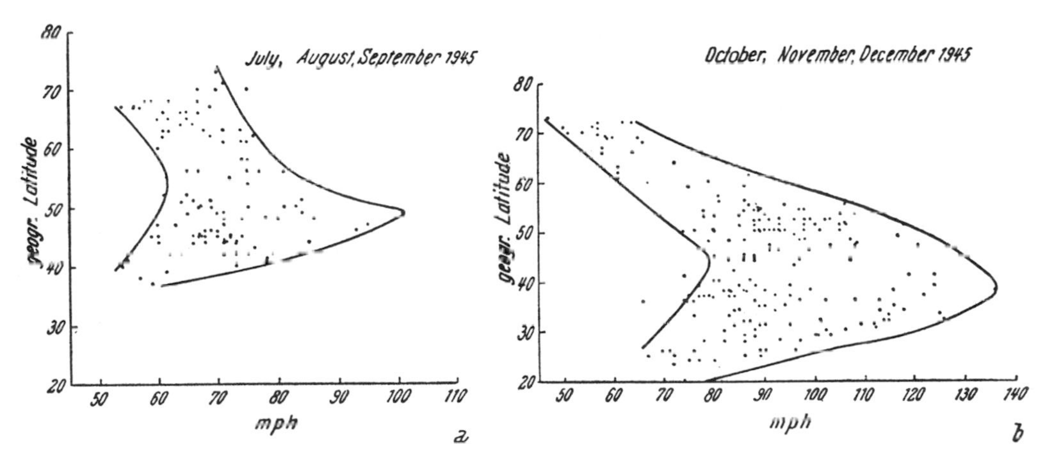

FIG. 4.121.3.—Mean position and intensity of hemispheric jet streams between July and September, 1945, and October and December, 1945. The curves indicate the envelope of the point distribution. (Cressman, 1950.)

In Figure 4.121.3 each point shows the speed and geographical location of the jet axes in a sector 270° wide, between 110° E and 20° E, for each single day during the months of July through December of 1945 (Cressman, 1950). During the summer the high tropospheric wind maximum on the average lies farther to the north, and is weaker, too, than during winter. This shift is connected with the dislocation of the subtropical high-pressure belt and with the variations in the polar cold-air reservoir, and is also reflected in the migrations of the polar front (Berry, Haggard, and Wolff, 1954). From Figure 4.121.3 interesting conclusions are possible. During winter, the mean jet-stream maximum may be found at about 40° of latitude and with about 105 mph, during summer, however, at about 50° N with 78 mph.

Considering the angular momentum which an air particle would have at these latitudes when *at rest* relative to the earth's surface, we obtain from 1.236 (9)

$$G = u \cdot R \cdot \cos \varphi. \qquad 4.121\ (1)$$

Let $C_E = 2R\pi/86{,}400 = 0.46$ km/sec be the equatorial speed of rotation of the earth. We, then, may express u in per-cent of C_E and we obtain ($u/C_E = \cos \varphi$)

$$G = C_E R \cdot \cos^2 \varphi. \qquad 4.121\ (2)$$

The variation of the angular momentum between two different geographic latitudes is given by the ratio

$$G_1 : G_2 = \cos^2 \varphi_1 : \cos^2 \varphi_2. \qquad 4.121\ (3)$$

For $\varphi_1 = 50°$ and $\varphi_2 = 40°$ of latitude one arrives at $G_1 : G_2 = 0.70$, i.e., the angular momentum of air at rest at 50° latitude amounts to only 70 per cent of the momentum at a latitude of 40°.

The mean decrease in the wind speed of jet streams from winter to summer amounts to about 26 per cent according to Figure 4.121.3, i.e., on the average the jet streams reflect the conditions of angular momentum of the earth's surface at their respective geographic latitude. This is not surprising, for the earth's surface constitutes the only source of momentum for the atmosphere, because of surface friction: braking of the easterlies in the trade wind region is equivalent to the generation of westerly (positive) angular momentum. Braking of the westerlies in temperate latitudes equals the consumption of such momentum. Therefore, angular momentum has to be transported by the general circulation of the atmosphere from low toward higher latitudes in order to keep the circulation in a stationary equilibrium.

The momentum transport from one hemisphere into the other, as it is necessary to explain the differences in stratospheric circulation from summer to winter, will be discussed in further detail in Chapter 4.414.

If in the course of the seasons the quasi-stationary high- and low-pressure areas under whose influence the general circulation occurs are shifted into other positions, the magnitude of the momentum transport will change with variations in the intensities of sources and sinks of angular momentum. The momentum is to a large degree concentrated within the jet streams. It, therefore, is readily understood that the mean wind speeds will react upon changes in the hemispheric momentum transport. That this occurs in such good agreement with the laws of angular momentum of the rotating earth, as is shown by the above estimate, may serve as proof that the jet streams are a phenomenon of the rotation of the earth.

Figure 4.121.4 shows the term $\cos^2 \varphi$, which is a measure of the angular momentum, and $\cos^2 \varphi_2 / \cos^2 \varphi_1$ for $(\varphi_2 - \varphi_1) = 10°$ of latitude, as a function of geographic latitude. From the latter expression it follows that a decrease of about 26 per cent in the angular momentum within 10° of latitude corresponds to a region which lies approximately 5° farther south than the mean jet-stream maxima of Figures 4.121.3. Figure 4.121.4 shows that at 45° latitude the angular momentum amounts to about 74 per cent of the momentum measured at 35°. The dashed line in Figure 4.121.4 intersects the ordinate $(\varphi_1 + \varphi_2)/2 = 40°$ at a value of about 0.74. If one were to characterize jet streams as phenomena which occur under conservation of angular momentum, this would imply that air masses would have to undergo only a relatively small meridional shift from south toward north in order to obtain the observed jet-stream speeds. The following estimate may serve as an example: Let an air mass travel under conservation of its angular momentum from 42° to 46° N. According to Eq. 1.236 (14) its increase in speed relative to the earth's surface would be 29 m/sec.

A comparison with Figure 4.121.7 reveals that this width of latitudinal shift corresponds approximately to the region of sloping isentropic surfaces in the frontal zone below the jet core. The upward motion which will have to be expected here would lead to an increase in wind speed, as it is actually observed on the anticyclonic side of the jet stream in Figure 3.211.

Therefore, the southern sides of well-developed jet streams seem to show a tendency of conservation of angular momentum. As already mentioned in Chapter 1.236, this is also evident from the fact that the absolute vorticity approaches zero in a relatively narrow band to the south of the jet axis.

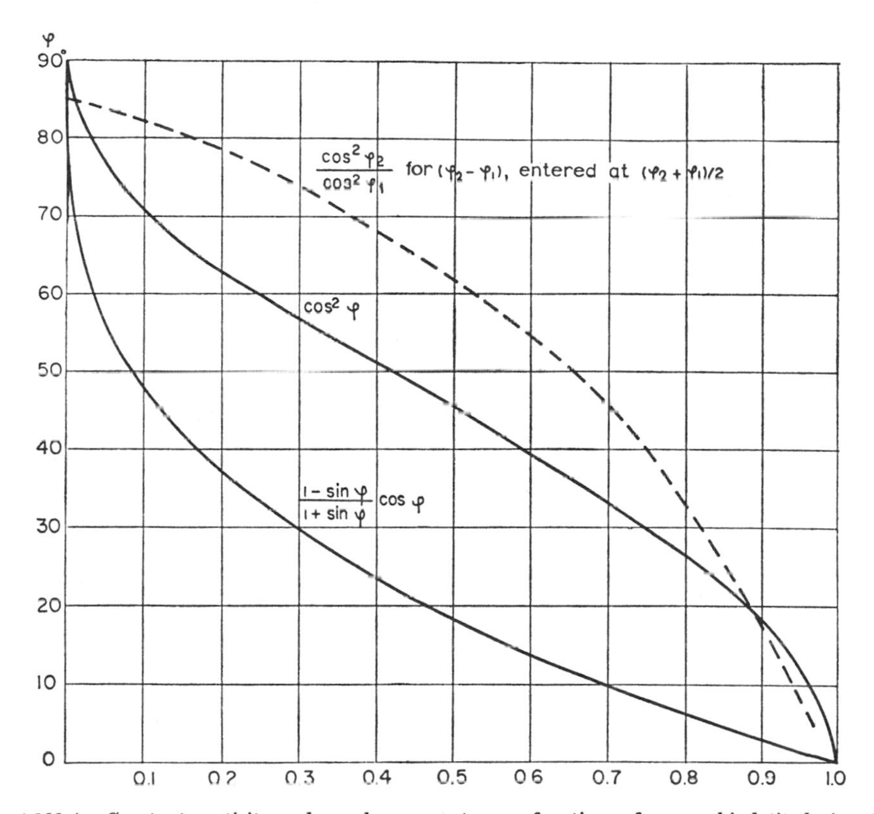

FIG. 4.121.4.—Constant vorticity and angular momentum as functions of geographic latitude (see text). The ratio $\cos^2 \varphi_2/\cos^2 \varphi_1$ has been computed for belts of 10° latitude and has been entered at the center of each of these belts.

On the cyclonic side of the jet axis the average situation is much different. Figure 4.121.5 shows that there is a tendency for the establishment of a horizontal profile of constant absolute vorticity (Riehl, Alaka, *et al.*, 1954; University of Chicago, 1947). From this figure, as well as from Figure 4.121.3, it may be seen that the intensity of jet streams decreases with increasing latitude. In Figure 4.121.5, wind-speed values are given in units of the rotation speed C_E of the equator. By this it is possible to compare values from different rotating bodies with each other, as has been done here with solar and terrestrial data (see also Chapter **4.431**).

The vertical component of relative vorticity for zonal motion may be written in the form [see **3.247 (13)**]:

$$q_z = -\partial u/\partial y + \frac{u}{R}\cdot \tan \varphi.$$

Substituting $\partial u = \partial(\omega R \cdot \cos \varphi)$ and $\partial y = R\cdot\partial\varphi$, where ω stands for the *absolute angular velocity* relative to the pole, of an atmosphere with only zonal motion (Rossby, 1947), and in considering only the *absolute* motion, one obtains from the above expression directly the *absolute* vorticity

$$Q_z = -(1/\cos \varphi)[\partial/\partial\varphi(\cos^2 \varphi \cdot \omega)]. \qquad \textbf{4.121 (4)}$$

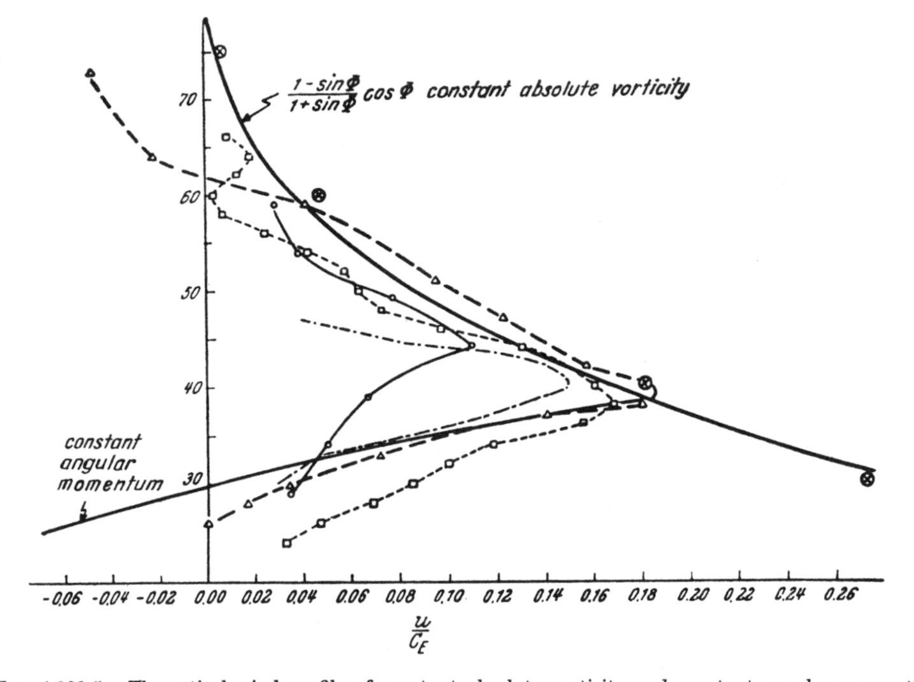

FIG. 4.121.5.—Theoretical wind profile of constant absolute vorticity and constant angular momentum (heavy solid line) and several observed geostrophic wind profiles at tropopause level (thin lines). Rotation data from the sun are indicated by circles. All speeds are expressed in units of equatorial speed C_E. (University of Chicago, 1947.)

For *constant* absolute vorticity which should be the result of mixing effects of northward and southward currents, one arrives at

$$\omega \cdot \cos^2 \varphi + Q_z \cdot \sin \varphi = \text{const} \qquad 4.121\ (5)$$

by integration of 4.121 (4). The integration constant is determined by the condition that the angular velocity ω of the atmosphere at the pole shall be finite. For $\varphi = 90°$ one obtains from 4.121 (5) $Q_z = \text{const}$, and therefore,

$$\omega \cdot \cos^2 \varphi = Q_z(1 - \sin \varphi). \qquad 4.121\ (6)$$

For the angular velocity ω of the zonally moving air this leads to

$$\dot{\lambda}=\omega=2\omega_p/(1+\sin\varphi). \qquad 4.121\ (7)$$

because $Q_z=2\omega_p$, where ω_p is the angular velocity of the atmosphere at the pole. This results from 4.121 (6) for $\varphi=90°$, if one substitutes $\cos^2\varphi=1-\sin^2\varphi$ and divides the expression by $(1-\sin\varphi)$.

Equation 4.121 (7) states the distribution of angular velocity in a portion of the atmosphere, which covers the polar cap and which assumed a constant vorticity by the action of meridional exchange processes.

The linear speed u in this atmosphere, measured relative to the earth's surface, amounts to $u=(\omega-\Omega)R\cdot\cos\varphi$, or with the aid of 4.121 (7),

$$u=R\cdot\Omega\,\frac{(2\omega_p-\Omega)/\Omega-\sin\varphi}{1+\sin\varphi}\cos\varphi. \qquad 4.121\ (8)$$

Ω is the angular speed of the earth's rotation. The linear speed of the earth at the equator is

$$C_E=R\cdot\Omega=0.46\ \text{km/sec}. \qquad 4.121\ (9)$$

The zonal wind distribution is obtained in non-dimensional form

$$u/C_E=\frac{(2\omega_p-\Omega)/\Omega-\sin\varphi}{1+\sin\varphi}\cos\varphi. \qquad 4.121\ (10)$$

At $Q=2\omega_p<2\Omega$ easterlies appear in high latitudes. Assuming that the vorticity of the completely mixed air over the polar cap is at the most equal to the vertical component of the vorticity of the earth, i.e.,

$$Q=2\omega_p=2\Omega, \qquad 4.121\ (11)$$

one obtains the limiting value of the *zonal wind distribution at constant absolute vorticity* in non-dimensional form

$$u/C_E=\frac{1-\sin\varphi}{1+\sin\varphi}\cos\varphi. \qquad 4.121\ (12)$$

As has been shown in Figure 4.121.5, the mean wind profiles on the north side of jet maxima correspond well with this theoretical limiting value (heavy curve). (The dashed curve has been taken from a cross section at the 300-mb level from Havana to Thule on 17 January, 1947, 0300 GCT. The thin solid line stands for nine-day mean values over North America during approximately zonal upper-flow conditions.)

From this good agreement between meridional profiles of zonal wind speed at constant absolute vorticity with observed mean profiles, the University of Chicago Department of Meteorology under Rossby (1947; A. Defant, 1949; University of Chicago, 1947) derived the "mixing theory" of jet-stream formation. Since the atmospheric motions are not only due to forces acting in meridional planes, but since east-west components in the horizontal pressure gradients and, thus, meridional components of flow play an important role, too, the conclusion is obvious that mixing processes will lead to a large-scale exchange of Q_z, the vertical component of vorticity. The free mixing length of these exchange processes has the order of magnitude of the low- and high-pressure areas of temperate latitudes (A. Defant, 1921). The proof of the effectiveness of these mixing processes may be established in the following way:

In the west wind belt surface friction produces ageostrophic components of flow toward the north. A compensating current at higher levels which is directed toward the south should have an easterly component of motion, if its angular momentum were conserved. That this is not the case, and that a profile of constant absolute vorticity tries to establish itself, as has been shown above with the aid of Figure 4.121.5, has to be attributed to large-scale exchange processes. Such profiles may in extreme cases reach as far equatorward as 35° or 30° latitude. Here, the profiles become unstable because of the large horizontal shears. South of this area a profile of $Q_z = q_z + f = 0$ will be established, which corresponds to constant angular momentum. Hsieh (1950*b*) assumes that there is not only one but several zones with pronounced lateral vorticity exchange (see also Freeman, 1953).

In analogy, mixing has to be assumed for the polar cap of the southern hemisphere. Here, however, in contrast to the northern hemisphere, cyclonic vorticity has a negative sign. If the mixing of the air masses, and the subsequent establishment of a meridional wind profile of constant absolute vorticity would reach all the way to the equator, a discontinuity between positive and negative vorticity values would appear here. Wind shears of corresponding greatness would have to be expected. According to observations, however, the mixing zones extend only to about 30° to 35° latitude, where the jet streams occur.

In the jet-stream region there is a strong horizontal vorticity gradient which, by virtue of exchange processes, causes a continuous vorticity transport toward the south in the direction of this gradient. Rossby (1947) assumes, that this vorticity transfer has a *constant value* and that it transports positive vorticity from the northern into the southern hemisphere, or negative vorticity in the opposite direction. In the transition zones between the two regions in which on the one hand Q_z = constant, and on the other hand $Q_z = 0$, the vorticity which is carried away will have to be replenished by ascending motions or the vorticity of the polar cap would be rapidly diminished. This corresponds to actual observations, according to which in the delta region of a frontal zone there are maximum ascending motions to be found underneath the jet axis (see Chapter 4.221 and 4.232).

Because of the mixing processes north of the polar-front jet, the absolute angular momentum is only redistributed, without its total amount

$$G = 2\pi R^4 \int_{\phi_0}^{\pi/2} \dot{\lambda} \cos^3 \varphi \, d\varphi \qquad 4.121\ (13)$$

being changed. φ_0 is the geographic latitude to which the mixing extends. In this equation it has been assumed that the mass per unit area of the polar cap, which is bounded by the polar front, has the magnitude 1.[1]

After complete mixing, $\dot{\lambda}$ assumes the value given by 4.121 (7), and one obtains for the total angular momentum by integration of 4.121 (13)

$$G = 2\pi R^4 \omega_p (1 - \sin \varphi_0)^2. \qquad 4.121\ (14)$$

[1] According to Eq. 1.236 (9) the angular momentum per unit mass amounts to $R^2 \cos^2 \varphi \cdot \omega$. This expression is integrated over the area $2R\pi \int_{\varphi_0}^{\pi/2} \cos \varphi \cdot R \, d\varphi$ of the polar cap.

Starting with the assumption that the atmosphere originally was in solid rotation with the constant angular velocity $\dot{\lambda}_i$, one obtains by integration of 4.121 (13)

$$G = 2\pi R^4 \dot{\lambda}_i (1 - \sin \varphi_0)^2 (2 + \sin \varphi_0)/3. \qquad 4.121\ (15)$$

For the latitude φ_0 in which the maximum angular velocity establishes itself, one obtains from 4.121 (7)

$$\dot{\lambda}_{\varphi_0} = 2\omega_p/(1 + \sin \varphi_0). \qquad 4.121\ (16)$$

Substituting this expression into 4.121 (14) for $2\omega_p$, one arrives at

$$G = \pi R^4 \dot{\lambda}_{\varphi_0} (1 + \sin \varphi_0)(1 - \sin \varphi_0)^2. \qquad 4.121\ (17)$$

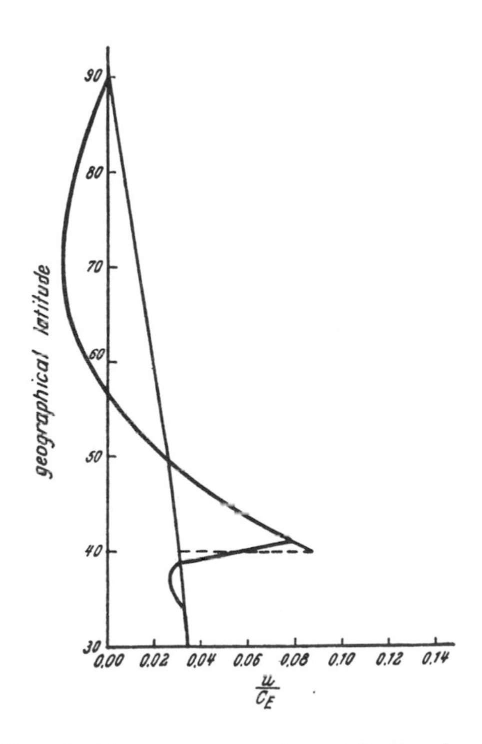

FIG. 4.121.6.—Effect of lateral mixing processes upon the distribution of vertical vorticity within a cap of polar air, centered at the pole. The original wind distribution with constant angular velocity is given by the thin line. The resulting wind distribution—obtained under conservation of the total angular momentum within the polar air—is indicated by the heavy line. The mixing processes are assumed to reach all the way to 40° of latitude, where the wind speed shows a maximum. All speeds are expressed in units of the equatorial speed of rotation. (University of Chicago, 1947.)

Figure 4.121.6 shows the wind profiles in units of the equatorial speed C_E (thin, almost straight line), which would be established under constant angular velocity (solid rotation). The heavier line gives the new velocity distribution, which establishes itself with constant vorticity under the effect of lateral exchange processes. The southern limit of the cap of polar air has been assumed at 40° latitude. The total absolute angular momentum within this polar cap is conserved. (The areas with decrease and increase of angular momentum are not equal in this diagram because the geographic latitude has been entered linearly and not after its sine.) At the southern limit of the thoroughly mixed polar cap there is a sharp decrease of velocity to the original value of solid rotation. The magnitude of this decrease is obtained from 4.121 (15 and 16):

$$\Delta\dot{\lambda}=\dot{\lambda}_{\varphi_0}-\dot{\lambda}_i=\tfrac{1}{3}\dot{\lambda}_i(1-\sin\varphi_0)/(1+\sin\varphi_0). \qquad 4.121\ (18)$$

$\dot{\lambda}$ corresponds in first approximation to the speed of rotation Ω of the earth. We obtain in approximation

$$\Delta\dot{\lambda}=(\Omega/3)(1-\sin\varphi_0)/(1+\sin\varphi_0). \qquad 4.121\ (19)$$

Correspondingly, the decrease of velocity at the discontinuity amounts to

$$\Delta(u/C_E)=\tfrac{1}{3}\cos\varphi_0(1-\sin\varphi_0)/(1+\sin\varphi_0). \qquad 4.121\ (20)$$

because of $\Delta u=\Delta\dot{\lambda}R\cos\varphi_0$ and because of 4.121 (9). For $\varphi_0=30°$ latitude the decrease in speed is approximately 100 mph (45 m/sec), which, because of $\dot{\lambda}_i\simeq\Omega$, is of the same order of magnitude as the speed in the jet stream. If the mixing zone ends farther to the north, the speed of the polar-front jet will be smaller accordingly. This, on the average, also agrees with observations (see 4.121.3). The smaller jet-stream speeds to the south in this diagram obviously stem largely from subtropical jet streams, which have not been included in these considerations. As has been indicated in Figure 4.121.6 the discontinuity on the southern border of the mixing zone spreads out because of lateral exchange processes, until a horizontal shear of the order of $+\partial u/\partial y=f$ is reached. One obtains the width of this dynamically unstable zone by dividing Δu through this critical shear. For 30° N, one obtains 615 km or $5\frac{1}{2}°$ of latitude, which, again, is confirmed by observations (Fig. 4.121.5 and Chapter 4.122). It has been pointed out earlier that the average decrease of velocity of extremely strong jet maxima from winter to summer corresponds to a decrease in angular momentum of a zone which lies approximately 5° south of the jet axis. This estimate, again, agrees well with the above results.

In the derivations made so far, we have assumed that the lateral mixing processes are confined to a cap of polar air, which has a sharply defined southern border. This restriction, of course, is not necessary for the initial state. The mixing zone will rather spread out slowly toward the south, and with the increase of the area with constant absolute vorticity the intensity of the jet streams on its southern border will mount (see Fig. 4.121.6), until dynamic instability is reached. This gradual intensification process under conservation of the total angular momentum of the cap of polar air may be observed in mean meridional wind profiles and is expressed in a southward trend of the wind maxima as revealed by trend diagrams. Simultaneously with the intensification of the wind maxima the baroclinicity of the atmospheric layers underneath the maximum increases, too. As soon as critical values of dynamic instability are reached, meridional circulation cells will develop. The vorticity transfer toward the south along these meridional components of flow at jet-stream level will be compensated by ascending motion. According to analyses by Newton (see Chapter 4.221), such circulations which permit a vorticity transfer toward the south at jet-stream level are to be expected in the frontolytically active delta region of a frontal zone. They are indicative of an indirect circulation, i.e., rising of cold air, and sinking motion in the warm air to the south of the jet-stream zone. The ageostrophic component of motion, which causes the vorticity transfer toward the south, is also directed toward *higher* pressure, which agrees well with the observed surface pressure tendencies. The ascending motion is corroborated by the precipitation maxima underneath the jet-stream axis.

The entrance region of a frontal zone is characterized by ageostrophic components of flow toward lower pressure and, therefore, by an acceleration of the air masses. Dynamic instability is not yet reached here.

In many individual weather situations the meridional wind profile on the cyclonic side does not follow constant absolute vorticity values but shows a well-pronounced vorticity maximum instead. Therefore, the "mixing theory" of the formation of jet streams is not universally satisfactory (see also Chapter 4.123; Bolin, 1952; Kuo, 1951*a*, *b*, 1953*a*).

Figure 4.121.7 shows such a pronounced vorticity maximum on the cyclonic side of the jet stream through which the air masses are rapidly moving and, therefore, are subject to strong convergence and divergence (see also Hsieh, 1950*b*). In view of the "mixing theory" of jet-stream formation this means that the ageostrophic components in the entrainment area of a frontal zone, directed toward lower pressure in the north, transport larger values of angular momentum from the south against the vorticity gradient at a rate which does not allow immediate and complete mixing, leading to a constant vorticity profile. Apparently, the prevailing exchange coefficients (Rossby, 1947) are not sufficient for this. Correspondingly, we may find higher wind speeds in the jet center and stronger wind shears on the cyclonic side of the jet axis in individual cases than would conform to constant absolute vorticity profiles (Nyberg, 1949). Thereby a vorticity maximum develops on the northern side of the jet maximum (see also Fig. 3.247.5). Only farther to the north the vorticity gradient becomes weak enough to consider Q_z as constant.

4.122. Wind Profiles and Vorticity in Special Cases

The results reported here have mainly been obtained from aircraft measurements (Dickson, 1955*a*; Reiter, 1960*d*, *e*, 1961*a*, *b*, *d*, *e*, *f*; *et al.*, 1961; Riehl, 1954*b*, *c*; Riehl and Maynard, 1954; U.S. Bureau of Aeronautics, 1953*a*, *b*). As has been mentioned in the previous section, well-developed jet-stream centers are characterized by maxima of positive vorticity on their cyclonic side (Figs. 4.121.7 and 3.247.5). These vorticity values are mainly caused by horizontal wind shear. Only in strongly elongated troughs the contributions from curvature vorticity may be considerable. The question arises whether the wind shears on both sides of fully developed jet streams follow some relationship by which the mean structure of a jet could be derived.

For the anticyclonic side, we already have obtained such a limiting value of wind distribution in the condition $Q=0$ (Chapter 1.236), which is synonymous with the fact that the motion on an isentropic surface in this area proceeds under constant angular momentum. For the cyclonic side, so far, only statistical and empirical correlations between wind speed and distance from the jet axis have been worked out. From these it results that the horizontal wind shear on this side usually surpasses the shear on the anticyclonic side by far (Johnson, 1952, 1953*a*, *b*, *c*).

Aircraft traverses of the jet stream over North America rendered the following interesting results (Riehl and Maynard, 1954; Riehl, Berry, and Maynard, 1955):

on the anticyclonic side of well-developed jet streams which have been flown through in four cases, the condition $Q=0$ is fulfilled within about 150 to 200 km to the south of the jet axis. The small negative values of absolute vorticity, which appear in some cases near the jet axis (Gustafson, 1949), are still within the limit of errors of the calculation of velocities in the measurements by Riehl. (The "omnirange system" has been used for navigation during this project.)

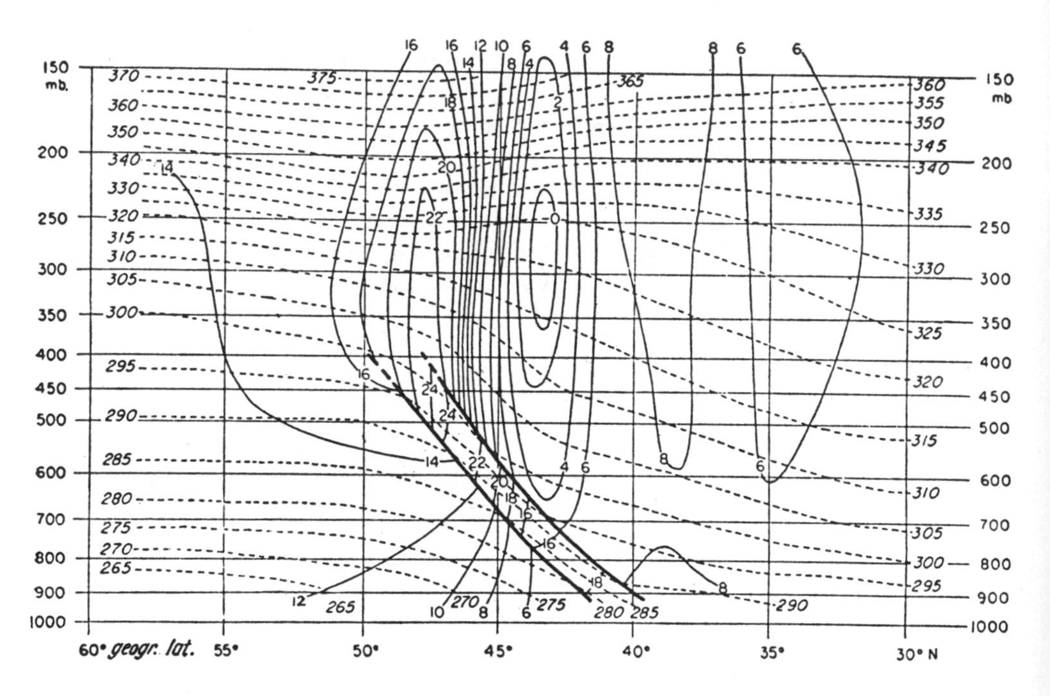

FIG. 4.121.7.—Mean absolute vorticity (10^{-5} sec^{-1}) and potential temperature (° K), computed from the cross section shown in Figure 3.211. (Palmén and Newton, 1948.)

Somewhat higher values of negative absolute vorticity ($-0.4 \cdot 10^{-4}$ sec^{-1}) are reported by Brundidge (1956) and by the author (Reiter 1960*d*, *e*, 1961*d*, *e*) to the south of the jet axis, based upon better methods of measurement. Dynamic instability, therefore, seems to be possible on the anticyclonic side of strong jet maxima.

At a larger distance from the jet axis (>150 km), again, weak positive values of vorticity assume an approximately constant value of about 0.3 to $0.4 \cdot 10^{-4}$ sec^{-1} (Riehl) or $1.6 \cdot 10^{-4}$ sec^{-1} (Brundidge). The flights have been carried out at an altitude of 30,000 ft (9 km). It will have to be assumed that, if measured along an *isentropic surface*, the area with $Q=0$ might under certain circumstances have extended to a distance of about 500 km from the jet axis.

A comparison of wind and vorticity conditions on the *cyclonic* side of four jet streams of Riehl's series of measurements showed, that between the two quantities there is an almost linear correlation:

$$Q/V=K. \qquad 4.122\ (1)$$

For K the empirical value $(150\text{ km})^{-1}$ has been obtained. Combining 4.122 (1) with 1.231 (3) one arrives at

$$f+(K_S-K)V-\partial V/\partial n=0, \qquad 4.122\ (2)$$

where $K_S=1/r_s$ is the magnitude of curvature of the streamlines. In the cases under investigation one could take $K_S \ll K (K_S<(2200\text{ km})^{-1})$, so that one may write in approximation:

$$f-KV-\partial V/\partial n=0. \qquad 4.122\ (3)$$

Neglecting also the latitude dependency of the Coriolis parameter, one may easily integrate this equation, and one obtains

$$dV/(V-f/K)=-K\cdot dn$$

and from this

$$V=f/K+(V_0-f/K)e^{-Kn}. \qquad 4.122\ (4)$$

$V=V_0$ for $n=0$. V_0 is the wind speed in the jet axis. Assuming $f=10^{-4}\text{ sec}^{-1}$, which corresponds to the value of the Coriolis parameter at about 45° latitude, and for $K=(150\text{ km})^{-1}$, we obtain an expression for V in m/sec

$$V=15+(V_0-15)\cdot e^{-n/150}. \qquad 4.122\ (5)$$

This equation depicts the conditions on the cyclonic side of the jet streams in Figure 4.122.1, while the anticyclonic side shows profiles with $Q=0$ to $Q=0.2\cdot 10^{-4}$. The abscissa contains wind speeds and the ordinate gives the distance n from the jet axis. The various wind profiles which have been observed during these research flights agree well with the cyclonic conditions of shear, as given in 4.122 (5), as do two profiles measured by Hurst (1952, 1953) over England, one of which has been entered into this diagram. One may assume, however, that this equation gives *maximum* conditions of shear rather than *average* for the cyclonic side of a jet stream. (According to Riehl's equation the shear in a jet stream with a peak velocity of 100 m/sec would amount to $4.3\cdot 10^{-4}\text{ sec}^{-1}$ measured over an area which extends to about 100 km to the left of the jet axis [Saucier, 1958*b*].) The latitude dependency of this equation was negligible during these investigations.

From 4.122 (4) it may be seen that the observed wind profiles may be expressed by straight lines in a semi-logarithmic co-ordinate paper, with log V and the distance n from the jet axis as co-ordinates. The same holds, if log $V^2/2$, the logarithm of kinetic energy, is chosen for the ordinate, which, too, corresponds to an exponential wind profile:

The condition for a straight line in such a co-ordinate system is

$$d(\ln V^2/2)/dn=-A=\text{const.} \qquad 4.122\ (6)$$

By transformation one obtains from this

$$(dV/dn)=-AV/2$$

and by integration

$$\ln (V_2/V_1)=-(A/2)(n_2-n_1)+B.$$

For the jet axis $(n=0)$ we have $V_1=V_0$. Therefore

$$V_2=V_0\cdot e^{-(An/2-B)}.$$

Because the condition $V_2 = V_0$ will have to be met for $n = 0$, one obtains for the constant of integration: $B = 0$. Therefore,

$$V_2 = V_0 \cdot e^{-An/2}. \qquad 4.122\ (7)$$

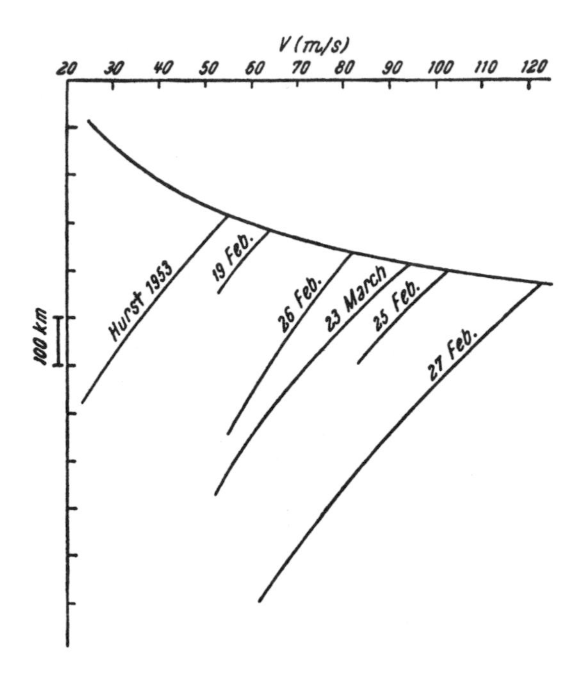

Fig. 4.122.1.—Horizontal wind profiles observed in jet streams, 1953. (Riehl, Berry, and Maynard, 1955.)

If one dependable wind observation were available for each side of the jet stream, from 4.122 (5) or (7) for the cyclonic side, and from $Q = 0.2 \cdot 10^{-4}$ sec^{-1} for the anticyclonic side the position of the jet axis, as well as the maximum wind speed in the axis may be computed (Fawcett and Snellman, 1959; see also Morley, 1957). Pauly and Menin (1954) propose an approximation equation for the calculation of the winds in the jet axis from observations on both sides of the jet stream. These computations are performed under the assumption of a double Couette flow (linear gradients of wind speed on both sides of the jet axis).

$$V_m = 2\overline{V} + \frac{V_1 + V_2}{2} + \frac{(V_1 - V_2)^2}{4\overline{V}} \qquad 4.122\ (8)$$

where

$$\overline{V} = \frac{g}{f}\,\frac{z_A - z_B}{L}.$$

It will have to be assumed that this expression is less accurate than the one given above, if the distance from the jet axis exceeds 200 km. In the latter expression z_A and z_B are the heights of an isobaric surface between the two stations on either side of the jet stream. L is the distance between these stations, V_1 and V_2 are the wind components normal to the connecting line $\overline{AB}$; V_m is the component of flow in the jet axis perpendicular to this connecting line.

Wind profiles as shown in Figure 4.122.1 would cause a *discontinuity* of the vorticity in the jet axis. In the cross sections analyzed by Palmén and Newton (1948) (see Fig. 4.121.7) we find a strong vorticity gradient in the jet axis; there is no pronounced discontinuity, however. We, therefore, would have to assume in this case a rounded wind profile in the jet center. Which of these two possibilities of analysis is to be preferred is difficult to decide because none of the measurements permit a dependable estimate of the micro- and meso-structure (order of magnitude to about 10^5 m).

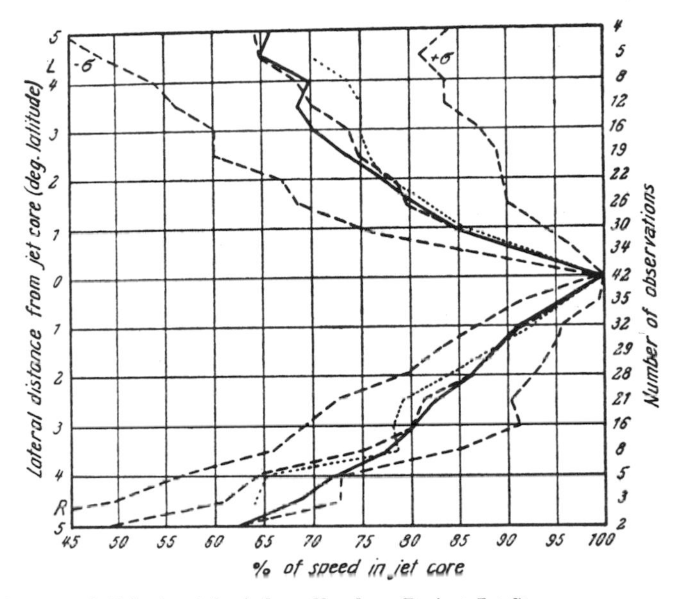

FIG. 4.122.2.—Average of 42 horizontal wind profiles from Project Jet Stream measurements. Solid line, $(V_0 - V)/\overline{V}_0$; dashed: V/V_0 and standard deviation $\pm\sigma$ of this quantity; dotted, distribution of median values. (V_0=speed in the jet axis.) (Saucier, 1958*b*.)

Wind profiles which have been obtained from research flights of Project Jet Stream in the Florida region, i.e., mainly under the influence of the STJ and of some PFJs which have advanced far to the south (Saucier, 1956*b*, 1958*b*), within their accuracy of measurement reveal a tendency for the formation of peaked wind profiles. The wind speeds in these profiles have been calculated as mean values over flight legs of 56 km in length, and so, at best, have only meso-structural accuracy. Figure 4.122.2 contains the mean ratio of velocities V/V_0 (dashed curve in the center) for 42 wind profiles. The solid curve gives the mean value of $(V_0 - V)/\overline{V}_0$ in per cent. $\overline{V}_0$ is the average wind speed in the jet axis. Larger differences between this and the dashed curve appear only at some distance from the jet axis. It appears from Figure 4.122.2 that during these research flights the cyclonic side also shows larger shears on the average than does the anticyclonic side, at least in a region on both sides of the jet axis with distances less than 350 km from the axis. As is shown by the standard deviation σ of the quantity V/V_0, the scattering of the wind profiles about the mean profile is larger on the cyclonic side than on the anticyclonic side. The median value of the distribution (dotted curve) indicates that on the cyclonic side the weakly shearing profiles are slightly more frequent than the strongly shearing ones. Horizontal wind profiles with large cyclonic shears, therefore, are relatively infrequent, at least in jet streams which have penetrated far to the south.

As far as the detailed flow pattern at the jet-stream level near 300 mb is concerned, one may draw certain conclusions from theoretical considerations (Faust, 1959*a*; Hollmann, 1959*a*; Reiter, 1959*c*, *f*), as well as from results of measurements (Riehl, 1954*b*). It has been pointed out in Chapter 3.248 that a maximum of divergence corresponds to an inflection point in the distribution of vertical velocities [see 3.248 (10)]. At the level of maximum we have

$$\frac{\partial \mathbf{v}}{\partial p}=0. \quad 4.122\ (9)$$

If we assume the surface of maximum wind to be quasi-horizontal, we also obtain

$$\partial D/\partial p=0,$$

i.e., the horizontal divergence has an extreme at jet-stream level.

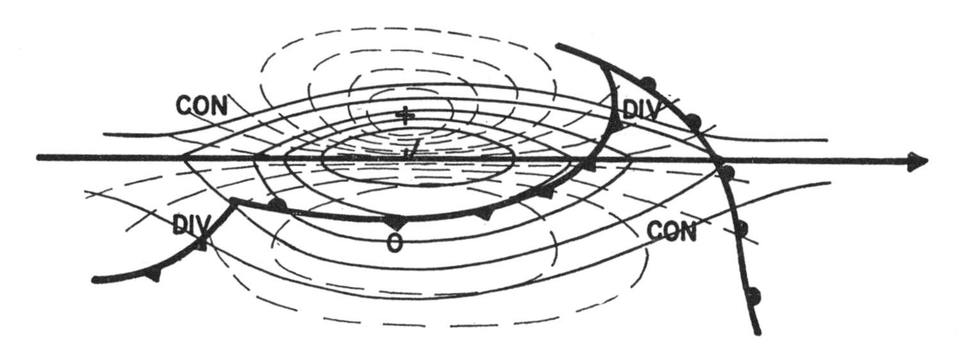

FIG. 4.122.3.—Schematic representation of surface fronts, as well as of vorticity distribution (dashed) and of divergence at the 300-mb level in the vicinity of a jet maximum (isotachs = full lines).

As has been mentioned already in Chapter 3.248, the geostrophic wind is non-divergent except for the term

$$D_g=-(v_g/R)\cot\varphi, \quad 4.122\ (10)$$

which is caused by the latitude dependency of the Coriolis parameter and which usually is neglected because of its smallness. The maximum of divergence at jet-stream level, therefore, has to be caused by *ageostrophic* components of flow. If we denote these by u^* and v^* following Eq. 1.224 (2) we obtain

$$D=\partial u^*/\partial x+\partial v^*/\partial y=\nabla\cdot\mathbf{v}^*. \quad 4.122\ (11)$$

The maximum of positive vorticity is located to the left of the jet maximum. The air masses flowing through this pattern experience divergence in the region of positive vorticity advection, i.e., in the left front quadrant of a jet maximum. In the region of negative advection (left rear quadrant) there will be convergence (Fig. 4.122.3). In the right front and rear quadrants of a jet maximum the vorticity distribution is ambiguous and depends on the predominance of curvature or shearing terms in Eq. 1.231 (3). Accordingly, convergence and divergence in these two quadrants are less well developed.

It has been shown already by 1.224 (1) that the acceleration acts at a right angle to the ageostrophic component:

$$\dot{\mathbf{v}} = f\mathbf{v}^* \times \mathbf{k}.$$

In the left front quadrant we have $D > 0$, therefore, according to 4.122 (11)

$$\nabla \cdot \mathbf{v}^* = \partial V^* / \partial s > 0,$$

i.e., the positive ageostrophic component increases in the direction of flow. Therefore $\dot{\mathbf{v}}$ is directed toward higher pressure in this area, at a rate which increases downstream. There will be a mass outflow toward higher pressure, which is caused by the divergence of flow and, hence, by the vorticity distribution.

One arrives at the same result if one considers that for $\mathbf{v}^* = \mathbf{v} - \mathbf{v}_g > 0$ the actual wind speed is larger than the geostrophic one. Since the wind field tries to adapt itself to the given pressure field (principle of adaptation), a deviation of the wind toward higher pressure and a deceleration of the motion will result because the Coriolis force is greater than the gradient force.

The existence of these super-gradient components of flow have been confirmed by Faust (1955*a*) and others (Böhme, 1956; Dahler, 1955; Flohn, 1956*b*; Hollmann, 1955*b*; Reinecke, 1950, 1951; Schneider-Carius, 1956). Palomares (1956) computed the influence of turbulent exchange acting from the jet-stream region upon the layers of air below. He also arrives at components of flow directed toward higher pressure, probably because the additional momentum creates super-gradient velocities. Faust called this outflow toward higher pressure the "zero layer effect" ("Nullschichteffekt") (Faust, 1955*c*, 1959*b*). This ageostrophic component of flow accounts for the "evacuation" of low-pressure vortices and is opposed in its effect to the inflow in the surface layers, which is caused by friction (Schneider-Carius and Faust, 1953). With this view, we arrive at a cyclone model which is able to explain the surface pressure falls in a frontal wave disturbance. The super-gradient winds in the jet-stream region, which have been found by Faust to be present on the average, have not been confirmed by experiments with rotating dishpans. A mean *direct* circulation has been revealed by these experiments in the jet-stream region, which is based upon a mass flow from higher toward lower pressures. If, on the average, an indirect circulation were found at the maximum wind level in the atmosphere, the jet stream apparently would have to draw its kinetic energy from a source different from the ageostrophic meridional mass circulation. Such a source would remain in the action of large-scale horizontal vortices of the magnitude of planetary waves.

It will be shown in more detail in Chapter 4.433 that the question whether the jet stream is associated on the average with a direct or indirect circulation, i.e., whether the meridional mass circulation acts to accelerate or impede the jet stream, cannot be solved without difficulty because the results are decisively influenced by the choice of the co-ordinate system.

That Faust's "zero-layer effect" cannot exist everywhere in the jet-stream region is easily realized, because it would rapidly consume the kinetic energy and convert it into potential energy. Thus, within the jet stream there also have to be processes which transform potential energy into kinetic energy. As in model experiments, the circulation processes in the atmosphere which produce or consume kinetic energy depend on the position of the point of observation with respect to the long-wave phase and the jet maximum. Therefore, the choice of co-ordinate system may influence the results, too. Although the instantaneously measured winds may reveal in their *streamlines* a component, which, on the average, is directed toward higher pressure, the motion of the pressure field is superimposed upon this instantaneous streamline pattern. It might be possible, therefore, that the total effect showed a flow toward lower pressure in the *trajectories*. Statistical investigations to this end would be a rewarding enterprise. The consideration of the rate of displacement of wave disturbances in the computation of gradient wind velocities has been pointed out in Chapter 3.243.

We now shall investigate a case in which the vertical component of the wind velocity not only has an inflection point at jet-stream level but becomes actually zero. In this case the jet-stream level has the true character of a "zero layer" (defined as a layer in which $\omega=0$)—following the terminology used by Faust (1953).

By differentiation after ∂p and by considering Eq. 4.122 (9) and $\partial^2\mathbf{v}/\partial p\,\partial t=0$, the equation of motion yields (Hollmann, 1959*b*):

$$\omega\frac{\partial^2\mathbf{v}}{\partial p^2}=-\nabla\frac{\partial\Phi}{\partial p}.$$

With the aid of the hydrostatic equation and the equation of state this renders

$$\omega\frac{\partial^2\mathbf{v}}{\partial p^2}=\frac{R}{p}\nabla T. \qquad 4.122\ (12)$$

Finally applying the operator $\nabla\times$ to this equation, one obtains the differential equation for the vertical motion on an isobaric surface of extreme wind velocity

$$\frac{\partial^2 v}{\partial p^2}\frac{\partial\omega}{\partial x}-\frac{\partial^2 u}{\partial p^2}\frac{\partial\omega}{\partial y}+\frac{\partial^2 q}{\partial p^2}\omega=0. \qquad 4.122\ (13)$$

From 4.122 (12 and 13) the following deductions can be made with regard to the layer of maximum wind:

1. Vertical motions vanish in an isobaric, isothermal surface of maximum wind speed.

2. Since, because of $-\partial^2\omega/\partial p^2=0$, the vertical velocity at the same time shows an inflection point in this layer, the sign of the velocity ω has to reverse itself in this layer.

3. Since the vertical motion is zero in the "zero layer," the vertical vorticity advection $\omega\dfrac{\partial q}{\partial p}$ and the turning of horizontal vortex tubes (see Chapter 1.233) $\dfrac{\partial v}{\partial p}\dfrac{\partial\omega}{\partial x}-\dfrac{\partial u}{\partial p}\dfrac{\partial\omega}{\partial y}$ also vanish. From 4.122 (13) we may conclude, therefore, that on either side of an isobaric surface of extreme wind velocity, which at the same time constitutes a "zero layer," the sum of vorticity advection and turning of vortex tubes has equal sign.

As Hollmann (1959*a*) showed, 4.122 (13) has a non-trivial solution $\omega \neq 0$ at the level of maximum wind, if the characteristics of this differential equation are isotherms at the same time. The nodal curves, for which $\omega = 0$, then, are *isotherms of extreme temperature*, because of 4.122 (12).

For practical purposes, the assumption of an *isobaric* layer of maximum wind will have to be abandoned, as is shown by Figure 3.246.4. At jet-stream level vertical velocities may still be observed which have an order of magnitude comparable to the ones at the 500-mb surface (Danielsen, 1959; Endlich, 1953; Reiter, 1961*a*, *e*; *et al.*, 1961; Vuorela, 1957*a*). This indicates that the "zero layer" nature of the jet-stream layer is preserved only on the average; it does not have to hold true in single cases. Many times the results contradicting the "zero layer" conditions are revealed only by the meso-structure of detailed flight measurements. According to recent investigations (Reiter, 1961*e*) in which the vertical velocity has been estimated from true air speed and pitch of the aircraft (Kuettner and McLean, 1958) vertical motions of either sign as high as 2.5 m/sec may be expected at jet-stream level.

In a recent paper Hollmann (1959*b*) abandoned the condition that the layer of maximum wind has to be isobaric. He introduces a vertical co-ordinate $\zeta = \frac{z}{H(x,y,t)}$. H is the height of the surface of maximum wind. At jet-stream level ($z = H$), ζ assumes the value of 1, at the ground the value of 0. $\zeta' = d\zeta/dt$ is the generalized vertical velocity in this new co-ordinate.

From the equations of motion in a natural co-ordinate system the following relation for $\zeta = 1$ and $\partial V/\partial\zeta = 0$ may be derived, which is valid at the layer of maximum wind:

$$\zeta' = \left(\frac{\partial G_s}{\partial \zeta} - V\left(\frac{\partial V}{\partial n}\right)_\zeta \frac{\partial \alpha}{\partial \zeta} - \frac{\partial F_s}{\partial \zeta}\right) \Big/ \frac{\partial^2 V}{\partial \zeta^2}.$$

The subscript ζ indicates a differentiation in which this variable remains constant. G_s is the gradient force along a streamline: $G_s = -(1/\rho)(\partial p/\partial s)$ and α is the wind direction (the angle between the wind vector and the positive x-direction). At jet-stream level $\partial^2 V/\partial\zeta^2 < 0$. F is the force of friction.

The level of maximum wind has the nature of a "zero layer" ($\zeta' = 0$, i.e., the vertical velocity vanishes at jet-stream level) under the following conditions:

1. Here G_s shows an extreme value in its vertical distribution, because $\partial G_s/\partial\zeta = H\,\partial G_s/\partial z$. This is equivalent to extreme ageostrophic conditions of flow.
2. The horizontal shearing vorticity $(\partial V/\partial n)_\zeta$ vanishes only in the jet axis and attains high values on either side of it. Then, at the level of maximum wind, $\partial\alpha/\partial\zeta = 0$, i.e., the wind direction has to attain extreme values here.
3. $\partial F_s/\partial\zeta$ also has to be zero, i.e., the friction also must show an extreme value at jet-stream level, if the latter should have the nature of the "zero layer."

As Hollmann indicated, however, these conditions are only valid if the level of maximum wind is a physical surface, i.e., if it is at all times formed by the same air particles. This condition is hardly ever met in reality.

From these and from statistical results obtained by Faust and his collaborators (Attmannspacher, 1959, 1960*a*, 1960*b*; Faust, 1954*a*, *b*, 1955*a*, *b*, 1960; Harsány, 1960; Soos, 1959), one may conclude that layers of extreme wind velocity and "zero layers" are located at approximately the same level in quasi-stationary pressure patterns. In the region of jet streams, however, one will have to expect a rather complicated structure of the three-dimensional field of flow. This is the case because here the layer of maximum wind undergoes drastic height changes, and it also is not a substantial surface; therefore, a mass exchange between stratosphere and troposphere is possible. The tropopause cannot be regarded as a barrier for vertical mass exchanges, because of its leaflike structure (see Chapter 3.249).

For frictionless horizontal motion without vertical transport of momentum [see Eq. 1.224 (1)] the expression

$$\dot{\mathbf{v}} = -\alpha \nabla p + f\mathbf{v} \times \mathbf{k}$$

is valid. After scalar multiplication of this equation with $\mathbf{v}$ we obtain

$$\mathbf{v} \cdot \dot{\mathbf{v}} = -\alpha \mathbf{v} \cdot \nabla p + f\mathbf{v} \cdot (\mathbf{v} \times \mathbf{k})$$

or

$$\tfrac{1}{2}\, dV^2/dt = -\alpha V \cdot \partial p/\partial s.$$

Because of

$$dp/dt = \partial p/\partial t + V \cdot \partial p/\partial s,$$

we obtain

$$\tfrac{1}{2}\, dV^2/dt = -\alpha(dp/dt - \partial p/\partial t).$$

In a stationary state $\partial p/\partial t = 0$, and one obtains Bernoulli's equation in the form

$$V^2/2 + p/\rho = \text{const.} \qquad 4.122\ (14)$$

This equation also indicates that the speed increases if the horizontal streamlines are directed toward lower pressure. The contrary holds for decreasing velocities.

According to these assumptions, Bernoulli's equation derived here only holds for a horizontal and stationary current. These limiting conditions, however, are hardly ever fulfilled in a jet stream. Vertical motions are in process which—as far as they can be regarded as adiabatic—follow isentropic surfaces. In order to compute the velocity changes of an air particle, one would have to follow its trajectories in three dimensions and not on a horizontal surface (Danielsen, 1959; Reiter and Danielsen, 1960).

In spite of these limitations the theoretical considerations are confirmed by observational results. As an example, the weather situation of 23 March, 1953, will be considered again. In the late afternoon of this day, a research flight was conducted from the eastern coast of the United States to Lake Michigan (see Fig. 4.122.1). The jet maximum appears at 2100 GCT—the approximate time of the research flight—well marked over the state of Michigan. Rawins and aircraft winds were in good agreement. Figure 4.122.4 contains the jet axis which approximately corresponds to a streamline, and the mean 300-mb topography between 23 March, 1500 GCT, and 24 March, 0300 GCT, which approximately correspond to 2100 GCT. The jet-stream sector with positive accelerations coincides with a departure of the streamline toward lower pressures as compared to the geostrophic direction, corresponding to the above theoretical derivation. The sector with negative accelerations already lies beyond the border of the map. A comparison of the high-level flow with the surface weather map of 24 March, 1953, 0300 GCT (Fig. 4.122.5) shows that the upper divergence in the region of positive vorticity advection in the left front quadrant (delta region) of the jet maximum is superimposed upon a marked surface convergence in the region of a low-pressure vortex with cloudiness and precipitation, as has also been indicated in Chapter 3.248. The sector with upper convergence in the entrance region of the jet maximum is located above a marked low-level divergence within a high-pressure wedge with fair weather.

Flights which have been carried out at higher levels (at about 11 km = 35,000 ft) seem to indicate a splitting tendency of the jet stream. Figure 4.122.6 shows the measurements during a research flight conducted normal to a jet maximum, with flow from a northwesterly direction. The flight was carried out on 7 January, 1954, in the rear of an upper-level trough along the East Coast of the United States from Florence, South Carolina, to Poughkeepsie, New York. While at a height of 9 km the horizontal wind profile shows only one maximum; at a height of 10.5 to 11 km two maxima may

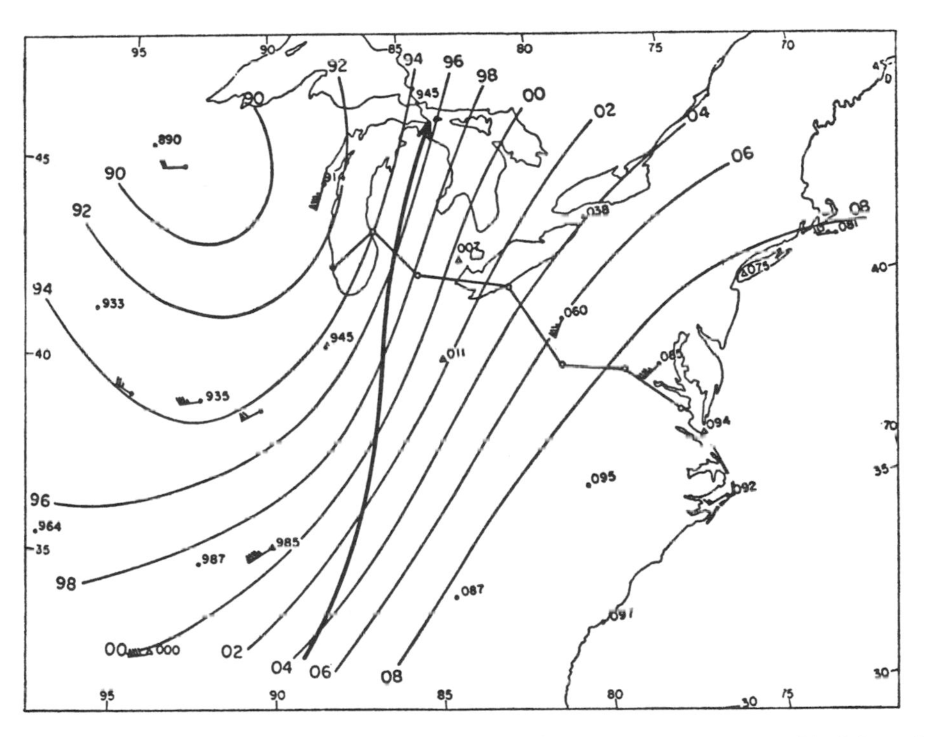

Fig. 4.122.4.—Absolute topography of the 300-mb surface (200-ft contour interval), combined from the synoptic map times 23 March, 1953, 1500 GCT and 24 March, 0300 GCT. The heavy line with arrow indicates the position of the jet axis. (Riehl, 1954*b*.)

be discerned distinctly, whose existence is also corroborated by the horizontal temperature gradients. Using mean cross sections, Reed and Danielsen (1959) arrive at similar results for the detailed structure of the upper wind field to the rear of a high-level trough. The warm tongue ("isentrope trough"), which appears at the 200-mb level on the cyclonic side of the jet stream (Fig. 4.112.2), extends far into the stratosphere and indicates strong sinking motion in this area (Reiter, 1961*e*). The vertical motion in the surroundings of a jet stream, therefore, influences drastically the vertical as well as the horizontal structure of the wind field by destroying the

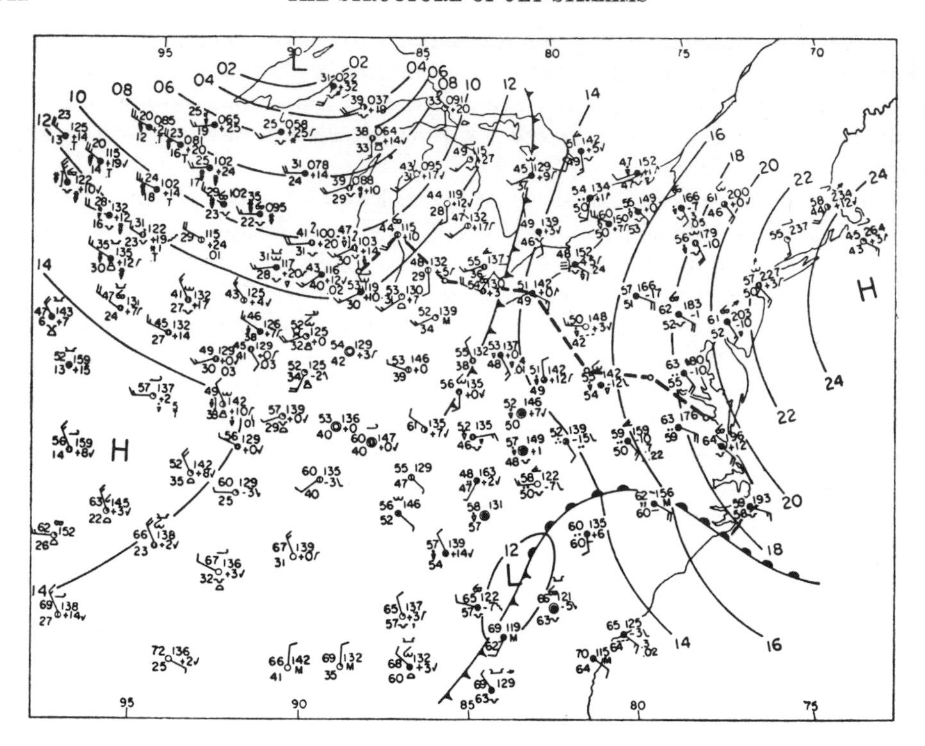

FIG. 4.122.5.—Surface weather map, 24 March, 1953, 0300 GCT. Route of research flight (also indicated in Fig. 4.122.4) entered with dashed lines. (Riehl, 1954b.)

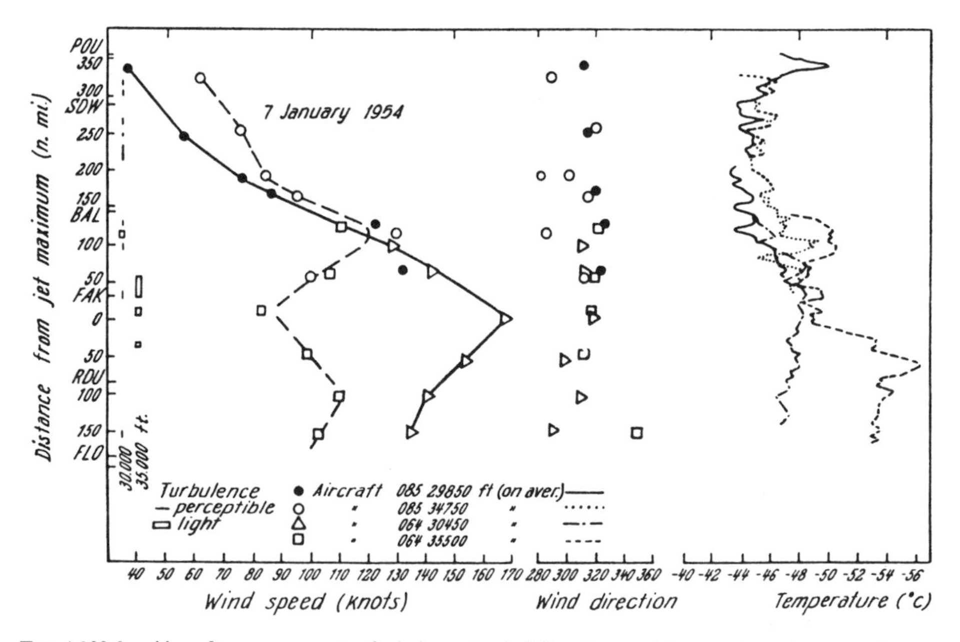

FIG. 4.122.6.—Aircraft measurements of wind speed, wind direction, and temperature along a route normal to the jet stream, 7 January, 1954. *POU* = Poughkeepsie, New York; *FLO* = Florence, South Carolina. (Dickson, 1955.)

baroclinicity in some places, and strengthening it in other places. Because of the *band-like* structure of the area of strongest sinking motion, the jet stream, which appears as a uniform and sharply concentrated ribbon of high wind speeds at the 300-mb level, is split into several branches at higher levels (Reiter, 1959*e*). (The same holds for the ascending motions which cause the cold tongue ("isentrope hump") at the 200-mb level to the right of the leading edge of a jet maximum.) The structure of jet streams, therefore, can be regarded and understood only in a three-dimensional view.

4.123. Jet Maxima and Their Origin

In the preceding chapters reference has been made on several occasions to maxima of wind speed which occur along the jet stream (see Fig. 4.122.3 and 4.122.4). These involve regions in which the air particles experience strong accelerations—and therefore are subject to *ageostrophic* components of flow. In the jet maximum itself $\partial V/\partial s=0$ and $\partial^2 V/\partial s^2<0$. (Strictly speaking, this differentiation should not be performed along the direction of the streamline s but rather in a curvilinear coordinate system whose main axis runs parallel to the jet axis (see Chapter 4.433).)

In essence, therefore, jet maxima are an ageostrophic phenomenon. This may be demonstrated most impressively from American transosonde flights (Durst and Gilbert, 1950; Neiburger and Angell, 1956). Figure 4.123.1 shows the ageostrophic flow of mass as it may be observed directly from transosonde flights. (For orientation purposes the boundaries of the state of Colorado have been entered in this figure.) Two-hour transosonde positions are given by dots and arrows. The length of the arrows and the numbers written above them indicate a four-hour mean value of the wind velocity. Conventional balloon data have been entered in the customary fashion. Furthermore, in the vicinity of each point of measurement of the transosonde, the contour gradients at the time of observation are indicated by two heavier lines. It is clearly visible from this figure that accelerations or decelerations of air particles are originated by flow toward lower or higher pressure. If the deviations toward lower and higher pressures, which the transosonde of Flight No. 993 underwent several times, were simple inertia oscillations, the periods of these fluctuations would have to correspond to the one of the inertia circles.

$$\tau_i=\frac{2\pi}{f} \qquad 4.123\ (1)$$

(see Kao and Neiburger, 1959). The *inertia period*, therefore, is equal to half a pendulum day, $[2\pi/(\Omega \sin \varphi)]\cdot\frac{1}{2}$. At 35° N (lower part of Figure 4.123.1) τ_i has the magnitude of about 21 hours. In fact, the transosonde needs little over 10 hours to cover the distance from the velocity minimum near El Paso (ELP) to the maximum near Fort Smith (FSM). There are, however, only 6 hours until the next minimum, southwest of Green Bay (GRB), is reached. Here the motion is strongly influenced by a traversing wave in the pressure field, so that an undisturbed inertia oscillation would seem rather unlikely to occur. The theoretical value of the inertia period for the geographic latitude of Green Bay (44° 29′ N) is approximately 17 hours. In good agreement with this, the transosonde traveled the distance to the next velocity maximum (south of Omaha) in about 8 hours.

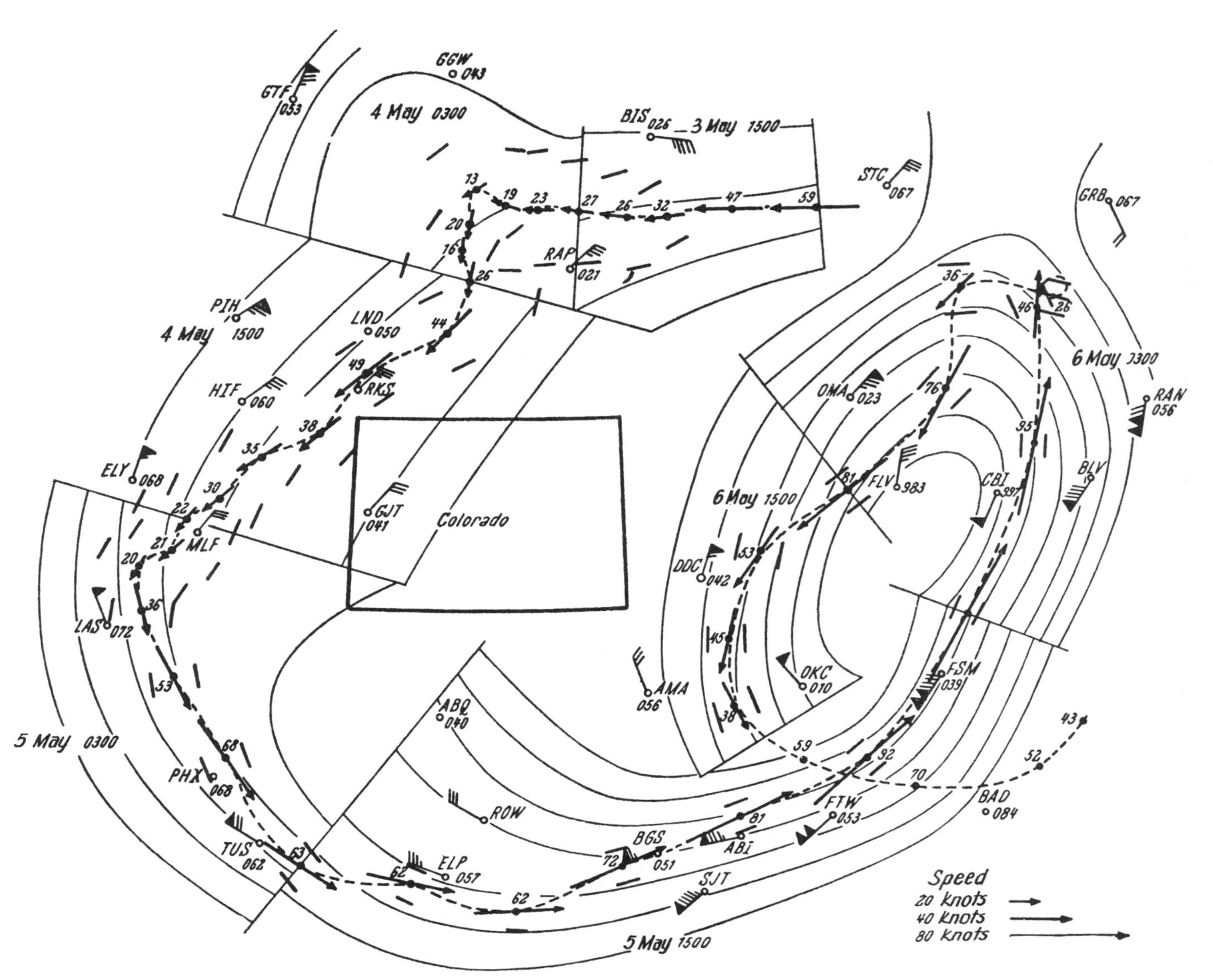

FIG. 4.123.1.—Trajectories of transosonde Flight No. 993, 3 to 7 May, 1953. For explanation see text.

Angell (1958*a*, *b*, 1960*a*, 1960*b*) investigated a series of transosonde flights statistically. He was able to show that, on the average of the flights analyzed, the strongest zonal wind components were found between *high-pressure* ridge and the *inflection point upstream from it*, i.e., in the region of increasing anticyclonic curvature. This would agree well with the considerations in Chapter 4.121: Air masses ascending east of the trough axis would import larger angular momentum from southern latitudes and would cause higher wind speeds in the anticyclonic part of the jet stream. This is congruent with some of Raethjen's (1958*a*) views on the origin of jet maxima. He considers convective motions to be responsible for disturbances of the geostrophic equilibrium in the upper-level flow, and for the appearance of ageostrophic components of motion. This ascending motion of relatively slow (subtropical) air masses also is to be expected in the warm-air region east of the troughs. In order to adapt the flow pattern to the pressure pattern, a pronounced component of flow across the isobars (contour lines), directed toward lower pressure, will have to establish itself here. In Angell's statistical work mentioned above, the strongest component of flow normal to the contour lines, in fact, is found at the *inflection point* upstream from the high-pressure ridge, or near the trough line, i.e., farther to the west of the point in which the strongest zonal speeds occur on the average.

Offhand, it will have to be expected that inertia oscillations as computed above will be met only under ideal conditions. Johannessen (1956*a*) derives an oscillation period of $\frac{1}{2}$ pendulum day for a perturbation motion, which is superimposed upon a *constant geostrophic wind field*.

This assumption will have to be abandoned, however, in the region of a jet maximum. The air particles traveling through the jet maximum are faced with a pressure gradient *variable in time and space*. At the same time, the accelerations observed at jet-stream level prove the existence of *ageostrophic* components of flow. From the deviations of the jet axis toward higher and lower pressures (see Fig. 4.122.4) one may conclude that in general wind speed maxima have super-geostrophic flow (or super-gradient flow in the case of curved streamlines), while wind speed minima have sub-geostrophic flow. Newton (1959*a*) assumes that in the jet core

$$\frac{d\mathbf{v}_g}{dt} = \frac{1}{2}\frac{d\mathbf{v}}{dt} \qquad 4.123\ (2)$$

The adaptation between flow and pressure patterns, therefore, should follow a simple statistical law. Because of Eq. 1.224 (2) $\dot{\mathbf{v}}^* = \frac{1}{2}\dot{\mathbf{v}}$, and because of 1.224 (1) we have

$$\frac{d\mathbf{v}^*}{dt} = \frac{d\mathbf{v}_g}{dt} = \frac{f}{2}\,\mathbf{v}^* \times \mathbf{k}. \qquad 4.123\ (3)$$

This follows from the assumption that half the observed accelerations are caused by changes in the pressure field and, therefore, in the geostrophic wind field; the other half, however, is brought about by ageostrophic processes of motion.

These conditions of speeds and accelerations are shown schematically in Figure 4.123.2. $\overline{\mathbf{v}}_g$ is the mean geostrophic wind, assumed to be $(\mathbf{v}_{max} + \mathbf{v}_{min})/2$, according to Newton. $\mathbf{v}_{max}$ is the velocity in the jet maximum, $\mathbf{v}_{min}$ is the average taken from the two adjacent velocity minima along the same jet axis. The total velocity, therefore, is $\mathbf{v} = \overline{\mathbf{v}}_g + \mathbf{v}_g' + \mathbf{v}^*$. $\mathbf{v}_g'$ stands for the variable component of the geostrophic wind, which is given by the variation in pressure gradients between the locations of jet maximum and jet minimum. According to 4.123 (3), $\mathbf{v}_g' = \mathbf{v}^*$. For $\bar{V}_g > 2V^*$ the total speed varies between

$$(\bar{V}_g - 2V^*) \leqq V \leqq (\bar{V}_g + 2V^*). \qquad 4.123\ (4)$$

The acceleration acts with constant magnitude toward the right of the vectors $\mathbf{v}_g'$ and $\mathbf{v}^*$ (see Fig. 4.123.2). The oscillation cycle has a radius of $|\mathbf{v}_g' + \mathbf{v}^*| = |2\mathbf{v}^*|$. According to Eq. 4.123 (3) and Figure 4.123.2 the cycle is completed with an angular velocity of $|f\mathbf{v}^* \times \mathbf{k}| / |2\mathbf{v}^*| = f/2$. The period of this perturbation motion, therefore, is

$$\tau^* = \frac{2\pi}{f/2} = \frac{1 \text{ day}}{\sin \varphi} = 2\tau_i. \qquad 4.123\ (5)$$

Thus, an air particle would require *one pendulum day* to travel from one jet maximum to the next, or from one minimum to the next.

The period of oscillations about the mean geostrophic wind speed $\bar{V}_g$, derived by Newton, is equal to *twice* the inertia period [4.123 (1)]. This result is due to the assumptions underlying 4.123 (2), which have been made arbitrarily, and which do not have to be met in each individual case. We, therefore, will have to expect a certain amount of scattering of the observed periods about the theoretical value of $2\tau_i$.

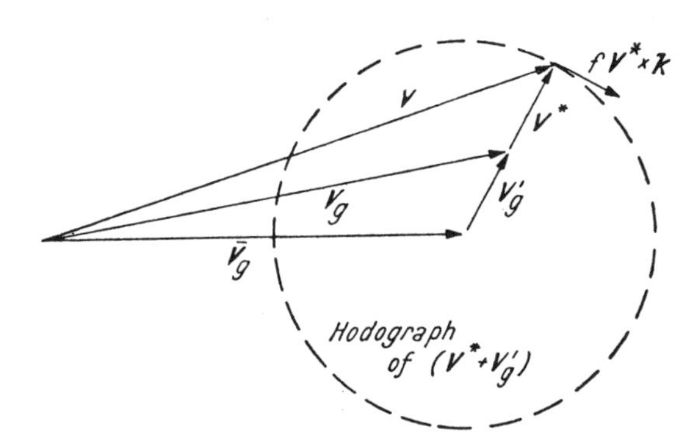

FIG. 4.123.2.—Velocity changes in the jet stream, for $\mathbf{v}_g = \frac{1}{2}\dot{\mathbf{v}}$ (see text). (Newton, 1959*a*.)

Figure 4.123.3 shows that *on the average* the observations are grouped about the period $2\tau_i$. The measurements were based upon 250-mb charts. The periods of oscillations were computed from

$$\tau^* = \frac{L_j}{\bar{V} - C_j}. \qquad 4.123\ (6)$$

L_j is the distance between two jet minima measured along the jet axis. $\bar{V}$ stands for the (also time-averaged) mean wind speed along the jet axis between the two jet minima. C_j is the rate of displacement of the jet maximum.

Equations 4.123 (5 and 6) are valid only for straight flow. Newton (1959*a*) was able to show by using gradient-wind conditions that in the case of curved streamlines the relationship

$$\tau^* = \frac{L_j}{\bar{V} - C_j} = 2\tau_i \left(1 - \frac{\Delta\alpha}{4\pi}\right) \qquad 4.123\ (7)$$

is valid. $\Delta\alpha$ indicates the change of wind direction (positive when counterclockwise) during the period τ^*.

The importance of the variable component $\mathbf{v}_g'$ of the geostrophic wind upon the flow patterns in the region of jet maxima is brought out by the fact that in Figure 4.123.3 only a few points lie in the close vicinity of oscillations with a period of τ_i. This component itself, however, has to be considered a perturbation superimposed upon the uniform basic current $\overline{V}_g$, leading to the formation of jet maxima, which, again, exist only by virtue of ageostrophic components of flow.

The results of Newton's investigations as presented in Figure 4.123.3 may also be interpreted in the following way: The formation in the atmosphere of jet maxima which are traversed by air particles having an *average* period of oscillation of about $2\tau_i$ clearly indicates the presence of a *mechanism of adaptation* (see Raethjen, 1950, 1957*a*, *b*, 1958*a*, 1959). This mechanism seeks to equalize the pressure and flow conditions. It acts, however, with considerable *damping*. If the ageostrophic components of flow did not influence the pressure field at all, one would have to expect a

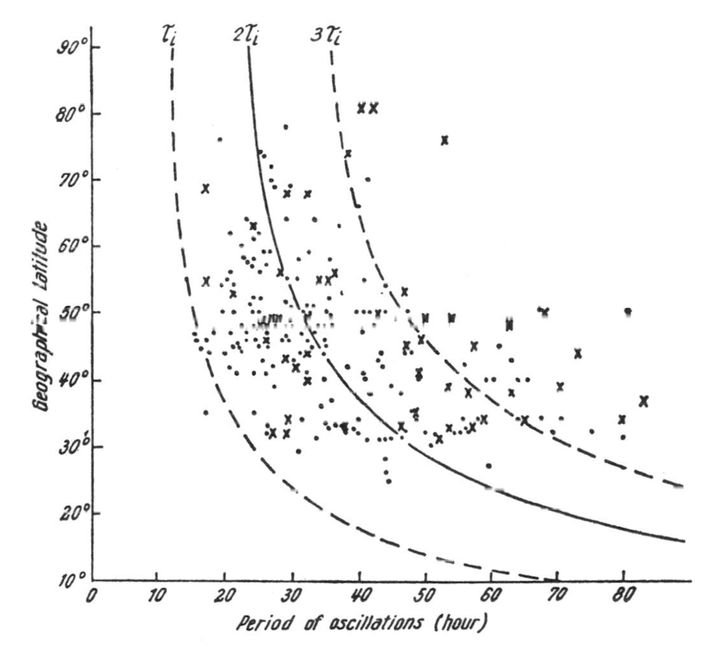

FIG. 4.123.3.—Period of observed velocity oscillations along jet axis at the 250-mb level, October through December, 1958. Crosses indicate unreliable measurements of wave lengths and wind speeds. (Newton, 1959*a*.)

mean oscillation period of τ_i. If, on the other hand, the pressure adjusted itself without any damping to the instantaneous ageostrophic flow conditions, i.e., if there were ideal adaptation, there should be no inertia oscillations at all.

From 4.123 (6) it might be expected that the "wave length" L of individual jet-stream sections is proportional to the relative wind speed $\overline{V}-C_j$. A corresponding evaluation made by Newton shows a rather wide scattering of values, which is perhaps due mainly to inaccurate estimates of $\overline{V}-C_j$ or of L_j.

It is worth mentioning that the jet maxima of the subtropical jet stream (see Fig. 4.412.2), analyzed by Krishnamurti (1959*a*), on the average fit well into Newton's theoretical considerations. The following quantities have been measured in the STJ: $\bar{V}=131$ knots, $\bar{L}_j=6330$ nautical miles (11,730 km), $\bar{C}_j=0$, $\bar{\tau}^*=48.4$ hours. From the mean geographic latitude (28°) 51 hours are computed for $2\tau_i$.

Newton's computations are valid for the jet-stream layer. Outside this layer one has to expect larger periods of the ageostrophic oscillations because of the smaller relative velocities. With this, also the ageostrophic components of flow **v*** appear greatly reduced outside the jet-stream core, which stands in agreement with the considerations made in the preceding chapter. Therefore, **v*** attains maximum magnitudes within the jet-stream layer.

The *trajectories* of air particles following the jet axis describe a cycloid which may be regarded as the sum of the straight motion $\bar{\mathbf{v}}_g$ and of the anticyclonically rotating vector $(\mathbf{v}_g'+\mathbf{v}^*)=2\mathbf{v}^*$ (Fig. 4.123.2). If $2V^*\geqq \bar{V}_g$, the trajectories will form loops or cusps wherever V attains minimum values.

The wave length of the trajectory cycloid is $\bar{V}_g\tau^*$, while the wave length of the jet axis is given by $(\bar{V}_g-C_j)\tau^*$. The amplitudes of the ageostrophic oscillations which lead to the formation of jet maxima are $(V_{\max}-V_{\min})/f=4V^*/f$ for a *wave*-shaped trajectory. (Johannessen [1956*a*] obtains an amplitude of V^*/f under the assumption $\mathbf{v}_g=$ constant. Raethjen [1958*a*] arrives at similar results assuming elliptic instead of circular perturbation motions.)

From the preceding considerations the existence of jet maxima may, therefore, be ascribed to the effect of ageostrophic perturbation motions which are superimposed upon a geostrophic basic current (*or a current which fulfils the gradient-wind equation*). *Because of the adaptation of the pressure field to the flow pattern these ageostrophic perturbations give rise to changes in the geostrophic basic current.*

Now the question arises to which mechanism these ageostrophic components of flow owe their existence. According to Raethjen (1957*a*, 1958*a*), their origin is to be expected where the ageostrophic components show a maximum, i.e., where the adaptation has not yet become effective. In this connection it seems noteworthy that the oscillations caused by the ageostrophic flow of mass lead toward an *increase* of wind speed *downstream*, even though the local effects may be *braking* the upper current, thus causing subgeostrophic conditions. Sutcliffe (1938) points out that in zones with strong confluence or diffluence pronounced ageostrophic motions will have to be present. The "confluence theory" by Namias and Clapp (1949 [Chapter 4.142]) is based upon similar considerations. Sekera (1949) also obtains theoretical distributions of wind-speed maxima which agree well with synoptic experience, by considering perturbations in the u and v components.

Confluence itself, however, may not be regarded as the ultimate cause of the ageostrophic mass circulation because it already constitutes a perturbation of a uniform and zonal basic current. It is not difficult, though, to localize regions under the influence of high mountain barriers (Himalayas, Rocky Mountains), in which the atmosphere constantly receives perturbation energy (see Chapter 7.3). The distribution of continents and oceans and their associated temperature gradients in the lower troposphere, too, may lead to perturbations of a uniform basic current.

Rossby (1951*b*) considers it possible that an *intensification of the upper current—*

and connected with it a pressure drop along the direction of the streamlines—may be caused by withdrawing momentum from the lower layers of the atmosphere (e.g., by mountain ranges), if the total volume transport in a current of constant width has a certain predetermined value.

In Chapter 4.121 it has been pointed out that a wind profile of constant absolute vorticity would establish itself on the cyclonic side of a jet stream under the influence of horizontal exchange processes. Cross sections through individual jet maxima may, however, reveal large departures from such a mean profile. Most of all, jet maxima are characterized by limited areas with maximum values of positive vorticity (Fig. 4.122.3) which, according to the vorticity equation, 1.233 (6), determine the divergence of the upper current, and with this the weather conditions in the jet-stream region.

It is easy to perceive that the vorticity maximum on the cyclonic side of a jet maximum, again, is due to ageostrophic components of flow. Let us assume a *geostrophic, zonal* basic current, in which shearing conditions are already present that conform to the "mixing theory." Let us, furthermore, consider a perturbation, perhaps due to orographic influences, in the axis of this geostrophic jet stream which does not yet show any velocity maxima. The perturbation will be assumed to *brake* air particles traveling through it. The wind speed now becomes sub-geostrophic at this place and results in a deviation of the trajectories toward the low-pressure side. Simultaneously, however, due to the reduced wind speed in the jet axis, the horizontal wind shear, and with this the absolute vorticity, will also be reduced.

Downstream from this location the air particles having deviated toward the cyclonic side will now accelerate, finally attaining super-geostrophic speeds. By this, the absolute vorticity at the low-pressure side of the newly established wind-speed maximum assumes *higher* values than would correspond to the original distribution with constant absolute vorticity. Thus, a local vorticity maximum of limited extent develops.

The "mixing theory" of jet-stream formation, therefore, is not contradicted by the existence of vorticity maxima. Two processes are active in the atmosphere: On the one hand there are *exchange* and *mixing* processes, which tend to establish a large-scale state of equilibrium. On the other hand, there are *perturbation motions*, which oppose this equilibrium trend. To the latter correspond the processes which lead to the formation of jet maxima and vorticity maxima. The "mixing theory," however, accounts only for the equalizing processes. It might be pointed out that *mean* wind profiles (in which ageostrophic components of flow with different sign cancel each other) fit well into Rossby's theory.

4.13. The Horizontal Structure of the Layer of Maximum Wind

In the preceding chapters several characteristics of the jet stream have been treated in quasi-horizontal (isobaric) surfaces. Since the surface of maximum wind ($\partial \mathbf{v}/\partial p=0$) is not horizontal, one will have to assume offhand that a treatment of the conditions of flow on this surface will render different results, which perhaps take into account the three-dimensional structure of the jet stream more adequately (Reiter, 1957*c*, 1958*c*; and Riehl and Hinkelman, 1957; U.S. Air Weather Service, 1956*d*).

In Chapter 4.122 it has been pointed out that the distribution of wind speeds on the cyclonic and on the anticyclonic sides of a jet stream may be represented by potential laws of the form

$$V_0 = V_s \cdot e^{An} \qquad 4.13\ (1)$$

V_0 is the wind speed in the jet axis, V_s is the speed at a distance n from the axis.

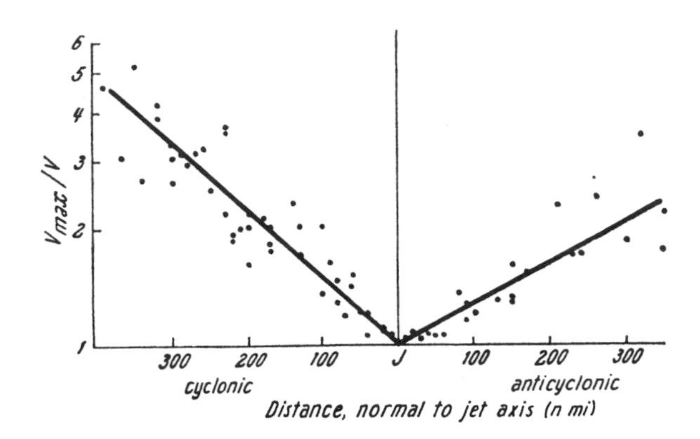

FIG. 4.13.1.—Ratio of wind speed in the jet axis to wind speed in the LMW for stations to the left and right of axis.

The distribution of the mean speed of the LMW is given by the data points in Figure 4.13.1. The velocity decay in the LMW at both sides of the jet axis, thus, may be approximated, too, by a potential law of a form as given above. For the examples

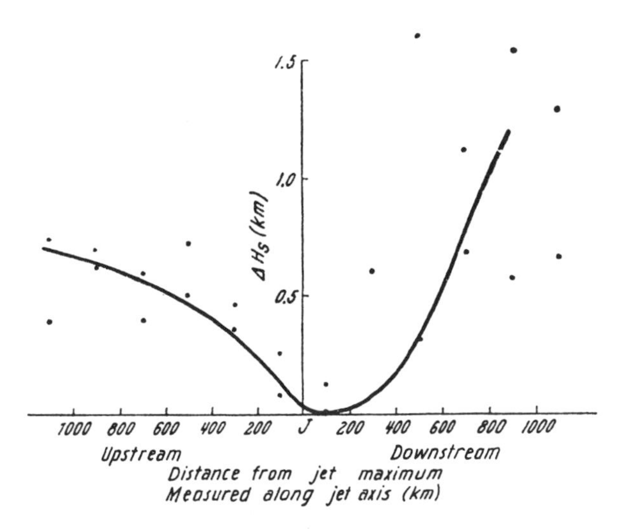

FIG. 4.13.2.—Mean height of the LMW, relative to the height of the jet maximum, evaluated along the jet axis.

available from the papers quoted above, on the *cyclonic* side the constant A had the value $1.72 \cdot 10^{-3}$, on the *anticyclonic* side $1.03 \cdot 10^{-3}$ (n. mi.)$^{-1}$, if V is expressed in knots or m/sec, and n is given in nautical miles. For the horizontal shearing conditions on the 300-mb surface [4.122 (5)], one obtains the exponent $12 \cdot 10^{-3}\ n$, if n, again, is measured in nautical miles. Therefore, on the cyclonic side the relation between average shear on an isobaric surface and the shear in the LMW is given by

$$(V_p-15)/(V_0-15):(V_s/V_0)=1:1.0140. \qquad 4.13\ (2)$$

V_p is the wind speed at the distance n from the jet axis on an isobaric surface. The difference in the shears, thus, amounts to about 1 per cent on the cyclonic side. On the anticyclonic side it has the same order of magnitude.

Equation 4.13 (1) may be used as well as 4.122 (5) in order to determine the position of the jet axis from reliable wind observations on either side of the axis and to calculate the wind speed at the location of the jet axis.

From careful analyses of the LMW (see Figs. 3.246.3, 3.246.4, 3.246.5) several characteristics of the three-dimensional wind field have been obtained which facilitate the analysis of the LMW charts:

1. If one follows the jet axis the LMW reaches its point of lowest elevation on the average approximately 100 km downstream from the tropospheric wind maximum. Upstream from this point the core of strongest wind velocities rises slowly; downstream the height of the LMW rises rapidly. However, the observed values scatter rather much here (Fig. 4.13.2).

2. A "trough" of low elevation of the LMW extends along the cyclonic side of the jet-stream axis, with the lowest heights on the average at about 100 km distance from the axis (Fig. 4.13.3; see also Fig. 3.246.4). The core of the polar-front jet lies close to

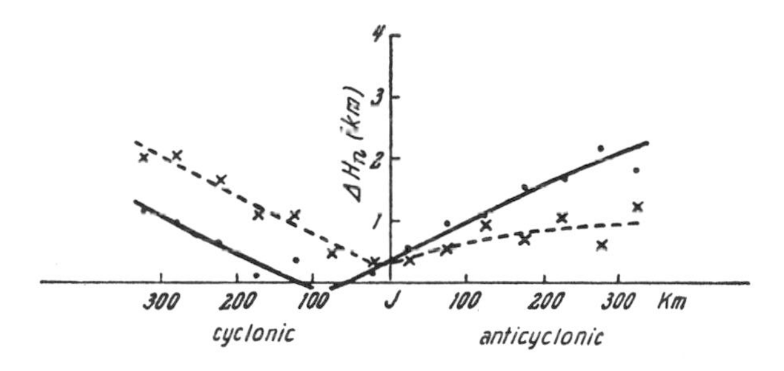

FIG. 4.13.3.—Mean height of the LMW relative to the height of the jet axis, evaluated normal to the jet axis (dots, solid line), and mean deviations of measurements (crosses, dashed line).

the 9-km level. By means of analyses of the "zero layer" Attmannspacher (1959) also finds that the jet-stream layer shows a trough of low elevations which runs parallel to the jet axis.

3. Analyses of the thickness of the LMW also show a "trough" of small values along the cyclonic side of the jet axis, with its center at a distance of about 150 km from the axis (Fig. 4.13.4; see also Fig. 3.246.5). This coincides with the area of strongest vertical wind shear, into which Berggren (1953*a*) places his stratospheric front (see Fig. 4.112.3). The relatively large scattering of the data points on the anticyclonic side of the jet axis, which is expressed by the mean deviation in Figure 4.13.4, is partly due to the fact that in this area the confluence of subtropical and polar-front jet streams has been observed, as is indicated in the charts (Figs. 3.246.3 to 3.246.5).

From the foregoing it follows that, at least during winter, on the cyclonic side, the LMW rapidly rises to high elevations. It, therefore, may be expected to lie here on the average *above* the tropopause, while on the anticyclonic side (right side of Fig. 4.13.3) the layer of maximum wind in general is located below the tropopause (see Chapter 3.249).

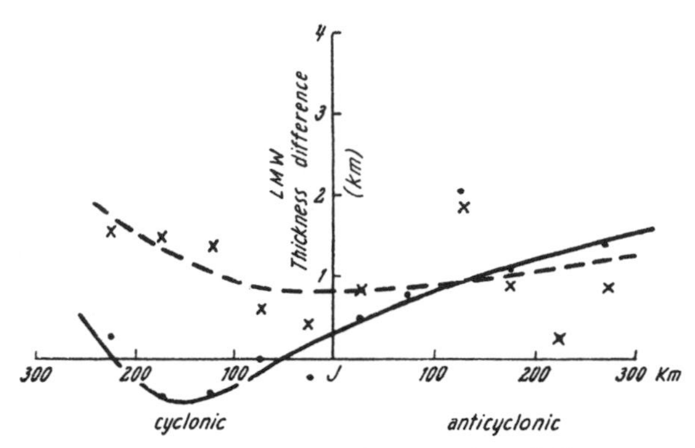

FIG. 4.13.4.—Thickness of LMW (km), evaluated as departure from thickness measured at location of jet axis (dots, solid line), and mean deviations of measurements (crosses, dashed line).

4.14. Multiple, High Tropospheric Jet Streams of Temperate Latitudes

4.141. Polar and Subtropical Jet Streams

The structural characteristics of jet streams described in the preceding chapter have been taken from observational data which have mainly been gathered over the United States. Either the jet streams occurring there are associated with a well-pronounced polar front in the lower troposphere, i.e., they are polar-front jets (PFJ), or the baroclinic zone characteristic for jet streams is present only in the upper troposphere, while the lower troposphere is quasi-barotropic. Jet streams of the latter kind are called subtropical jets (STJ). Since transitions between the two jet-stream systems seem to be possible (Reiter, 1959*b*, Reiter *et al.*, 1961), the PFJ and STJ may not always be distinguished clearly. A short account of both jet-stream types is given in Chapter 4.41. In the following the interaction between several adjacent jet-stream branches will be pointed out, one of which may usually be called STJ and the other PFJ, although in some cases, such a discrimination is not possible.

It has already been pointed out in several earlier papers (see Riehl and Teweles, 1953) that the jet stream does not surround the hemisphere as a uniform closed band, but it frequently appears split into several jet streams lying side by side. Such velocity distributions are characteristic for the North American continent: the jet stream associated with the polar front traverses the northern states and Canada, while over the southern states and Mexico the jet stream emerging from the southwest is especially well pronounced at the 250- and 200-mb level. The southernmost of these two jet streams is not connected with a frontal zone that would reach down to the earth's surface; instead, the baroclinic zone in which this jet stream is rooted is confined to the upper troposphere (Defant and Taba, 1957). Both bands meander around the hemisphere, as Cressman (1950) was able to show.

From Cressman's analyses we may conclude the following:

1. It has been pointed out already (see Chapter 3.251) that the jet-stream maxima show a hemispheric tendency of migration. This tendency, as described by Cressman, apparently corresponds to processes which characterize the transition from low to high index. A polar jet maximum (connected with the polar front) forms in the north.

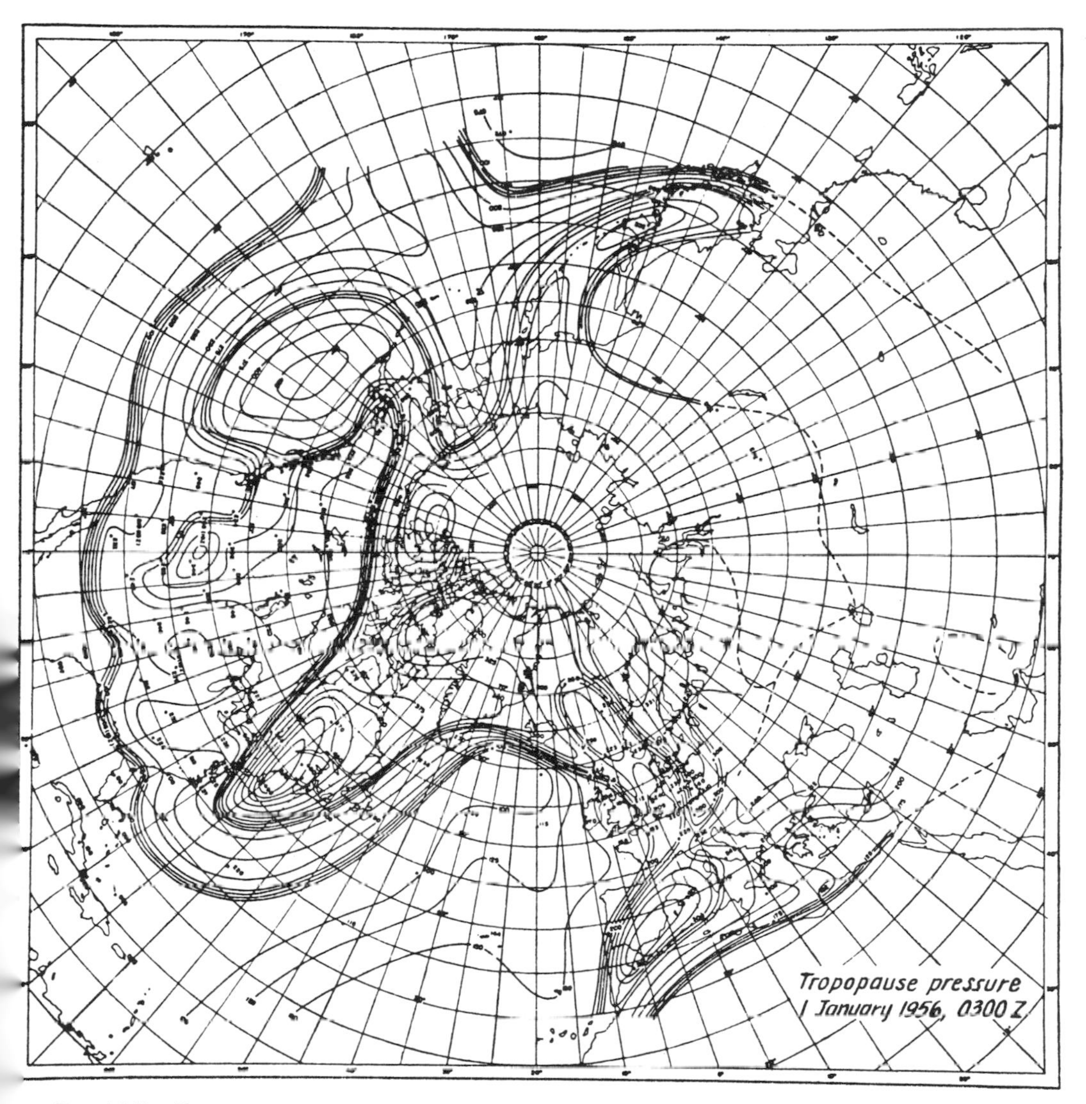

FIG. 4.141.—Tropopause pressure (mb) of 1 January, 1956, 0300 GCT. Discontinuities are indicated by crowding of isobars. (Defant and Taba, 1958b.)

While it penetrates toward lower latitudes, following a southward trend, and simultaneously progressing toward higher altitudes, the wave amplitude increases. A new formation of the polar front in the north finally establishes two (at times also three) separate jet-stream bands, the southernmost of which usually may be termed as subtropical jet (see Murray, 1952). Some of the jet streams called STJ, therefore, when considering their case history, could be regarded as remnants of a baroclinic zone which has survived in the upper troposphere from an old polar front. Near the ground, where the influences of divergence in the subtropical high-pressure area, which modify the air mass properties, become active, this baroclinicity has been largely destroyed, and therefore the subtropical jet does not appear to be connected with any frontal zone near the ground. Simultaneously with the southward propagation of the jet axis its potential temperature increases (Phillips, 1950; see Chapter 4.412).

2. There are regions in which the two jet streams approach each other within several degrees of latitude, and sometimes may merge into one single jet-stream band. Then, again, the two streams flow into diverging directions: the polar-front jet follows a northeasterly course, while the subtropical jet bends to the southeast. A comparison with the pattern of planetary waves shows that the areas with confluence are most frequently situated in strongly developed cold upper troughs, in which from the tight contour gradient one may expect great wind velocities.

The diffluent areas are to be sought upstream from blocking anticyclones or from cut-off lows. Defant and Taba (1957, 1958*a*, *b*) arrive at similar results. Figure 4.141 shows an analysis of the tropopause heights (in mb) of 1 January, 1956, 0300 GCT. As has been reported in Chapter 3.249 the jet streams coincide with a steep rise in the tropopause heights. Therefore the crowding of isobars in Figure 4.141 may be interpreted as the jet-stream positions.

From this figure we may easily recognize an area over the American West Coast in which PFJ and STJ are diffluent. On the other hand, over the West Atlantic there is a confluent zone. Furthermore, over Europe there is a well-marked shear line along which two jet streams flow in opposite directions.

Confluence and diffluence are not only possible between two different jet-stream systems, as for instance PFJ and STJ, but they are also present in the entrance and delta regions of single jet maxima.

4.142. The Confluence Theory of Jet-Stream Formation

From the relationship between confluence and increased jet stream velocities Namias and Clapp (1949) derived their "confluence theory."

Baroclinic zones are formed in the atmosphere whenever air masses from different latitudes with different temperatures are brought together. The effectiveness of the advection mechanism depends on the one hand upon the angle between isotherms and isobars, and the superimposed effect of vertical motions, and on the other hand on the wind speed itself. All three factors together determine the rate of propagation of the isotherms. From the turning of wind with height (Barbé, 1956), which usually is different on the warm and cold sides of a jet stream, one may discover the effectiveness of the confluence and diffluence mechanism (Dahler, 1957, 1960). A mechanism which brings about the confluence effect may be found in different speeds and wave length of the planetary waves in higher and lower latitudes (Czapski, 1952; Namias, 1947*b*).

According to the "mixing theory," a possibility of confluence is also allowed by the fact that trajectories of absolute vorticity have longer wave length with higher wind speeds, except when their amplitudes increase at a compensating rate [see 1.234 (11 and 12)]. CAV trajectories, therefore, have larger amplitudes in the jet axis than in the areas on both sides of it. This should lead to an increase of the gradients at the south side of large troughs (University of Chicago, 1947).

If there is a superposition of wave trains so that cold air is brought cyclonically from the north and warm air is imported anticyclonically from the south, the baroclinicity of the troposphere will be increased in the entrance region of the two jet streams. A new formation, or an intensification of an already existing jet-stream maximum will be the result (Clapp and Winston, 1951; Nyberg, 1949). Because of the increased crowding of streamlines (isobars) the ageostrophic flow of mass toward lower pressure will be increased simultaneously in this area. As the air particles enter the jet maximum, they experience an acceleration which makes them deviate from the geostrophic direction of flow. The confluent area, therefore, will be characterized—especially in its cyclonic sector, as has been shown in Chapter 4.122—by upper-level convergence and low-level divergence. This explains why the confluent part of strong jet-stream maxima runs across regions in which the cores of high-pressure areas associated with cold outbreaks and of subtropical anticyclones with strong low-level divergence may be found.

An effective advection of different air masses is possible only when there are relatively large meridional components of flow present in the upper current. This, again, agrees with the considerations made in Chapter 4.121, according to which a relatively small meridional displacement under conservation of angular momentum leads toward the formation of strong zonal components of flow. According to both points of view strong jet maxima should be expected along the northwestern slopes of the subtropical high-pressure cells, where warm air and westerly momentum are carried out of the trade wind region toward the north. On the other hand, we have to expect that the easterly jet stream of the tropics (see Chapter 4.413) receives its momentum on the southeastern slopes of these high-pressure cells, where the subtropical belt of high pressure is interrupted by a low pressure incision, which reaches far into the tropics.

A careful analysis of the entrance region of the jet maximum shows that the confluence mechanism reveals itself by the convergence of several "jet fingers." These are relatively narrow branches of the jet stream which enter into the main jet axis from the north and from the south and which contribute to the intensification of the baroclinicity mentioned above by advecting air masses of different temperature. Figure 4.232.2 contains the 250-mb isotach analysis of 4 April, 1957, 1500 GCT, which shows rather clearly such a confluence zone with "jet fingers" over the states of the American Middle West.

In the right rear quadrant of a jet maximum which has been newly formed by the confluence of two jet streams, weak upper divergence may appear if the cyclonic curvature is not very strong and the increasing anticyclonic shear predominates. This would be the area in which secondary wave disturbances may form along the polar front. The left rear quadrant of the jet maximum is characterized by strong upper convergence and low-level divergence. Here we observe the formation of cold surface anticyclones, which eventually merge with the subtropical high-pressure cells due to the frontolytical processes active in this area.

The delta region of a frontal zone (Scherhag, 1948*b*) shows the opposite characteristics with respect to the divergence distribution: The cyclonic sector shows strong upper divergence and low-level convergence as has been mentioned earlier. This is the sector of the jet maximum with the strongest cyclogenetic activity, coinciding with the location of a more or less intensive surface cyclone. The anticyclonic sector shows more or less pronounced anticyclogenetic tendencies, depending on the predominance of the shearing or the curvature vorticities. This is the area in which warm high-pressure ridges form.

While this holds for any entrance or delta region of a frontal zone, we may assume that during the confluence or diffluence of two *jet-stream systems* similar vergences are active in an *increased* magnitude and that thereby widespread readjustments in the general circulation will result.

Although the "confluence theory" contains a possible qualitative explanation for the intensification of jet streams and for the formation of velocity maxima, the origin of the jet stream itself, and its maxima, cannot be explained by this theory. The confluence of air masses with different temperatures in a deep atmospheric layer is synonymous with convergence of flow; the diffluence is synonymous with divergence of flow. By virtue of the vorticity distribution around a jet maximum and the resulting vorticity advection, however, the divergence distribution is already pre-determined [see 1.233 (6)]. Therefore, the divergence and convergence in the region of the jet maximum would be cause and effect of this maximum and therefore cannot be used as an explanation for its formation. Namias (1952*b*) himself admits this; other authors, however, sometimes do not consider these facts properly (see Dahler, 1957, 1960). Basically, the confluence theory is nothing else but a statement of the fact that the thermal wind equation is valid in the free atmosphere with good approximation (Jansá and José, 1956). Each wind velocity maximum is associated with a maximum of baroclinicity in the layers below. The baroclinic zone, again, owes its temperature contrast largely to advective processes, which in the relatively unstable troposphere overshadow by far the influence of vertical motions.

Thus, the confluence of air masses of different temperatures results in an *increase* of the wind speed in the upper troposphere in accordance with the thermal wind equation. The principal cause of confluence, however, must be sought elsewhere, e.g., in the effectiveness of perturbation motions, which are superimposed upon a basic current, and which may be produced for instance by mountain ranges (see Chapters 4.123 and 7.3).

4.2. THE VERTICAL STRUCTURE OF JET STREAMS

4.21. Mean Meridional Cross Sections

4.211. Seasonal Differences

It has been pointed out in Chapter 4.111 and 4.121 that with the seasonal displacement of the baroclinic zone in the troposphere the jet streams, too, are migrating. Figure 4.211.1 shows the mean geostrophic zonal component in winter and summer (averaged over the northern hemisphere) (Petterssen, 1950; see Koslowski, 1958). From this diagram it may be seen that during winter the high tropospheric westerlies double their intensity. During winter the zonal wind maximum lies near 25° N, and during summer near 42° N. A separate maximum of the subtropical jet stream cannot be found because this representation constitutes a hemispheric and seasonal average. Subtropical and polar-front jet streams merge into one maximum because of the meandering which they are subject to. Only the rise of the surface of maximum wind toward the south, which is especially pronounced in the winter cross section, indicates

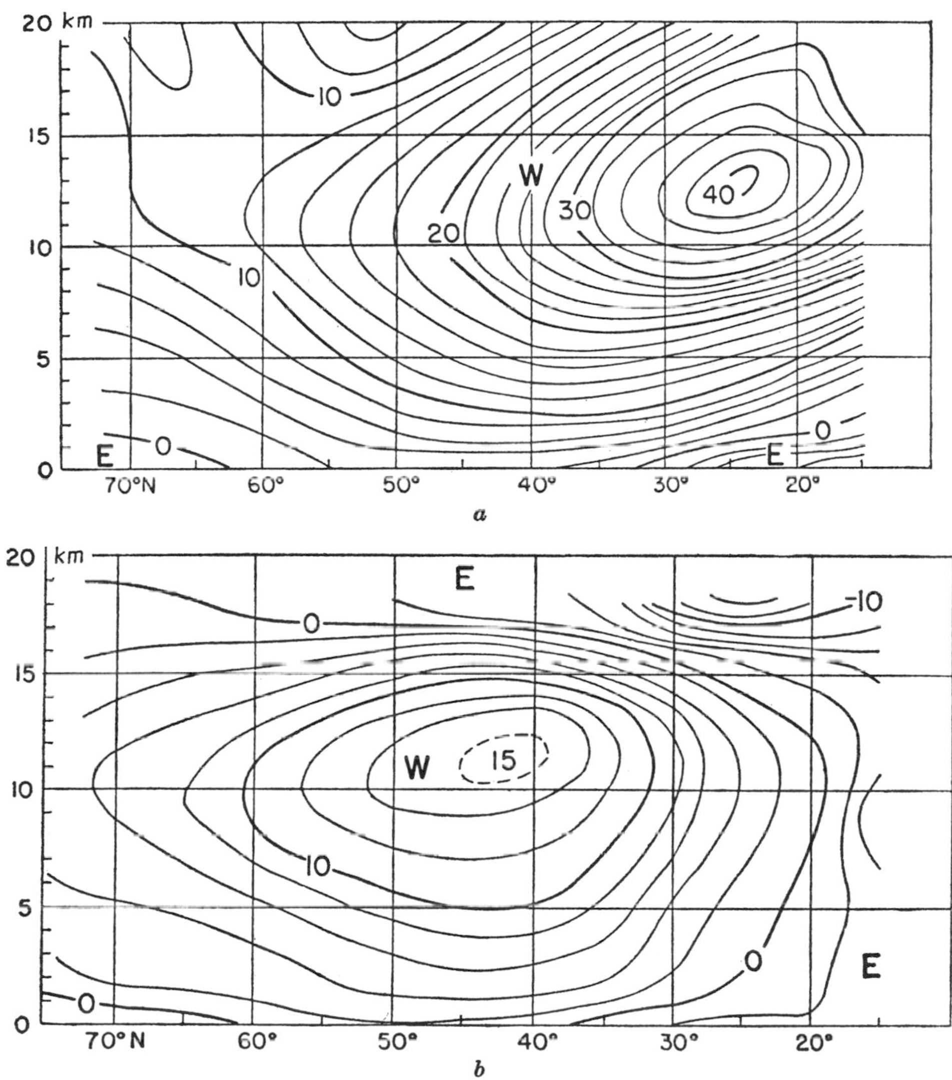

FIG. 4.211.1.—Mean zonal component of geostrophic wind (m/sec); (*a*) during winter, (*b*) during summer. (Petterssen, 1950.)

the influence of the subtropical jet at higher levels. During summer the stratospheric easterlies are well established, while during winter a branch of the *Arctic* stratospheric jet becomes visible at about 70° N and at 20 km (Moore, 1956).

Comparing this Figure 4.211.1 with Figure 4.121.3, we see that the position of the average wind maximum agrees only poorly with the frequency maximum of jet-stream positions. The mean wind maximum according to Petterssen (1950) may be found close to the southernmost position which the jet stream assumes occasionally but by no means most frequently. This discrepancy between the location of the *mean* wind maximum and the *most frequent* position of the jet axis has been pointed out by Davis (1951). These differences are brought about by the different magnitude of wind shears on the cyclonic and anticyclonic sides of the jet stream, which, in averaging, makes the position of the *mean* jet stream appear displaced toward the anticyclonic side and at the same time makes the horizontal wind shears appear strongly reduced.

The following example may serve to illustrate this. Let three westerly jet streams be available for averaging, with their axes at 28°, 34°, and 40° latitude. The horizontal wind shears are assumed to be 100 knots per 10° of latitude on the anticyclonic side, 100 knots per 4° of latitude on the cyclonic side. The following results are obtained:

Latitude	18	20	22	24	26	28	29	30	31	32	34	36	38	40	42	44	46
Jet at 28°	50	70	90	110	130	*150*	140	130	105	80	30	30	30	30	30	30	30
Jet at 34°	10	20	30	50	70	90	100	110	120	130	*150*	130	80	30	30	30	30
Jet at 40°	10	10	10	10	20	30	40	50	60	70	90	110	130	*150*	130	80	30
Mean Jet	23	33	43	57	73	90	93	*97*	95	93	90	90	80	70	63	47	30

The position of the mean jet stream at 30°, thus, lies very close to the most southerly position the jet stream ever assumes in this experiment.

Figure 4.211.1 shows, furthermore, that the shear on the anticyclonic side of the mean jet stream is larger than the shear on the cyclonic side: this is in direct contradiction to individual synoptic cases. The same phenomenon is evident from a comparison of the single jet streams with the mean jet in above table. Thus, by averaging, completely different shearing conditions from those present in reality may be simulated.

The structure of wind shears peculiar to jet streams may bring it about that of two stations at different geographic latitudes the southern one may show the larger *mean* wind speed; nevertheless, the jet stream may be most frequently encountered above the northernmost of the two stations. One has to be careful, therefore, not to draw conclusions about the mean position of the jet stream from average cross sections as shown in Figure 4.211.1.

The meridional distribution of the relative vorticity (Fig. 4.211.2) reflects primarily the influence of the wind shear. The location of the zero line indicates the position of the jet axis at different levels. The smallness of the relative vorticity values, again, has its reason in the averaging process.

The mean distribution of the absolute vorticity is given in Figure 4.211.3. Maxima and minima in the vertical distribution are indicated by dashed lines.

A closer inspection of these diagrams reveals several facts which are of importance for the understanding of the general circulation of the atmosphere (Petterssen, 1950). In the cold polar anticyclone, negative relative vorticity is consumed by friction; this is equivalent to the generation of cyclonic (positive) vorticity. This vorticity is exported approximately along isentropic surfaces into the subpolar low-pressure belt, where the polar jet stream is located and is consumed here by surface friction.

Accordingly, the distribution of relative and absolute vorticity (Figs. 4.211.2 and .3) reveal a gradient in this area which is directed toward the ground and from which one can surmise a vorticity transport toward the ground, maintained by exchange processes. In the subtropical high-pressure belt, mainly in the trade-wind region, positive vorticity is generated. The vorticity gradient in the lower part of the troposphere is directed upward in this area. Part of this vorticity is transported into

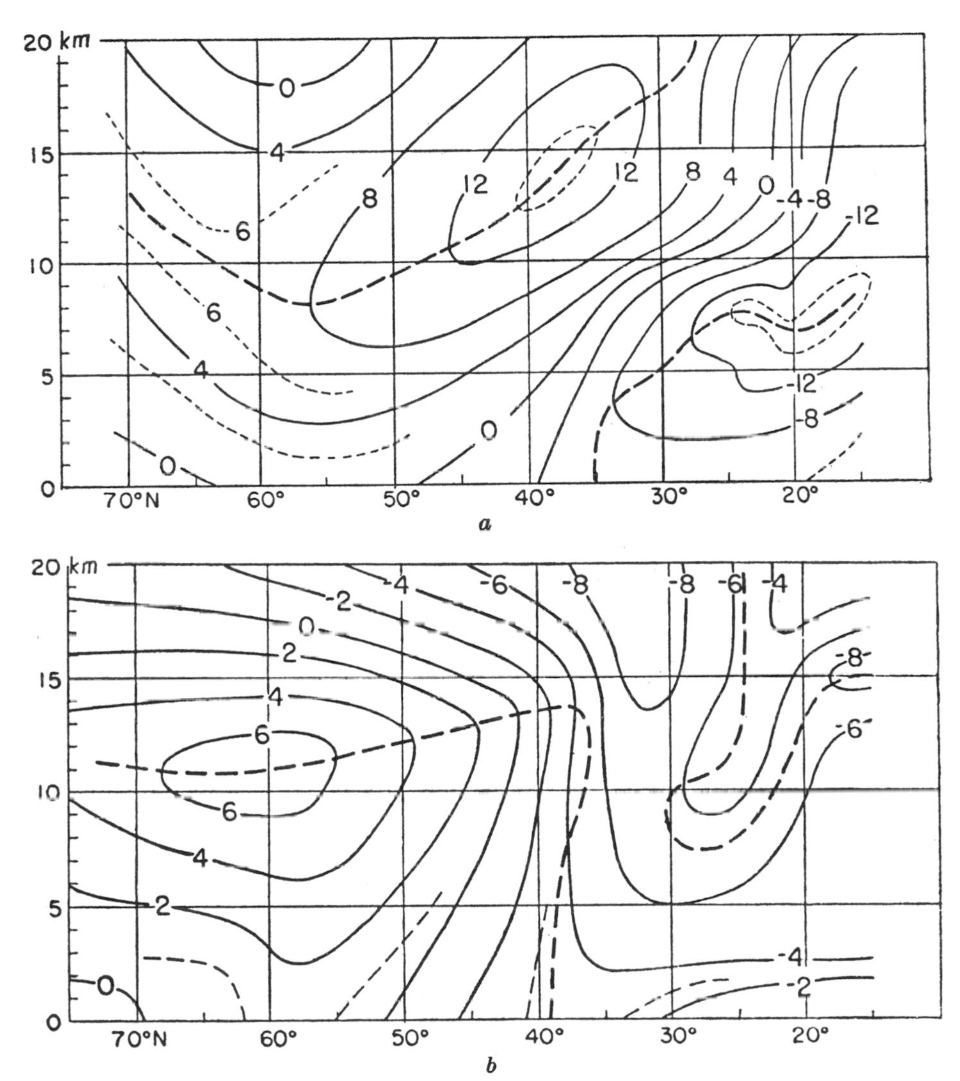

FIG. 4.211.2.—Mean meridional distribution of relative vorticity (10^{-5} sec^{-1}); (*a*) during winter, (*b*) during summer. (Petterssen, 1950.)

the equatorial doldrums and is consumed there. Another part is carried into the monsoonal low-pressure areas, especially during summer. A sizable portion of this vorticity, however, is carried around the western edges of the subtropical high-pressure cells toward the north and helps to maintain the jet streams of the temperate latitudes.

It is especially these western edges of the high-pressure cells which are characterized by confluence of polar and subtropical jets (Chapter 4.14), thus giving rise to especially intense jet streams. The intensification of jet streams in this area, thus, may be explained not only by thermal considerations—confluence of air masses of different temperature—but also by vorticity considerations: strong injections of cyclonic

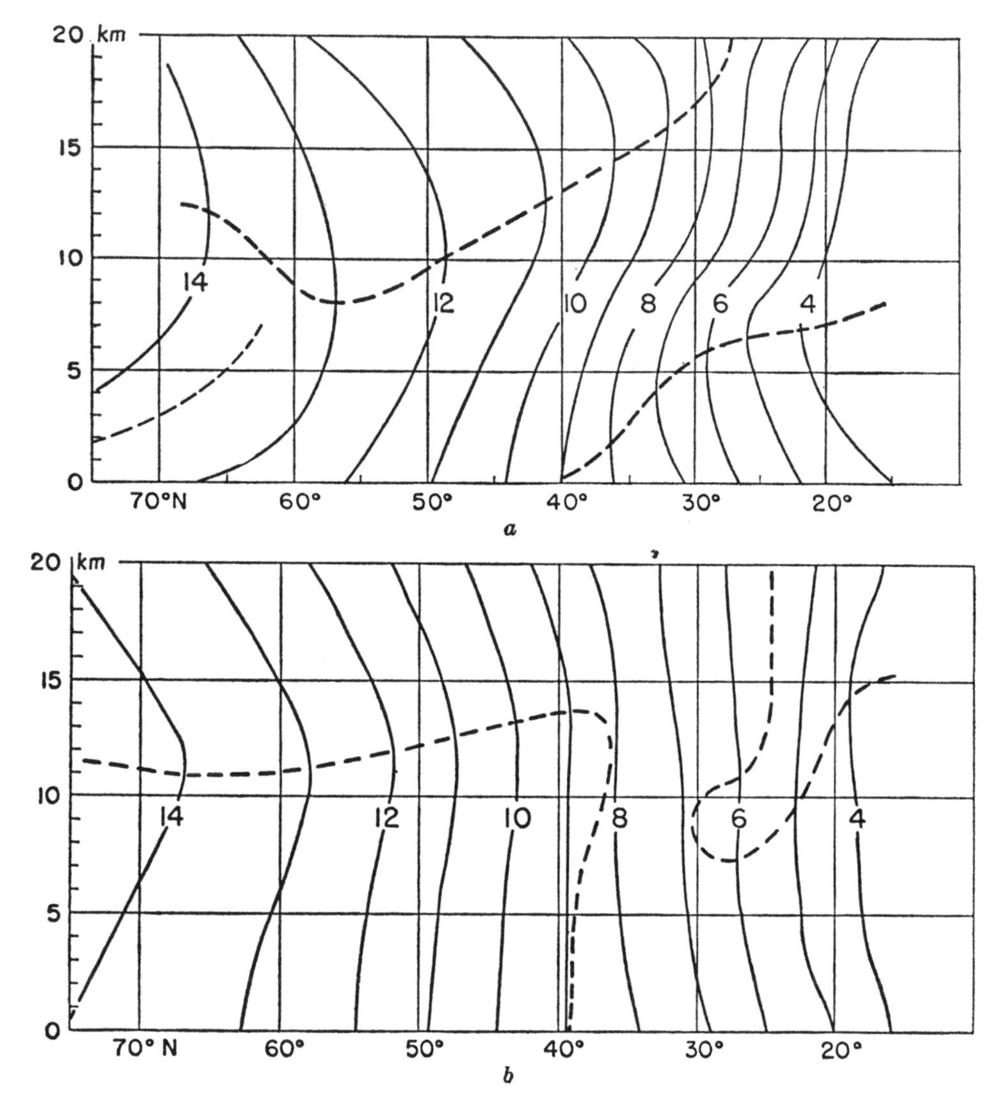

FIG. 4.211.3.—Mean meridional distribution of absolute vorticity (10^{-5} sec^{-1}); (*a*) during winter, (*b*) during summer. (Petterssen, 1950.)

vorticity occur here from the south. Downstream from these confluent areas, blocking anticyclones form frequently (see Chapters 6 and 7). Large-scale changes in the circulation of the hemisphere originate in these areas of preferred vorticity injections into the westerlies.

From Figures 4.211.2 and 4.211.3 we may, therefore, draw the conclusion that the jet streams are mainly fed from two source areas of cyclonic vorticity: one located in polar, the other in subtropical latitudes. Vorticity injections, changing the circulation pattern, may therefore be expected from both high and low latitudes (Defant, 1954; Elliot, 1956).

Studies by Riehl, Yeh, and La Seur (1950) revealed that on the 500-mb surface cyclonic angular momentum is carried in well-established surges from south toward north in two-thirds of the cases investigated, and only in the remaining third of the cases is it carried in the opposite direction. (These surges may be seen from a trend diagram, which, instead of the wind speed, contains anomalies of the mean angular momentum of the respective season.) The largest horizontal transport of momentum is accomplished at jet-stream level (Mintz, 1955). This northward transport carries angular momentum across the mean position of the jet axis (Bolin, 1952). The large-scale "eddies" of the planetary waves maintain this transport in a decisive way, because an inclination of the trough axes from southwest toward northeast, as it is usually observed, helps to carry more cyclonic angular momentum northward on the east side of troughs than is carried southward on the west side of the same troughs. By this asymmetry of the long waves a mean transport of angular momentum toward the north is accomplished, although the mass budget of the hemisphere remains undisturbed.

Since, during a high-index stage, the meridional exchange of heat and momentum is impeded, it may be understood at least qualitatively that during such a circulation stage vorticity as well as positive (negative) heat energy will be stored in subtropical (polar) regions. This leads to an acceleration of zonal circulation until a critical value is reached which brings about a breakdown of the circulation. A low-index stage will then be established, with an increased meridional exchange.

Kuo (1951*a*, *b*, 1953) has considered this in detail. A decrease in the amplitude of wave disturbances may be considered equivalent to a transition of kinetic energy from the disturbance to the basic current. Angular momentum will be concentrated in the jet stream, and vorticity is transported from south toward north, i.e., against the direction of the vorticity gradient. (See Chapter 4.121.) If, however, the amplitude of the wave disturbances increases, apparently the basic current gives off kinetic energy to these disturbances. A large-scale meridional mixing takes place, combined with a vorticity transport from north toward south, as has already been postulated by the "mixing theory" of jet-stream formation (Chapter 4.121). Thereby, an index cycle with an average duration of about four weeks is characterized by impulses from different directions: Vorticity injections from the north increase the amplitudes of the wave disturbances, as may be actually observed during the formation of blocking high-pressure ridges (Elliot, 1955, 1956). Injections from the south, however, contribute to an intensification of the zonal index and to a breakdown of low-index stages (Defant, 1954). As mentioned earlier, such impulses mainly appear on the western edges of the subtropical high-pressure cells. A preferred area of this kind is located in the subtropical West Atlantic. A similar area exists in the Pacific, near the east coast of Asia.

Regional meridional cross sections show some differences from the hemispheric mean values in the cross sections reproduced in Figures 4.211.1 to 4.211.3. The meridional section of the northern hemisphere along 80° W has been subject to study on several occasions (Hess, 1948; Kochanski, 1955; Mintz and Dean, 1952). An extension of this cross section into the southern hemisphere may be expected from the results of the International Geophysical Year (Reiter, 1957*d*). In the northern hemisphere this section is characterized by a quasi-stationary upper-level low with its center of gravity near 70° N.

In Figure 4.211.4*a* and *b* cross sections along the meridian 80° W are shown for the winter and summer months January and July, and for the transition months April and October. The sections constitute an average over the years 1948 through 1951. In January the high tropospheric jet maximum appears at about 40° latitude with 100 knots; a secondary maximum with 60 knots may be found at about 27° of latitude. Thus, there is an indication of the subtropical jet stream. Similar conditions prevail during the months of April and October. This double structure of the tropospheric

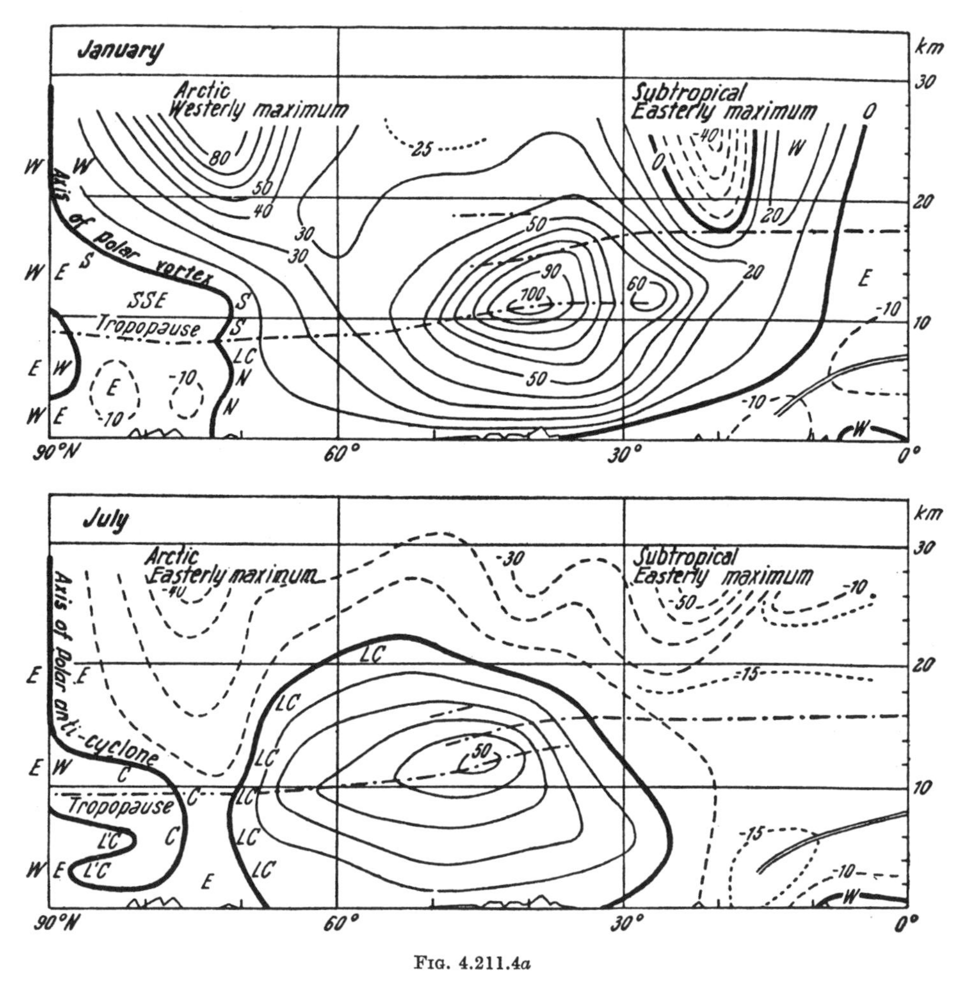

Fig. 4.211.4*a*

Fig. 4.211.4.—Mean geostrophic zonal component (knots) along meridional cross section at 80° W. (*a*) January and July, (*b*) April and October. *LC* = low pressure core, *C* = col, *N* = average northerly current, *S* = average southerly current. East winds, dashed lines; tropopause, dashed-dotted. (Kochanski, 1955.)

jet stream appears in some, but by no means in all, cross sections which have been analyzed for this area (Gilchrist, 1953; Hess, 1948). Thus, it seems it is not equally pronounced in each year. In the July cross section shown here, there is no indication of a double maximum either (Landsberg, 1958). During winter a stratospheric westerly jet stream may be found over the Arctic at levels above 25 km, which is replaced by an easterly jet during summer (Brasefield, 1950). Easterlies are present during summer over the whole North American region already at the 50-mb level (Chiu, 1958; Conover and Wentzien, 1955; Hubert and Dagel, 1955; Kochanski, 1955; Kochanski and Wasko, 1956*b*; Wege, 1957), because the stratosphere undergoes a strong warming trend during the summer months, due to continuous insolation (Ohring, 1958).

An easterly subtropical jet stream appears to be strongest in this cross section during summer; it is best defined, however, during winter. Toward the equator from this subtropical jet, westerly winds appear again in the stratosphere, except in July.

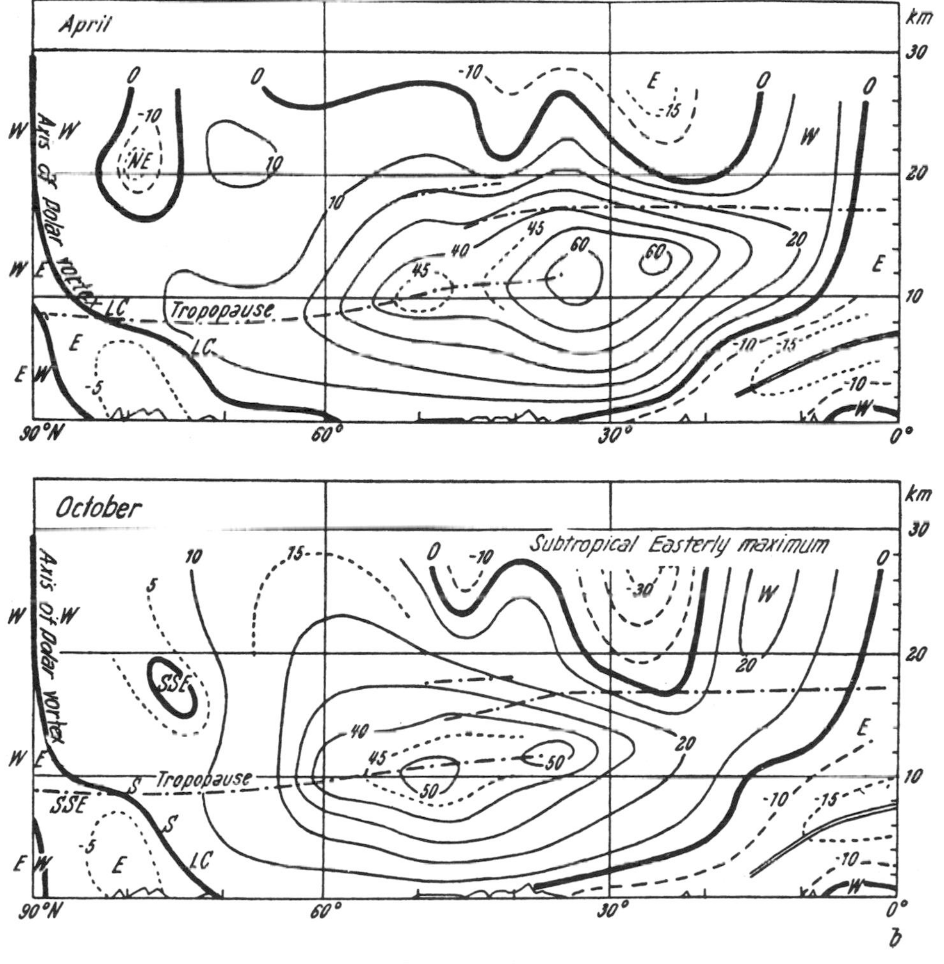

FIG. 4.211.4*b*

During the transition seasons all jet streams are less well defined, more diffuse, with the exception of the upper tropospheric westerlies. The reason for this lies, on the one hand, in the reversal of the radiation budget of the stratosphere during these seasons and, on the other hand, in the strong meandering these jet streams are subject to.

A mean cross section constructed by Palmer and others (1955) (see Lettau, 1956), which extends over the tropical latitudes of both hemispheres, shows the complicated structure of the atmospheric circulation and the presence of a number of jet streams which will be discussed further in Chapter 4.4 (Fig. 4.211.5). Besides the high tropospheric westerly jet streams in both hemispheres (W_J) and the subtropical easterly jet streams (E_J) there appears an easterly trade wind maximum (E_T). Over the equator above the height of 20 km we find a *westerly* jet stream embedded in the easterly flow, which Palmer called "Berson westerlies" (W_B), thus differentiating them from the low-level equatorial westerlies which appear in certain areas (Palmer, 1954). Above these westerlies one again finds the "Krakatoa easterlies" (E_K) at great heights. They became evident when ashes were transported from the Krakatoa explosion. In the oceans one finds a similar sequence of jet streams with different directions on top of each other, as has been discovered during the International Geophysical Year by the Dolphin Expedition in the Pacific Ocean: below the south equatorial current which flows westward, one finds at a depth of 100 to 800 ft (30 to 250 m) the *Cromwell current,* which flows toward the east and which attains a width of about 250 miles and a speed of about 3.5 miles per hour, and thereby is almost 2 mph faster than the south equatorial current. The Cromwell current transports approximately as much water as the Gulf Stream in the Florida straits. Below this, there is again a slow current directed toward the west. Thus, the existence of three streams with opposite directions of flow stacked on top of each other could be verified in the Pacific Ocean (National Academy of Sciences, 1958*a*), similar to the conditions in the atmosphere as shown in Figure 4.211.5.

A mean meridional cross section by Mohri (1953) along the meridian 140° E (Japanese Islands) for the months of December, 1950, to February, 1951, shows marked deviations from the analyses by Kochanski (1955) and Hess (1948): the latter show a predominance of the polar-front jet stream; in the former the subtropical jet stream, which runs tangential to the southern slopes of the Himalayas, reaches highest velocities near the eastern slopes of the high mountains by confluence of subtropical air masses from the Gulf of Bengal, and of polar air from the Chinese–Siberian region (Yeh, 1950). The *mean* wind speeds of 70 m/sec (*ca.* 135 knots) measured here surpasses the value given by Kochanski for the North American area (100 knots) by far. This has its reason in the greater stability of this jet stream in space and time. The channeling influence of the mountain ranges of the Himalayas is felt even at jet-stream level and causes a very regular seasonal weather sequence in this area. This will be discussed further in Chapter 7.

4.212. Hemispheric Differences

In the southern hemisphere the conditions are somewhat different, as the study of cross sections by Loewe and Radok (1950) and Hutchings (1950, 1952) shows (see also Hofmeyr, 1957; Lamb, 1952, 1958; Taylor, 1960). The west wind maximum with its seasonal changes of intensity is clearly established (Gabites, 1952, 1953). Schwerdtfeger (1960*a*, *b*) points out a semiannual periodicity in the zonal index of the 300-mb surface (maxima in March and September) which he thinks is caused by the radiation budget and which is more pronounced in the southern hemisphere than in the northern hemisphere, due to the more homogeneous surface of the former. In the summer cross sections for the southern hemisphere there is no indication of easterlies in the

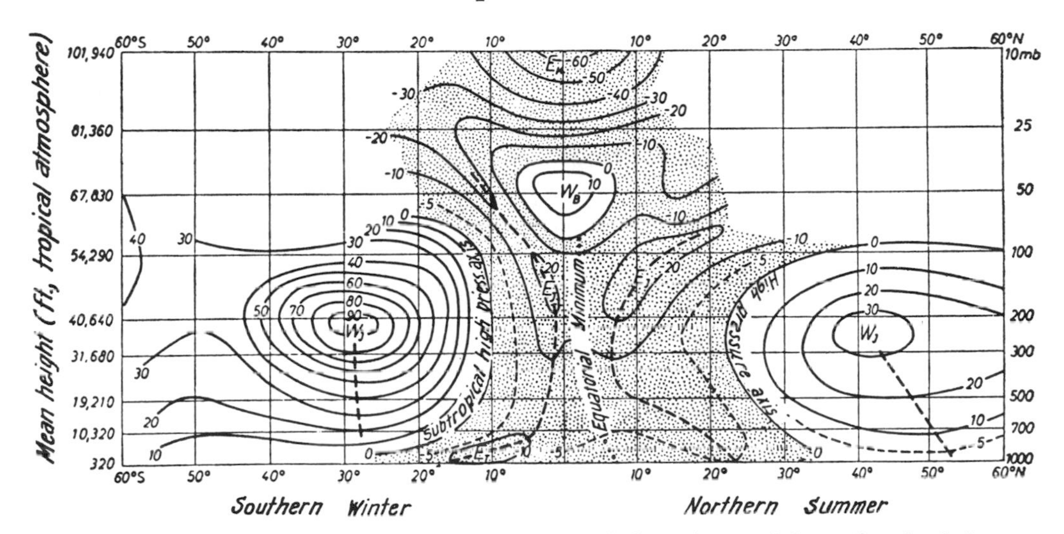

FIG. 4.211.5.—The zonal circulation during the southern hemisphere winter and the northern hemisphere summer. W_J = westerly jet stream, E_J = easterly jet stream, E_T = trade wind maximum, W_B = "Berson" westerlies, E_K = Krakatoa easterlies. (Palmer *et al.*, 1955; from Lettau, 1956.)

lower stratosphere of the polar region (Gibbs, 1953) (Fig. 4.212.1*a*, *b*). In summer a splitting of polar and subtropical jet stream may be recognized. The cross sections presented here have been made approximately along 170° E (New Zealand). Sections along the 150th easterly meridian (Australia) (Gibbs, 1952) show a double structure of the jet stream also during winter, while cross section along 130° E (Central Australia) as well as the ones constructed over the Indian Ocean (Van Loon, 1955), show only a single maximum of wind speed in winter and in summer. Therefore, on the average, there seems to be a confluent region over Western Australia (Fig. 4.212.2; see Phillpot, 1959).

Downstream from this confluence region we would have to expect an area of relatively frequent blocking anticyclones. This is actually the case according to investigations made by Lamb (1959).

The seasonal migration of jet-stream maxima also is dependent on geographic location. While Loewe and Radok (1950) find a displacement of the wind maximum from 26° S in winter to 40° S in summer for 150° E longitude, over the Indian Ocean, a displacement is observed of the order of magnitude of only about three degrees latitude (Van Loon, 1955).

The most pronounced differences in the upper-flow patterns of the southern hemisphere as compared with those of the northern hemisphere are these:

1. The southern summer on the average shows a stronger zonal wind component than the northern summer, while the winter conditions are about the same in both hemispheres. It may be assumed that the strong zonal component over the southern

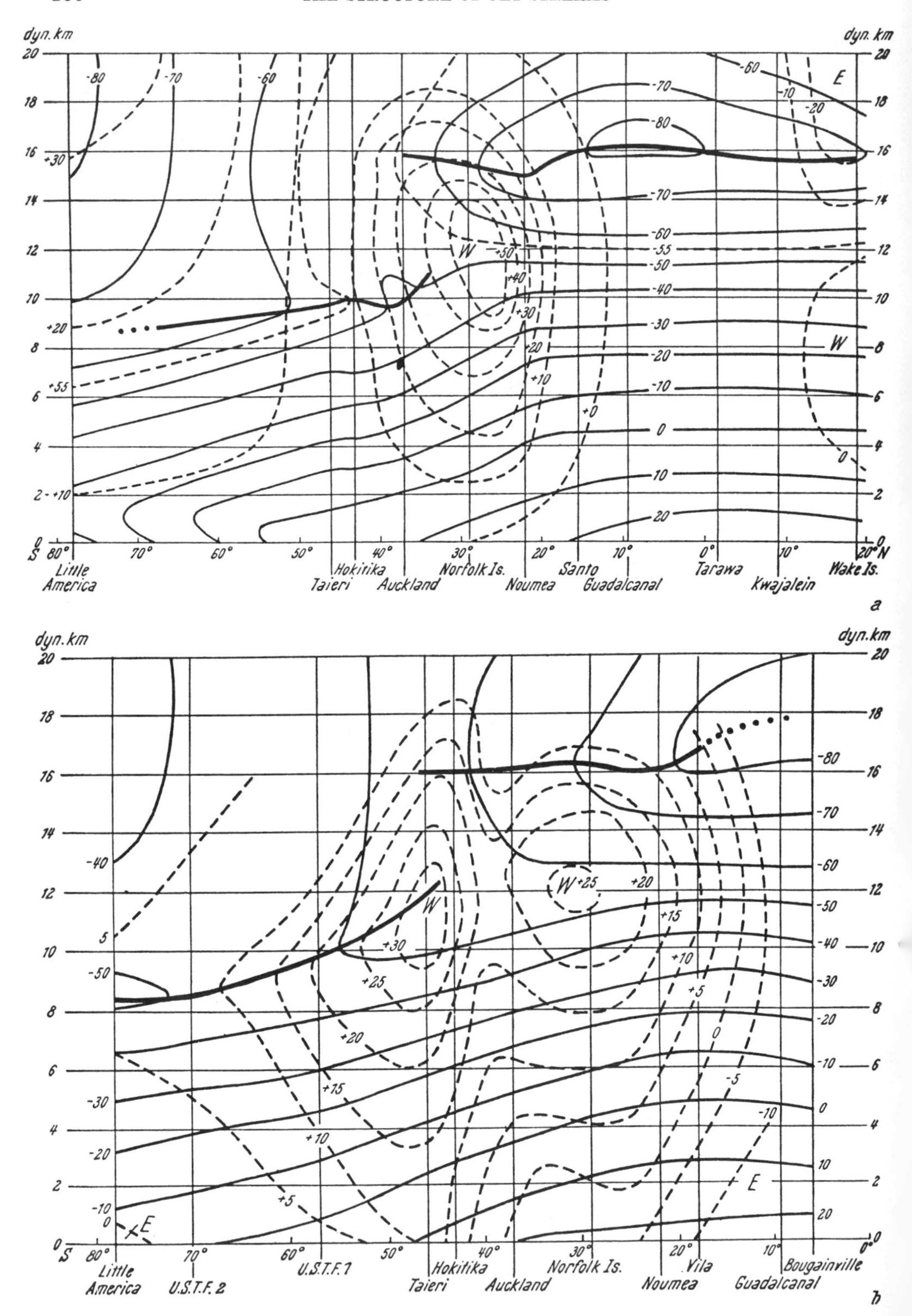
dyn. km
Little America
Hokitika
Taieri
Auckland
Norfolk Is.
Noumea
Santo
Guadalcanal
Tarawa
Kwajalein
Wake Is.
a
U.S.T.F. 2
U.S.T.F. 1
Vila
Bougainville
b

hemisphere is caused by a stronger thermal contrast between pole and equator. A certain influence also may be exerted by the smaller frictional forces over the oceanic areas of the southern hemisphere as compared with the continents of the northern hemisphere (Lamb, 1959). These differences in frictional effects should primarily show up in the hemispheric angular momentum budget. Model experiments by Clarke

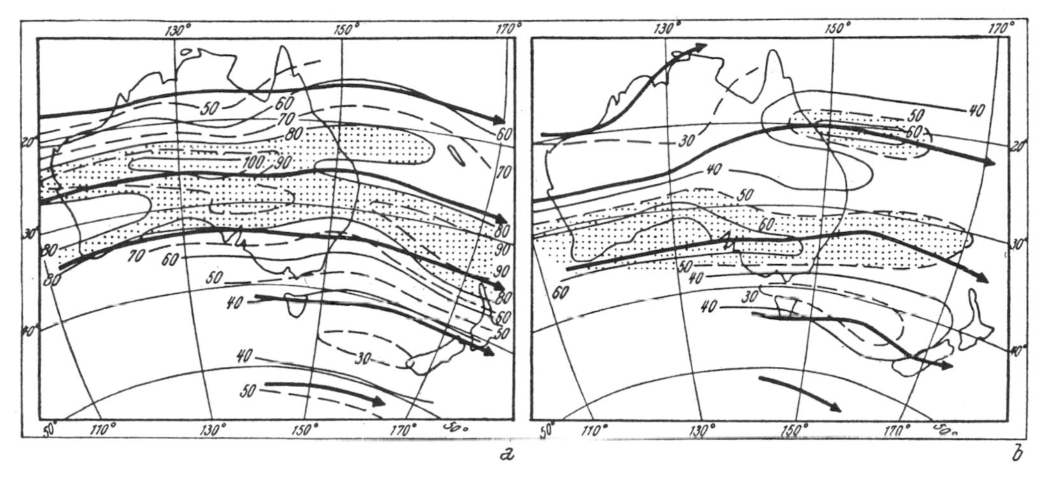

FIG. 4.212.2.—Mean geostrophic wind speeds (knots: $V > 80$ or > 50 knots, respectively, indicated by shading) and wind directions (heavy lines with arrows) during (*a*) July (winter) and (*b*) January (summer). (Gibbs, 1952.)

(1960) seem to point in this direction and also seem to indicate an increase in baroclinicity due to the higher elevation of the cooling surface of the Antarctic continent.

2. The stratospheric easterlies of the summer season are only weakly indicated in some longitudes of the southern hemisphere and do not reach jet-stream intensity. In several locations they are completely absent (Barnett, 1951; De Q. Robin, 1957; Farkas, 1955; Hofmeyr, 1953; Lamb, 1959; Porter, 1952*a*). The Antarctic troposphere of summer is substantially colder than the Arctic troposphere during the same season, so that no reversal of the pressure gradient with height is observed. This difference has been explained by the higher albedo of Antarctica (*ca.* 89 per cent) (Flohn, 1950*a*, *b*; Mintz, 1953, 1954; Mironovitch, 1953*a*, *b*; Schumacher, 1955; Van Rooy, 1957). It may, however, be assumed that the influences of the upper current, especially of the weaker meridional circulation, also play an important role in the establishment of the observed temperature changes. This will be discussed further in Chapter 4.414.

4.22. The Structure of the Frontal Zone in the Region of the Polar-Front Jet

4.221. Entrance and Delta Regions

In a detailed study Newton (1954) investigated the flow conditions in a well-established frontal zone, making a distinction between entrance and delta regions. In the lee of the Rocky Mountains the first indications of a wave disturbance on a surface

FIG. 4.212.1.—Mean meridional cross sections through the southern hemisphere from Wake Island to Little America. (*a*) southern winter, (*b*) southern summer. Thin solid lines, isotherms (° C); dashed, isotachs (m/sec) of the geostrophic zonal component; heavy solid lines, tropopause. (Hutchings, 1950.)

front extending from California to New England became apparent. A large precipitation area north of the front from Nebraska to Indiana indicated that large-scale ascending motions were taking place. Figure 4.221.1 shows the absolute topography of the 500-mb surface of 3 April, 1950, 1500 GCT (full lines). The heavy lines indicate the position of the frontal zone, the thin lines give the location of the cross sections, of which only *A*, *C*, and *D* are reproduced in Figure 4.221.2. Cross section *A* (Fig. 4.221.2*A*) lies in the entrance region of the frontal zone and shows the following characteristics:

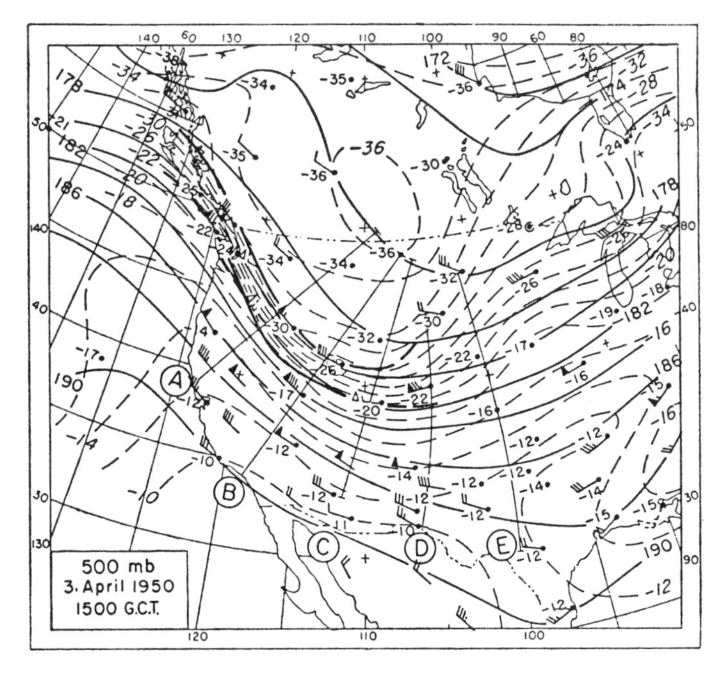

FIG. 4.221.1.—Absolute topography and isotherms of the 500-mb surface, 3 April, 1950, 1500 GCT. Heavy lines mark the boundaries of the frontal zone. Thin lines *A* through *E* indicate the position of cross sections. (Newton, 1954.)

(1) The cold air is flowing out in a shallow layer near the surface.

(2) The baroclinic zone extends with almost constant intensity throughout the whole troposphere. The horizontal temperature gradient has a maximum near the 600-mb level.

(3) This cross section shows the highest wind speeds of all, namely 140 knots in the jet axis; therefore, it lies approximately in the region of the jet maximum while all other sections are located downstream from the maximum.

Cross section *C* (Fig. 4.221.2*C*) is already approaching the delta region of the frontal zone. Although the baroclinic layer remains throughout the troposphere, its greatest intensity is already confined to the region above the 500-mb surface.

In cross section *D* (Fig. 4.221.2*D*), which lies in the frontal zone delta, no well-established frontal zone can be defined any longer. There is only a more or less diffuse baroclinic area, in which the strongest horizontal temperature gradient may be found immediately underneath the jet-stream level (McIntyre, 1955). The surface front is present only in the lowest layers (see Nyberg, 1945).

The frontal zone is moving downstream at a rate of 30 knots, i.e., somewhat slower than the air on the cold side of the frontal surface. At the point indicated by A in Figures 4.221.2C and D the velocity of the air *relative* to the motion of the frontal

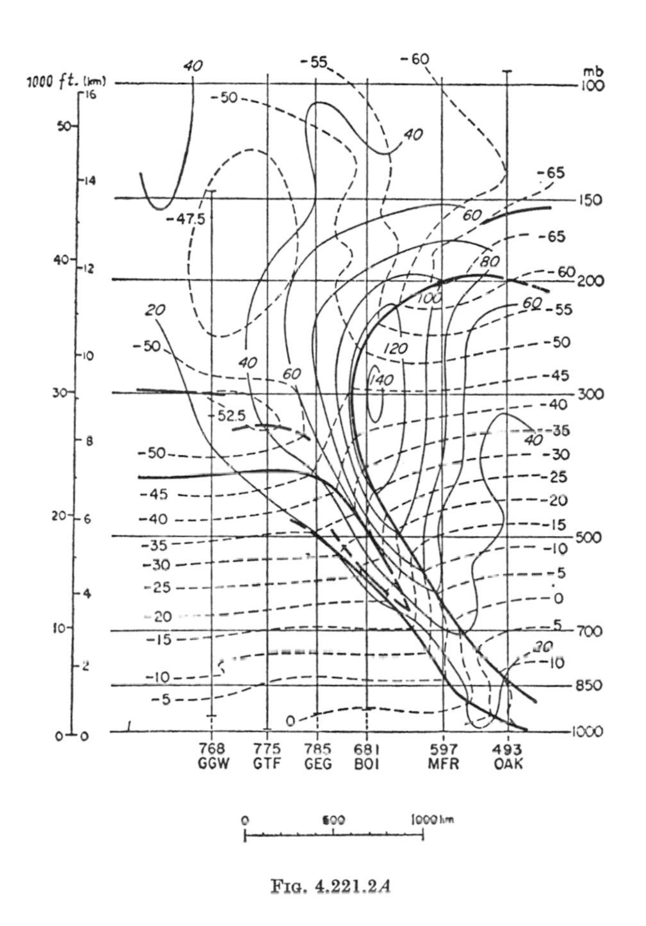

FIG. 4.221.2A

FIG. 4.221.2.—Cross sections through the atmosphere along the lines indicated in Figure 4.221.1. The notation used for these lines corresponds to the letters of this figure. Full lines, isotachs (knots); dashed, isotherms (° C); heavy lines indicate frontal zone and tropopause (Newton, 1954.)

zone amounted to about 30 knots. Therefore, the air masses, while flowing through the frontal zone, are undergoing *frontogenetic* effects in the entrance region and *frontolytic* influences in the delta region.

Frontogenesis and frontolysis may be expressed by the variation of the gradient of a quantity in time, e.g., of potential temperature (Miller, 1948a). We shall assume in the following that the x-axis is oriented parallel to the streamlines at the level under consideration. d/dt gives the individual changes of the quantity under consideration, measured on a particle which flows through the frontal zone.

We, then, obtain

$$(d/dt)(\partial\Theta/\partial y) = (\partial/\partial t + u\cdot\partial/\partial x + v\cdot\partial/\partial y + w\cdot\partial/\partial z)(\partial\Theta/\partial y)$$
$$+1.39$$
$$= -(\partial u/\partial y)(\partial\Theta/\partial x) - (\partial v/\partial y)(\partial\Theta/\partial y) \qquad 4.221\ (1)$$
$$+0.41 \qquad\qquad +0.60$$
$$-(\partial w/\partial y)(\partial\Theta/\partial z)$$
$$+0.54\ (10^{-9}\ {}^{\circ}\mathrm{K\ m^{-1}\ sec^{-1}}).$$

$$(d/dt)(\partial\Theta/\partial z) = -(\partial u/\partial z)(\partial\Theta/\partial x) - (\partial v/\partial z)(\partial\Theta/\partial y) - (\partial w/\partial z)(\partial\Theta/\partial z)$$
$$-1.67 \qquad -0.52 \qquad -0.97 \qquad +0.20 \qquad 4.221\ (2)$$
$$(10^{-7}\ {}^{\circ}\mathrm{K\ m^{-1}\ sec^{-1}}).$$

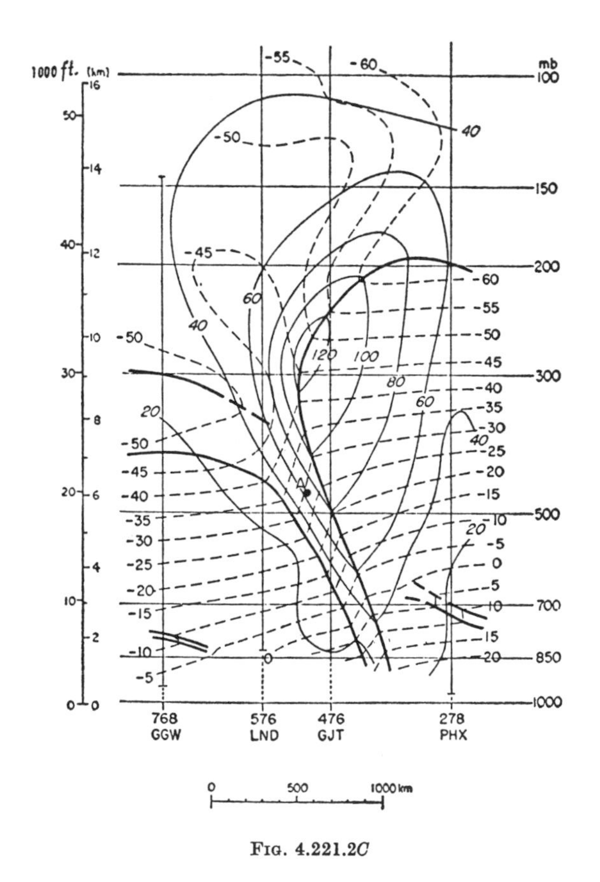

FIG. 4.221.2*C*

(The numbers indicate the values of the different terms computed by Newton at the points *A* in Figures 4.221.2*C* and *D*). The distance between the two cross sections *C* and *D* is 275 miles (440 km). The air requires about 8 hours to travel this distance.

The horizontal gradients of non-adiabatic temperature changes, $(\partial/\partial y)(d\Theta/dt)$, and also $(\partial/\partial z)(d\Theta/dt)$, in general are rather small, as long as condensation processes are of no importance, and therefore have been neglected in the above equations. Reed and Sanders (1953) also neglected terms which contain $\partial\Theta/\partial x$.

From the complete vorticity equation, 1.233 (7) on an isobaric surface (on this surface the solenoidal terms vanish because $dp=0$) we obtain

$$\begin{aligned} dQ_z/dt &= -Q_z D_{xy} + (\partial u/\partial z)(\partial w/\partial y) \\ -1.91 \quad & \quad -0.67 \qquad -1.07 \quad (10^{-9}\ \text{sec}^{-2}) \end{aligned} \qquad 4.221\ (3)$$

if only the most important terms are considered. In this equation $D_{xy}=\partial u/\partial x+\partial v/\partial y$ is the divergence in the x-y-plane. Terms with $\partial w/\partial x$ have been neglected, as well as frictional forces.

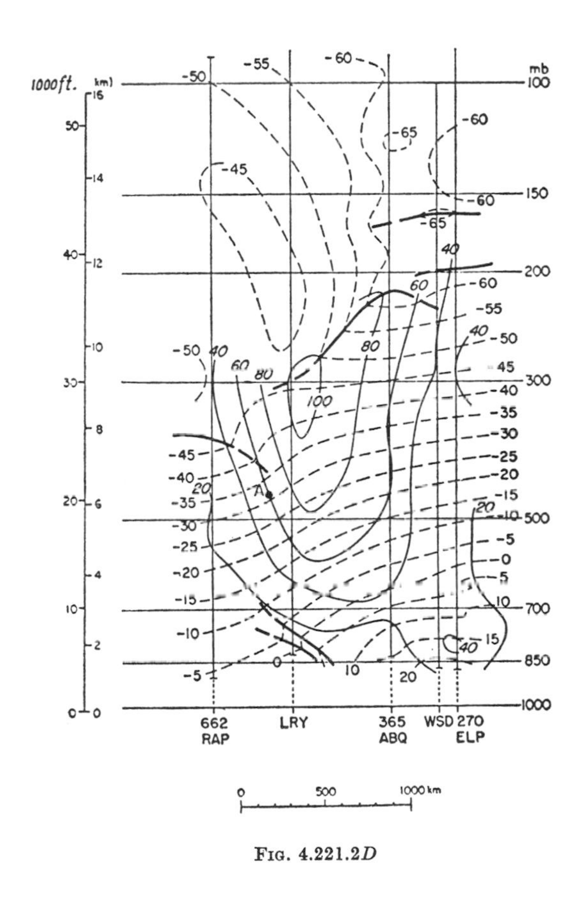

FIG. 4.221.2D

For the vorticity component in the y-direction we obtain an equation analogous to 1.233 (7), also neglecting frictional forces,

$$\begin{aligned} (d/dt)(q_y - e\cdot\cos\psi) = &-(q_y - e\cdot\cos\psi)\cdot D_{xz} \\ &+(\partial v/\partial z)(f-\partial u/\partial y)+(\partial v/\partial x)(\partial w/\partial y) \\ &+(\partial/\partial x)(\alpha\cdot\partial p/\partial z)-(\partial/\partial z)(\alpha\cdot\partial p/\partial x). \end{aligned} \qquad 4.221\ (4)$$

In this equation $q_y=\partial u/\partial z-\partial w/\partial x$, $e=2\Omega\cos\varphi$ is the horizontal component of the Coriolis parameter and $D_{xz}=\partial u/\partial x+\partial w/\partial z$ is the divergence in the x-z-plane; ψ is the angle between x-axis and the direction east.

The third term on the left-hand side of this equation gives no significant contribution; the fourth term becomes zero when considering the hydrostatic equation 1.222 (3). The geostrophic wind component may be substituted into the fifth term. If only considering the most important terms of 4.221 (4), i.e., neglecting $\partial w/\partial x$ and e, one obtains

$$(d/dt)(\partial u/\partial z) = -(\partial u/\partial z)D_{xz} + f(\partial/\partial z)(v - v_g) - (\partial v/\partial z)(\partial u/\partial y). \quad 4.221\ (5)$$

$$-3.19 \qquad +1.55 \qquad -1.89 \quad -1.35 \qquad -1.97$$

$$(10^{-7}\ \text{sec}^{-2}).$$

That the numerical values of the left-hand side do not agree exactly with the one on the right-hand side of this equation is due to inaccuracies in the analyses. Nevertheless, these estimates render usable results as far as the order of magnitude is concerned.

Let us first consider 4.221 (1): $-(\partial u/\partial y)(\partial \Theta/\partial x)$ indicates that the cold air advection is larger on the warm side of the frontal zone, because of the higher wind speeds there, than on the cold side. The term $-(\partial v/\partial y)(\partial \Theta/\partial y)$ indicates a lateral diffluence. $-(\partial w/\partial y)(\partial \Theta/\partial z)$ stands for the frontolytic effect of ascending motions and of adiabatic cooling in the warm air relative to the cold air. In Newton's investigations all three terms have been of the same order of magnitude, while Reed and Sanders (1953) found that the last term, i.e., the influence of the horizontal gradient of the vertical velocity normal to the direction of flow (strongest sinking motion on the warm side of the frontal zone), is almost exclusively responsible for frontogenesis in the horizontal temperature field. Reed's results have also been corroborated by the application of Ertel's equation 1.235 (3). It turned out that the upper part of the air masses inside the frontal zone came from the stratosphere (see Chapter 6.2).

The thermal stability [4.221 (2)] changes because of differential advection at different heights; because wind speed increases with height $-(\partial u/\partial z)(\partial \Theta/\partial x)$, and mainly because advection normal to the direction of flow differs at different levels $-(\partial v/\partial z)(\partial \Theta/\partial y)$. Vertical shrinking $(\partial w/\partial z)(\partial \Theta/\partial z)$ contributes only by a small amount of opposite sign.

The decrease of the vertical component of vorticity [4.221 (3)] mainly (according to Reed and Sanders exclusively) is due to vertical shearing and vertical motion $(\partial u/\partial z) \cdot (\partial w/\partial y)$ and only about one-third to divergence.

All terms contribute by the same order of magnitude toward the change of vertical shear [4.221 (5)]. This indicates that flow patterns which are frontogenetically or frontolytically active in essence have to be *ageostrophic*, because with geostrophic flow the second and third term on the right-hand side of 4.221 (5) would cancel each other, and the last term would be positive in the delta area by virtue of the observed diffluence and temperature distribution. Equation 4.221 (5), therefore, would not be fulfilled, not even in order of magnitude. The actually observed decrease of vertical shear (see Figs. 4.221.2 *A*, *C*, and *D*), therefore, is mainly an effect of ageostrophic components of flow. Studies of Hovmöller (1948) showed that the ageostrophic components may attain large values especially on the anticyclonic side of the frontal zone (see Endlich, Solot, and Thur, 1955). There the actually observed wind speeds in general are higher than the computed ones, even though the *configuration* of the isotachs may be reproduced well by using the geostrophic or thermal wind equations (Boville, Creswick, and Gillis, 1955).

For frontogenesis near the ground the terms $(\partial w/\partial y)$ in 4.221 (1 and 3) are of no significance. The vorticity changes, therefore, are caused in the lower layers by divergence, and the changes in horizontal temperature gradient by horizontal advection.

To these considerations of Newton's one might remark that vorticity and stability have been treated separately. Since, however, during adiabatic conditions of flow, the potential vorticity equation, 1.235 (4) has to be satisfied, 4.221 (2 and 3) are interrelated, so that under these circumstances a regrouping of terms might be indicated. This may explain the different results which Reed and Sanders obtained in some places.

Figure 4.221.3 shows the horizontal and vertical motions which correspond to cross section D (Fig. 4.221.2D). With the exception of the layers near the surface of the earth, frontolytic processes are predominant. In the frontogenetically active rear sector of the frontal zone the direction of the arrows would have to be reversed by 180°. From this diagram one may see that the frontogenetic processes near the

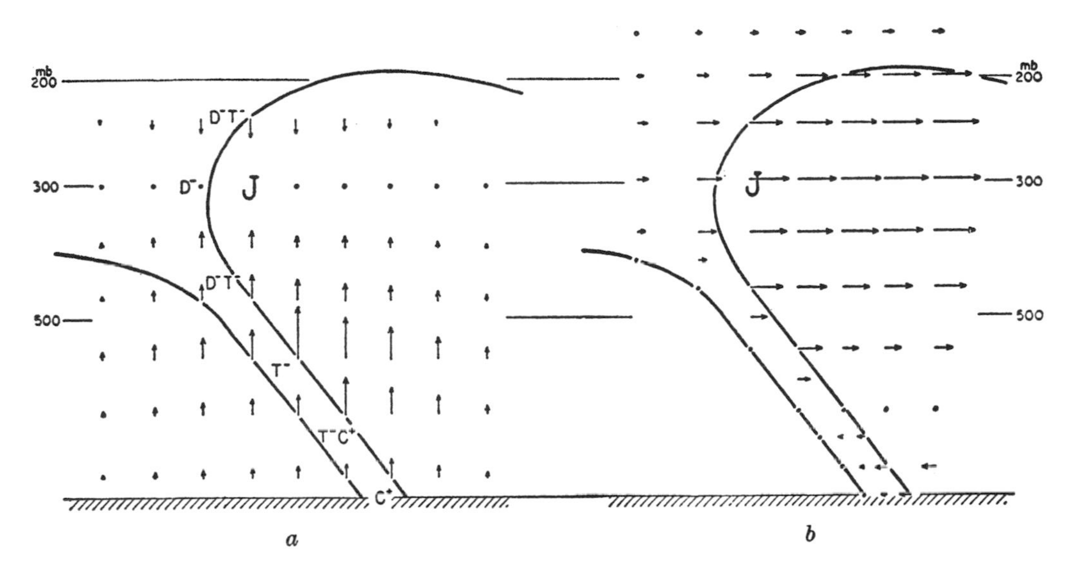

FIG. 4.221.3.—Schematic representation of the vertical motions (a) and of the "cross-stream circulation" (b) in the frontolytically active delta region of a frontal zone. (In the frontogenetically active entrance region the orientation of the arrows will have to be reversed.) J = position of the jet stream. The other capital letters indicate the effect of various terms upon the vorticity changes of the current (the sign of the terms has been entered as exponent): C = convergence, D = divergence, T = tilting of horizontal vortex tubes. (Newton, 1954.)

ground become active before the arrival of the main frontal zone and of the jet maximum, i.e., already in the delta area. When the upper front then moves eastward, it will be superimposed upon the front near the surface of the earth, and the two baroclinic zones will merge into a single one, which now reaches from the ground to the tropopause. According to the surface weather map ascending motions are active only in the frontolytic forward quadrant of the jet maximum.

It follows from Newton's analyses that the air masses which travel through the jet maximum that is connected with the frontal zone are subject to frontogenetic and frontolytic processes. The *frontolytic* leading edge of a jet maximum, where positive vorticity is advected (and where, according to the vorticity equation 1.233 (6), upper divergence has to be expected), lies over the area with largest surface pressure falls, i.e., with largest *cyclogenetic* activity.

This apparent paradox is explained in the following way: The air masses move faster than the frontal zone itself, and thereby they undergo strong frontolysis in the delta region. Since, however, the frontal zone progresses slowly, over the region which formerly has been occupied by the delta area gradually a pronounced front will be generated. This process manifests itself as frontogenesis over the respective area (see Kaznacheeva, 1958).

The sequence of surface weather in connection with the jet stream will be treated in more detail in Chapter 6. Here, we will only supplement Newton's studies with those of Berggren (1953*a*, *b*), who continued the analysis of the frontal zone into the stratosphere. In Chapter 4.112 it has already been mentioned that one may find a strong horizontal temperature gradient at the 200-mb level, which is of opposite direction to the one at the 500-mb level, which, however, is located in approximately the same position (Murray and Johnson, 1952). Figure 4.112.3 shows the analysis of a cold front over northern Europe of 7 November, 1949, 1500 GCT. The same considerations are valid for air masses which travel through the stratospheric baroclinic zone as have been made by Newton for the tropospheric frontal zone. Therefore, also in the stratosphere the delta region of the frontal zone would act frontolytically upon the transient air masses.

4.222. The Characteristic Field of Flow in a Frontal Zone

Palmén and Newton (1948) have analyzed the mean cross section along the meridian 80° W, averaged over 12 cases of December, 1946, with approximately zonal flow, which has been shown in Figure 3.211. The bulge in the 35 m/sec isotach indicates the presence of a weak subtropical jet stream. Some cross-section analyses, especially those in areas with diffluence between polar and subtropical jet streams, may, at times, show both equally well developed (Defant and Taba, 1958*a*; Hubert, 1953). From Figure 3.211 one may see that the wind maximum in the troposphere lies on the warm side of the frontal zone; in the stratosphere, however, it lies on the cold side of this zone. It appears approximately in the region in which the frontal zone intersects the 500-mb level.

Figure 4.121.7 shows the isotherms of potential temperature and the absolute vorticity in units 10^{-5} sec^{-1} of the frontal zone represented in Figure 3.211. The jet maximum lies near 46° N and 270 mb. A discontinuity in the horizontal wind shear has been assumed at the two boundary surfaces of the frontal zone, while in the jet axis itself only a strong vorticity gradient has been analyzed, and not a real discontinuity. This may be justified for a *mean* cross section. The resolution of >30 miles (45 km) of the measurements made during research flights seems to reveal a discontinuous vorticity distribution (Endlich and McLean, 1957). More recent measurements with a resolution of about 15 miles (23 km) show, however, a rounded horizontal wind profile in a well-established jet stream, with maximum cyclonic shear ($1.17 \cdot 10^{-4}$ sec^{-1}) approximately 180 km away from the jet axis, on its left side. Maximum anticyclonic shears ($0.94 \cdot 10^{-4}$ sec^{-1}) have been measured in about the same distance to the right of the jet axis (Saucier, 1958*a*). The roundness of the wind profiles would have to be considered a part of the meso-structure of the jet stream. For macro-structural analyses this question is of no significance.

It should be pointed out that in Figure 4.121.7 there is an area with $Q=0$, which extends along the anticyclonic side of the jet stream between 230 and 360 mb. One may assume that in some cases this area may be considerably larger. Because of the large horizontal wind shears in the frontal zone itself, one finds positive values of vorticity there. The vertical wind shear, too, has a discontinuity in the frontal zone (Reed, 1957*b*; see Fig. 3.211).

4.23. The Mean Vertical Structure of the Jet Stream

4.231. The "Average" Jet Stream

While in Chapters 4.21 and 4.22 the global structure of jet streams and their relation to the tropospheric and stratospheric frontal zones has been discussed, we shall now attempt to find statistical values of the vertical structure of the field of flow which will be easily applicable to problems of aviation (Endlich, Solot, and Thur, 1955; Reiter, 1957*c*, 1958*c*).

A frequency analysis has been made from 261 wind profiles with peak velocities >80 knots, obtained from rawinsondes over the United States between 1 November, 1952, and 31 March, 1953. Figure 4.231.1 shows the per cent frequencies of the

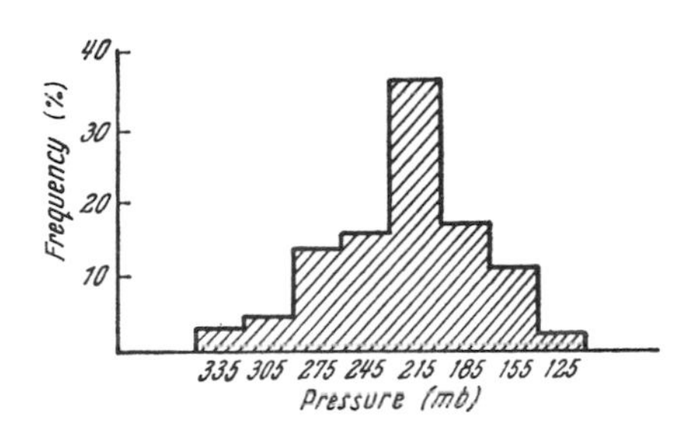

Fig. 4.231.1.—Per cent frequency distribution of pressure at the level of maximum wind. (Endlich, Solot, and Thur, 1955.)

occurrence of jet maxima at certain pressure levels. The jet stream will be found most frequently slightly below the 200-mb level (at about 37,000 ft = 11.3 km). The total variation of this statistical population of jet streams lay between 345 mb and 120 mb (27,000 to 50,000 ft = 8.2 to 15.2 km), which is considered rather large and may be due to the incorporation of polar and subtropical jet streams into this sample, with the latter probably the more frequent ones. No correlation could be found between height and wind speed of the jet maximum.

In the mean vertical wind profiles the vertical wind shear seems to have a maximum in the immediate vicinity of the jet maximum itself; this effect has been blamed on interpolation errors, but it could also reflect an actual situation. Since in the present sample the subtropical jet streams are predominant, and since in their influence region the baroclinic zone is confined to the upper troposphere and the lower stratosphere, one will have to expect the maximum vertical shears to occur in the immediate vicinity of the jet maximum. Endlich, Solot, and Thur (1955) give the following expression as best approximation for the observed wind profiles:

$$V_p = V_0 \cdot e^{-k(p-p^*)/100}. \qquad 4.231\ (1)$$

V_p is the wind speed at the pressure level p, V_0 is the peak velocity, and p^* is the pressure at the level of the wind maximum. Below the jet maximum k has the value $+0.33 \pm 0.15$; this expression is valid within the limits $(p-p^*) \leqq 260$ mb. Above the jet maximum $k = -0.56$ and the expression is valid within $(p^*-p) \leqq 100$ mb.

In this expression the peak velocities appear reduced by about 10 per cent. One, therefore, obtains profiles as may be expected from the analyses of the layer of maximum wind. Average values of LMW analyses over an area of 1000 km length and 250 km width with its center in the jet maximum render a profile indicated by the full curve in Figure 4.231.3. Thus, when averaging vertical wind profiles in the jet-stream region without regard to the absolute wind speed of the jet maximum, one obtains in first approximation nearly constant vertical gradients of wind speed, with a discontinuity at the level of maximum wind. The shear above this level seems to be slightly larger than below, so that the geometric center of the LMW—whose mean thickness is 4.2 km—lies approximately 200 m below the level of maximum wind. For flight planning it will suffice in most cases to assume a constant vertical gradient of wind speed above and below the level of maximum wind as long as one stays in the vicinity of this level and within the LMW.

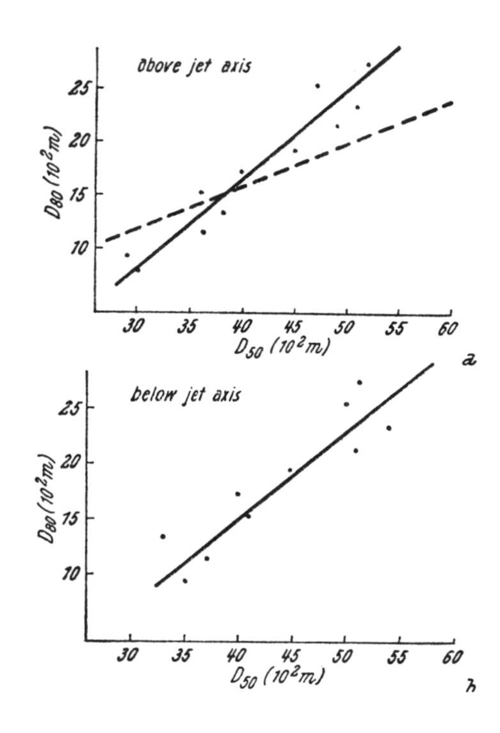

FIG. 4.231.2.—Mean correlation between thicknesses D_{50} and D_{80}, characterizing the layer in which the wind speed decreases to 50 and 80 per cent, respectively, of the peak wind, (*a*) above, (*b*) below the level of maximum wind. The dashed line in (*a*) indicates the correlation, which would have to hold for linear vertical wind profiles.

For extrapolations of the velocity pattern outside the LMW, the quantity $\partial^2 V/\partial z^2 \neq 0$ may already be of a certain significance. Therefore, the thickness of the layer above and below the level of maximum wind has been calculated, within which the speed drops to 80 per cent and 50 per cent, respectively, of the peak value. These thicknesses have been indicated by D_{80} and D_{50}, and they have been correlated with each other in Figure 4.231.2. On the average, there seems to be a linear relationship between these two quantities in the following form

$$D_{50}=19.6+1.36 \cdot D_{80} \quad \text{below} \qquad 4.231\ (2)$$
$$D_{50}=20.7+1.17 \cdot D_{80}. \quad \text{above}$$
the level of maximum wind.

In the wind profiles thus calculated, the value D_{50} will correspond to the actual observations within an error limit of 1 km in 85 per cent of the cases. Since the constants in these two expressions are very similar to each other, one may, in first approximation, assume an average of these two equations for the shears above and below the level of maximum wind. In two-thirds of the cases under investigation the vertical wind shear has been larger above the jet-stream level than below.

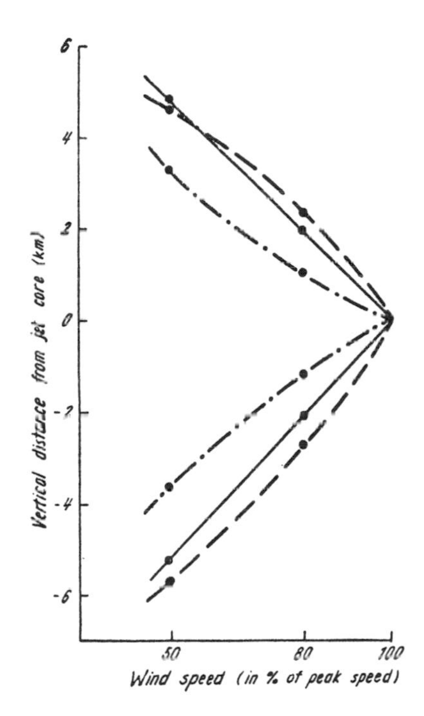

FIG. 4.231.3.—Schematic wind profiles computed from the regression shown in Figure 4.231.2. It has been taken into account that on the average 45 per cent of the thickness of the LMW is found above, 55 per cent below the level of the jet axis. Dashed-dotted: thickness of the LMW = 2200 m; dashed: thickness = 5000 m; the full line corresponds to a linear profile.

The regression for constant shear, assuming $D_{50}=2.5D_{80}$, has been entered as a dashed line in Figure 4.231.2*a*. That this regression line, which has been based upon an average value of the thicknesses, intersects with the actually observed regression indicates that a linear wind profile can only be expected with a thickness of the layer *above* the jet-stream level $D_{80}=1500$ m. With smaller thicknesses D_{80} the profile assumes a concave curvature; with larger thicknesses the profiles become convex. This is shown in Figure 4.231.3 for *total thicknesses* of the LMW of 2200 and 5000 m (dashed-dotted and dashed lines). In this diagram it has already been considered that, on the average, 45 per cent of the thicknesses of the LMW are found above, and 55 per cent below the jet-stream level.

The investigated sample is not large enough to study the distribution of "concave" and "convex" wind profiles with respect to entrance and delta areas of a frontal zone. Some results give the impression that the smaller thicknesses and the "concave" wind profiles were characteristic for the entrance region of a jet maximum, where strong accelerations take place (U.S. Bureau of Aeronautics, 1953*a*, *b*) while the convex, blunt profiles may rather be found in the delta region of a frontal zone. This would be in agreement with the analysis of the thickness of the LMW shown in Figure 3.246.5.

In the immediate vicinity of a frontal zone the thickness of the LMW, i.e., the layer in which the wind speeds are within 80 per cent of the peak velocities, may show the opposite distribution of "concave" and "convex" wind profiles. This has its reason in the fact that in the entrance area the vertical wind shears are larger in the well-developed tropospheric and stratospheric frontal zone. Since, however, in this region the baroclinic zone immediately underneath the jet axis is relatively weakly established, the vertical wind profiles within the LMW are blunt. In the delta area of a jet maximum, however, where only the high tropospheric baroclinic zone is present, the shears are strongest in the immediate vicinity of the jet axis (see Serebreny, Wiegman, and Hadfield, 1960). From a study by Taba (1959) it may be assumed that during winter convex vertical wind profiles may on the average be found on the anticyclonic side of the subtropical jet stream at a distance >200 km from the jet axis. On the cyclonic side, however, the average minimum distance of convex profiles is about 600 km. In the PFJ concave wind profiles appear at an even greater average distance from the jet axis.

4.232. The Structure of the Jet-Stream Core

During the winter months of 1953–54 and 1954–55 reconnaissance flights through jet maxima were conducted from Florida, with aircraft of the type B-29 and B-47, mainly exploring the STJ. From 1956 to 1958, during a second phase of the project, flights were carried out with an aircraft of the improved type B-47E from Wright-Patterson Air Force Base near Dayton, Ohio, mainly penetrating the PFJ (Saucier, 1958*c*; Endlich and Rados, 1959). The results of these flights constitute the most detailed measurements which so far could be obtained near the jet stream core, i.e., the area in the immediate vicinity of the jet axis.

In Figure 4.232.1 a cross section through the atmosphere of 4 April, 1957, to the rear of an upper trough is reproduced. The upper flow pattern and the position of the cross section as well as the track of Flight No. 29 are given in Figure 4.232.2. The shaded areas in Figure 4.232.1 indicate stable layers. In the present case a jet stream located above a stable baroclinic zone that reached throughout the whole troposphere was investigated. The isentropes (thin lines) clearly indicate that this stable layer has the character of a frontal zone. The dashed rectangle shows the position of the detailed analyses given in the following chapters, which have been made with the aid of measurements of Project Jet Stream Flight No. 29. Wind and temperature measure-

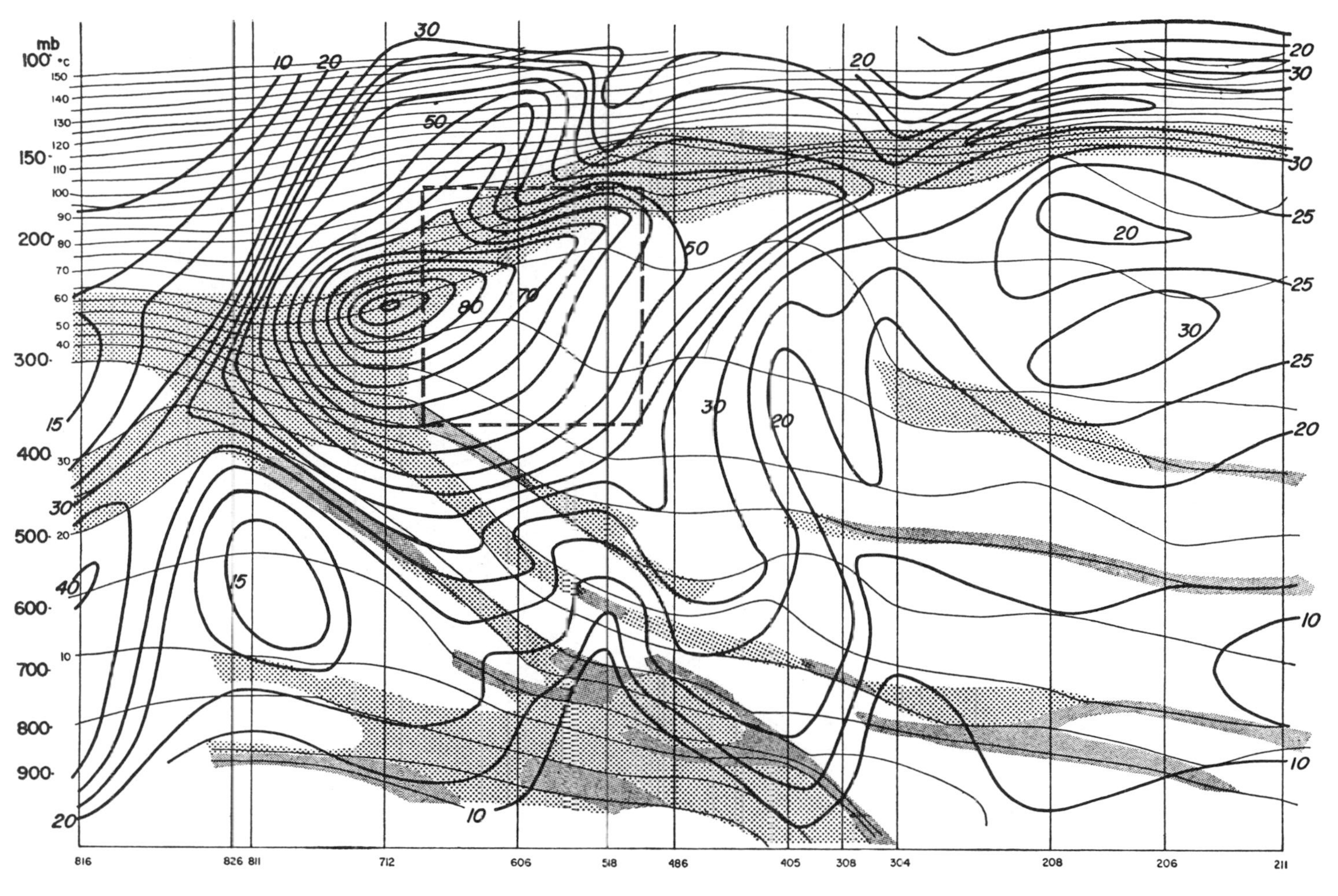

FIG. 4.232.1.—Cross section through the atmosphere, 4 April, 1957, 1500 GCT, from Goose Bay (816) to Tampa, Florida (211). Stable zones and stratosphere are indicated by coarse shading, inversions by fine shading. Wind speeds: heavy lines (m/sec), potential temperatures: thin lines (°C).

ments were made every 30 sec; with a true air speed of about 830 km/h this corresponds to a distance between the points of measurements of about 7.6 km (Brundidge and Goldman, 1958). Since, on the average, three consecutive points of measurement are necessary in order to distinguish a trend in the wind and temperature measurements from irregular fluctuations, the resolution of the present measurements is about 23 km in the horizontal. Thus, according to the definitions of structure at the beginning of

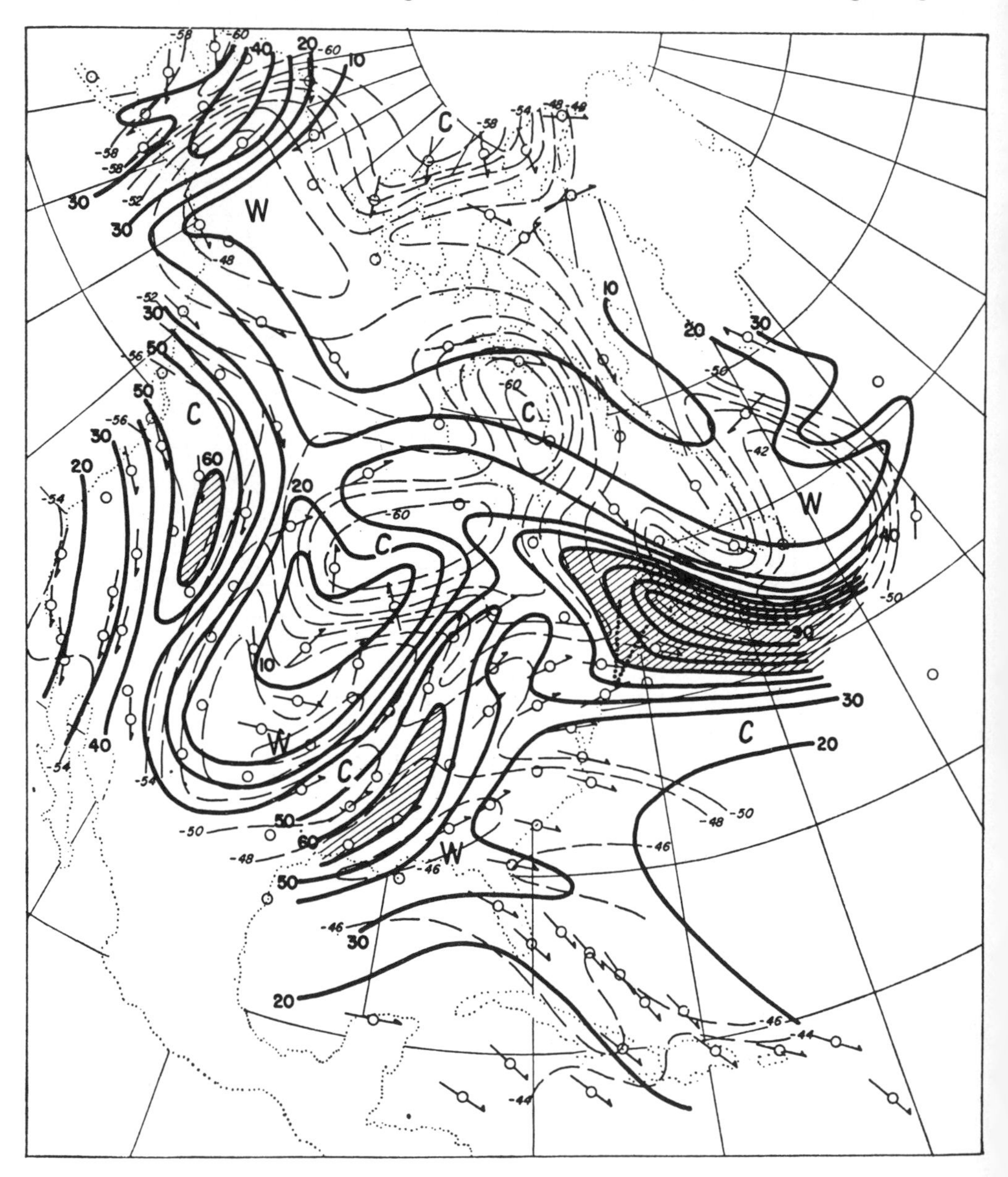

FIG. 4.232.2.—250-mb chart, 4 April, 1957, 1500 GCT. Heavy solid lines, isotachs (m/sec); thin dashed lines: isotherms (° C). Wind directions are given by arrows. The route of Flight No. 29 has been entered as a dotted line. C = cold, W = warm.

Chapter 4, this resolution still lies in the meso-scale range. This, however, will be discussed in more detail in the following chapter. Here it will suffice to point out several characteristics of the jet-stream core.

From a comparison of the isotherm pattern of potential temperatures (Fig. 4.232.3) with the isotachs of actual wind speed (Fig. 4.232.4, heavy lines) the validity of the

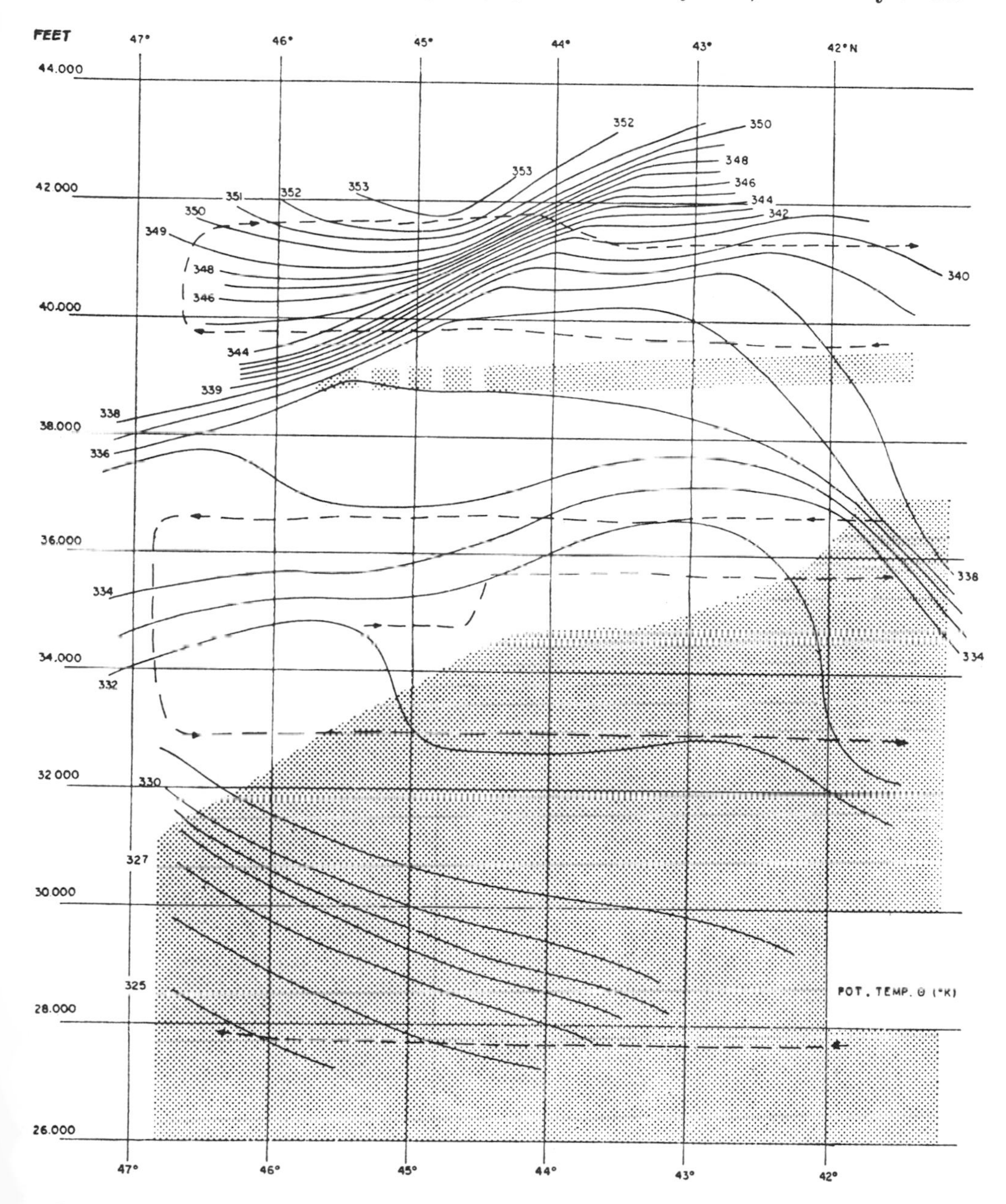

FIG. 4.232.3.—Cross section through the jet-stream core, as in Figure 4.232.4; however, isotherms of potential temperature (° K). The shaded areas indicate cloudiness.

thermal wind equation may easily be checked. It has already been established from the measurements by Endlich and McLean (1957) that the actually observed wind shears do not agree with the ones calculated by means of the thermal wind equation. While, for instance in one of the cross sections analyzed by them, at a certain location a mean vertical wind shear of 6 knots per 1000 ft of height difference has been measured, the horizontal temperature gradient of 1.0° C per degree of latitude observed at the same time and location would indicate a shear of 2.4 knots per 1000 ft. The actually present shears were *more than twice as large* on the anticyclonic side of the jet stream than the shears determined theoretically. On the cyclonic side of the same jet stream in certain places, the shear of −1.5 knots/1000 ft has been observed, and +4.8 knots/1000 ft has been calculated. Here not even the signs are in agreement between theory and observations. Similar discrepancies have been found by Cunningham (1956*a*) and by Brundidge and Goldman (1958) and may also be recognized from a comparison of Figure 4.232.3 with Figure 4.232.4. In spite of the double smoothing process to which the measurements of wind speed and temperature have been subjected in these two analyses, and by which micro-structure as well as meso-structure have been eliminated, the velocity *decrease* with height which would be indicated by the slopes of the isentropes near 36,000 ft in Figure 4.232.3 is not at all present in Figure 4.232.4. Therefore, strong ageostrophic components of flow have to be active in this region, which are not expressed in the (geostrophic) thermal wind equation 3.212 (2).

In the upper left portions of Figures 4.232.3 and .4 a strong baroclinic zone appears, with marked decrease of wind speeds with height; this is the stratospheric "jet-stream front" with negative baroclinicity. In the lower parts of these diagrams is another baroclinic zone, which extends underneath the wind speed maximum and apparently corresponds to the "jet-stream front" after terminology introduced by Endlich and McLean (1957) (see Reiter, 1960*d*, *e*; 1961*a*; U.S. Air Force, 1960). This front runs approximately along isentropic surfaces as may be seen from Figure 4.232.1. According to Figure 4.232.5, which contains the absolute vorticity pattern corresponding to the cross sections shown in Figures 4.232.3 and .4, rather high values of positive vorticity are measured on the cyclonic side of the jet stream. (Analyses by Brundidge [1958] show values as high as $2.8 \cdot 10^{-4}$ sec^{-1} on the cyclonic side of the jet-stream front). On the anticyclonic side of the jet stream dynamic instability $((\partial u/\partial y)_{\theta} > f)$ is indicated in this example and also during other flights. This, however, is characteristic of extreme situations rather than average conditions (Saucier, 1958*b*). Investigations by Reed and Danielsen (1959) revealed that on the cyclonic side of this jet-stream front sinking motions from the stratosphere predominate. Correspondingly, we may expect relatively dry air and cloudless conditions in this area (McLean, 1957). The formation of condensation trails will also be suppressed here (Endlich and McLean, 1957). During several Project Jet Stream flights the sinking motion in the jet maximum could also be determined directly from the attitude of the airplane (Endlich and Rados, 1959; Kuettner and McLean, 1958; Reiter, 1961*e*).

The order of magnitude of the effect of vertical velocities may be seen directly from registrations of true air speed and pitch angle of the aircraft. In an effort to maintain altitude the aircraft will assume a nose-down attitude (negative "pitch") when ascending

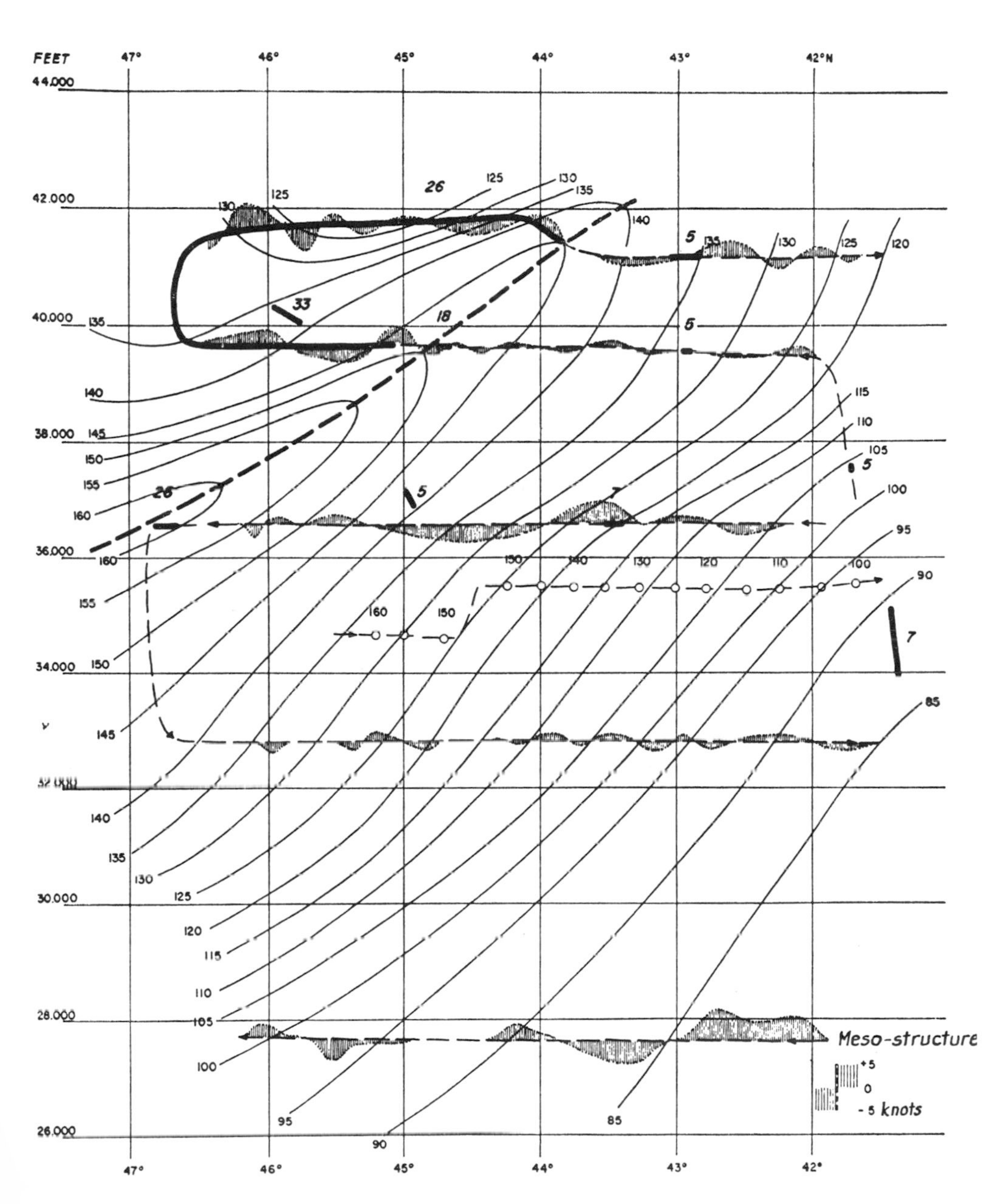

FIG. 4.232.4.—Cross section showing wind speeds (knots), 4 April, 1957, 1537 GCT to 2211 GCT. The heavy lines are isotachs of the wind field which has been subjected to a double smoothing process. The heavy dashed line indicates the position of the vertical jet core. The meso-structure of the wind field is given by the hatched areas (the amplitudes of which may be read in knots, with respect to the flight route as base line). The dashed lines mark the route of Flight No. 29, heavy lines along this route indicate turbulence zones which have been measured with a VGH(=velocity, acceleration in g-units, height recording) instrument. Numerical values give maximum gust velocities (ft/sec) measured within the respective turbulence zone. The flight leg near 35,000 ft (dashed line with circles) was flown farther to the east and therefore was not included in the analysis.

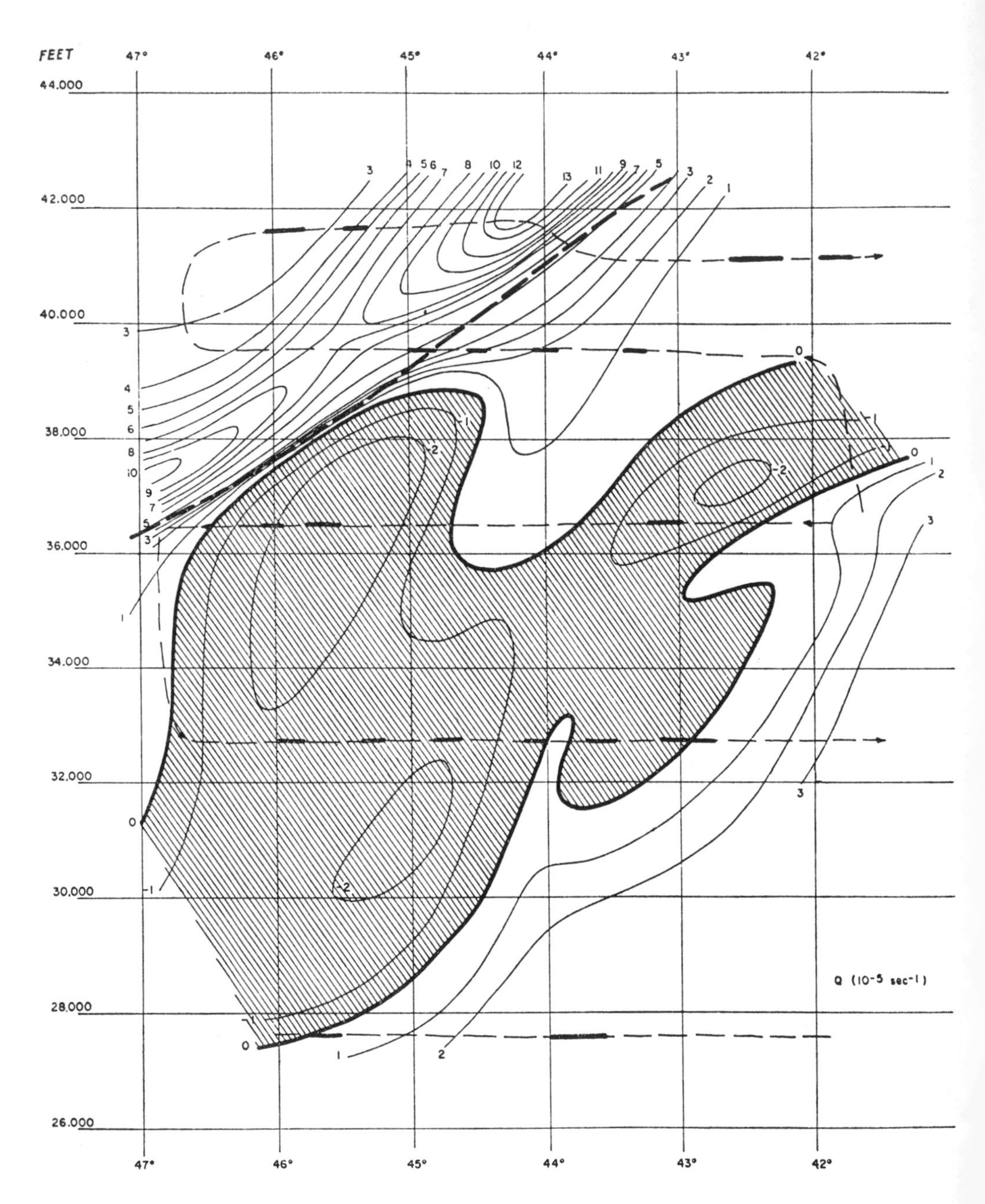

FIG. 4.232.5—Absolute vorticity Q (in units 10^{-5} sec^{-1}), computed under the assumption that the values of V/r, which are obtained from the 250-mb map of Figure 4.232.2, are valid throughout the vertical extent of this cross section. Shaded area, negative absolute vorticity; heavy lines along the flight route, zones in which the meso-structure of the wind field causes the absolute vorticity to be of the opposite sign from what is shown by the analysis of the smoothed field. The position of the jet axis has been taken from Figure 4.232.4.

air motions are encountered. At the same time the true air speed will increase. In sinking air motions the opposite applies. According to Kuettner and McLean (1958) a vertical motion of about 0.1 to 0.2 m/sec produces a corresponding change in true air speed of about 1 knot with an aircraft of the type B-47E.

According to recent studies one may expect small-scale vertical motions of both signs of a magnitude up to 2.5 m/sec in the jet-stream region near the level of maximum wind. This figure should be taken only as a crude order-of-magnitude estimate, however. Sinking motions are predominant in the region of the isentrope trough (warm tongue to the north of the jet axis at the 250-mb level), while the anticyclonic side of the isentrope hump (cold area south of the jet axis at the 250-mb level) is characterized by ascending air motions (Reiter, 1961*e*).

The air masses on the anticyclonic side of the jet-stream front are of a different origin from the ones in the frontal zone, as may be seen from a distribution of the potential vorticity, which according to 1.235 (4) has to be considered a conservative quantity. While on the low-pressure side of the baroclinic zone in the upper left portion of the cross sections presented here the potential vorticity assumes values larger than $90 \cdot 10^{-9}\, g^{-1}\, cm \cdot sec \cdot degree$, on the anticyclonic side values of the order of magnitude of $1 \cdot 10^{-9}$—in places even with negative sign—are prevailing. This is an area with preferred ascending motion, as may be seen from the cloud distribution in Figure 4.232.3. It also indicates that in the region of the jet-stream core areas with vertical motions with different sign are in close proximity to each other. *The idea of a large-scale vertical circulation wheel has to be corrected insofar as the vertical motions in the vicinity of a jet stream occur as sliding processes within relatively thin layers.* In the region of a frontal zone the potential vorticity of individual air particles, in general, is not conserved (Staley, 1960) because of the presence of a gradient of non-adiabatic temperature changes and because of a component of $\nabla \times \mathbf{F}$ normal to the isentropic surfaces. Probably these two factors are also responsible for the establishment of areas with negative absolute and potential vorticities.

During several research flights wind maxima lying closely *side by side* or on *top of each other* have been observed. This multiple structure of the jet stream may be observed frequently during winter over the southern United States, especially after the passage of a cold front (Brundidge, 1956; Endlich *et al.*, 1954; Reiter, 1959*b*; 1960*d*, *e*; 1961*a*, *e*). The individual wind maxima usually are in good agreement with the complicated thermal structure of the atmosphere on top of these shallow cold outbreaks. This peculiarity has been found during several Project Jet Stream flights, so that Brundidge and Goldman (1958) summarized them in three jet-stream models (Fig. 4.232.6). The wind speeds in these diagrams are expressed by the mean anomalies relative to the wind values in the jet axis. Only models 1 and 2 reveal several basic differences. Model 1 is very similar to a mean cross section which Endlich and McLean (1957) regarded as characteristic for jet streams. The essential feature in this diagram is the presence of a marked frontal zone, the polar front, and a relatively thin stable layer underneath the jet maximum, Endlich's "jet-stream front," which is not directly connected with the polar front. This has already been found by Van Mieghem (1939) in a study of a well-established polar front (see also Reiter, 1961*a*, *d*). Furthermore, the jet-stream core contains distinct bulges toward the north, which also appear in Endlich's model. The wind-speed maximum lies slightly above the 300-mb surface.

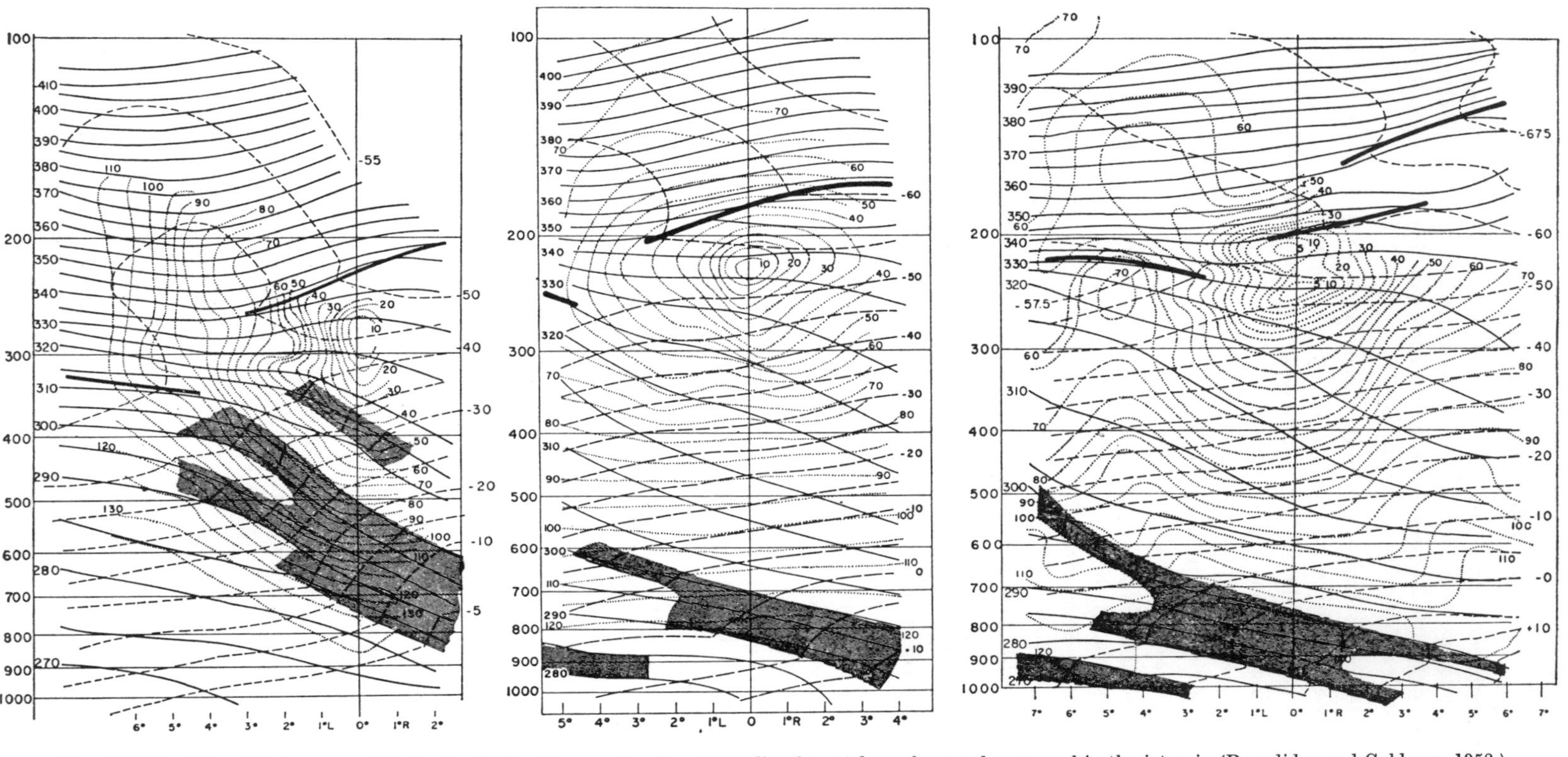

Fig. 4.232.6.—Mean jet-stream models (see text). Speeds are entered as anomalies (knots) from the speed measured in the jet axis. (Brundidge and Goldman, 1958.)

Model 2 corresponds to a STJ, which has its greatest intensity near 250 mb. A weakly developed baroclinic stable layer in the lower troposphere, which at times may assume the character of a subsidence inversion with dry air masses on top of it, has no longer an immediate connection with the jet-stream front. The horizontal wind shear in the lower part of the troposphere is almost zero. Only in the region of a weakly developed baroclinicity in the upper troposphere, which in many cases is so diffuse that it can no longer be called "jet-stream front," does the jet stream begin to establish itself. The wind maximum itself has its strongest horizontal shears on the cyclonic side. On the southern side, however, the jet core shows a distinct bulge, and only weak horizontal shears (Reiter, 1959*b*; 1961*a*).

Model 3 (Fig. 4.232.6) shares with model 2 the diffuse character of the frontal zone and the weakly established "jet-stream front." The structure of the jet-stream core, however, especially on its northern side, has great similarity with model 1. A distinct characteristic is the double jet-stream core. In all probability, this indicates a transition stage (Reiter *et al.*, 1961). Figure 4.232.7 shows the isotachs in a cross section which has been obtained from Flight No. 19 of Project Jet Stream on 16 February, 1957, near the tip of a trough over Ohio. This jet stream has a double structure as indicated in model 3. From the peculiar flight pattern (dashed lines in Fig. 4.232.7), it is possible to compute the change of the wind field with time over part of this cross section. (The numbers at the end of each flight leg indicate the time [GCT] at which this point was reached.) The results are presented in Figure 4.232.8, as the rate of southward displacement (m/sec) of the isotachs of Figure 4.232.7. At the location of the lower jet-stream core the rate of displacement clearly indicates a minimum; on its cyclonic side, however, a maximum is present. Kinematic considerations, therefore, would indicate that the isotachs of smaller speed, north of the core, will eventually overtake the jet axis. Thus, the lower core is subject to a dissipating tendency.

The upper core shows its greatest rate of displacement on its anticyclonic side. Therefore, from a kinematic point of view, it should expand and probably also intensify. Simultaneously with a general southward displacement of the whole jet-stream system, the jet core of strongest wind speeds, therefore, seems to be displaced *discontinuously* toward higher levels with higher potential temperatures (see Chapter 4.412).

Brundidge and Goldman indicate that model 1 may be found on the leading edge of long wave troughs, i.e., in regions of a well-developed frontal zone, according to the results described in Chapter 4.221. (An arrangement of jet stream and frontal zone which would correspond to type 1 has been found by the author [Reiter, 1961*d*] also on the western side of a trough.) Model 2 is mainly found on the rear side of troughs, and in cross sections through high-pressure ridges and through the western extremities of a polar front, which is subject to strong sinking motions in the influence region of a (cold) intermediate high (Reiter, 1961*a*).

Endlich and McLean (1957) investigated the mean structure of the jet-stream core, making use of 65 traverses of the jet stream in the Florida region. Because of the geographic location of the flight legs, the following results should be regarded as mainly valid for the STJ. Figure 4.232.9 contains mean profiles arranged according to different classifications. The numbers written down along each profile indicate the

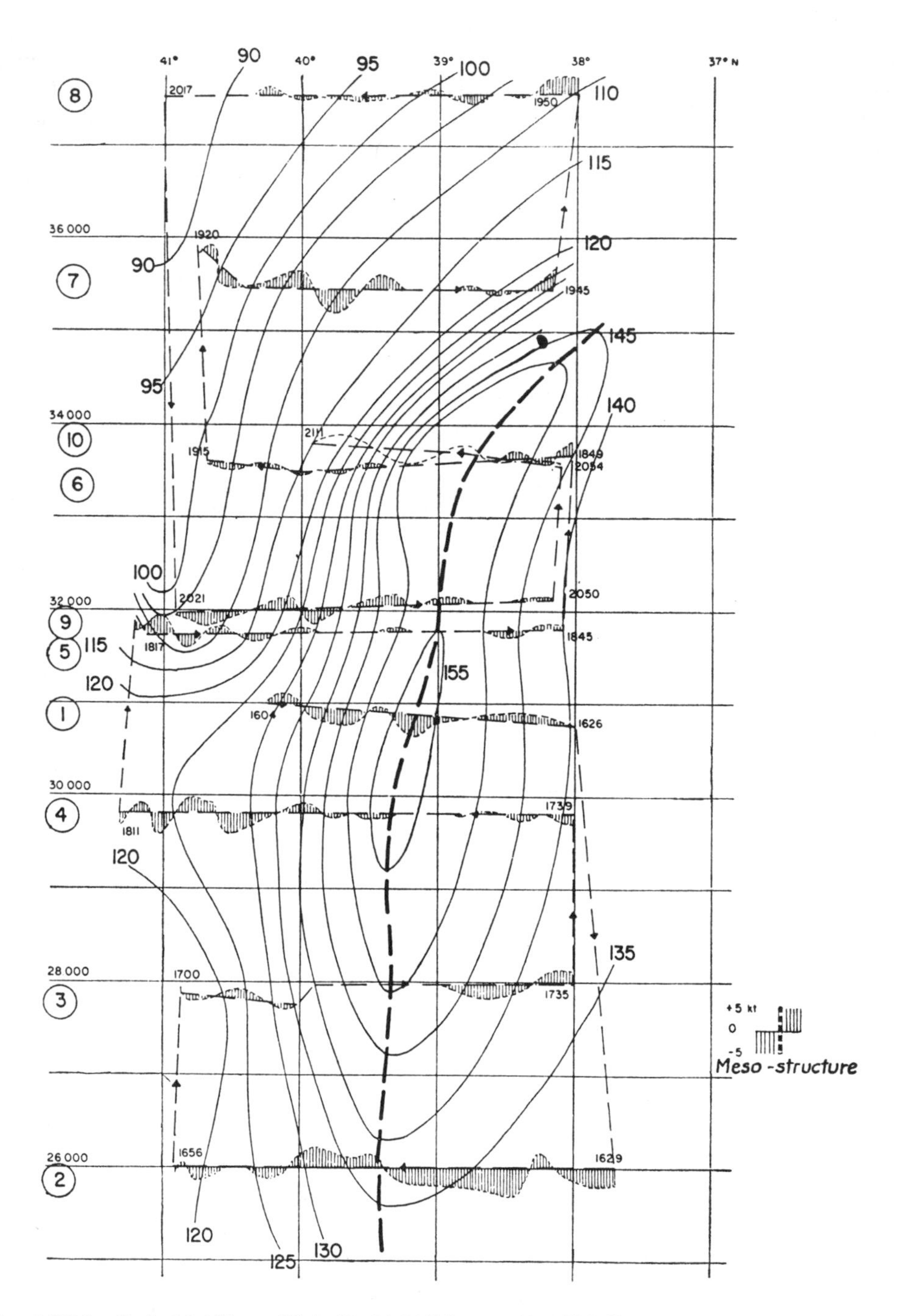

Fig. 4.232.7.—Project Jet Stream Flight No. 19, 16 February, 1957. Thin lines, isotachs (knots) of the twice-smoothed wind field; heavy dashed line, vertical jet axis; light dashed line, flight route. The numbers on the end of the various flight legs indicate the time (GCT) at which these points were reached by the aircraft. The circled numbers along the left margin of the diagram mark the sequence of the flight legs. Ordinate, height in feet. Shaded areas, meso-structure of wind speeds.

number of observations contained in each class interval. The wind speeds are given in per cent of maximum wind speed, whereby the horizontal distance of the vertical grid lines corresponds to 10 per cent.

Classification:

A.—Mean profile;
B.—Strong jet streams, ≧130 knots maximum wind speed;
C.—Cross section more than 1000 ft (300 m) above the jet axis;
D.—Cross section at the level of the jet axis (±1000 ft, 300 m);
E.—Cross section 1000 to 9000 ft (300 to 2750 m) below the jet axis;
F.—Cyclonically curved flow;
G.—Straight flow;
H.—Anticyclonically curved flow.

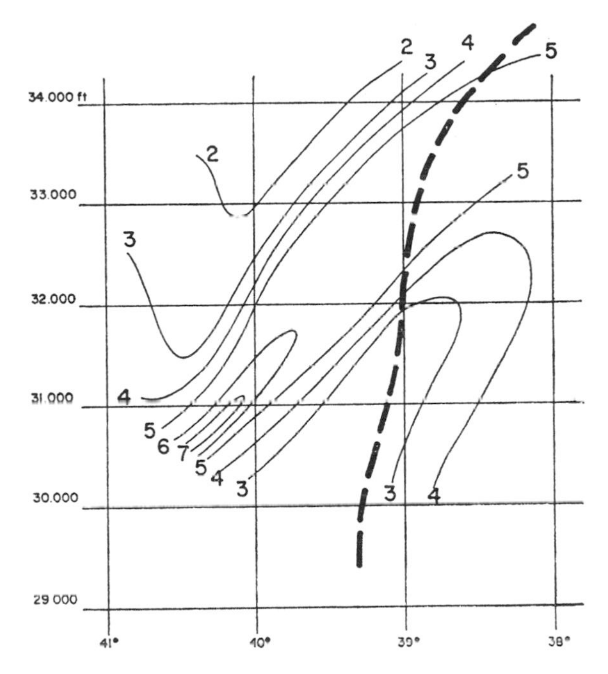

Fig. 4.232.8.—Rate of displacement (m/sec) toward the south, of the isotachs shown in Figure 4.232.7. Heavy dashed line, jet axis.

The mean profiles thus classified show several characteristic properties. First of all, the discontinuity in the horizontal shear, and therefore also in the vorticity, which had been shown by Riehl, Berry, and Maynard (1955; see also Riehl and Maynard [1954]) seems to be valid at a scale which corresponds to the accuracy of positioning the aircraft. The per cent of wind shear on the anticyclonic side of the jet stream is the same for almost all classes. On the cyclonic side the stronger jet streams seem to have larger shears on the average, and the same holds for profiles measured with cyclonic curvature and those obtained underneath the jet axis; the latter ones, of course, intersect the jet-stream front. Saucier (1958*b*) arrives at similar results when incorporating flights through the PFJ. According to these more recent results, the anticyclonic shear seems to be strongest at the jet-stream level and slightly above it (corresponding to profile *D*).

Endlich and McLean (1957) arrive at the following characteristic properties, based on the observations mentioned above, of a *fully developed* PFJ in the temperate latitudes:

1. A marked decrease of tropopause heights is observed north of the jet stream, amounting to at least 1 km in 2° of latitude. (The term "discontinuity" used by Endlich seems to be slightly misleading in view of more recent studies by Danielsen [1959; see Chapter 3.249], since the tropopause reveals a more or less laminated structure.)

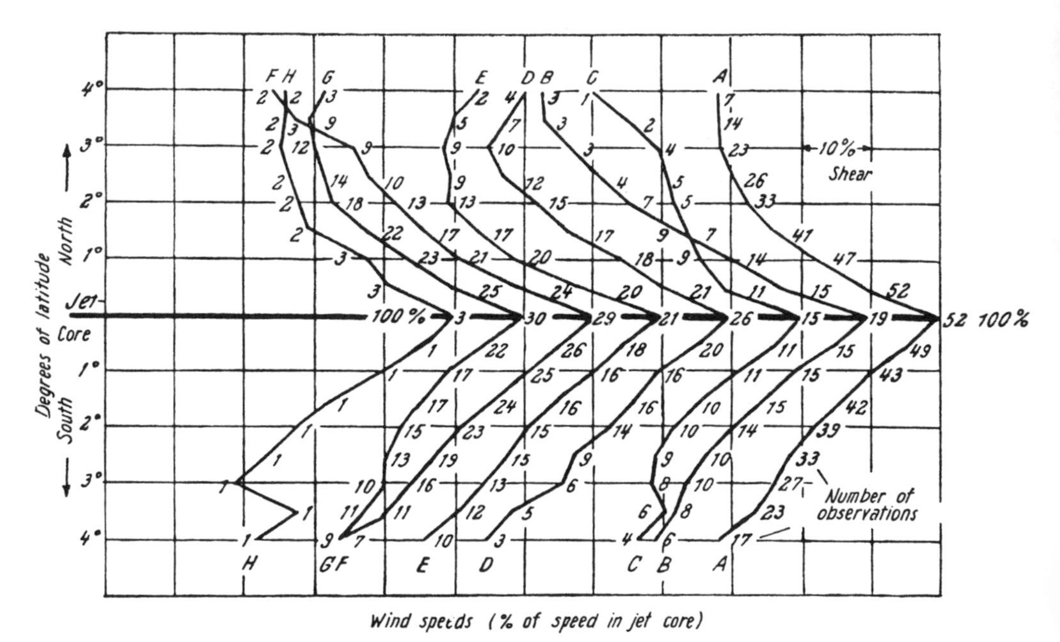

FIG. 4.232.9.—Horizontal wind profiles (in per cent of maximum speeds) for various classes (see text). (Endlich and McLean, 1957.)

2. The wind speed in the center is higher than 100 knots and decreases to 80 per cent of the maximum value within 2.5° of latitude on the south side and within 1.5° of latitude on the north side of the jet stream.

3. A more or less pronounced layer of thermal stability is sloping southward underneath the jet core. Isentropes and isotachs reveal a tendency within this layer to run parallel to its boundary surfaces. Horizontal temperature gradients and horizontal as well as vertical wind shears are concentrated within this jet-stream front.

Especially for the PFJ the following holds:

4. The position of the polar front underneath the jet stream of the temperate latitudes is largely variable with respect to the position of the jet axis; on the average, however, the intersection of the frontal zone with the 500-mb surface approximately lies underneath the jet core.

As has already been mentioned, during some of the flights several velocity maxima have been found at levels increasing toward the south. Several of these maxima have been connected with small changes in tropopause height. These maxima should only be separated from the meso-structure of a uniform jet stream, however, if each of them meets the criteria listed above (Endlich *et al.*, 1954).

Some jet streams may be weaker than postulated in point 2, and nevertheless show a marked horizontal and vertical wind shear. The interpretation of the above points, therefore, has to be handled liberally. McLean *et al.* (1955), for instance, found a small cold-air vortex at about 35,000 ft over Florida during one of the research missions of Project Jet Stream, mentioned earlier, which was bisected by a well-pronounced shear line in the upper wind field. On the western side of this shear line a "miniature jet stream" was observed with peak velocities of about 80 knots. The tropopause also showed an indentation. The vortex, however, had such small dimensions that it probably would have eluded the rawin observations.

4.3 THE FINE STRUCTURE OF JET STREAMS

In the introduction to Chapter 4 an arbitrary classification of the structure of jet streams according to macro-, meso-, and micro-scale has been made. In the preceding sections mainly the macro-structure has been considered. The small-scale and short-lived fluctuations of wind speed and of wind direction are of considerable importance, too. On the one hand they are responsible for exchange and mixing processes as well as the heat transport in vertical and horizontal direction, and on the other hand they may be of interest for air traffic with fast-flying jet aircraft because they may appear as bumpiness and clear-air turbulence.

4.31. Observations and Measurements of the Fine Structure

It is difficult to determine within which frequency range the wind fluctuations in the free atmosphere occur, because the measurement techniques are not yet far enough advanced to allow a continuous and accurate measurement of upper wind changes for any small or large time interval. "Power spectrum analyses," as they have been made by Panofsky and his collaborators from wind measurements in the atmospheric layers near the ground (literature given by Flohn, 1959*a*), are not yet available for the free atmosphere in such a wide frequency range. The variance σ^2 of the wind speed (which may be computed from the standard deviation from the mean value and which is proportional to the kinetic energy of the wind speed fluctuations) shows two maxima near the ground: one of them occurs at "wave lengths" of about 100 hours (4 days), thus belonging to the macro-meteorological range, and a second one is found at about 1 minute, which falls into the micro-meteorological range. The statistical significance of a secondary maximum at about 12 hours has not yet been fully established. A broad gap of velocity fluctuations appears between the wave length of 10 minutes to one hour. Thus, this region of the turbulence spectrum is only rarely used by atmospheric turbulence processes near the ground.

For the free atmosphere in the vicinity of jet streams we may conduct several qualitative considerations only, which are based upon detailed measurements of the upper winds, which, unfortunately, have not been made too frequently.

"Power spectra" of *long-wave* disturbances may be computed from synoptic upper-air charts. The results of these investigations of the general circulation of the atmosphere will be described further in Chapter 8. Short-wave disturbances have only been treated inadequately so far.

Series of ascents which have been made at Trappes, France, and which have been investigated by Barbé (1956, 1957) have already been discussed in Chapter 2.123 (Figs. 2.123.1 and .2). As has already been mentioned, however, such measurements give only little information on the fine structure of jet streams, because the velocity fluctuations measured in a height interval of 600 m are rather crudely determined and unreliable, and the distance in time between these measurements (1 hour in the series mentioned above) is too long.

Further information on the structure of *short wave fluctuations* of the wind and temperature field are available through research flights of Project Jet Stream. The results of these flight measurements will be discussed separately according to meso- and micro-structure.

4.311. The Meso-Structure of Jet Streams

It has been pointed out in several publications (Reiter, 1959*b*; 1960*c*, *d*, *e*; 1961*a*, *b*, *d*, *e*, *f*; Reiter *et al.*, 1961) that fluctuations in a meteorological parameter (e.g., wind speed, temperature, etc.) may be studied to advantage only if it is possible to define these local fluctuations as perturbations superimposed upon a smooth "laminar" basic state of the atmosphere.

For this purpose the author proposed a double smoothing process which may be applied graphically to aircraft measurements: First, all fluctuations are smoothed out if a certain trend in the measured quantities prevails only over less than three consecutive points of measurement. (This has already been pointed out in Chapter 4.232.) These oscillations, which have been eliminated by this first smoothing process, are regarded as "instrument errors," although they may in part stem from a genuine micro-structure of the atmosphere.

In a second process of smoothing the remaining fluctuations of wave lengths of about 10^5 m—belonging to the meso-structure—are eliminated. Unfortunately, these smoothing methods are not free of a certain subjectivity, which could be removed easily by a numerical computation of overlapping means. Then, however, sharp discontinuities which may exist in the horizontal gradients, would also be lost.

The analyses shown in Figures 4.232.3, .4, .5, and .7 are based upon data which have been smoothed twice as described above. The "meso-scale" fluctuations of wind speed have been entered as shaded areas in Figures 4.232.4 and .7. They should be regarded as differences between the data after the first and after the second smoothing. Thus, they are local "anomalies" of the wind field with respect to a "quasi-laminar" basic current. (The amplitudes of the meso-structure have been entered with respect to the dashed flight route as zero line. Bold sections of the flight route in Figure 4.232.4 indicate zones with clear-air turbulence according to objective measurements of accelerations, obtained from a special air-speed indicator.) Since the indicated fluctuations in temperature are not necessarily real (Endlich and Rados, 1959), they have not been considered in Figure 4.232.3.

A superficial comparison of Figures 4.232.3 and .4 already shows that the meso-structure of wind speed attains its maximum amplitudes in *stable* and *baroclinic* zones. This is in qualitative agreement with a simplified, "geostrophic" form of Richardson's number R_i^*, which will be described further in Chapter 4.322. Although no clear-cut correlation exists between the amplitudes of meso-scale oscillations and the number R_i^*, as may be seen from Figure 4.311.1, a distinct trend is evident which points in the same direction as Eq. 4.322 (9). From this one may conclude that the meso-structure of the wind field has the character of perturbations, which mainly form as waves on stable layers (Kasahara, 1956). Observations of smoke clouds (Durst, 1952) show that the greatest short-period variability of the wind occurs near the tropopause, which, again, corresponds to the above considerations.

These conclusions are corroborated by analyses of horizontal research flights. Figures 4.311.2 and 3 contain isotherms and isotachs of the 222-mb surface of 24 January, 1957, 1500 GCT, including the measurements of Project Jet Stream Flight No. 14. Again, the meso-structure of wind speed (the fine structure of temperature should not be given too much consideration, since it may be influenced by turbulence) attains its largest amplitudes where the horizontal gradient of temperature indicates the existence of a stable, baroclinic layer which intersects the 222-mb surface. The amplitudes of the fluctuations are largest in the vicinity of the Rocky Mountain ranges (marked by hatching). This indicates a certain orographic effect which may lead to the formation of standing lee waves (see Reiter *et al.*, 1961).

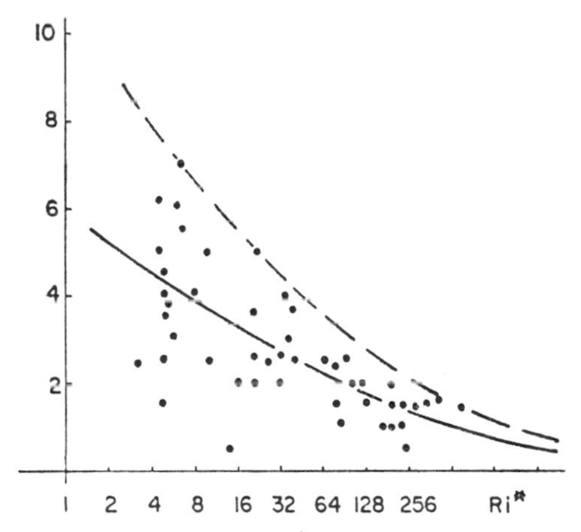

FIG. 4.311.1.—Correlation between amplitudes of meso-structure of wind speed (ordinate) and R_i^*-number (abscissa). Dashed line, envelope curve.

From the small sample of flight data analyses presented here (see also Reiter, 1961*a*, *d*) several interesting conclusions which characterize the detailed structure of the atmosphere in the jet-stream region may be drawn:

1. Detailed temperature measurements reveal a fine structure of atmospheric stratification such as will never be evident from coded radiosonde messages. Danielsen (1959) has already pointed out the existence of shallow stable layers embedded in a

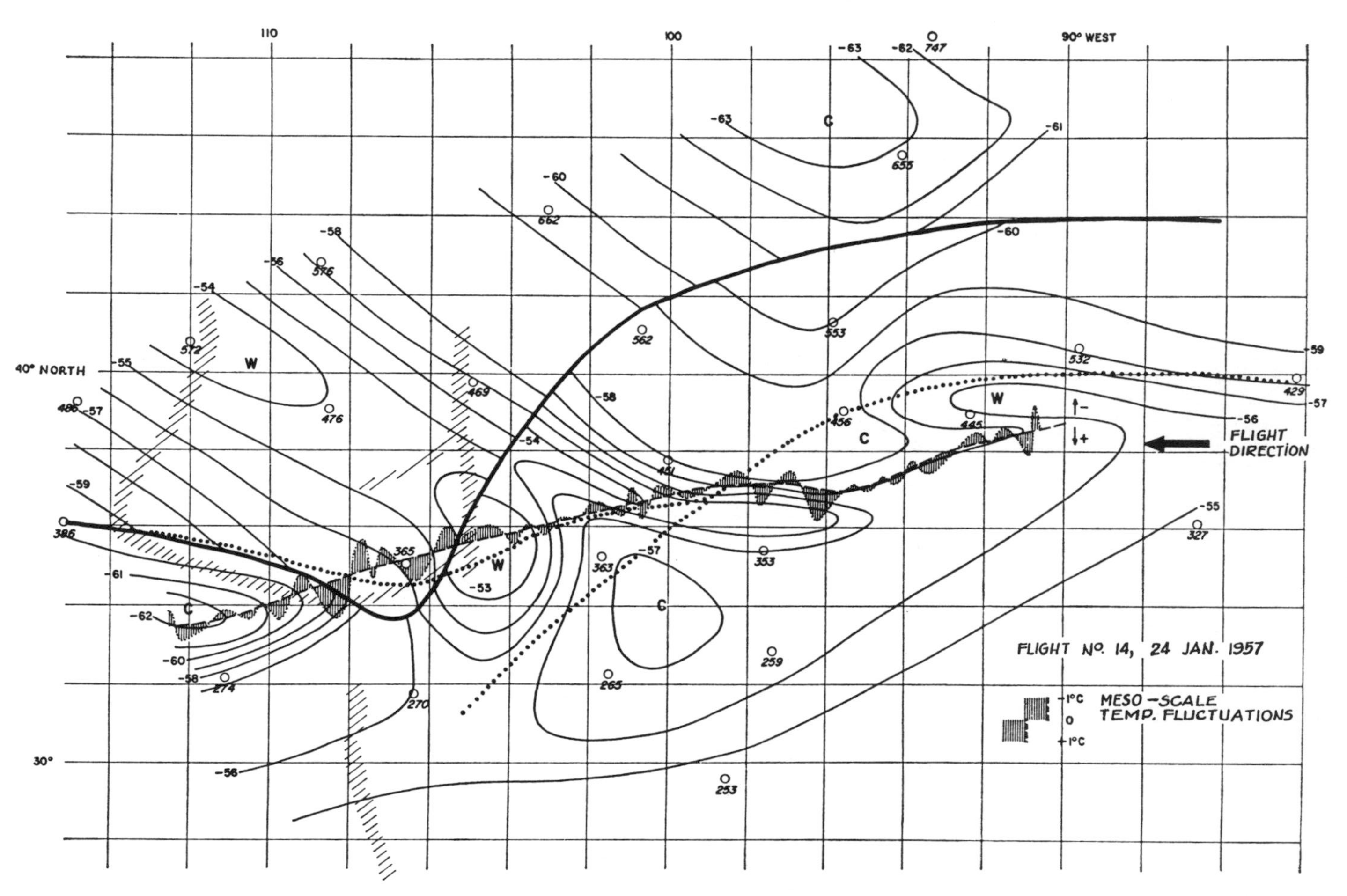

Fig. 4.311.2.—Isotherms (° C) of the 222-mb surface, 24 January, 1957, 1500 GCT (Flight No. 14). The meso-structure of temperature is indicated by shading (negative anomalies plotted above, positive anomalies below line of flight route; amplitudes to be measured off with respect to this line). Dotted line, jet axes; heavy line, tropopause intersection with flight level; slant hatching, main range of Rocky Mountains.

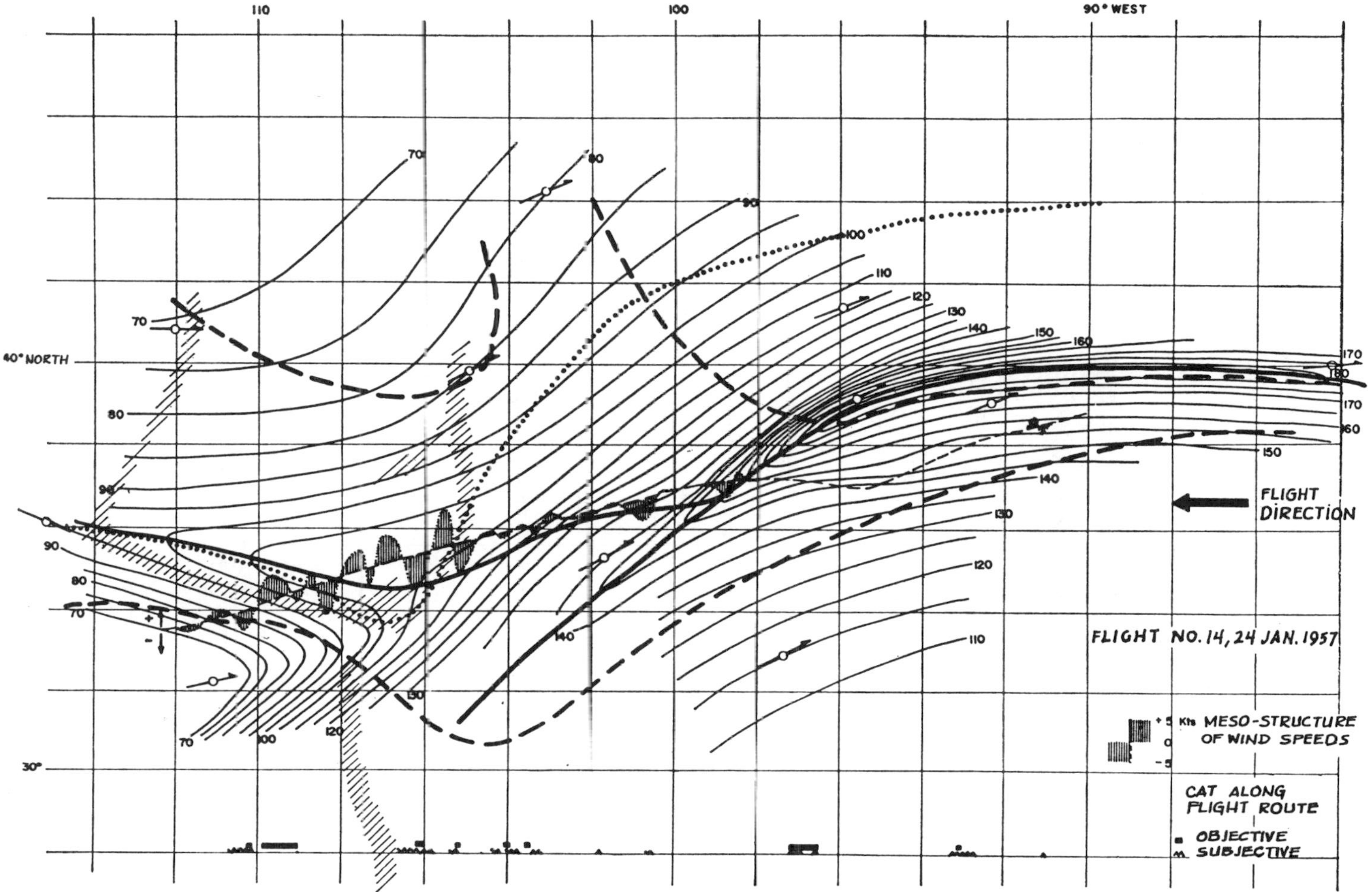

Fig. 4.311.3.—Isotachs (knots) of the 222-mb surface (36,000 ft pressure altitude). The meso-structure of wind speeds is indicated by hatching (positive anomalies plotted above, negative anomalies below line of flight route; amplitudes (knots) to be measured off with respect to this line). Heavy lines, jet axes; heavy, dashed line, intersection of level of maximum wind with 222-mb level; dotted line, tropopause intersection. Objective and subjective observations of CAT are entered along the lower margin of the diagram in the fashion indicated.

nearly adiabatic surrounding. Although these layers may be evaluated from the original ascent measurements, they are smoothed out during the coding process. Figure 4.232.3 clearly indicates such a zone in the lower left portion of the diagram, and again near 36,000 ft (11 km) on the right margin of this figure.

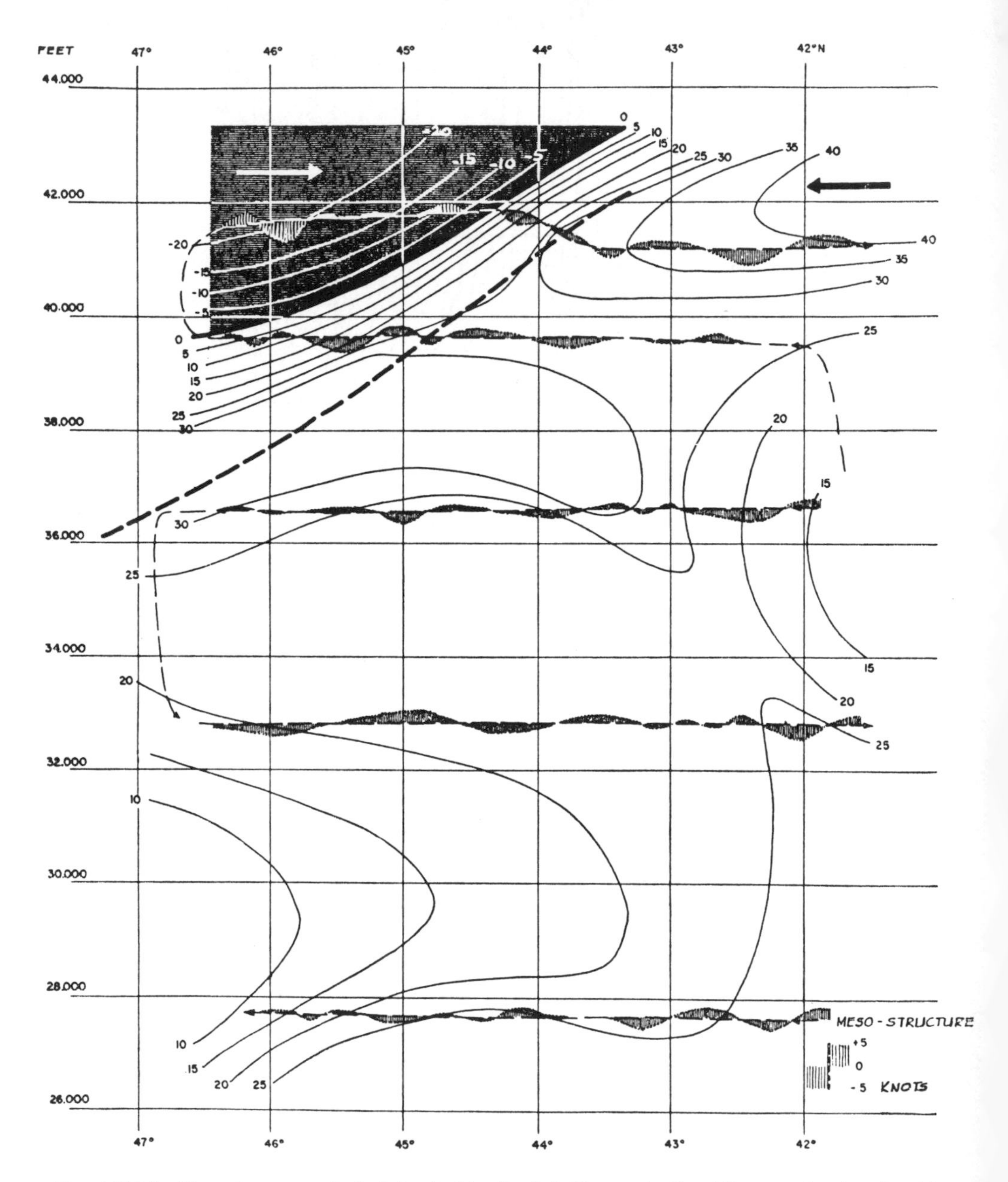

FIG. 4.311.4.—Normal component of wind velocities (for definition see text) and its meso-structure (knots), Flight No. 29. Flow from the anticyclonic toward the cyclonic side of the jet stream has positive sign. Areas with negative normal components are shaded. Jet axis as in Figure 4.232.4.

Because of their influence upon the meso- and micro-structures of the wind field, these thin stable layers are of great importance. They, furthermore, seem to indicate a mechanism of mixing processes in the vicinity of the jet-stream core. Figure 4.311.4 shows the "normal component" of wind velocity (defined as the velocity component normal to the direction of flow at the place of greatest wind speed encountered in the course of the respective research flight). The zero line of this quantity does not intersect the jet axis anywhere in Figure 4.232.4 because the greatest wind speeds have been measured along the flight level 34,600 ft, which, however, has not been included in the analysis of Figure 4.232.4, since it ran farther to the east than the rest of the flight cross section. Maximum south-wind components (positive) seem to be wedged between the two stable zones of Figure 4.232.3 mentioned above. Similar observations could be made in other cross sections (Reiter, 1961*a*, *b*, *d*, *e*, *f*). It appears, therefore, that air masses of different origin are "interlocked" with each other near the jet-stream core, and especially near the jet-stream front. This "interlocking" becomes apparent from minute changes of wind direction across these shallow stable layers. They, again, constitute "miniature frontal zones" along which the meso- and micro-structures are responsible for further mixing.

2. If we accept the order of magnitude of the dimensions of meso-structure in the wind field outlined in the introduction to Chapter 4, and corroborated by the aircraft measurements presented here, a "wave length" of 10^4 sec as upper boundary of meso-structure would fall into the vicinity of the secondary maximum near 10 hours, which has been found by Van der Hoven (1957)—although not very well established—in "power spectra" of wind measurements near the ground (see Flohn, 1959*a*). The meso-structure of jet streams, therefore, seems to gain a certain justification also from the results of the statistical theory of turbulence. It should be mentioned that fluctuations in wind speed are evident from aircraft measurements along the direction of the streamlines (Fig. 4.311.3) as well as normal to it (Fig. 4.232.4). Their amplitudes are great enough to be considered real. Maximum values of these fluctuations amount to 4 m^2/sec^2 to 9 m^2/sec^2, values which agree well in order of magnitude with what should be expected from Van der Hoven's statistics.

In this connection a few interesting perspectives are worth further research. The fact that turbulent processes in the free atmosphere as well as near the ground share similar "spectral ranges" may give rise to a number of speculations. It should be anticipated here that clear-air turbulence as a manifestation of velocity fluctuations of a duration of about 0.001 hours indicates another spectrum range of turbulence. Van der Hoven finds a maximum of micro-structure near 0.02 hours. Such oscillations lie, however, beyond the range of acceleration measurements—and not yet within the range of wind and temperature observations. It might well be that the clear-air turbulence measured by the presently employed jet aircraft constitutes only the extreme short-wave margin of a spectral range which plays the same important role in the mixing processes of the free atmosphere as it does in the short-period turbulence of the surface layer that has been attributed primarily to the effect of surface friction. One, therefore, would have to expect frictional forces to be active also in the vertical wind-shear zone in the jet-stream region, which may give rise to the formation of these turbulence elements.

As is evident from the diagrams of this chapter and of Chapter 4.232, clear-air turbulence seems to occur primarily near shallow stable and baroclinic layers in which the vertical wind shear should be concentrated according to the thermal wind equation.

Unfortunately, the data available from the free atmosphere are too sparse and incomplete to give an experimental basis to the conjectures expressed here.

3. In Figure 4.232.5 the distribution of absolute vorticity has been shown, and an area of dynamic instability has been pointed out to the right of the jet axis. This analysis has been obtained from the doubly smoothed data of Figure 4.232.4. If we consider, however, the meso-structural velocity fluctuations, we obtain locally confined horizontal gradients $\partial V/\partial n$ which may reverse the sign of the vorticity Q measured macro-meteorologically. Such zones of a reversal of sign by meso-structural effects are indicated by heavy lines along the (dashed) flight routes in Figure 4.232.5. Thus, the region of negative absolute vorticity is traversed by narrow zones of dynamic stability, while the area with positive vorticity Q contains zones with $\left(-\frac{\partial V}{\partial n}+f\right)<0$.

4. According to 1.235 (4) the potential vorticity on the cyclonic side of the "jet-stream front" and of the stratospheric stable layer in Figure 4.232.3 attains values of the magnitude of $>60\cdot 10^{-9}$ g^{-1} cm·sec·degree, while on the anticyclonic side of this "frontal zone" only small positive or even negative values of this quantity prevail (Reed and Danielsen, 1959; Reiter, 1961*d*). If we consider $Q_z\cdot\partial\Theta/\partial p$ to be a conservative quantity, we may conclude that the air masses within and outside of the jet-stream front are of different origin. According to the findings of Reed and Danielsen, the jet-stream front and the high-tropospheric portion of the frontal zone, therefore, cannot be considered a "blurred" discontinuity between two adjacent air masses of different temperatures. Apparently within the "jet-stream front" air is descending from the stratosphere.

5. The quantities $\partial v/\partial y$ and $\partial u/\partial x$, and from these the horizontal divergence, may be computed from the horizontal gradients of the normal component (Fig. 4.232.4) and from upper-wind charts. Studies by the author (Reiter, 1961*a*, *d*) indicated that the divergence distribution evident from the vorticity advection in Figure 4.122.3 is valid only in a macro-meteorological sense. Although one finds convergence predominating in the entrance region of a jet maximum, to the left of the axis (in Fig. 4.311.5 indicated by shading), and divergence to the right of the axis, vergences of opposite sign may be interspersed in this large-scale distribution. These meso-structural disturbances with a wave length of about 400 km seem to correspond to the extent of cloud fields observed by Schaefer and Hubert (1955). The meso-structure of the wind field (in total speed V as well as in the normal component) with wave lengths of the order of magnitude of 50 to 100 km also allows one to expect a certain influence upon the vergences. In spite of the small variations in wind direction, the fine structure in the normal component may be appreciable because of the high wind speeds (Saucier and Brundidge, 1956). Cirrus bands which, according to Conover (1960), have a mean distance of 185 km may be due to this detailed structure in the wind field. Kuettner (1952*b*) deems it possible that vertical motions resulting from this meso-structure might be utilized in soaring.

6. The vertical motion of the air may be qualitatively deduced from the normal component of wind velocity and from the isentrope slope in the cross-section analyses.

The cloud distribution (in Fig. 4.232.3 indicated by shading) seems to match these considerations. Vertical motions in the jet-stream region may also be expected from the temperature gradients along the direction of the streamlines, as shown in Figure

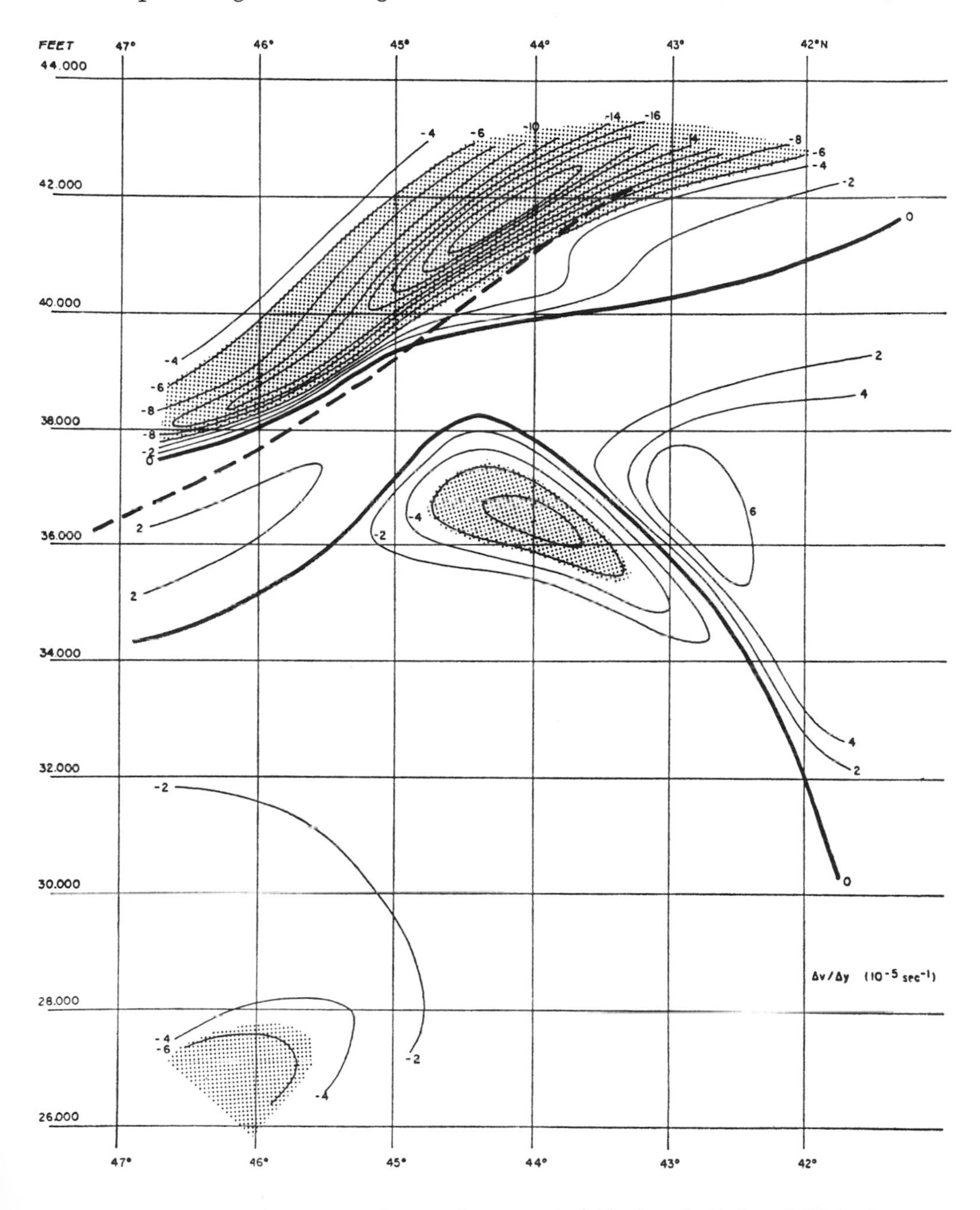

FIG. 4.311.5.—Horizontal gradient of the normal component, $\Delta v/\Delta y$, in units 10^{-5} sec^{-1}, Flight No. 29. Areas with horizontal convergence, indicated by shading, have been computed under the assumption that $\Delta u/\Delta x$ is equal to $5.7 \cdot 10^{-5}$ sec^{-1} throughout this cross section. Jet axis as in Figure 4.232.4.

4.311.2. So, for instance, at the grid point 38° N and 102° W a velocity component $w = 0.65$ m/sec could be computed.

Direct estimates of the vertical velocity from variations in true air speed and pitch render much stronger vertical motions (see Chapter 4.232). The diameter of areas with positive or negative velocity component w has the order of magnitude of 150 km, when measured normal to the direction of flow. It, therefore, may be compared with the "wave length" of 400 km, which has been obtained from the divergence distribution.

Fluctuations of a smaller diameter in the vertical velocity (order of magnitude in the wave length normal to the direction of flow: *ca.* 50 km) indicate the presence of meso-scale vortex tubes with horizontal axes, through which the air particles flow in a "screwlike" motion. Long banks of cirrus clouds corroborate such motions (Kuettner, 1959*b*).

The meso-structure of the wind and temperature measurements of Project Jet Stream, thus, is by no means a random phenomenon but manifests a well-organized pattern of atmospheric flow processes. Narrow bands with positive and negative anomalies of wind speed have been found, oriented side by side along isentropic surfaces, and more than 400 km long. Some of these meso-scale fluctuations seem to retain their identity for several hours (Reiter, 1961*a*; Reiter *et al.*, 1961). The long and narrow cloud bands which are frequently observed in the jet-stream region, therefore, are in good agreement with these flight measurements (see Chapter 6.3), and they confirm the existence of a *banded* structure of the atmosphere. These cloud streaks also appear in photographs taken by the weather satellite Tiros I. A similar structure with less distance between bands is also observed in the "cloud streets" of the lower troposphere, which are usually connected with an inversion wind maximum or a low-level jet (see Chapter 4.416). Kuettner (1959*b*) attributes this banded structure to a *convective motion* within a current with a vertical wind profile that is curved as in a jet stream. The curvature of the wind profiles acts to stabilize the current. In essence, this reasoning conforms with the derivations in Chapter 4.32, if we consider the convective motions as perturbations superimposed upon a shearing current. The importance of the stable and baroclinic layers in Figures 4.232.3 and 4.311.2 is accentuated by the fact that vertical and horizontal gradients are concentrated in these layers.

Since the stable layers in the cross sections analyzed here are oriented almost isentropically, one may assume that their slope regulates the vertical gliding motions of air masses near the jet core. The shallow layers of cirrus—sometimes even several of them—which frequently are observed in the vicinity of a jet maximum, corroborate the *laminated* and stratified structure of the atmosphere.

4.312. The Micro-Structure of Jet Streams. Clear-Air Turbulence

Besides the large-scale turbulent processes near the jet stream described so far, there is also a short periodic "noise"—especially in the wind speeds—which, in the form of clear-air turbulence, is of importance to air traffic. This micro-structure may be shown by various methods of observation (see Reiter, 1960*b*).

The rate of diffusion of smoke clouds released from aircraft or anti-aircraft shells (Durst, 1948, 1952; Roberts, 1923; Sutton, 1932), the dissipation of condensation trails (Clodman, 1958), the spreading of artificial "clouds" of aluminum foil (Warner and Bowen, 1953) may be utilized in the study of small-scale exchange processes.

From various balloon observations conclusions may also be drawn about the prevailing degree of turbulence. Especially some of the old meteorograph records near the tropopause show strong, short periodic oscillations in the recorded elements, which are due to vibrations of the sonde in a turbulent air stream (Mironovitch and Viaut, 1938; Poncelet, 1935). Fluctuations in wind speed as they have been observed from radiosonde ascents (Scrase, 1954) do not necessarily have to be caused by turbulence but may be simulated by errors in measurement. This has been discussed in detail in Chapter 2.122. Measurements with "gust sondes" carrying an accelerometer are more reliable for turbulence detection (Anderson, 1957*b*; Junge, 1938).

Indications of atmospheric turbulence may also be gained from the scintillation of stars, which is caused by small heterogeneities in density (Boutet, 1950; Gifford and Mikesell, 1953; Keller, 1952; Protheroe, 1955; Royal Meteorological Society, 1954). The scintillation amplitudes may be recorded photographically. There seems to be a significant correlation between wind speed and wind shear at jet-stream level and the scintillation. The high-frequency oscillations (150 cps) of the star image seem to have their main source region near the mean tropopause level, while the low-frequency scintillation (25 cps) shows no clear correlation to wind speeds below 20 km (Gardiner *et al.*, 1956; Gifford, 1955).

The density variations caused by turbulence act not only upon electromagnetic waves in the wave-length range of visible light, but also upon radio short waves (Kazès and Steinberg, 1957; Staras, 1955), and radar waves (Fleisher, 1959; Rogers, 1957). The scintillation of radio stars may have its origin in ionospheric turbulence elements (Booker, 1957; Wells, 1958).

Our main concern, however, will be with small-scale and short-period turbulence phenomena, which may be felt by an aircraft as "bumpiness," and which, in cloud-free regions, is called clear-air turbulence (CAT). An extensive bibliography on this subject has been published by the author elsewhere (Reiter, 1960*b*; see also 1960*a*). It may suffice, therefore, to give here only a short review of the problems which seem to be connected immediately with the jet stream.

A large part of CAT observations are made by pilots (Farthing, 1959). Although these are subjective reports, they may, when collected systematically (Lake, 1956), give valuable insight into the space distribution of CAT. Since the turbulence conditions in flight are of importance not only to passenger comfort but also for the life expectancy of the aircraft (Reiter, 1959*g*), the exploration of CAT by objective methods has received a tremendous impetus during the last few years. First, one determines from recording accelerometers the vertical accelerations which the aircraft experienced in flight. From this one may compute in first approximation the vertical wind speed which led to the observed vertical displacement of the aircraft, by assuming a "sharp-edged gust" (Pratt, 1953).

$$W_{de}=\frac{2b\,\Delta n}{\rho_0 ka V_i}. \qquad 4.312\ (1)$$

W_{de} is the derived gust velocity (ft/sec), ρ_0 the air density at sea level, b the wing load (lb/ft^2), Δn the observed increment of acceleration in units of the acceleration of

TABLE 4.312.1. CHARACTERISTICS

1	2	3	4
SOURCE OF INFORMATION	ALTITUDE RANGE	ALTITUDE RANGE OF FREQUENCY MAXIMUM	INTENSITY OF TURBULENCE
1. Bannon (1951*a*,*b*)		28,000 to 32,000 ft	
2. Bindon (1951)	24,000 ft		
3. Clem (1957)	25,000 to 45,000 ft	40,000 to 44,000 ft. Secondary maximum at 34,000 ft over northeast U.S.	light CAT moderate severe
4. Clodman (1953)	18,000 to 40,000 ft	No significant height dependency over southern Canada between 18,000 and 38,000 ft	all intensities moderate and severe severe
5. Cunningham (1958)			
6. Estoque (1958)	150 mb 200 mb 250 mb 300 mb 350 mb	250 mb (Europe, Turkey, U.S., Japan)	10 5 2 ft/sec 10 5 2 ft/sec 10 5 2 ft/sec 10 5 2 ft/sec 10 5 2 ft/sec
7. Heath-Smith (1955)		Decrease to 25,000 ft. Increase above	
8. Hislop (1951)	25,000 ft 35,000 ft		4 ft/sec 8 ft/sec 12 ft/sec
9. Hyde (1954*a*)	49,000 to 36,000 ft 22,000 to 28,000 ft		light or moderate severe extremely severe
10. Kuettner (1952*a*)	40,000 ft		
11. Murray (1953)	400 to 200 mb		$\geqq 0.1$ g $\geqq 0.2$ g $\geqq 0.3$ g
12. Pinus (1957)		Decrease to middle troposphere, increase above by 15 to 20% to tropopause level	
13. Press *et al.* (1953)			

OF VARIOUS CAT OBSERVATIONS

5	6	7	8	9	10
FREQUENCY OF OCCURRENCE	EXTREME ACCELERATION	EXTENT OF TURBULENT AREAS			
		Horizontal		Vertical	
		Average	Extreme	Average	Extreme
	0.7 g				
	3 g				
19% of all flights 12% 2%		15 to 60 km longer than wide		500 to 2000 ft	
1: 35 km 1: 85 km 1:440 km		~90 km	≧450 km	3000 ft	100 to 15,000 ft
		Areas with strong turbulence usually are larger and thicker			
		50% < 30 km	6.9 to 328 km	~1500 ft	500 to 3000 ft
0.02 0.16 2.0% 0.09 0.75 9.0 0.15 1.2 15.0 0.11 0.88 11.0 0.08 0.72 9.0 of km flown					
	0.8 g 20 ft/sec				
1 gust in 13 km 1 gust in 97 km 1 gust in 650 km	1.5 g≃35 ft/sec	75 to 100 km		900 m	
28% of all flights 7% 1%	2.5 to 4 g (estimated)				
	+3 g −2.5 g (sailplane) (21 m/sec)				
37.4% of all flights 4.9% 0.2%	0.4 g				
		50% < 80 km	>800 km	50% < 2000 ft	100 to 10,000 ft
		Areas with severe CAT usually are larger and thicker			

gravity ($\Delta n = n - 1$). n is the total acceleration in g-units. k is the non-dimensional gust alleviation factor, V_i the horizontal true air speed, and a the slope of the lift curve. b and a depend upon the aircraft type. Thus, gusts of a certain intensity may cause different accelerations on different types of aircraft. CAT, therefore, is not a quantity which would describe an atmospheric state objectively.

Horizontal velocity changes, too, may cause vertical accelerations of the airplane, because they change the lifting force. The effect, however, is only about one-quarter of what vertical gusts of the same intensity would accomplish (Hislop, 1951). In order to represent the horizontal gusts adequately, during recent measurements, variations in the indicated air speed of the airplane have been recorded. This method of measurement has been employed successfully primarily during the research flights of Project Jet Stream (Endlich and Rados, 1959).

Results of the measurements of horizontal gust velocities cannot be assumed equivalent to subjective turbulence observations. The latter respond primarily to vertical accelerations, thus indicating a different component of gustiness from the former. Clodman and Ball (1959) believe they have detected a certain anisotropy of CAT from the discrepancies between measured horizontal and estimated vertical gust velocities. According to their statistical investigation horizontal gusts seem to prevail in the stratosphere, vertical gusts, however, in the troposphere. This would be in good agreement with stability conditions: In a stable stratification vertical motions will be suppressed, because a large amount of work would be required against the gravitational force.

Light turbulence occurs rather frequently. Estoque (1958) finds that at tropopause level (250 mb) about 15 per cent of the distance flown will show gusts with more than 2 ft/sec. In a continuous vibration 0.25 g will already be experienced as uncomfortable, while 0.5 g amounts to severe turbulence. Cases with severe turbulence are, however, rare, as may be seen from Table 4.312.1 (Clodman and Ball, 1959; Reiter, 1960*b*). Based upon the research flights of two British Mosquito aircraft, Hislop (1951) arrives at the conclusion that a fleet of 20 Comets with about 3000 hours of flying time per year might expect a report on turbulence of 1.5 g (36 ft/sec = 10.5 m/sec) once every two weeks, and a report of 2.0 g (50 ft/sec = 15.2 m/sec) once every four years. Under the influence of orographic obstacles which are traversed by a flight route, the turbulence frequencies may be much larger than indicated in Table 4.312.1, due to the formation of standing lee waves.

The horizontal dimensions of turbulent areas usually are small; occasionally one may, however, run into turbulence extending over several hundreds of kilometers. As an average value one may take 900 m in the vertical and 75 to 100 km in the

TABLE 4.312.2. HORIZONTAL EXTENT OF TURBULENCE REGIONS

Extent (miles*)	< 10	10–19.9	20–29.9	30–39.9	40–49.9
Per cent of cases	31.5	21.4	9.5	10.1	6.5
Extent (miles*)	50–59.9	60–69.9	70–79.9	80–89.9	90–99.9
Per cent of cases	4.8	2.4	2.4	0.6	1.2
Extent (miles*)	100–149.9	150–199.9	> 200		
Per cent of cases	6.5	2.4	0.6		

* 1 mile = 1.61 km

horizontal. Table 4.312.2 contains a per cent frequency distribution for 168 turbulent areas experienced in the course of Project Jet Stream flights (Fetner, 1956), according to classes of horizontal diameter (Cunningham, 1958).

According to considerations made by Richardson (1920), which will be discussed further in Chapter 4.322, it follows that vertical—and maybe horizontal—wind shears are important for the formation of turbulence (see Berenger and Heissat, 1959*a*). From this point of view the jet stream should be a preferred location of CAT. This becomes clearly evident from a classical study by Bannon (1952), which has been reproduced many times since (Berggren, Gibbs, and Newton, 1958; Reiter, 1960*b*; Riehl, Alaka, *et al.*, 1954; Weber, 1959). Into a normalized cross section through the jet stream CAT cases with $\geqq 0.4$ g have been entered, which have been observed above 20,000 ft (6 km). Of a total of 92 CAT observations 56 lay in the proximity of the jet stream. The main portion of the observed cases was concentrated on the cyclonic side and below the mean jet maximum, i.e., where according to Endlich's and McLean's (1957) model one would find the "jet-stream front" (see Balzer and Harrison, 1959; Harrison, 1959). A second turbulent zone extends near the tropopause, with its center again on the cyclonic side of the jet stream. Both zones coincide with

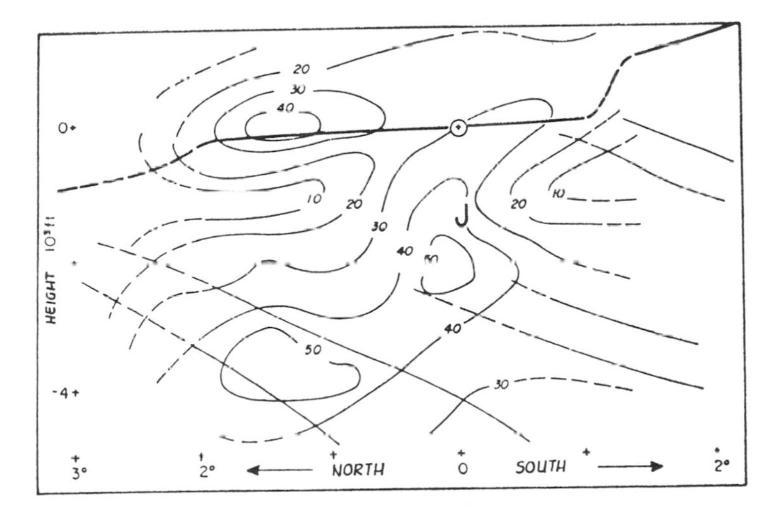

FIG. 4.312.1.—Mean distribution of CAT expressed in per cent turbulent flying time of total flying time, for nine Project Jet Stream flights 1956/57. (Sasaki, 1958.)

regions of small Richardson number (Defant, 1959*b*). Figure 4.312.1 contains an average distribution of CAT expressed in terms of turbulent flying time in per cent of total flying time for nine Project Jet Stream flights of the 1956–57 season. Bannon's results are corroborated by this diagram: the turbulence frequency on the cyclonic side exceeds the one on the anticyclonic side, although the latter still shows a relatively large number of CAT cases.

The position of the individual turbulence maxima coincides with the location of stable baroclinic zones. Figures 4.232.3 and .4, and 4.311.2 and .3, too, indicate a relationship between turbulence and stability as well as baroclinicity of the atmosphere, as could already be shown for the meso-structure of jet streams (Chapter 4.311). CAT, therefore, constitutes a turbulence phenomenon which, although belonging in another range of wave lengths than the meso-structure, obeys the same dynamic principles as the latter. This fact may be expressed by the perturbation theory (see Chapter 4.32).

If one accepts the assumption that, aside from vertical gusts in convective currents of an unstable atmosphere ("thermo-convective" turbulence, according to Georgii [1956*a*, 1958*b*]), mainly stable atmospheric stratifications are responsible for the occurrence of CAT, it may seem paradox at first sight, when Cunningham (1958) observes largest frequencies of turbulence with negligibly small horizontal gradients of temperature (Fig. 4.312.2). This apparent discrepancy can, however, be explained in a very simple way (Reiter, 1961*a*): In view of the analyses shown in Chapters 4.232 and 4.311, Danielsen's (1959) conclusion seems to be justified, whereby the stable and

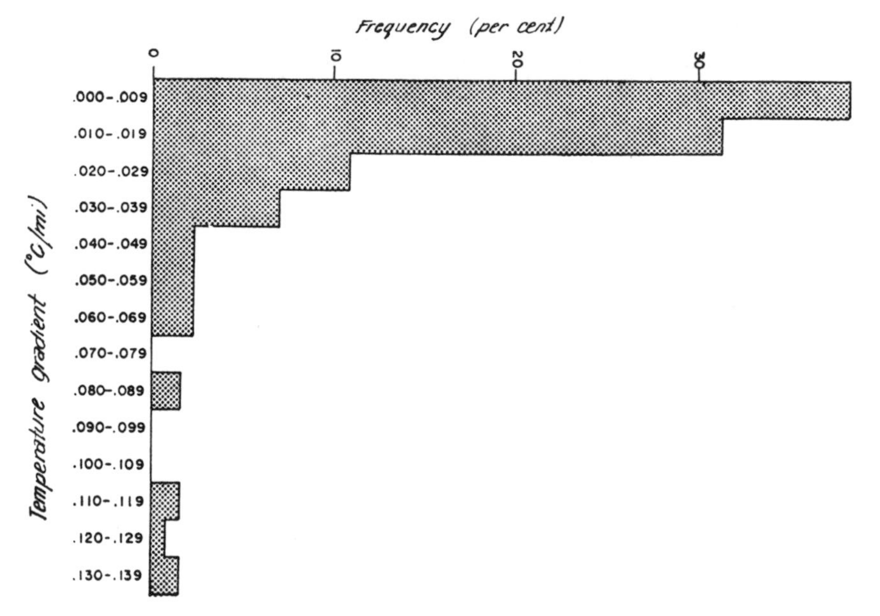

FIG. 4.312.2.—Frequency distribution of 128 CAT zones according to classes of horizontal temperature gradients. (Cunningham, 1958.)

baroclinic zones involved in CAT formation may be rather thin. An aircraft which traverses these layers at right angles may record a certain temperature change, the probability of CAT occurrence is, however, small. At best CAT will be experienced in a few short bumps. It will be different, as soon as the aircraft intersects such a stable layer at an oblique angle: the recorded temperature gradients will be rather small; the aircraft will, however, be exposed to this layer for a longer time and the probability of the occurrence of CAT will be relatively large. Under these circumstances, it also seems plausible that Figure 4.232.4 shows only few (objective) CAT reports within the shallow, and therefore rapidly traversed, stable layers on the anticyclonic side of the jet stream, while Figures 4.311.2 and .3 indicate a much better correlation between CAT and such zones.

Many observers describe CAT as being a "random phenomenon." The reason for this lies in the difficulties of measuring the meso-structural, stable layers in the atmosphere, and in their small extent. So, for instance, there are reports, according to which an aircraft experienced CAT at a certain location, and a following aircraft did not (Hislop, 1951). During the measurement program with gust sondes (Anderson, 1957*b*), it was found over the United States, among other things that, within the same 5000 ft (1400 m) layers, turbulence was recorded during at least three consecutive ascents (i.e., during at least 48 hours) only in about 8.4 per cent of all cases. This does not yet prove, however, that the statistics were concerned with identical turbulence layers from one ascent to the next. The station Grand Junction experienced "persistent turbulence" in 49 per cent of the cases, thus deviating from the pattern set by the rest of the stations. Since, however, Grand Junction lies in the Rocky Mountain region, much of the turbulence observed there might have been caused by high-level standing mountain waves. (Sixty-two per cent of all cases with persistent turbulence over this station have been recorded within the height range between 9 and 15 km.)

Even small hills may, at times, cause an increase in turbulence frequencies. This is understandable, for a (laminar) basic current constantly receives energy in the perturbation components of motion from orographic sources. If the flow conditions of the basic current are stable, standing lee waves may be formed whose amplitudes strongly depend upon the vertical patterns of stability and shear. (A theory of lee waves by Scorer will be treated briefly in Chapter 4.323). Clodman and Ball (1959) were able to show the influence of a small range of hills upon turbulence by means of a frequency distribution of CAT cases in the vicinity of Wright-Patterson Air Force Base, Dayton, Ohio. Orographic obstacles are not a necessary condition for the occurrence of CAT, however. A study by Clodman, Morgan, and Ball (1960) indicates that one may expect CAT also over oceans (see also Crossley, 1961). Here, mainly the presence of vertical shears seems to support turbulence formation. In contrast to the measurements over land, which are expressed representatively by Figure 4.312.1, over the oceans CAT seems to occur more on the anticyclonic side of jet streams—especially in the region above the jet axis. The tropopause, again, shows a maximum of turbulence frequency, just as it does over land. The delta region seems to be more turbulent over oceans than any other jet-stream sector.

4.32. The Perturbation Theory and the Fine Structure of Jet Streams

4.321. Principles of the Perturbation Theory

The components u, v, w, p of the three-dimensional velocity and pressure field at any given point in space may be considered resultants of an undisturbed, *quasi-stationary* basic current $\bar{u}$, $\bar{v}$, $\bar{w}$, $\bar{p}$ and a superimposed *perturbation motion* u^*, v^*, w^*, p^* which is variable in space and time. The latter is rather small in comparison with the former, so that its quadratic terms may be neglected wherever they appear. The hydrodynamic equations, thus linearized, are more easily accessible to mathematical treatment. In meteorology, the perturbation theory has been applied successfully by V. Bjerknes (1926, 1929; *et al.*, 1933; see Haurwitz, 1941). According to the above definition we have

$$\begin{aligned} u &= \bar{u} + u^* \\ v &= \bar{v} + v^* \\ w &= \bar{w} + w^* \\ p &= \bar{p} + p^*. \end{aligned} \qquad 4.321\ (1)$$

The equations of motion 1.221 (1) are not only valid for the total motion but also for the undisturbed basic flow. Neglecting frictional effects we obtain in component notation

$$\frac{\partial u}{\partial t} + u\frac{\partial u}{\partial x} + v\frac{\partial u}{\partial y} + w\frac{\partial u}{\partial z} + 2\Omega_y w - 2\Omega_z v = -\frac{1}{\rho}\frac{\partial p}{\partial x} \qquad 4.321\ (2)$$

and

$$\frac{\partial \bar{u}}{\partial t} + \bar{u}\frac{\partial \bar{u}}{\partial x} + \bar{v}\frac{\partial \bar{u}}{\partial y} + \bar{w}\frac{\partial \bar{u}}{\partial z} + 2\Omega_y \bar{w} - 2\Omega_z \bar{v} = -\frac{1}{\rho}\frac{\partial \bar{p}}{\partial x}. \qquad 4.321\ (3)$$

Analogous expressions may be written down for the v- and w-components. For simplicity's sake we will, however, assume *zonal* and *horizontal* conditions of flow in the basic current (Sasaki, 1958). Introducing into 4.321 (2) the definitions 4.321 (1) we obtain

$$\frac{\partial \bar{u}}{\partial t} + \frac{\partial u^*}{\partial t} + (\bar{u}+u^*)\frac{\partial(\bar{u}+u^*)}{\partial x} + v^*\frac{\partial(\bar{u}+u^*)}{\partial y} + w^*\frac{\partial(\bar{u}+u^*)}{\partial z} + 2\Omega_y w^* - 2\Omega_z v^* = -\frac{1}{\rho}\frac{\partial(\bar{p}+p^*)}{\partial x}.$$

Subtracting 4.321 (3) from this, and neglecting quadratic terms in the perturbation motions we arrive at:

$$\frac{\partial u^*}{\partial t} + u^*\frac{\partial \bar{u}}{\partial x} + \bar{u}\frac{\partial u^*}{\partial x} + v^*\frac{\partial \bar{u}}{\partial y} + w^*\frac{\partial \bar{u}}{\partial z} + 2\Omega_y w^* - 2\Omega_z v^* = -\frac{1}{\rho}\frac{\partial p^*}{\partial x}. \qquad 4.321\ (4)$$

The continuity equation, 1.221 (2) may be transformed in a similar manner.

Let us further assume two atmospheric layers (subscripts $i=0, 1$), in which ρ_0, ρ_1 and $\bar{u}_0$, $\bar{u}_1$ are constant. Furthermore, we will only consider perturbations u^* and w^*, and we will neglect Ω_y. Under these conditions 4.321 (3) assumes the form:

$$\frac{\partial u_i^*}{\partial t} + \bar{u}_i\frac{\partial u_i^*}{\partial x} = -\frac{1}{\rho_i}\frac{\partial p_i^*}{\partial x}. \qquad 4.321\ (4a)$$

For the vertical component one obtains the expression

$$\frac{\partial w_i^*}{\partial t} + \bar{u}_i\frac{\partial w_i^*}{\partial x} = -\frac{1}{\rho_i}\frac{\partial p_i^*}{\partial z} \qquad 4.321\ (4b)$$

and from the continuity equation

$$\frac{\partial u_i^*}{\partial x} + \frac{\partial w_i^*}{\partial z} = 0. \qquad 4.321\ (4c)$$

At a large distance from the boundary ($z=0$) between the two layers the magnitude of the perturbation motions will become negligibly small ($u_i^* = w_i^* = p_i^* = 0$ for $z \to \pm\infty$). Furthermore, the pressure will be continuous across the boundary surface, which is expressed by the following boundary conditions:

$$\begin{aligned} \frac{\partial(p_0^* - p_1^*)}{\partial t} + \bar{u}_0\frac{\partial(p_0^* - p_1^*)}{\partial x} + w_0^*\frac{\partial(\bar{p}_0 - \bar{p}_1)}{\partial z} &= 0 \\ \frac{\partial(p_0^* - p_1^*)}{\partial t} + \bar{u}_1\frac{\partial(p_0^* - p_1^*)}{\partial x} + w_1^*\frac{\partial(\bar{p}_0 - \bar{p}_1)}{\partial z} &= 0. \end{aligned} \qquad 4.321\ (5)$$

The following solutions of 4.321 (4) satisfy these boundary conditions:

In the lower layer,

$$\begin{aligned} u_0^* &= A_0 e^{kz} \cos k(x-ct) \\ w_0^* &= A_0 e^{kz} \sin k(x-ct) \\ p_0^* &= \rho_0(c-\bar{u}_0)A_0 e^{kz} \cos k(x-ct). \end{aligned} \qquad 4.321\ (6)$$

In the upper layer,

$$\begin{aligned} u_1^* &= -A_1 e^{-kz} \cos k(x-ct) \\ w_1^* &= A_1 e^{-kz} \sin k(x-ct) \\ p_1^* &= -\rho_1(c-\bar{u}_1)A_1 e^{-kz} \cos k(x-ct). \end{aligned} \qquad 4.321\ (7)$$

$k=2\pi/L$ is the wave number, L the wave length, and c the wave speed of the periodic perturbation motions. If we substitute 4.321 (6 and 7) into 4.321 (5), giving the conditions at the boundary surface, we obtain for $z=0$ and by using the hydrostatic equation, 1.222 (3)

$$\begin{aligned} k(c-\bar{u}_0)[\rho_0(c-\bar{u}_0)A_0+\rho_1(c-\bar{u}_1)A_1]-g(\rho_0-\rho_1)A_0=0 \\ k(c-\bar{u}_1)[\rho_0(c-\bar{u}_0)A_0+\rho_1(c-\bar{u}_1)A_1]-g(\rho_0-\rho_1)A_1=0. \end{aligned} \qquad 4.321\ (8)$$

The two amplitude factors A_0 and A_1 may be eliminated from 4.321 (8).

$$\rho_0(c-\bar{u}_0)^2+\rho_1(c-\bar{u}_1)^2-\frac{g}{k}(\rho_0-\rho_1)=0. \qquad 4.321\ (9)$$

From this equation, which is quadratic in c, one may compute the phase velocity of the perturbation motion:

$$c=\frac{\rho_0\bar{u}_0+\rho_1\bar{u}_1}{\rho_0+\rho_1}\pm\sqrt{\frac{g}{k}\frac{\rho_0-\rho_1}{\rho_0+\rho_1}-\frac{\rho_0\rho_1}{(\rho_0+\rho_1)^2}(\bar{u}_0-\bar{u}_1)^2}. \qquad 4.321\ (10)$$

This expression corresponds to the velocity of gravitational shearing waves (Haurwitz, 1941). They have been given this name, because they form on the interface between two stably stratified (incompressible) fluids under the influence of a wind shear (u_0-u_1).

From the observational results reported in Chapter 4.31 it became evident that shallow stable layers occur in the jet-stream region which may be considered in first approximation as discontinuity surfaces. The vertical wind shears may be considerable, too. Gravitational shearing waves, therefore, are to be expected frequently in the vicinity of jet maxima.

The perturbation components in 4.321 (6 and 7) magnify exponentially, if the square root in 4.321 (10) becomes imaginary. The condition of stability of the disturbance, therefore, may be expressed by

$$\frac{g}{k}\cdot\frac{\rho_0-\rho_1}{\rho_0+\rho_1}\lessgtr\frac{\rho_0\rho_1}{(\rho_0+\rho_1)^2}(\bar{u}_0-\bar{u}_1)^2 \quad \begin{matrix}\text{unstable}\\ \text{stable.}\end{matrix} \qquad 4.321\ (11)$$

We introduce the following abbreviated notations:

$$\bar{\rho}=\frac{\rho_0+\rho_1}{2} \qquad \Delta\rho=\rho_0-\rho_1 \qquad \Delta\bar{u}=\bar{u}_1-\bar{u}_0 \qquad 4.321\ (12)$$

and we obtain as limiting condition between laminar and turbulent flow,

$$\Delta\rho\lessgtr\frac{k}{g}\frac{\rho_0\rho_1}{2\bar{\rho}}(\Delta\bar{u})^2. \qquad 4.321\ (13)$$

The factor $\rho_0\rho_1/2\bar{\rho}$ may be transformed in the following way:

$$\frac{\rho_0\rho_1}{2\bar{\rho}}=\frac{-(\bar{\rho}-\rho_0)^2+\bar{\rho}^2}{2\bar{\rho}}=\frac{-\left(\frac{\Delta\rho}{2}\right)^2+\bar{\rho}^2}{2\bar{\rho}}\approx\frac{\bar{\rho}}{2},$$

because $\Delta\rho \ll \rho_1, \rho_2$.

Under these simplifications the instability criterion assumes the form

$$R\equiv\Delta\rho-\frac{k\bar{\rho}}{2g}(\Delta\bar{u})^2\lessgtr 0 \quad \begin{matrix}\text{unstable}\\ \text{stable.}\end{matrix} \qquad 4.321\ (14)$$

4.322. The Instability Criteria by Richardson and Sasaki

In a stably stratified atmosphere the turbulence has to work against the gravitational force. The required energy is drawn from the wind shear and from the resulting stresses. A limiting condition, under which the turbulence of the motion will barely be maintained, apparently is reached whenever energy dissipation (work against gravity) and energy supply (from vertical shear) balance each other. This limiting condition derived by Richardson (1920)—also known by the name of *Richardson's turbulence criterion*—has the form (Haurwitz, 1941; Sutton, 1953)

$$R_i=\frac{\frac{g}{T}\left(\frac{\partial T}{\partial z}+\Gamma\right)}{\left(\frac{\partial u}{\partial z}\right)^2+\left(\frac{\partial v}{\partial z}\right)^2}=\frac{\frac{g}{\Theta}\frac{\partial\Theta}{\partial z}}{\left(\frac{\partial V}{\partial z}\right)^2}\lessgtr 1 \quad \begin{matrix}\text{unstable}\\ \text{stable.}\end{matrix} \qquad 4.322\ (1)$$

A factor k_T/k_M has been assumed to equal 1 in this criterion. k_T is the exchange coefficient of heat, k_M the corresponding exchange coefficient of momentum. In its original formulation this criterion is valid only for small-scale motions in which the Coriolis parameter is without significance (Van Mieghem, 1961).

A comparison of 4.322 (1) with 4.321 (14) shows the formal similarity between the two criteria. Thus, the Richardson number may also be derived by means of the perturbation theory. It states the limiting conditions, under which an arbitrarily small perturbation will magnify its amplitude. No indication is given, however, about the wave length of the disturbance.

The actual limiting value of R_i, which would indicate an increase of turbulence, may vary widely. On rigid boundary surfaces for example, critical values of $R_i=0.04$ have been determined in the laboratory. A limiting value of 1 may hardly ever be expected, because in the derivation of the R_i number several simplifying assumptions have been made (Calder, 1949; Dugstad, 1956). So, according to a paper by Petterssen and Swinbank (1947) the condition $k_T/k_M=1$ does not seem to hold in the free atmosphere. A statistical investigation over England yielding $k_T/k_M=0.65$ makes a limiting value of $R_i=1.54$ more likely.

Sasaki (1958) also considers the limiting value in the form of 4.322 (1) to be unsatisfactory. Most of all, it cannot explain the occurrence of CAT at the level of maximum wind ($\partial V/\partial z=0$) and at the tropopause ($\partial T/\partial z=0$).

A large part of the discrepancies in the correlations that have been found or not found between CAT and Richardson's number are due to the different scales of measurement in the correlated quantities. CAT constitutes a micro-scalar phenomenon. Richardson's number, however, is usually determined from radiosonde ascents which bear a macro-scale character. At best it is computed from flight cross sections, as e.g., obtained from Project Jet Stream.

The evaluations by Brundidge (1956) indicate that the wind field as well as the temperature field are subject to strong variations within relatively short periods of time. As may be seen from investigations by the author (Reiter, 1961*a*, *d*), meso-structural fluctuations of speed of ± 5 m/sec, and of temperature of $\pm 1°$ C, are by all means possible in the jet-stream region. These fluctuations may change the vertical stability and shear conditions in a small area decisively enough to render the R_i numbers computed from macro-scale observations unrepresentative (Reiter, 1960*b*).

The criterion given by 4.322 (1) indicates an increase in turbulence probability with decreasing stability. The analyses shown in Chapters 4.232 and 4.311, however, reveal a tendency of the meso-structural oscillations of speed (wave lengths up to about 100 km) as well as of CAT to be relatively well established within *stable* layers (see Fig. 4.311.1). These results may be made to agree with the turbulence criterion, if the thermal wind equation is substituted into 4.322 (1) in the following form (Radok and Clarke, 1958; Reed, 1960*a*; Reiter, 1960*b*, *c*, 1961*a*, *d*):

$$\frac{\partial}{\partial \Theta} \dot{v} + f \frac{\partial u}{\partial \Theta} = -\frac{g}{T} \left(\frac{\partial T}{\partial n}\right) \frac{\partial z}{\partial \Theta}. \qquad 4.322\ (2)$$

We then obtain

$$R_i = \frac{f^2 \Theta}{g \dfrac{\partial \Theta}{\partial z} \left[\left(\dfrac{\partial z}{\partial n}\right)_\Theta - \left(\dfrac{\partial z}{\partial n}\right)_p - \dfrac{\Theta}{g} \left(\dfrac{\partial \dot{v}}{\partial \Theta}\right) \right]^2}. \qquad 4.322\ (3)$$

This expression has been derived by utilizing the following relationships:

$$\frac{\partial \Theta}{\partial z} = \frac{\Theta}{T} (\Gamma - \gamma), \qquad 4.322\ (4)$$

$$\frac{c_p}{g} \left(\frac{\partial T}{\partial y}\right)_\Theta = \left(\frac{\partial z}{\partial y}\right)_p - \left(\frac{\partial z}{\partial y}\right)_\Theta, \qquad 4.322\ (5)$$

$$\left(\frac{\partial T}{\partial y}\right)_\Theta = \left(\frac{\partial T}{\partial y}\right)_p + \frac{\partial T}{\partial z} \left(\frac{\partial z}{\partial y}\right)_\Theta, \qquad 4.322\ (6)$$

$$\left(\frac{\partial z}{\partial y}\right)_\Theta = \frac{-\left(\dfrac{\partial \Theta}{\partial y}\right)_p}{\dfrac{\partial \Theta}{\partial z}} \qquad 4.322\ (7)$$

and

$$\frac{\left(\dfrac{\partial T}{\partial y}\right)_\Theta}{\left(\dfrac{\partial T}{\partial y}\right)_p} = \frac{\Gamma}{\Gamma - \gamma}. \qquad 4.322\ (8)$$

$(\partial z/\partial n)_\Theta$ stands for the slope of isentropic surfaces, $(\partial z/\partial n)_p$ for the slope of isobaric surfaces, and $\partial \dot{v}/\partial \Theta$ indicates the change of horizontal acceleration in the vertical, which gives a measure of the effect of changes in the wind field with time, as pointed out above.

Neglecting $(\partial z/\partial n)_p$ and assuming $\partial \dot{v}/\partial \Theta = 0$, which will hold true for geostrophic conditions of flow, we arrive at the simple expression,

$$R_i^* = \frac{f^2}{g} \frac{\Theta}{\frac{\partial \Theta}{\partial z} \left[\frac{\partial z}{\partial n}\right]_\Theta^2}. \qquad 4.322\ (9)$$

We, therefore, have to expect the occurrence of meso-structural velocity variations and CAT the more frequently, the more stable and, at the same time, the more baroclinic the atmospheric stratification is. The wind field now does not enter directly into this relationship; it is, however, implied in the slope of the isentropic surfaces.

With this method of reasoning the influence of the shallow stable layers in the jet-stream region is brought out clearly. This has already been emphasized in Chapter 4.311. The fine structure of the *wind field*, thus, appears closely related with the *thermal* fine structure of the atmosphere.

The criterion of dynamic instability [1.236 (4)]

$$\left(\frac{\partial u}{\partial y}\right)_\Theta \geq f,$$

may be transformed by means of the relationship

$$\left(\frac{\partial u}{\partial y}\right)_\Theta = \frac{\partial u}{\partial z}\left(\frac{\partial z}{\partial y}\right)_\Theta + \left(\frac{\partial u}{\partial y}\right)_z. \qquad 4.322\ (10)$$

From this one arrives at the critical slope of isentropic surfaces

$$\left(\frac{\partial z}{\partial y}\right)_{\Theta Cr} = \frac{f - \left(\frac{\partial u}{\partial y}\right)_z}{\frac{\partial u}{\partial z}}. \qquad 4.322\ (11)$$

If the horizontal wind shear $(\partial u/\partial y)_z = 0$, we obtain

$$\left(\frac{\partial z}{\partial y}\right)_{\Theta Cr} = \frac{f}{\frac{\partial u}{\partial z}}. \qquad 4.322\ (12)$$

This expression is substituted into 4.322 (9) under consideration of

$$\frac{\partial u}{\partial z} = \frac{g}{f\Theta} \frac{\partial \Theta}{\partial z} \left\{\left(\frac{\partial z}{\partial y}\right)_\Theta - \left(\frac{\partial z}{\partial y}\right)_p\right\}.$$

Under the simplifying assumption that $(\partial u/\partial y)_z = (\partial z/\partial n)_p = \partial \dot{v}/\partial \Theta = 0$ this results in

$$R_i^*{}_{Cr} = 1. \qquad 4.322\ (13)$$

One may, therefore, expect the critical value of R_i^*, which indicates the increase of originally small amplitudes in the disturbances, to be 1 only, if geostrophic conditions of flow without horizontal shear are prevailing. This will not be the case in the jet-stream region. It has already been pointed out in Chapter 4.232, that in the vicinity of the jet-stream core strong ageostrophic components of flow are present. The horizontal shear has an order of magnitude of 10^{-5} sec^{-1}. Nevertheless, a relationship of the kind given by 4.322 (9) seems to govern the *average* meso-structural conditions in the atmosphere. This becomes evident from Figure 4.311.1.

If we introduce 4.322 (11) and an analogous expression for $\left(\frac{\partial z}{\partial y}\right)_p$ into 4.322 (3) without neglecting the horizontal shear, we obtain for geostrophic conditions of flow (Radok and Clarke, 1958),

$$\frac{1}{R_{ik}} = 1 - \frac{1}{f}\left(\frac{\partial u}{\partial y}\right)_p . \qquad 4.322\ (14)$$

This corresponds to a criterion of "potential dynamic instability," which has been derived by Eady (1949).

In analogy to the criterion 4.321 (14), which may also be written in the form

$$R \equiv \Delta T + \Gamma - m_i \Delta V^2 \qquad 4.322\ (15)$$

where $m_i = (T/g\Delta z)\cdot(k_M/k_T)$, Sasaki (1958) derived a stability criterion which incorporates the *curvature* of the vertical wind and temperature profiles (second derivative with height):

$$\tau_i \equiv \overline{\Delta\Delta T} + 2m_i \overline{\Delta V}\cdot\overline{\Delta\Delta V}. \qquad 4.322\ (16)$$

This symbolic notation stands for

$$j \equiv \overline{\Delta\Delta V} \equiv \frac{\Delta V_{+1} - \Delta V_{-1}}{2} \qquad \begin{aligned} \Delta V_{+1} &\equiv V_{+1} - V_0 \\ \Delta V_{-1} &\equiv V_0 - V_{-1}. \end{aligned}$$

The subscripts $+1$, 0, -1 refer to the upper, intermediate, and lower layer of a three-layer model of the atmosphere. For m_i Sasaki found an empirical value of 0.0198° C/knot^2.

By means of this criterion critical conditions of flow may be studied at the tropopause and at jet-stream level. (A slightly more detailed review of this criterion has been given by Reiter [1960*b*]). Sasaki obtains:

1. At the tropopause: $|\tau_i| > m_i j^2$

stable	$0 < R < m_i j^2$	or $|\tau_i| + m_i j^2 < R$
unstable	$R < 0$	or $m_i j^2 < R < |\tau_i| + m_i j^2$.

2. At jet stream level: $|\tau_i| < m_i j^2$

stable	$m_i j^2 - |\tau_i| < R < m_i j^2$	or $m_i j^2 + |\tau_i| < R$
unstable	$R < m_i j^2 - |\tau_i|$	or $m_i j^2 < R < m_i j^2 + |\tau_i|$.

R is given by 4.322 (15).

From the evaluation of a number of Project Jet Stream flights it seems as though Sasaki's criterion might be superior to Richardson's [Eq. 4.321 (14)] when dealing with CAT areas (Sanford, 1958; Sasaki, 1958).

4.323. The Scorer Criterion of Lee-Wave Formation

To the lee of hill or mountain ranges, as well as of single peaks, one may observe under favorable conditions large lenticular clouds, the so-called Moazagotl clouds.

They indicate the existence of large "standing waves," which form in a strong upper current under the external forcing influence of a perturbation pattern, namely the ground elevation.[2]

[2] A review of this phenomenon with an extensive bibliography has been compiled by Alaka (1958*b*). See also Georgii (1956*b*), Queney *et al.* (1960) and Reiter (1960*b*).

The North American Rocky Mountains and the South American Andes contribute to a frequency maximum of lee-wave phenomena because of their capacity as a large barrier in the zone of westerlies. Research on lee-wave phenomena has also been conducted near other mountain ranges, and is rather far advanced in Europe (Ferrari, 1958; Förchtgott, 1956; Georgii, 1953, 1958*a*; Gerbier and Berenger, 1960*a*, *b*, 1961; Harrison, 1956, 1957*a*, *b*; Jenkins, 1952*b*; MacDonald and Harrison, 1960; Sinha, 1960).

The wave formation may, at times, reach to great altitudes. It could even be detected at the level of nacreous clouds and in the ozonosphere (Dietrichs, 1950; Jenkins and Kuettner, 1953; Paetzold and Zschörner, 1955; Palm and Foldvik, 1960).

Lee waves have been investigated theoretically by Lyra (1940, 1943; see also Koschmieder, 1951; Zierep, 1958) and by Queney (1941, 1947, also 1959*a*). Scorer and others succeeded in deriving expressions which may be evaluated in a comparatively simple manner from radiosonde data, and, therefore may be utilized for prognostic purposes (Döös, 1958; Palm, 1958; Sawyer, 1960; Scorer, 1949, 1951*a*, *b*, *c*, 1952, 1953*a*, *b*, 1954, 1955, 1957, 1958*a*, *b*, 1959; Scorer and Klieforth, 1959; Wurtele, 1956). Since lee waves occur especially in the jet-stream region and therefore constitute a meso- or micro-scale phenomenon of the jet stream, which is important to air traffic because of the occurrence of CAT, a short review of the results of Scorer's research efforts will be given here.

If one neglects the Coriolis parameter, the wave equation

$$\frac{\partial^2\psi}{\partial z^2}-\left(\frac{g}{C^2}+\beta\right)\frac{\partial\psi}{\partial z}+\left(\frac{g\beta}{V^2}-k^2-\frac{1}{V}\frac{\partial^2 V}{\partial z^2}\right)\psi=0 \qquad 4.323\ (1)$$

will describe disturbances of a wave length <50 km. Let the disturbances be periodic in the x-direction. The stream function ψ, then, is defined by

$$u=\frac{\partial\psi}{\partial z}-\frac{g}{C^2}\psi,$$
$$w=-ik\psi. \qquad 4.323\ (2)$$

C is the velocity of sound ($C=\sqrt{\kappa RT}$), and β is the vertical stability $(1/\Theta)\cdot(\partial\Theta/\partial z)$ [see Eq. 3.245 (5)]. Equation 4.323 (1) may be solved for constant coefficients, if the wind profile may be approximated by a solution of the equation

$$\frac{g\beta}{V^2}-\frac{1}{V}\frac{\partial^2 V}{\partial z^2}=l^2=\text{const.} \qquad 4.323\ (3)$$

l^2 is usually called the "Scorer parameter." $\frac{g\beta}{V^2}$ is Lyra's wave number. The term $\frac{1}{V}\frac{\partial^2 V}{\partial z^2}$ is of importance only in the lowest layers of the atmosphere (<900 m), and when strong vertical wind shears are present (Gazzola, 1956). Equation 4.323 (1) has the following solution for a two-layer atmospheric model:

$$\psi = A_1 e^{L_1 y} + A_2 e^{L_2 z}$$

$$L_1,\ L_2 = \frac{1}{2}\left\{\frac{g}{C^2} + \beta \pm \sqrt{\left(\frac{g}{C^2}+\beta\right)^2 + 4(k^2 - l^2)}\right\} \qquad 4.323\ (4)$$

$$\cong \pm\sqrt{(k^2 - l^2)} \qquad 4.323\ (5)$$

because of

$$\frac{g\beta}{V^2} \gg \left(\frac{g}{C^2}+\beta\right)^2. \qquad 4.323\ (6)$$

Not taking into account the trivial solution of 4.323 (3), $V=\text{const}$, the wind profile is periodic for $l^2 > 0$ and $\beta = \text{const}$, and contains maxima and minima of wind speed. At the inflection point $l^2 = g\beta/V^2$. The "Scorer parameter" l^2 characterizes the dynamic properties of the atmosphere at each level.

Considering expression 4.323 (6), 4.323 (1) may be reduced to the simple form

$$\frac{\partial^2 \psi}{\partial z^2} + (l^2 - k^2)\psi = 0. \qquad 4.323\ (7)$$

Scorer showed that lee waves are forming only, *if l^2 decreases with height.* A limiting condition for the appearance of waves is given by

$$l_1{}^2 - l_2{}^2 > \frac{\pi^2}{4h^2}. \qquad 4.323\ (8)$$

h is the thickness of the lower layer (subscript 1).

The deviation ζ_z of the streamline at the level z from an undisturbed state has been computed by Corby and Wallington (1956)

$$\zeta_z = -2\pi h b e^{-kb}\left(\frac{V_1}{V_z}\right)\psi_{z,k}\left(\frac{\partial \psi_{1,k}}{\partial k}\right)^{-1} \sin kx. \qquad 4.323\ (9)$$

(V_1 = surface wind, V_z = upper wind, k = wave number of lee waves, h = height of the mountain range, b = "half width" of the mountain, given by $\zeta = \frac{hb^2}{b^2 + x^2}$, where ζ is the height of the location which lies at a distance x from the crest of the mountain ridge.)

From this equation it may be seen that the longest waves which are still able to fulfil condition 4.323 (8) (smallest wave number k), are triggered to form the largest amplitudes. By the same token, narrow but steep obstacles induce large wave amplitudes.

A decrease of the parameter l^2 in the vertical, which is one of the prerequisites of wave formation, may be caused by a decrease in the stability β, or by an increase of the wind speed V with height. Of two identical l^2-profiles, the one with strongest surface winds, and therefore with the largest factor V_1/V_z in 4.323 (9), will produce the largest amplitudes.

Due to condition 4.323 (8) jet-stream situations seem to be especially favorable to the formation of standing lee waves, because the pronounced *increase* of wind speed with height warrants the decrease of the parameter l^2. An effective wave formation

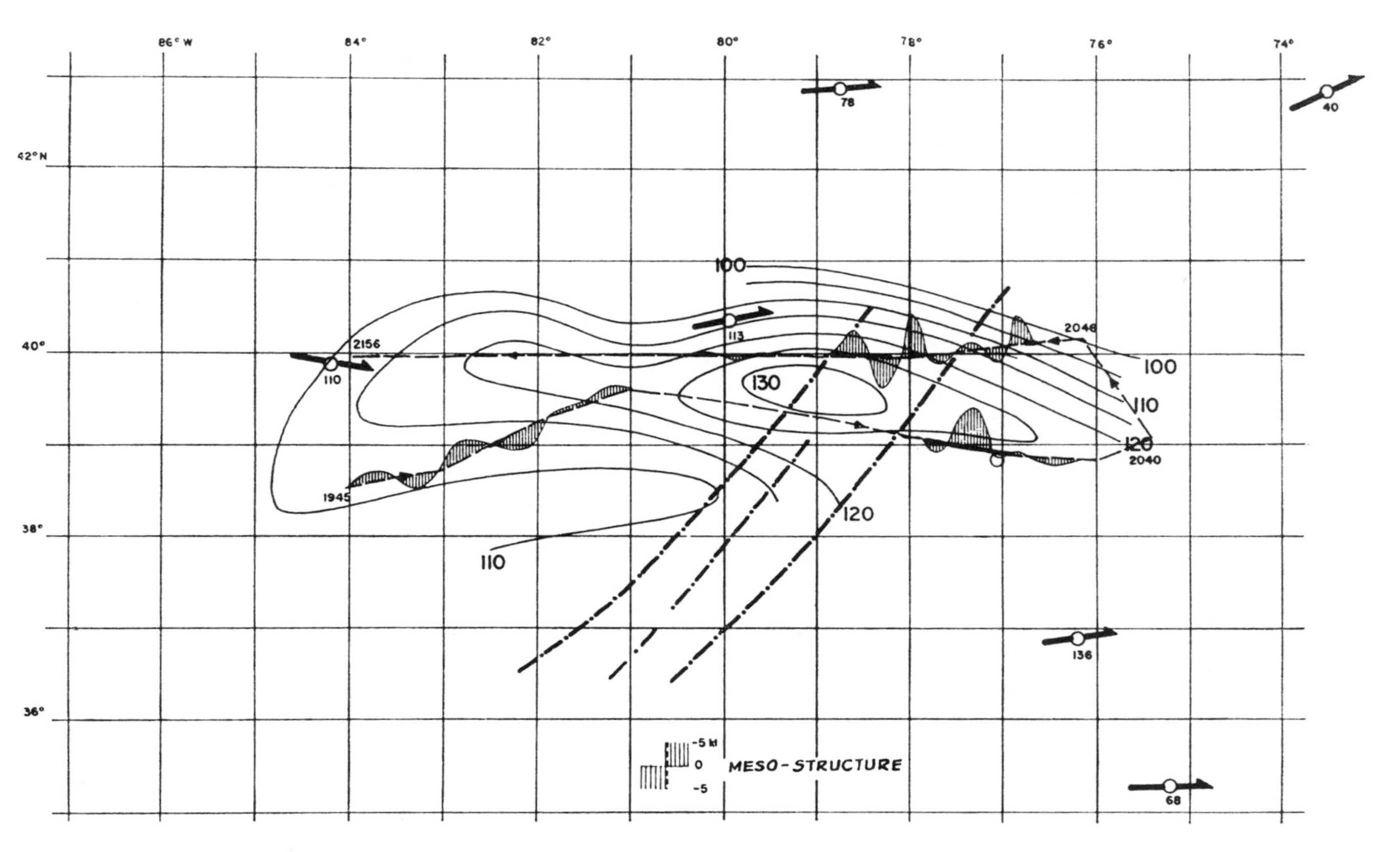

Fig. 4.323.1.—Isotachs (knots) at the 300-mb level, Flight No. 9. Wind speeds and directions of 10 January, 1957, 1500 GCT, are entered at the stations. The numbers at the ends of the flight legs indicate time (GCT). The ridges of the Alleghenies are marked by heavy dashed-dotted lines. Turbulence according to observations made by the co-pilot is indicated by heavy lines along the flight legs. The meso-structure of the wind speed is given by shading (positive anomalies are plotted upward, negative anomalies downward from the flight route, which serves as a base line).

should be expected, however, only if the flow near the earth's surface also shows a component normal to the direction of the mountain range. Only in this manner will a perturbation motion be generated which may influence higher levels. Because lee waves—especially when forming great amplitudes or even "rotors" (i.e., regions in which the actual flow runs in a direction opposite to the basic [undisturbed] current)—usually are associated with CAT and thus may be dangerous for air traffic (Gales, 1955; Kuettner, 1959*b*; Larsson, 1958; Wallington, 1959), Scorer's theory assumes a special position in considering the detailed structure of jet streams. It has already been mentioned in Chapter 4.312 that relatively low ranges of hills may have a distinct influence upon the space distribution of CAT. This effect will have to be considered especially during jet-stream weather situations and may improve turbulence warnings.

At times several levels may be present in which lee waves attain maximum amplitudes. *They may be expected wherever the vertical distribution of l^2 shows a maximum* (Alaka, 1958*b*; Corby, 1957). Thus, Scorer's lee-wave theory also allows one to expect maximum wave amplitudes within stable layers in the jet-stream region similar to what has been shown by means of the R_i^* criterion in Chapter 4.311. This does *not* mean, however, that all meso-structure of jet streams is a lee-wave phenomenon. The similarity of the results is rather caused by the similarities in the theoretical prerequisites: The derivation of the R_i^*-number as well as Scorer's lee-wave theory start from the perturbation equations. The difference lies only in the assumption of random disturbances on the one hand and forced orographic disturbances on the other hand.

As an example, the weather situation of 10 January, 1957, will be given here, which has been explored by Project Jet Stream research Flight No. 9 (Reiter *et al.*, 1961). Figure 4.323.1 shows the isotachs of wind speed at the 300-mb level obtained from aircraft measurements and from rawin data. (The four-digit numbers along the flight routes indicate the time [GCT] at which these points have been reached.) To the lee of the Alleghenies—the dash-dotted lines schematically indicate the position of the mountain ranges—the meso-structure of the flow, indicated by shading, clearly brings out the formation of standing lee waves. Figure 4.323.2 contains the temperature analysis of the same level. The numbers entered at the radiosonde stations give the temperature measurements on 10 January, 1957, 1500 GCT (upper number), and on 11 January, 0300 GCT (lower number). The intersection of the tropopause with the 300-mb level is indicated by a heavy line. Large amplitudes of the meso-structure caused by lee waves mainly occur along the northern flight leg, where the prevailing horizontal temperature gradient indicates the existence of a stable and baroclinic zone.

Figure 4.323.3 shows the radiosonde ascent of Pittsburgh, Pennsylvania, of 10 January, 1500 GCT (solid line) and of 11 January, 0300 GCT (dashed). From the first ascent the parameter $g\beta/V^2$ has been computed and entered in units of 10^{-6} m^{-2} (shaded area). As this diagram shows, this parameter has a minimum value at the 300-mb level and a secondary maximum above. Thus, this level would be favorable for the formation of standing lee waves. The minimum near 300 mb, in reality, probably would assume even smaller values, thus giving a better agreement with the observed wave lengths, because from the slope of the ascent curve on 10 January, between 300 and 400 mb, one might gather that a thin stable layer has been lost

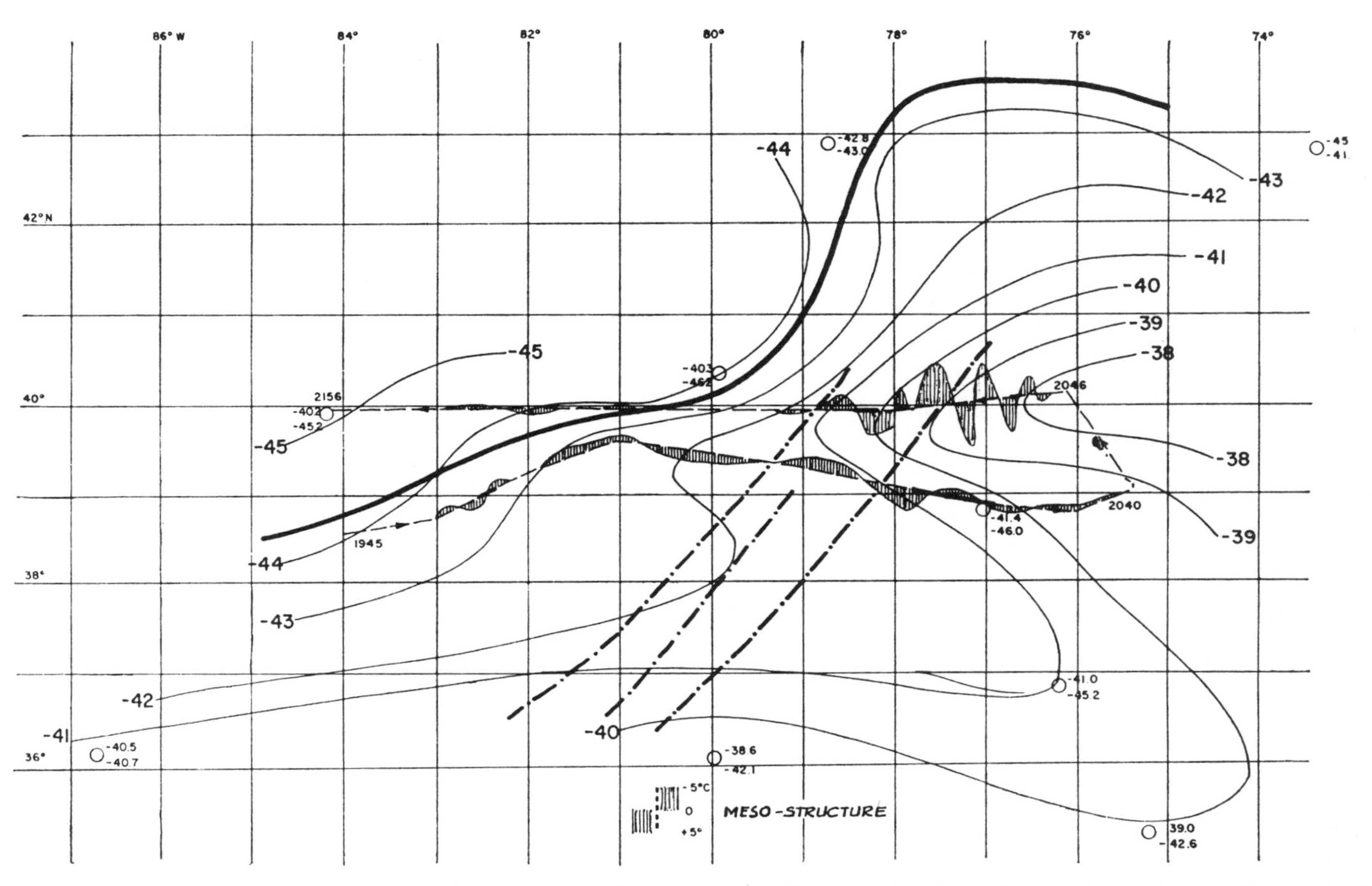

FIG. 4.323.2.—Isotherms (° C) at the 300-mb level, and meso-structure of temperature (positive anomalies plotted downward, negative anomalies upward) at the time of Flight No. 9. Temperatures of 10 January, 1957, 1500 GCT, are plotted at radiosonde stations (upper numbers), as are the temperatures of 11 January, 1957, 0300 GCT (lower numbers). Heavy lines, intersection of tropopause with 300-mb surface. Additional explanations may be taken from the legend to Figure 4.323.1.

during the coding process (see Danielsen, 1959; Reiter *et al.*, 1961). Twelve hours later (11 January, 0300 GCT) there is an additional kink in the temperature curve.

The term $(1/V)\cdot(\partial^2 V/\partial z^2)$, obtained from the vertical wind profile of Pittsburgh (small circles and thin line), has also been entered into Figure 4.323.3 in units of 10^{-6} m^{-2}. The reliability of these computations is not very great, however, because

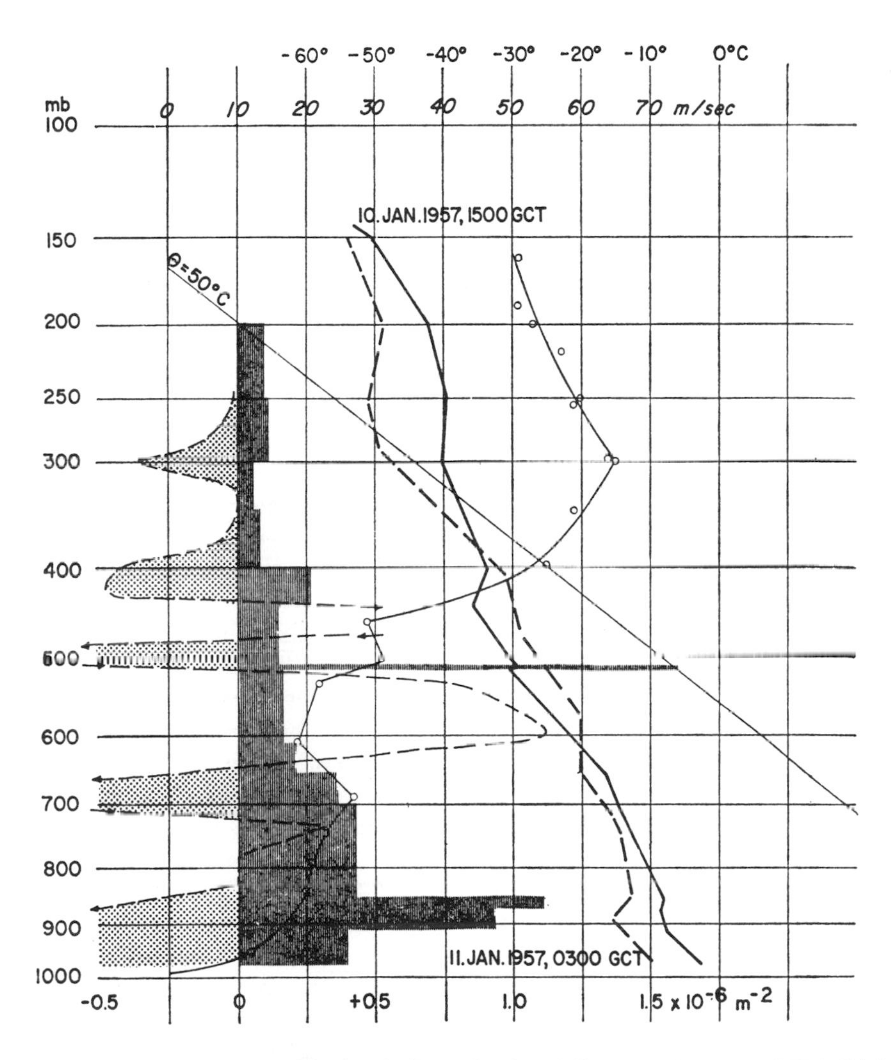

FIG. 4.323.3.—Radiosonde ascents, Pittsburgh, Pennsylvania, 10 January, 1957, 1500 GCT (solid line), and 11 January, 1957, 0300 GCT (dashed line), and vertical wind profile, 10 January, 1500 GCT (thin solid line with circles). Distributions of $g\beta/V^2$ (vertically shaded) and of $1/V\cdot\partial^2 V/\partial z^2$ (light dashed line and dotted area in the left portion of the diagram).

of possible errors of measurement in the wind profile. Since this term enters with a negative sign into the expression for l^2 [Eq. 4.323 (3)], the maxima of the Scorer parameter are indicated by the full amplitudes of the shaded area in Figure 4.323.3.

Additional aircraft measurements which have been made at the 264-mb level revealed much smaller lee-wave amplitudes in comparison with Figures 4.323.1 and .2. This stands in agreement with the distribution of the parameter l^2 with height in Figure 4.323.3.

The important contribution of lee-wave formation to the fine structure of the wind and temperature fields in the jet-stream region is stressed by the large amplitudes of meso-structural disturbances which occur over the ranges of the Rocky Mountains in Figures 4.311.2 and .3.

4.4. JET-STREAM SYSTEMS

4.41. Atmospheric Jet Streams

In the preceding chapters structural characteristics of high tropospheric jet streams have already been discussed in some detail. It proved to be necessary on several occasions to refer to two different types of jet streams. One of them, usually termed "polar-front jet" (PFJ) or "jet stream of the temperate latitudes," may be found near the 300-mb level (9 km), sometimes even lower. The other type occurs near the 200-mb level (12 km) and is commonly called "subtropical" or "southern jet stream" (STJ). In Chapter 4.14 several differences in these two jet-stream systems were pointed out, as far as was necessary for understanding the confluence theory.

A clear-cut differentiation between these two jet-stream types is not always possible, because there seem to be certain transition stages during which the jet axis may be found at the 200-mb level, or even higher up, although the lower troposphere still shows a marked baroclinicity at the edge of a fanning cold air mass (Reiter, 1959*b*).

The studies on the structure of jet streams reported in Chapter 4.1 and 4.2 were mainly confined to the polar-front jet, except for Endlich's measurements in the jet-stream core (Chapter 4.232), which have been gained predominantly from the sub-tropical jet stream. Most of the structural characteristics described in the preceding chapters probably are valid for both jet-stream systems, the PFJ and the STJ, however. In Chapter 4.211 (Fig. 4.211.5) reference has been made to several other jet-stream systems in the tropics: the tropical jet stream from the east, the Berson westerlies, and the Krakatoa easterlies. The two latter systems have only small lateral and vertical shears and, therefore, would not qualify as "jet streams" according to the WMO classification (Chapter 1.1). If, however, one accepts a horizontal shear of the order of magnitude of the Coriolis parameter as a threshold value, one could call them "jet streams" because of their proximity to the equator. Furthermore, mainly from observational data of the International Geophysical Year 1957/58, the existence of a laterally confined jet stream could be proven recently in the Arctic and Antarctic stratosphere which satisfies the WMO definition, and which blows from a westerly direction during winter, giving way to weaker easterlies in the northern hemisphere during the summer. It is the *Arctic stratospheric jet* (ASJ) (see Pogosian, 1957*b*).

In the lower troposphere during certain weather patterns a "*low-level jet stream*" (LLJ) is present, which will be treated separately in this book. The following section gives a short summary of the characteristics of these various jet streams.

4.411. The Polar-Front Jet Stream (PFJ)

Figures 3.211,4. 221.2, and Model No. 1 by Brundidge and Goldman (1958) (Fig. 4.232.6) may be regarded as typical cross sections through a PFJ. In all these cases the wind maximum lies near 300 mb (9 to 10 km) (Berg, 1949; Fotheringham, 1953). A strongly baroclinic zone extends through almost the entire troposphere. In some cases the "jet-stream front" immediately underneath the jet axis seems to be separated from this main zone. The "frontal zone" may appear as one continuous layer, as shown in Figure 3.211, in other instances it may be rather diffuse in the middle troposphere, as, e.g., in the delta region shown in Figure 4.221.2. This zone hardly ever is truly isentropic but in general has a layered structure (Danielsen, 1959; Reiter, 1961*a*). It is essential, however, that the atmosphere is baroclinic in a more or less wide zone, which extends from the lower troposphere up to the jet-stream level. This baroclinic zone even extends into the stratosphere—with negative baroclinicity, of course. The position of the jet axis will have to be sought approximately above the warm edge of the frontal-zone intersection with the 500-mb level (mostly a short distance to the right of this location), or underneath the intersection of the stratospheric frontal zone with the 200-mb level.

This strongly baroclinic zone, at times, may be traced around the whole hemisphere (Bradbury and Palmén, 1953); however, it is usually interrupted in places and undergoes new formation. It, therefore, should not be regarded as continuous in its longitudinal extent, but rather as a zone which constantly migrates, dissipates, and then re-forms elsewhere.

The pronounced baroclinicity in the lower troposphere probably is the reason that the PFJ was discovered first. The point of view that the frontal zone is a boundary "surface" between two air masses, combines in the perception of the PFJ the more recent dynamical aspects of the atmosphere with the older Norwegian polar-front theory and with the treatment of air mass properties, mainly promoted by the German school of thought. More recent investigations, which will be discussed further in Chapter 6, reveal, however, that the "frontal zone," at least in its high-tropospheric part, frequently is a separate body of air which has been imported from the stratosphere by sinking motion (Reed and Danielsen, 1959; see Reiter, 1960*d*, *e*, 1961*d*; Reiter *et al.*, 1961). The significance of the frontal zone as mixing layer between two adjacent air masses, thus, has receded into the background, while more emphasis now is placed upon the *dynamic aspects* of the *baroclinic region*. The term "front," therefore, will be used in the following synonymously with "baroclinic zone," and not so much as a surface along which different air masses move upward or downward, thus causing the classical weather patterns.

Since the PFJ is the only jet stream in which the baroclinic zone reaches the earth's surface—sometimes well enough defined to warrant the expression "front," this kind of jet will be characterized by intensive frontal cyclogenesis (Chapter 6). The term "polar-front jet" may be somewhat misleading insofar as this baroclinic zone, which becomes unstable for wave disturbances of a certain wave length does not necessarily have to lie between polar and tropical air masses. It may separate air masses, which, according to the existing air-mass classifications may have other properties (e.g., continental Arctic air and maritime polar air). Bergeron (1956) points out that the Arctic front, too, is associated with a more or less well-defined jet stream, depending on the magnitude of baroclinicity present. It, therefore, is possible to observe upper-tropospheric jet streams at relatively high latitudes, e.g., over Greenland (Bedel, 1954; Godson, 1955*a*). Cyclogenesis may occur not only along the polar front but along each baroclinic zone, even near the pole (Bugaev, 1947; Reed and Kunkel, 1960). This trend of thought has been further developed in the so-called Canadian three-front model (Galloway, 1958; McIntyre, 1958; McIntyre and Lee, 1953). In extending the Norwegian polar-front school one probably overshoots the target if one tries to analyze all three fronts (polar front between mT and mP air, maritime Arctic front between mP and mA air, and continental Arctic front between mA and cA air masses) together with the three associated jet streams in continuous bands clearly around the hemisphere. Granted, the one or other of these fronts will be very conspicuous in some areas, and in some cross sections three jet streams may exist at the same time (Newton and Carson, 1953; Serebreny, Wiegman, and Hadfield, 1960); one should, however, keep in mind that frontogenetic and frontolytic processes are *continuously* active. Fronts, therefore, are no rigid "boundaries," which one should try to trace all around the hemisphere; they are constantly forming and dissipating, instead. Even the studies on the hemispheric position of the polar front made by Bradbury and Palmén (1953) clearly indicate areas in which the seemingly continuous 500-mb frontal zone, as evident from an isotherm analysis, is interrupted. The difficulties of "frontal" analysis in a frontolytically active region are avoided, if, as mentioned earlier, the main emphasis is placed on the perceptions of baroclinicity and of the dynamics of the upper flow.

Since the term "polar-front jet" has enjoyed common usage in meteorological literature, although it may actually be associated with a variety of air masses, it will be retained here, however, in its broader sense outlined above:

"Polar-front jets" are jet streams whose baroclinic zone extends throughout the troposphere down into the layers near the ground. Under favorable conditions frontal cyclogenesis may occur.

The distribution of divergence and convergence near jet streams mentioned earlier (Fig. 4.122.3) is valid not only for the PFJ but for each jet stream with a pronounced vorticity pattern, which may have been caused by the presence of velocity maxima or by wave formation. A further discussion of these effects will be given in Chapter 6.

The cross sections obtained from radiosonde and aircraft measurements during the much-quoted Project Jet Stream provide us with means of studying in detail the PFJ over North America. It may well be that several characteristics of this jet stream, as for instance horizontal and vertical wind shears and maximum wind speed, should not be generalized for all areas which are under the influence of the northern and southern hemisphere westerlies, although so far no indications of significant deviations have been found (James, 1951*a*; Porter, 1951). Especially the *mean position* and *mean intensity* given in several of the cross sections should not be considered binding for other longitudes (Chapter 4.211). The cross sections along 80° W are characterized by the mean position of the PFJ being displaced rather far toward the south. (This may be the reason why Figure 4.211.4 shows only a weak indication of a subtropical jet stream, which frequently merges here with the PFJ.) The rather high mean wind speeds may be explained by the relatively small interdiurnal variability of the jet axis along this meridian. Cross sections farther to the west probably would show the PFJ farther to the north, and because of its migrating position its mean intensity would be less. The absolute wind maximum might even be found in the subtropical jet stream of this region, because of its greater steadiness. The latter seems to emerge from an area near Baja California, but due to the lack of upper-wind observations it cannot be traced accurately.

Over Eastern Asia and Japan the intense mean wind speeds at jet-stream level are also due to the small interdiurnal variability of the jet axis (see Chapter 4.211). So, e.g., the resulting wind vector over Tateno for winter at a height of 10 km is given as 260 km/h from the west (Flohn, 1944).

Essenwanger (1953; see Flohn, 1952*c*) conducted an interesting study on the frequency of wind-speed maxima at the 500-mb level as a function of geographic latitude (Fig. 4.411). As a comparison the frequency distribution obtained by Cressman (1950) for the 300-mb surface, and referred to already in Figure 4.121.3, is also

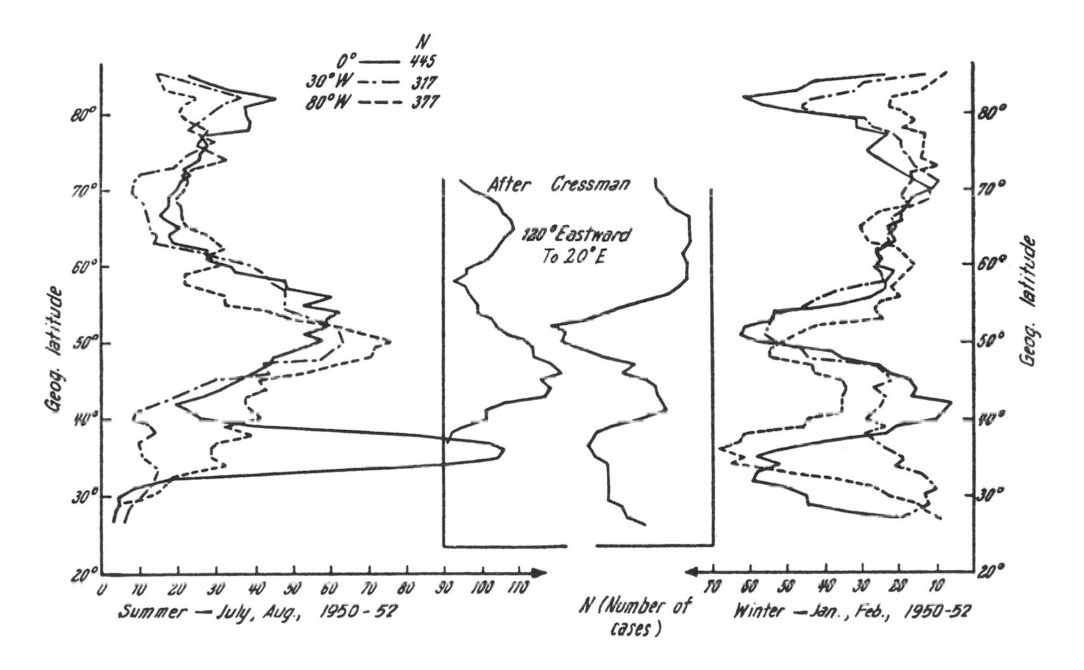

FIG. 4.411.—Frequency of wind maxima at the 500-mb level along 0°, 30°, and 80° W for summer (July, August) and winter (January, February) of 1950 to 1952 (N = number of cases). (Essenwanger, 1953.)

given in this diagram. The three meridians for which Essenwanger derived his statistics show considerable differences. First of all, three frequency maxima appear in winter as well as in summer: at about 80° N, 50° N, and 35° N. The northernmost of these three maxima, which, according to the Canadian point of view, might be associated with the baroclinicity between Arctic and polar air masses, is only weakly established over America (80° W), and there it is shifted toward lower latitudes than over Europe. The southernmost maximum in this investigation appears during summer only at the meridian 0°. Essenwanger surmises that this might be due to the thermal contrast between the Mediterranean and the North African continent. This frequency maximum probably is caused by the lower regions of the STJ which may be found over this area with relatively great steadiness. Over the Atlantic (30° W) we find the Azores' high during this season, and therefore the southern frequency maximum is missing at the 500-mb level. Over North America (80° W) this maximum is only weakly indicated. It also would correspond to the position of the STJ; however, as could be shown from the Project Jet Stream studies (Saucier, 1958*b*), the lower troposphere is quasi-barotropic in the STJ region, so that an indication of wind-speed maxima at the 500-mb level should be expected only rarely. During winter the southern maximum, again, is missing over the Atlantic. Over the United States and over Europe, however, it now is equally well established. Over the United States probably the deeply penetrating cold-air outbreaks in the lee of the Rocky Mountains are responsible for the presence of this frequency maximum. Therefore, this southernmost maximum still may be caused by polar-front jets, and it is not necessarily to be attributed to the STJ. The Arctic frequency maximum appears well pronounced over Europe and over the Atlantic at about 81° latitude, while it occurs at about 65° N over the United States. Here, the effect of the North American cold "pole" becomes apparent, which, on the average, is not far from the magnetic pole.

Upper-wind statistics which prove the existence of the PFJ, are available in large numbers for both hemispheres, e.g., North America: Henry and Armstrong, 1949; Europe: Berenger and Heissat, 1959*b*; Holzapfel, 1956*a*; Richter, 1952; Asia: Shimada, 1958; South Africa: Department of Transport, 1950; Australia: Porter, 1953; Row, 1951; Antarctica: Court, 1949; Falkland Islands: Gray and Carruthers, 1951.

In spite of the regional differences, there are certain general criteria which may be stated for the PFJ, based upon the results of the investigations quoted above (Saucier, 1958*b*).

1. At levels close to the jet-stream core the cyclonic shear to the left of the jet axis is somewhat larger than the anticyclonic shear to its right, where the absolute vorticity usually attains small positive values (order of magnitude $1 \cdot 10^{-5}$ sec^{-1}). In the immediate vicinity of the jet maximum, however, small negative values of absolute vorticity are possible.

2. The level and also the layer of maximum wind reflect well the baroclinic conditions in the atmosphere. Looking downstream, they both dip downward to the left of the jet axis, and rise upward to the right of the axis.

3. In agreement with this stands the observation that the region of strongest cyclonic shear is slightly below the level of the jet core; the region with strongest anticyclonic shear is slightly above the core level.

4. The level of maximum wind generally does not coincide with the tropopause. The jet core lies to the right of the "tropopause break." On the anticyclonic side of the jet axis the level of maximum wind lies *below* the tropopause.

5. At each level above and below the jet core the jet axis lies to the right of its position at core level.

6. The jet core is located slightly to the right of and above the isotherm concentration at the 500-mb level, and below the concentration at the 200- or 175-mb surface (Fig. 3.211) (Crocker 1952).

7. The baroclinicity below the jet core is in good agreement with observed vertical wind shears. Meso-structural departures from this may, however, be expected.

Information on the maximum wind speeds possible in jet streams, so far, is rather scanty. Extreme wind speeds cause considerable difficulties in measurements, so that the results are unreliable (see Chapter 2). A reported speed of 396 knots (732 km/h) over Philadelphia, Pa., has been simulated by malfunction of the instrument (Ratner, 1955*a*). The actual wind speed has been estimated to be about 265 knots (490 km/h). The highest wind speeds ever measured in a PFJ are not far from 300 knots (*ca.* 550 km/h) (Sheppard, 1951). An observation of 192 m/sec over Shinomisaki, reported by Mohri (1953) neglects the earth's curvature, and, therefore, was probably too high by about 20 per cent. Arakawa (1959) reports the highest value so far obtained from the STJ by means of radiosondes at the 13-km level over Tateno with 540 km/h. Frost (1953) observed about 650 km/h during a flight over Tokyo.

Lettau (1948) made a theoretical estimate of maximum geostrophic wind speeds. He made the arbitrary assumption, however, that the pressure gradient between a high and the adjacent low follows a cosine function.

Let the pressure distribution between high (p_H) and low (p_L) be given by

$$p = p_0 + \frac{p_H - p_L}{2} \cos \frac{\pi}{A} n. \qquad 4.411\ (1)$$

A = distance between high and low; n is the co-ordinate normal to the current, positive in the direction toward the low pressure; $p_0 = p_H + p_L/2$ is the mean pressure.

For $n = 0$, $p = p_H$.
For $n = A$, $p = p_L$.
For $n = A/2$, $p = p_0$.

The pressure gradient is given by

$$\frac{\partial p}{\partial n} = -\frac{\pi(p_H - p_L)}{2A} \sin \frac{\pi}{A} n. \qquad 4.411\ (2)$$

The maximum gradient is attained for $\sin (\pi/A)n = 1$. From this one arrives at the maximum geostrophic wind speed,

$$|V_{max}| = \frac{\pi(p_H - p_L)}{\rho f 2A}. \qquad 4.411\ (3)$$

The maximum possible pressure difference between high and low is given by the condition of dynamic instability described in Chapter 1.236 (Lettau, 1947). According to Eq. 1.236 (8),

$$\frac{\partial V}{\partial n} < f \qquad 4.411\ (4)$$

if we neglect the curvature of the streamlines. Therefore, for geostrophic conditions of flow,

$$-\frac{\partial^2 p}{\partial n^2} < \rho f^2 \qquad 4.411\ (5)$$

if the latitude dependency of f is neglected. By differentiating 4.411 (2) again, and by considering 4.411 (5), we arrive at the condition for maximum gradient,

$$(p_H - p_L) < \frac{2\rho f^2 A^2}{\pi^2}. \qquad 4.411\ (6)$$

An additional limitation is imposed upon the pressure field in the anticyclonic influence region by the condition given in Eq. 1.223 (5), whereby the square root has to render real values. Therefore, the maximum gradient wind speed is given by

$$V_{\max}=\frac{rf}{2}$$

(r is the radius of curvature, pointing in the direction of n). Since according to Eq. 1.223 (6) $V_{\max}=2V_g$, we obtain for the maximum geostrophic wind shear

$$\left(\frac{\partial V}{\partial n}\right)_{\max}=\frac{f}{4}. \tag{4.411 (7)}$$

A comparison with 4.411 (4) shows that this condition is much more (four times more) restrictive. Thus, we have for the anticyclonic region ($n=0$ to $A/2$)

$$p_H-p_0<\frac{2\rho f^2A^2}{4\pi^2}\cdot\frac{1}{2},$$

and for the cyclonic side

$$p_0-p_L<\frac{2\rho f^2A^2}{\pi^2}\cdot\frac{1}{2},$$

and together

$$p_H-p_L<\frac{5\rho f^2A^2}{4\pi^2}. \tag{4.411 (8)}$$

Introducing 4.411 (8) into 4.411 (3), we obtain

$$V_{\max}<\frac{5}{8}\frac{fA}{\pi}. \tag{4.411 (9)}$$

Assuming the low pressure at the 10-km level to occur at the pole and the high pressure at the equator, 4.411 (8) would give a maximum wind speed of 738 km/h (*ca.* 400 knots). Since, however, the maximum pressure is to be sought not at the equator but rather at about 30° latitude (Riehl, 1954*c*), this value would have to be decreased by about one third. The approximately 300-knot maximum speed which, then, would result, is in good agreement with observations.

4.412. The Subtropical Jet Stream (STJ)

In its structure the STJ is very similar to the PFJ: it is a belt of strong westerly winds which reaches its maximum intensity near the 12-km level (200 mb) (Nojima, 1954).

In various cross sections the STJ may lie appreciably higher (150 mb). This is primarily the case when a well-defined polar front has advanced far to the south of its normal position. In such cases even the wind maximum, which would have to be classified as PFJ because of its baroclinic zone, may already lie between 200 and 250 mb.

Since the latitudinal variations of the STJ intrude into the zone of the PFJ, its separate structure usually is lost in mean cross sections (see Fig. 4.211.1 and .4).

In Chapter 4.141 it has been mentioned that over the United States the jet maxima of the PFJ in general show a tendency of southward displacement (see Fig. 4.232.7 and .8). Because of a new formation of the baroclinic zone farther to the north, there may be two or more jet streams present at the same time. According to investigations by Phillips (1950), the jet axis seems to be displaced toward higher levels and higher potential temperatures during this southward drift (Knepple, 1960). It, therefore,

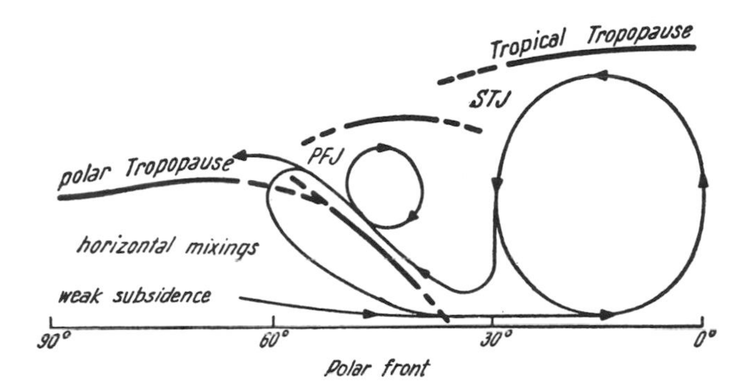

FIG. 4.412.1.—Schematic representation of the mean meridional circulation in the northern hemisphere during winter. Heavy lines, tropopauses and polar front. (Palmén, 1954*a*.)

appears as though the STJ genetically were attached to the remnants of a baroclinic zone which originally belonged to the PFJ. McIntyre and Lee (1953), on the other hand, arrive at the conclusion that jet maxima proceed toward lower levels during their southward migration. Some of them, however, seem to give off part of their kinetic energy to higher levels in a discontinuous process, so that new jet maxima form at higher potential temperatures while the old ones slowly disappear. Palmén believes that the subtropical jet stream is caused by an import of angular momentum from the south (see Mohri, 1958*a*; Sawyer, 1957), as may also be seen from the circulation scheme (Fig. 4.412.1) devised by him. According to this, the jet streams would form on the northern edge of meridional circulation cells (Saito, 1951). This scheme is corroborated by quantitative studies conducted by Palmén and Alaka (1952).

The meridional transport of momentum from the south, which would be necessary to maintain the STJ, may be produced in different ways. While in several theoretical papers, which will be referred to in Chapter 8, the momentum transport necessary to maintain the zonal circulation in the region of the PFJ is assumed to be accomplished by large-scale turbulence (turbulence elements of the magnitude of planetary waves), Palmén and Alaka proved in their paper that for the maintenance of the STJ a mean meridional circulation of the kind shown in Figure 4.412.1 is necessary. The large-scale turbulent exchange of angular momentum would lead to a divergence in the momentum flow within the zone of maximum westerlies (between 25° and 30° N during winter), i.e., more momentum would be carried northward by the action of the planetary long waves than would be replenished by these turbulence elements from the south (Mintz, 1951; Widger, 1949). This divergence in the flow of momentum, however, would cause the decay of the hemispheric jet stream. Processes of this kind may be of importance during an index cycle. Since the west wind zone is constantly regenerated, the necessary angular momentum will have to be replenished through some other process. In order to understand the existence of the STJ in terms of the angular momentum budget (transition of absolute angular momentum into relative angular momentum, the latter becoming apparent in zonal wind speed [see derivation of Eq. 1.236 (14)]) consideration of the horizontal turbulent exchange does not suffice. The following quantities will have to be taken into account in addition:

1. *Horizontal and vertical transport of angular momentum* is caused by the mass transport of a *mean meridional circulation* (Fig. 4.412.1). This mass transport between the isobaric surfaces p_2 and p_1 across the latitude circle φ has the magnitude

$$m_\varphi = \frac{2\pi R \cos \varphi}{g} \int_{p_2}^{p_1} v \, dp. \qquad 4.412\ (1)$$

v is the mean meridional component of flow at the pressure level p.

2. *The turbulent exchange of angular momentum* has the magnitude

$$M_z = -\mu \frac{\partial u}{\partial z} AR \cos \varphi. \qquad 4.412\ (2)$$

The exchange coefficient μ for angular momentum has been computed by Palmén and Alaka for the 700-mb surface to be 120 g cm^{-1} sec^{-1}, if one assumes for $\frac{\partial u}{\partial z} = 4 \cdot 10^{-3}$ sec^{-1}. A is the area between the latitude circles 20° and 30° N.

3. *The angular momentum exchange between earth's surface and atmosphere due to shearing stresses of the wind on the ground* has been calculated by Palmén and Alaka as a residual from 4.412 (1 and 2). Between equator and 30° N it amounted to $61 \cdot 10^{25}$ g cm^2 sec^{-2} during January, 1949. Since this corresponds to the total transport toward the north across the 30th parallel ($62 \cdot 10^{25}$ g cm^2 sec^{-2} according to Table 4.412), no replacement of angular momentum from the southern hemisphere would be necessary to maintain the circulation of the STJ.

TABLE 4.412. TOTAL TRANSPORT OF ANGULAR MOMENTUM TOWARD NORTH IN JANUARY (units 10^{25} g cm^2 sec^{-2})

Latitude	30°	25°	20°
Transport by meridional circulation	6	11	14
Transport by turbulent exchange	56	47	32
Ratio of the two transports in per cent	11	23	44

Thus, the contribution of the meridional circulation toward the total transport is relatively high in low latitudes. It is strong enough to balance the divergence in the flow of momentum, which would result from the transport by turbulent exchange (planetary long waves) only. More recent investigations by Tucker (1960) corroborate these results.

The value of the preceding considerations is somewhat diminished in view of the research conducted with geophysical models, which will be referred to in more detail in Chapter 4.433. There, it will be shown that the effect of the meridional circulation as well as of the large-scale, horizontal eddies upon the transport of various meteorological elements (heat, momentum, etc.) depends upon the choice of the co-ordinate system.

One will have to assume that meridional circulation as well as planetary waves play a role in the formation of the STJ. Palmén's model receives its justification from the observation that below the southernmost of the two jet streams indicated in Figure 4.412.1 frequently large subsidence inversions may be found (Brundidge, 1956) and that some of the subtropical jets may have a strong effect upon weather without any evidence of frequent intrusions of sinking cold air from the north, as is, for instance, the case over India during winter, or over the east Atlantic. There, a circulation cell seems to be in existence which follows Palmén's scheme.

On the other hand, some of these inversions, especially in the lower levels, may be recognized as remnants of old polar fronts, whose cold air has undergone a sinking process. These fronts are only very weakly baroclinic. The jet streams above such inversions apparently follow a dissipation tendency, because they frequently show a marked meso-structure and a disintegration into several secondary maxima ("jet fingers"). Below the 400-mb level the isotachs are almost horizontal, in marked contrast with the polar-front jets. This is also the reason why subtropical jets hardly ever become evident from isotach analyses at lower levels.

Brundidge (1956) observed several cases which, without doubt, correspond to Phillips' model: a frontal zone progresses as far as the Gulf of Mexico and there undergoes frontolysis, while the associated jet stream—now split into several sub-maxima—remains active for several more days. With a renewed advance of fresh polar air associated with a new jet stream, several possibilities offer themselves now: in some cases a merger of the two jet streams is observed. In other cases the southern jet stream intensifies with the approach of a new jet from the north, while the northern jet stream weakens. Sometimes the two jet streams separate again without losing their identity.

The southern jet streams usually occur at higher potential temperatures than the polar-front jets. This serves to show that the baroclinic zone of the former is not identical with the upper part of the original frontal zone. Therefore, if one were to explain the subtropical jets as the remnants of a baroclinic zone which originally belonged to the PFJ, one would have to look for a mechanism which incorporates other ranges of potential temperature into the frontal zone than have been present there originally. Such a mechanism may be found in the direct circulation of the entrance region of a jet maximum. The dry adiabatic sinking of cold air and the moist adiabatic rising of warm air decreases the baroclinicity of the frontal zone. The stable layer in the lower troposphere becomes nearly barotropic, due to the outflow of cold air near the ground in a migrating high-pressure system. The high-level wind field in the upper troposphere remains more or less conserved, and with it—perhaps slightly weakened—the vorticity pattern. With this, however, the distribution of divergence and convergence continues to exist at jet-stream level. Since above the "zero layer" (layer in which $\omega = 0$) the vertical component of velocity reverses its sign, the direct circulation, which decreased the tropospheric temperature gradient, appears reversed in the stratosphere (see Fig. 4.221.3*a*, however, opposite direction of arrows), i.e., acting in the sense of a generation of a south-north temperature gradient. In the stable stratification of the stratosphere vertical motions have at least the same large influence upon the temperature pattern as horizontal advection (Sawyer, 1951*b*). By this, the maximum wind level will proceed toward greater heights and higher potential temperatures as long as this mechanism is active. Thus, this mechanism would constitute a *continuous* process of transition between PFJ and STJ. The latter will be fully developed as soon as the baroclinicity below about 400 mb is completely deleted.

Besides this, also a discontinuous transition mechanism might be possible, which also would fit into McIntyre's (and Lee, 1953) model. If in the influence region of a jet maximum ascending warm air, whose circulation is amply verified by the existence of cirrus clouds (see Chapter 6.3), cools moist adiabatically and finally reaches the level of maximum wind in the PFJ, this cooling may be sufficient to produce a baroclinic layer on the southern edge of the lifting zone, within the originally barotropic air mass. This would give rise to a second wind maximum at greater heights. The tongues of cold air at the 250- and 200-mb surfaces, occurring along the anticyclonic side of a jet maximum, give evidence of these lifting processes. The secondary wind maximum, which is frequently found along the southern side of a PFJ at a somewhat higher level, which, however, is not always developed as a separate entity in the form of an STJ, might be explained by such a mechanism (see Figs. 3.211 and 4.232.7 and .8).

This jet-stream branch with the characteristics of an STJ also emerged from the PFJ in this case of a discontinuous transition; it appears, however, as a *new formation* of a second wind maximum. According to this hypothesis, one would have to expect the formation of this branch to occur whenever large bodies of warm air are caught in a lifting process. Indications of this sort seem to be present over the United States. A well-established STJ with anticyclonic curvature appears in general over the Gulf of Mexico whenever a polar-front jet maximum reaches the tip of a deep and elongated long-wave trough. (This happens primarily over the Colorado area.) Near the tip of the trough frequently very strong cyclogenesis is observed, which leads to the formation of intensive storms (Colorado lows) traveling northeastward and causing great amounts of precipitation. The latter results from ascending warm air. At such times the STJ usually is well-pronounced and runs almost parallel to the PFJ, slightly south of the latter.

Which of the proposed mechanisms dominates in the formation of the STJ is difficult to decide with the present data. The study of the life cycle of the STJ is rendered almost impossible by the acute lack of aerological stations in the subtropical belts. The situation is further complicated by the fact that only rarely may one observe the forming of an STJ. Usually, an already existing broad band of high-level winds is intensified. More detailed studies would be necessary to shed some light on the life history of jet streams. Probably both, vertical circulations around the PFJ as well as impulses from tropical regions, maintain the STJ. The latter might be of a certain importance during the warm-air intrusions to high latitudes, which will be discussed in Chapter 6. If only the former were active, the STJ would be subject to continuous dissipation. This, however, does not seem to hold true in the winterly jet stream south of the Himalayas, mentioned earlier.

It may be assumed that the various mechanisms which have been listed as possibly being of influence in the formation of the STJ may be of different effectiveness in different regions. The studies by Phillips (1950) and Brundidge (1956) mentioned earlier have been made over the United States. The geographic position in the lee of the Rocky Mountains leads one to expect a predominance of weather situations with intensive cold-air outbreaks in a long-wave trough. It is possible, therefore, that the

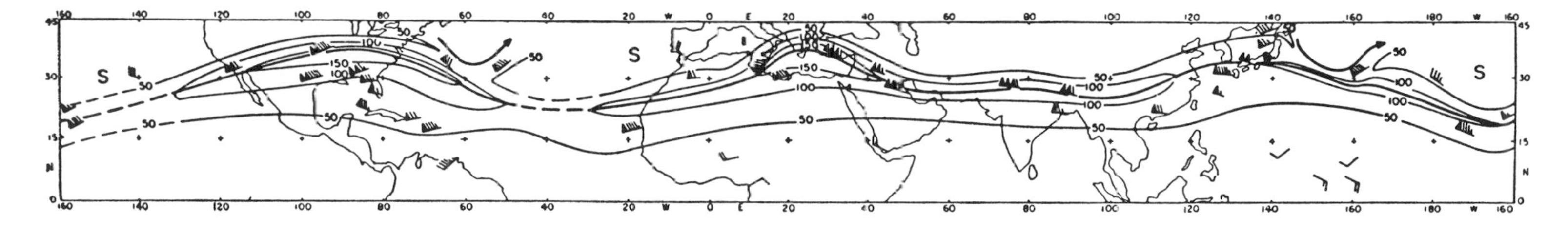

FIG. 4.412.2.—Isotachs (knots) of the STJ at the 200-mb level, 25 February, 1956. (Krishnamurti, 1959*a*.)

"characteristics" of the STJ obtained from this area may not at all be applicable to the rest of the hemisphere. Although there are some indications over the United States that the STJ emerges from the PFJ, this might be a result of some orographic effects. Unfortunately we do not yet have any dependable and detailed measurements in the subtropical jet stream from other parts of the world to make any definite statements in this matter.

On the average the STJ seems to come from a southwesterly direction over the southern United States (Cunningham, 1956*b*). Its origin has scarcely been explored, but it seems to emerge from the eastern Pacific. Aerological measurements over this region are lacking, however. Farther to the west, over the Hawaiian Islands upper-wind measurements, again, are available which indicate a clear differentiation between PFJ and STJ (Hoyle, 1955*a*).

Krishnamurti (1959*a*) studied the position of the STJ over the continents in one of his reports. Figure 4.412.2 shows the isotach pattern of the 200-mb surface of 25 February, 1956, in the subtropical belt. The American jet maximum is clearly evident from this figure.

From studies by F. Defant (1954) it appears that the STJ frequently shows great activity over the Atlantic and penetrates far toward the north in warm-air intrusions, leading, at times, to the formation of blocking anticyclones (see Chapter 6). These intrusions may be traced back to the western edge of the Bermuda high and into the Antilles region, and apparently have their origin in impulses from tropical latitudes. It seems, therefore, that here, to the east of the orographically induced long-wave trough, Palmén's circulation model (see Fig. 4.412.1) is applicable.

Over the Mediterranean coast of North Africa and over the Middle East the STJ sometimes assumes a rather stable position (see Fig. 2 and Fig. 4.411) (Austin and Dewar, 1953; Bannon, 1953*a*, 1954*a*; Buroleau, 1937; Genève and Jacquemard, 1957; Lamb *et al.*, 1957; Lamb and Robinson, 1957; Reiter, 1959*e*; Serra, 1955; Sutcliffe, 1960). Unfortunately, the aerological measurements from this region leave much to be desired. It is difficult to determine, therefore, whether the stability of this jet-stream position is induced by the temperature contrast between the Sahara and the Mediterranean Sea, which is concentrated along a shore line running approximately in a west-east direction (see Chapter 4.411).

Figure 4.412.3 shows the 200-mb streamlines and isotachs of July. A clear differentiation between STJ and PFJ is not given in this diagram. A relatively broad jet maximum which occurs over the northeastern United States during winter (not reproduced here) and which shows an extension into the North Atlantic may partly be due to the PFJ. In general, the jet maxima indicated here correspond well to the position of the STJ.

Most distinctly the STJ is present over northern India during the months of the winter monsoon (Fig. 4.412.2). During this season wind speeds of 150 knots have been measured over India (Ramamurthi, 1955). According to a study by Jenkinson (1955) *mean values* lie already near 120 knots, and over Japan they even reach 140 knots. This will be brought up again in Chapter 7.413 in conjunction with the Indian monsoon. Near the eastern slopes of the Himalayas and over the China Sea the STJ reaches the greatest intensities ever measured in the northern hemisphere during winter, and also shows its greatest steadiness here (see Fig. 7.33.1) (Bell and Kwai,

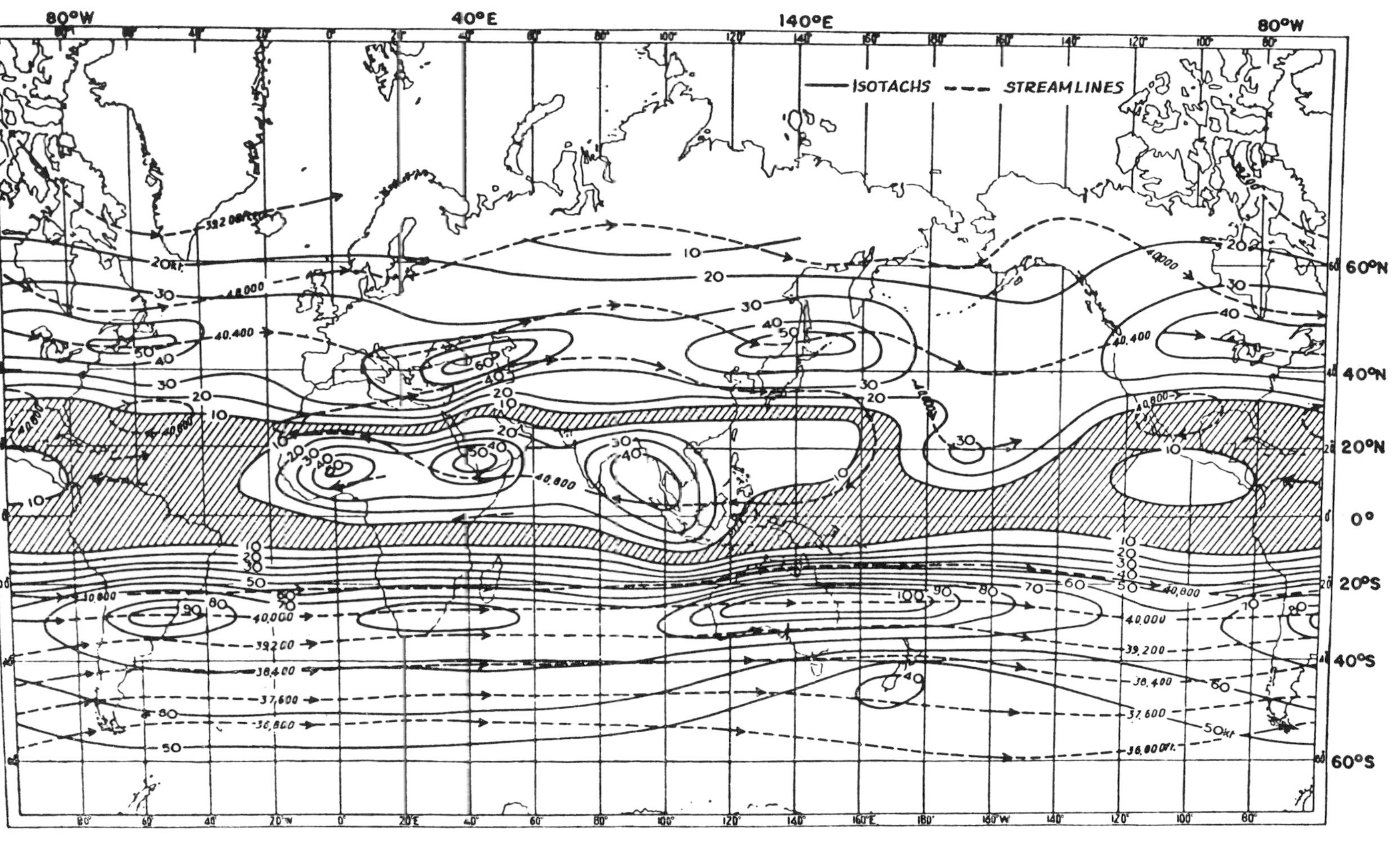

FIG. 4.412.3.—Streamlines and isotachs (knots) of the mean wind vectors, 200 mb, July (Jenkinson, 1955.)

1953; Great Britain Meteorological Office, 1945; Kawamura, 1956; Kobayashi, 1950; Matsumoto, Itoo, and Arakawa, 1953; Mohri, 1956, 1958*b*; Sugimoto, 1957; U.S. Air Weather Service, 1954*b*, 1955; Yamada and Matsuhashi, 1951, 1957; *et al.*, 1954; Yamada and Nakamura, 1954). Arakawa (1959) reports a maximum velocity of 150 m/sec (540 km/h), which was measured on 2 March, 1954, over Tateno by means of a relay ascent made from Honjo.

Over the Pacific the STJ at times advances to comparatively low latitudes. So, e.g., during the atomic tests over Bikini (*ca.* 12° N, 165° E) westerlies have been measured at heights between 3 and 17 km with maximum velocities of 100 knots (Otsuka and Shimada, 1954).

In other parts of the northern hemisphere the reports on maximum velocities in the STJ seem to fall slightly short of those in the PFJ. Therefore, Rossby's mixing theory (see Chapter 4.121) cannot be used to explain its existence. Because of the lower latitudes in which this jet stream occurs, its wind speed would have to be higher according to this theory than in the PFJ flowing farther to the north.

The studies by Jenkinson (1955) reveal that during the southern hemisphere winter the STJ is most pronounced over Australia (Edwardes, 1952; Porter, 1952*b*). Here, mean wind vectors of more than 100 knots occur during July, which speaks for the great steadiness of this wind system. A detailed study of the Australian STJ was made by Radok and Clarke (1958). They found that this jet stream, whose baroclinic zone comprises only the upper half of the troposphere, reaches its maximum frequency during winter between 25° and 30° S, and its maximum intensity between 20° and 25° S. Equatorward the wind speeds of jet maxima observed at 147.5° E rapidly decay. Their envelope describes approximately a curve of constant angular momentum, as was the case in Figure 4.121.5. From this it may be concluded that the position of the main axis of the subtropical high-pressure ridge regulates the jet maxima between 12° and 22° S. Air masses flowing southward from this axis obtain their westerly momentum according to Palmén's model. South of the critical geographic latitude (*ca.* 22° S) the intensity of the observed jet maxima, again, decreases rapidly. These maxima, therefore, cannot be due so much to intrusions from subtropical regions occurring under conservation of angular momentum but rather to processes which are induced from the PFJ zone. A certain scattering of the observations certainly will be caused by the seasonal displacements of the subtropical high-pressure belt, too.

Radok and Clarke could prove that zones of constant angular momentum, i.e., with $Q=0$, also occur on the anticyclonic side of individual subtropical jet maxima. In some instances the vertical shear is large enough to render Richardson's number R_i smaller than 1.

On the cyclonic side of individual maxima a vorticity maximum may be found—similar to what we have found in the PFJ—which speaks against the unlimited validity of the mixing theory in this region (Chapter 4.121). Only poleward from this maximum the vorticity seems to assume a quasi-constant value, which, however, at the most corresponds to only about 80 per cent of the earth's vorticity at the pole. Even when accepting the mixing theory as applicable in this case, the mixing could not take place all the way to the pole but could comprise only a somewhat smaller zone (see Estoque, 1950).

According to Jenkinson (Fig. 4.412.3) another wind maximum is present over South America at about 30° S with mean velocities of about 90 knots. A weak mean maximum is also indicated over the southern tip of Africa (Hofmeyr, 1952, 1953, 1954; Madagascar Service Météorologique, 1948). In special synoptic cases even here, however, considerable wind speeds have been measured (Boogard [1954], e.g., reports 130 knots north of Pretoria).

Since over the oceans hardly any upper-air wind measurements are available, the course of the STJ cannot be given with accuracy, either in the northern hemisphere (Fig. 4.412.2) or in the southern hemisphere. It might well be that additional wind maxima are found over the oceans. They should be expected wherever the subtropical high-pressure belt is interrupted by long-wave troughs in the westerly circulation. In these places impulses from tropical regions may penetrate into temperate latitudes and may give rise there to the formation of jet maxima.

Precipitation falling over northern India during winter, and over other areas underneath the STJ, indicates that disturbances travel along this jet stream just as they do along the PFJ (Mooley, 1957; Pisharoty and Desai, 1956). Precipitation activity has been observed in the southern United States when STJ and PFJ acted together (Riehl, 1945). Palmén's circulation model of Figure 4.412.1, therefore, is valid only *on the average*. Special cases may bring ascending motion with increased convective and thunderstorm activity, even in the STJ region. Since the lower troposphere is almost barotropic underneath the STJ, there will be no large-scale lifting motion along sloping isentropic surfaces, and, since there are no fronts, no frontal cyclogenesis can occur. There will be only a general destabilization of the atmosphere, which becomes apparent from the cloud pattern by cumulus formation.

The *mean* descending motion within the STJ which flows over the *subtropical high-pressure centers* is confirmed by observations (Koteswaram and Parthasarathy, 1954; Matsumoto, Itoo, and Arakawa, 1953). According to Palmén's circulation model (Fig. 4.412.1), the strongest upper convergence in the STJ region is to be expected over the areas with maximum low-level divergence, i.e., over the cores of the subtropical high-pressure areas. Therefore, in this line of reasoning, the subtropical high-pressure belt is not a stationary phenomenon but undergoes continuous dissipation and new formation because of the dynamics of the upper flow pattern.

The structure of the STJ over the United States is mainly revealed from research flights of Project Jet Stream (Saucier, 1958*b*). According to these, the baroclinic zone extends only through the upper half of the troposphere and varies greatly in width and intensity. A "jet-stream front," as analyzed by Endlich (and McLean, 1957), corresponds only to an extreme case of this baroclinicity. In this zone strong ageostrophic components of flow seem to be active. A tendency of the jet axis above and below core level to occur to the *right* of its position in the core, as found in the PFJ, could not be verified in the STJ.

Just as the PFJ, the STJ is connected with a "tropopause break," and it lies below the higher, tropical tropopause, on the average about 150 km to the right of the "break line." As compared with the PFJ, in the STJ in general the ratio of vertical to horizontal extent is somewhat smaller. The vertical shear frequently becomes significant only at greater heights (7 to 8 km) (Bannon, 1954*b*; see Brundidge and Goldman, 1958). The cyclonic shear surpasses the anticyclonic shear up to a distance of 450 to 600 km from the jet axis. The former also is more variable from case to case than the latter. In general the horizontal wind shear increases with the wind speed in the jet axis; because of the greater variability, no clear correlation could be found, however, as with the PFJ (see Chapter 4.122 and 4.13).

The slope of the level of maximum wind corresponds to what has been found for the PFJ: ascending level to the south, descending level to the north of the jet core. The distribution of shear also is analogous to the one in the PFJ: strongest cyclonic shear is found slightly below, strongest anticyclonic shear somewhat above the level of the jet core.

4.413. The Easterly Jet Stream of the Tropics (TJ)

As is evident from the studies by Jenkinson (Fig. 4.412.3) which have been mentioned earlier, a strongly developed easterly jet stream may be found over India and North Africa during summer. The magnitude of the mean wind vector at the 200-mb level is about 50 knots. The level of maximum wind in this jet stream lies between 100 and 150 mb, as may be seen from cross-section analyses by Koteswaram (1956; see Austin, 1952). The section of 25 July, 1955, 0300 GCT is reproduced in Figure 4.413.1. It extends from the southern tip of India (Trivandrum) to the slopes of the Himalayas (New Delhi). In this jet stream velocities of more than 100 knots have been observed.

Figure 4.413.2 shows an analysis of the 100-mb isotachs and streamlines, again for 25 July, 1955. According to this analysis, a marked easterly jet maximum with more than 100 knots lies between the two Indian peninsulas. Its leading edge reaches into the Sudan (Austin, 1952; Clarkson, 1956, 1958; Davies and Sansom, 1952; Emery, 1956; Frost, 1952, 1953; Gilchrist, 1955; Hay, 1952*a*, *b*, 1953; Ryan, 1958; Sutcliffe and Bannon, 1956). The entrance area of this TJ may be traced back over Guam (Otsuka and Shimada, 1955; Ramsey, 1955). A second maximum appears over the African west coast with velocities of about 60 knots.

The easterly upper current also is evident clearly from topographies of the 96- and 41-mb surfaces of the northern hemisphere in July published by Scherhag (1948*b*). From Figure 4.412.3 it may be concluded that the influence of the TJ does not reach far into the tropical Atlantic. Vuorela (1948) was able, however, to identify it clearly over the Cape Verde Islands with wind speeds of about 40 meters per second at a height of 14 km during summer. Above the tropopause (according to Vuorela in this area at about 17 km height) the easterly current of the TJ seems to merge gradually with the Krakatoa easterlies (Flohn, 1958*b*). Kuhlbrodt (1952*a*) also found an easterly current in this region.

Although easterlies may be found in this latitude region around the whole hemisphere, nowhere else *on the average* do they reach jet-stream intensity. Over Central America only a weak wind maximum appears with average velocities of slightly more than 10 knots (mean taken over the month of July).

Even though over the oceans only few reliable upper-wind measurements are available, one may conclude from the data material which is present so far that the TJ is a phenomenon which only over the Indian sub-continent and over Africa is characterized by *quasi-stationary conditions*, and therefore also appears in mean charts as shown in Figure 4.412.3. Furthermore, the TJ reaches considerable intensity here only during summer. During winter (January) only the indication of two easterly wind maxima with 20 knots each are found in the mean velocity distribution. One of them lies over Indonesia and the other one over Central Africa. The axes of both wind maxima appear close to the equator. They can hardly be called jet streams, however.

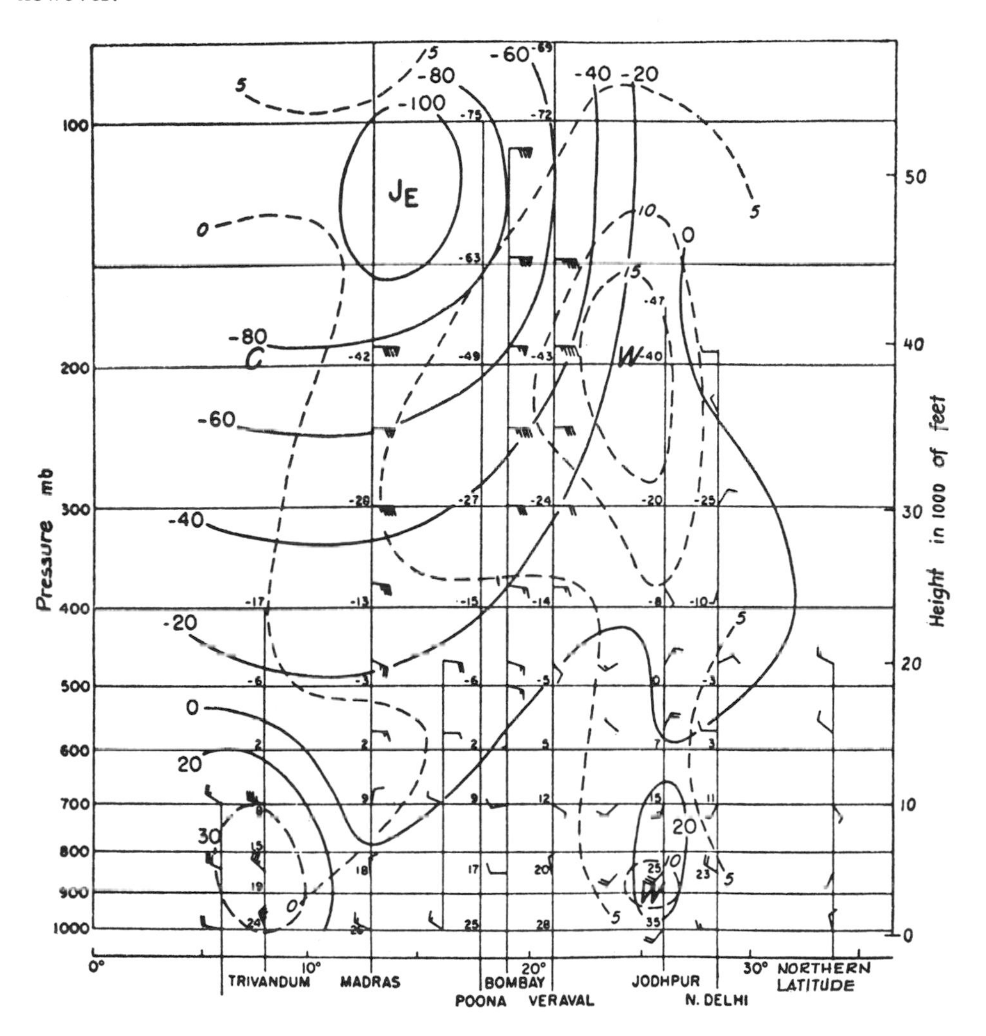

FIG. 4.413.1.—Cross section through the atmosphere over India, 25 July, 1955. J_E = easterly jet stream. Solid lines, isotachs (knots); dashed lines, isotherms of temperature anomalies (° C) from the mean tropical atmosphere. (Koteswaram, 1956.)

With this locally and seasonally confined existence of the TJ in monthly mean charts the search for a cause of this jet stream is not difficult. The association with the South Asiatic and African summer monsoon and with the inner tropical convergence zone, which is displaced far toward the north, is evident (Bannon, 1953*b*). As will be further discussed in Chapter 7, the monsoon circulation over India is closely related with appearance and disappearance of the STJ south of the Himalayas. Since this transgression of the jet stream across the mountain barrier occurs relatively quickly—within only a few days—the "burst" and the "retreat" of the summer monsoon constitute very pronounced discontinuities in the weather sequence over India. The monsoonal flow (the moist southwest monsoon of summer and the dry northeast monsoon during winter) over India has a vertical thickness of only several kilometers. Above the southwesterly flow of summer, and above the intertropical convergence zone along which the monsoonal precipitation occurs and which has far advanced into northern India during summer, an intense easterly flow is present: the tropical jet stream. The precipitation pattern over India and also over Africa corresponds to the distribution of convergence and divergence as we have seen it in Figure 4.122.3 and which has only to be adapted for an easterly jet stream. Figure 7.413.3 shows the precipitation maxima in the right rear and in the left front quadrant of the tropical jet maximum. This precipitation pattern is not only valid for large-scale conditions, but Ramanathan (1955) found that individual disturbances which are responsible for precipitation over India and the Himalayan Peninsula during the monsoon season are associated with waves in this jet stream also.

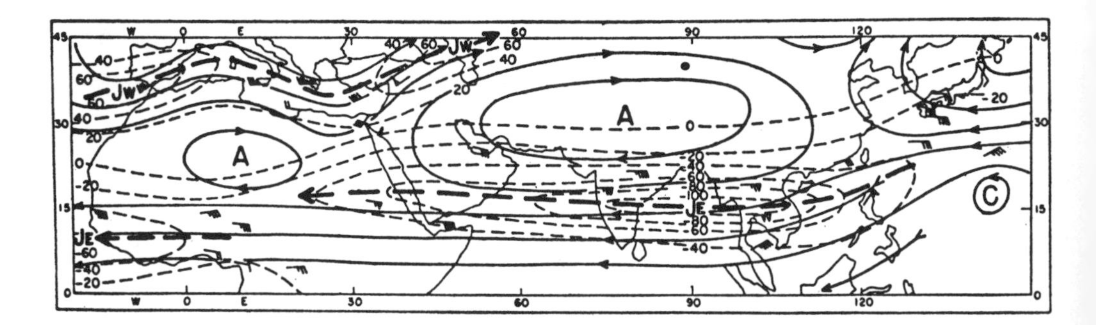

FIG. 4.413.2.—Streamlines (solid lines) and isotachs (dashed) at the 100-mb level, 25 July, 1955, 0300 GCT; J_W = westerly jet maximum; J_E = easterly jet maximum. A = anticyclones; C = cyclones. Heavy dashed lines with arrows indicate positions of jet axes. (Koteswaram, 1956.)

The Indian monsoonal rains and the rainy season in equatorial Africa therefore are dependent upon the TJ and its *position* and not so much upon the sun's proximity to the zenith, as has been implied in the expression "zenithal rains." It would be difficult to visualize that the convective activity in the cumulonimbus clouds of the rainy seasons should mainly depend upon the elevation angle of the sun rather than upon the slope of the terrain and upon differences in albedo, which, it is believed, are much more prominent in their effect. The start of the rainy season in conjunction with a strong *upper divergence* in the influence region of the TJ, however, offers a dynamically justifiable explanation. Tschirhart (1959) connects the occurrence of thunderstorms and squall lines with the presence of the intertropical convergence line (F.I.T., front intertropical) and with the African equatorial front (F.E.A., front équatorial Africaine). The latter separates the moist "monsoonal air masses" traveling from the southwest over the Gulf of Guinea and intruding over the African continent from the dry air masses flowing from the east. It should, however, be noted that the thunderstorm precipitation occurs far removed from both fronts and on the southern side of the inner-tropic front, where one would expect the presence of the TJ at great heights. Furthermore, it should be pointed out that the thunderstorms usually migrate toward the west, i.e., into a direction opposite to the one of the surface winds, which also indicates the presence of an easterly upper current that prevails above the monsoonal air masses which are only about 2 km thick. This should show that a "frontal analysis" in the tropical regions does not help too much. If it should be decided to install additional radiosonde stations and wind-measuring equipment in the tropics, we would come to a closer understanding of the very complex weather sequences in this latitude belt of our earth.

The question where this TJ draws its momentum is not difficult to answer in a qualitative and quantitative way. Figure 4.413.2 shows that during the season of the summer monsoon a quasi-stationary anticyclone establishes itself over the Asiatic Plateau (this will be discussed further in Chapter 7). On the eastern slopes of this anticyclone air masses are flowing toward the south, carrying along easterly angular momentum. As expected, the entrance area of the Indian maximum of the TJ lies exactly where this momentum transport toward the south occurs, i.e., in the region of Burma and South China. The second jet maximum which may be recognized over

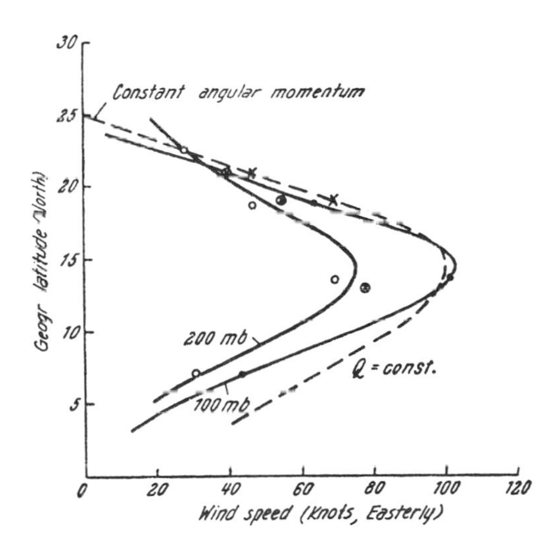

FIG. 4.413.3.—Meridional wind profile of the east-wind component over India and Thailand, 25 July, 1955, at 200 and 100 mb, together with theoretical wind profiles of constant angular momentum and constant absolute vorticity (dashed). (Koteswaram, 1958.)

equatorial West Africa draws its energy from an anticyclone whose center of gravity lies over the Sahara Desert and which is separated by a low-pressure trough from the Asiatic anticyclone. Over India the jet axis lies near 15° N. According to Eq. 1.236 (14), air masses which would be traveling from 25° N to 15° N under conservation of angular momentum would experience an increase in easterly velocities of about 105 knots (54.2 meters per second). The detailed studies of the TJ over India by Koteswaram (1956, 1958) reveal that the meridional wind profiles over India and Thailand (Fig.

4.413.3) actually correspond on their anticyclonic side to conditions of constant angular momentum (the dashed line is valid for a wind distribution in which the speed at 25 degrees latitude has been assumed with zero). Even mean wind profiles over this area during summer, when the TJ is active, correspond on their anticyclonic side approximately to the condition $Q=0$. On the cyclonic side of these profiles observations are rather scarce. It seems, however, as though at the 100-mb level horizontal shears were present which were slightly larger than would correspond to constant vorticity. For the dashed curve on the cyclonic side, Q has been assumed to be equal to $f_{15°}$.

It has been pointed out that the mean conditions of flow represented in Figure 4.412.3 do not so much prove the *existence* of the TJ as its *persistence* (Bannon, 1953*b*). It has been shown, furthermore, that the TJ draws its angular momentum from an area in which the subtropical high-pressure zone has been interrupted. Such interrup-

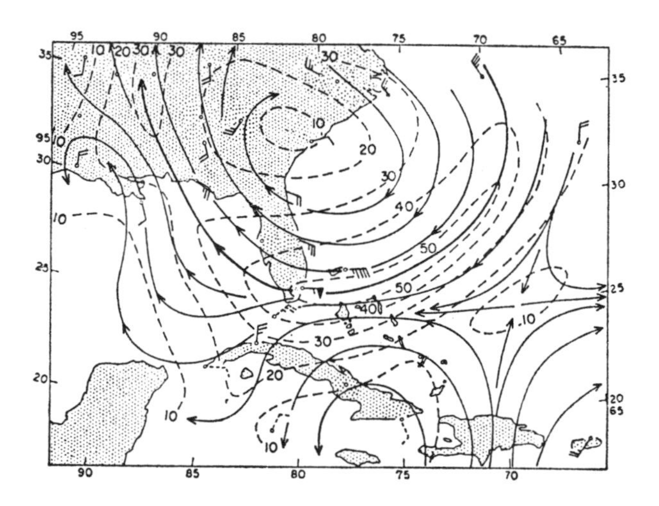

Fig. 4.413.4.—200-mb streamlines (solid lines) and isotachs (dashed), 1 August, 1953, 0300 GCT. The heavy line indicates the position of the jet axis. (Alaka, 1958*a*.)

tions of the subtropical high-pressure belt also occur in other areas, wherever well-developed troughs in the west wind zone penetrate toward low latitudes. Arakawa (1953*b*) considers such trough axes which are tilting from the southwest toward the northeast responsible for the coupling of extratropical and tropical circulations. Since, however—with the exception of the Afro-Asiatic region—such interruptions have no quasi-stationary character, one may assume that they may lead to the formation of an easterly jet stream on the southern side of the subtropical highs, but that this TJ will not appear in mean charts because of its rather sporadic occurrence. This could be proven by Alaka (1955, 1958*a*), who followed a TJ over the Caribbean area (Fig. 4.413.4) in a synoptic study from 1 to 4 August, 1953. The origin of this jet stream could be established clearly in a long-wave trough of the west wind belt, which broke through the Bermuda high. Curiously enough, Alaka found that the cyclonic shear of this jet stream followed the conditions given for a PFJ in Eq. 4.122 (5). Similar to the Indian TJ the divergence and convergence pattern of Figure 4.122.3

adapted for an easterly flow was clearly corroborated by the cloud distribution. A maximum of cloudiness over Cuba and Haiti coincided with the divergent left front quadrant of the jet stream shown in Figure 4.413.4.

Lowenthal and Arnold (1955), too, established the existence of an easterly jet stream over Florida at a height of about 30 km during August of 1954 by means of high-flying radiosondes. This jet stream, however, in all probability belonged to the Krakatoa wind system. The formation of TJ wind maxima at the locations of "breaks" of the subtropical high-pressure belt may be of importance for the formation of tropical cyclones (hurricanes, typhoons). Riehl's (1951) model envisions the formation of surface disturbances in the influence region of an anticyclonic and strongly divergent upper current, as it usually occurs in such regions of a "break." In order to keep the "heat engine" of a tropical cyclone going, a rather effective cooling mechanism is necessary which carries away the moist adiabatically ascending air masses in a powerful upper current. The kinetic energy of the upper current in part stems from the direct circulation and from the release of latent heat within the tropical cyclone. If these air masses were to sink in the close proximity of the cyclone, they would be heated adiabatically and thereby would destroy the solenoids that cause the direct circulation, and the hurricane would die out even before it could reach maturity (Riehl, 1954*c*, 1959). The upper current which causes this cooling effect does not necessarily have to be of jet-stream intensity (Riehl, 1948*b*).

In the southern hemisphere the situation seems to be similar. So, for instance, Bond (1953) observed an easterly jet stream of 80 knots between 14.5 and 17.5 km height over Australia in January and February of 1953.

Even though the easterly current in the tropics may not always assume the character of a jet stream, it still contains well-pronounced wave disturbances (Colon, 1951; Vuorela, 1950) which regulate the weather sequence in a large part of the tropical regions because of the relationship between vorticity changes and divergence expressed in Eq. 1.233 (6) (Arakawa, 1953*c*). A further discussion of this, however, would be beyond the scope of this book. For a lucid resumé, see Riehl (1954*c*).

4.414. The Arctic Stratospheric Jet Stream (ASJ)

From Figure 4.211.4 one could see that in the stratosphere above 20 km a pronounced seasonal change in the flow pattern occurs in temperate and higher latitudes. While during winter a strong westerly jet stream occupies a mean position near about 70° N, a relatively weak easterly jet stream dominates the picture during summer (Goldie, 1950; Haurwitz, 1954; Kochanski, 1959; U.S. Navy, 1959*b*; Wege *et al.*, 1958). This summer jet stream shows relatively few disturbances (Hare, 1960*b*). The seasons of transition (April and October) are characterized by relatively weak stratospheric winds in Arctic latitudes which show rather large meridional components. Over the Antarctic regions a westerly jet stream also is observed at great heights during winter (Alt, Astapenko, and Ropar, 1959).

This seasonal change of the stratospheric flow pattern which became known by measurements of the propagation of sound, by observations of noctilucent clouds, meteor trails, artificial shrapnel clouds (Murgatroyd and Clews, 1949) and high-flying balloons (Trowbridge, 1907) constitutes one of the most spectacular phenomena of the general circulation of the atmosphere. The designation "monsoonal current" therefore may not be unwarranted. The reversal of the current from winter west winds to summer east winds (Bannon, 1955; Darling, 1953; Goody, 1954; Holzapfel, 1958; Kamata and Horiuchi, 1955; Murgatroyd, 1955; Paetzold, 1956*a*; Pogosian, 1959*b*; Scrase, 1951; U.S. Office of Naval Operations, 1948–50) is clearly caused by the radiation and heat budget of the upper atmospheric layers, especially of the ozonosphere (Godson, 1957; Lee and Godson, 1957). This will be discussed in detail further below. First, however, a few characteristic properties of the ASJ will be listed.

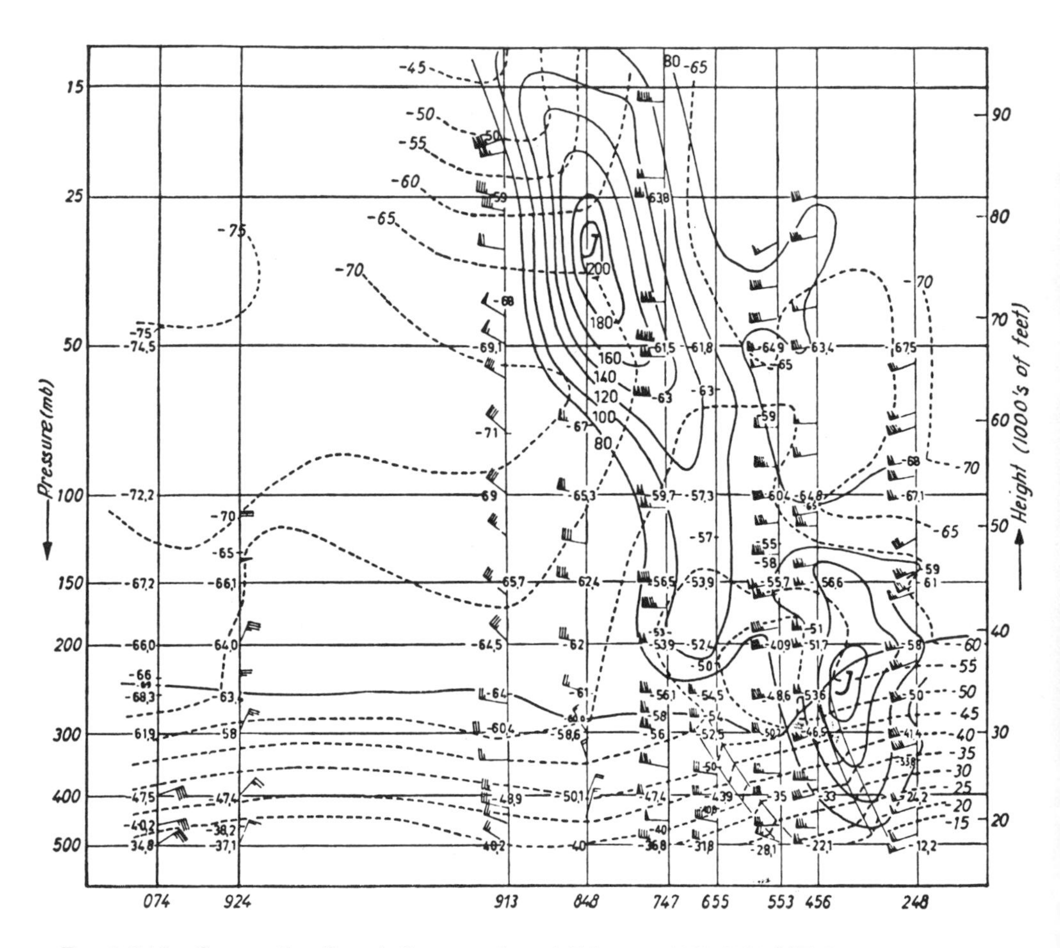

FIG. 4.414.1.—Cross section through the atmosphere, 1 February, 1957, 1500 GCT. Isotachs (knots) and tropopause indicated by solid lines, isotherms (° C) by dashed lines. (Godson and Lee, 1958.)

Figure 4.414.1 shows a meridional cross section from Isachsen, Northwest Territory (074) to Shreveport, Louisiana (248), of 1 February, 1957, 1500 GCT. This cross section runs in the vicinity of the 95th western meridian (Godson and Lee, 1958). The polar-front jet may be found well established near 300 mb north of Shreveport. The baroclinicity within the polar front is expressed by the isotherm pattern. The PFJ lies near the break of the tropopause, the latter being indicated by heavy lines in the analysis. A second frontal zone somewhat north of the polar front apparently indicates the Arctic front. A well-established tropospheric jet stream, however, does not seem to be connected with this front. Instead, there is an ASJ with more than 200 knots very sharply defined between 25 and 50 mb (see also Krishnamurti, 1959*b*). An extension of this jet stream reaches throughout the lower stratosphere all the way down into the influence region of the Arctic front. Whether this connection is merely coincidental cannot be decided with the few analyses available so far. In the meridional cross sections of winter published so far one may, however, in general find a zone of relatively strong winds slanting upward from the PFJ and ending in the ASJ, similar to that shown in Figure 4.414.1 (see also Meyer, 1960).

The rise in the LMW which is observed during winter north of the PFJ is correlated with this zone (see Fig. 3.246.4) (Reiter, 1958*c*). This increase in height is also apparent from the isotherm pattern of high-level isobaric surfaces (Reiter, 1959*e*). With this shift of the level of maximum wind toward greater heights, a tongue of warm air appears to the north of the jet axis at each respective upper pressure level, farther to the north, however, there still is a baroclinicity in the sense of increasing wind speed with height. More recent meridional cross sections which have been obtained by means of the data of the International Geophysical Year along 170° E show such a warm zone between 50° and 60° N during the winter even *on the average*, and during the southern winter between 40° and 50° S. In both cases this warm zone extends from the tropopause to at least the 20-mb surface (Taylor, 1960). The isotherm pattern in Figure 4.414.1 also shows this very clearly. A baroclinic zone extends from the earth's surface to above the 50-mb level. Here a very conspicuous reversal of the meridional temperature gradient is observed. Over the polar cap the temperature increases with height while south of the ASJ almost isothermal conditions prevail. Similar distributions may be observed in other cross sections which intercept the stratospheric level of maximum wind. This temperature distribution is remarkable insofar as it is opposed to what we might expect from the radiation budget. Over the polar cap there is no incoming radiation during the polar night. Therefore, one would have to expect lowest temperatures here. In reality, however, a temperature increase with height is observed above the stratopause (dividing surface between stratosphere and ozonosphere) (Chapman, 1950). This increase in temperature is indicated only weakly above Resolute (74° 41′ N), where the ascent terminated prematurely. Although Churchill (58° 45′ N) lies in the region of temporary incoming radiation, the high ozonospheric temperature at about 30 km height cannot be explained by radiation because the latter should call for an increase in temperature toward the south. Therefore, there has to be a *dynamic warming* in the influence region of the ASJ and its vertical circulation.

Actually, vertical velocities of the order of magnitude of centimeters per second have been observed in the stratosphere. These values appear large in view of the stable stratification (Craig and Hering, 1957; Epstein, 1959; Kochanski, 1954). Considering what has been said earlier about the PFJ and the STJ, the temperature distribution in Figure 4.414.1 now becomes understandable. A warm zone extends along the vertical jet-stream axis from the ozonosphere throughout the whole stratosphere into the region of the PFJ (see also cross section by Teweles [1958]). From this one has to conclude that the ASJ contains an area of maximum sinking motion similar to what has been found in the PFJ and its "jet-stream front" by means of cloud observations, moisture and ozone measurements, as will be further discussed in Chapter 6.

Thus, the old opinion (which still may be found in many textbooks) that the stratosphere—as indicated already by its name—is a zone which is mainly "stratified" by radiation balance now becomes obsolete. The dynamics of flow patterns have as much influence here as they have in the troposphere, and therefore we may by all means talk about a "stratospheric weather."

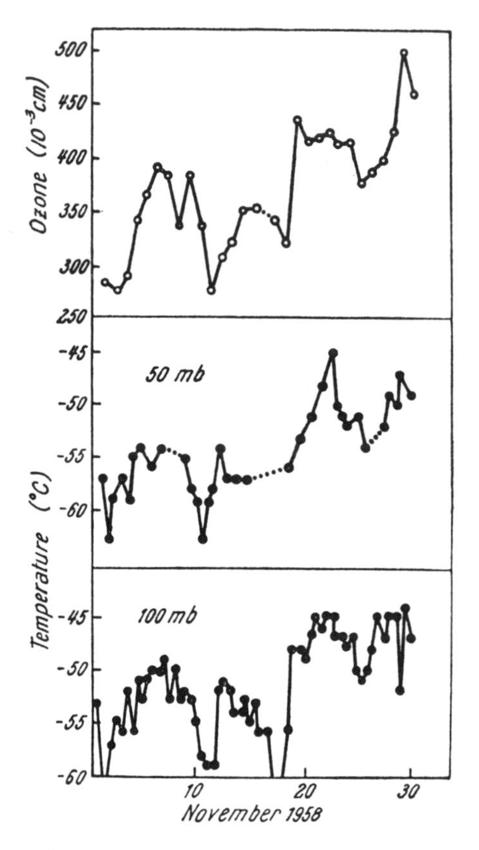

FIG. 4.414.2.—Comparison of the total amounts of ozone with the 50- and 100-mb temperatures over Moosonee, Ontario, November, 1958. (Teweles, 1959.)

The vertical circulation established by means of the temperature distribution in Figure 4.414.1 is also corroborated by other measurements. Figure 4.414.2 shows a correlation between total amounts of ozone in the atmosphere at standard temperature and pressure with 50- and 100-mb temperatures over Moosonee, Ontario (51° 16′ N). High stratospheric temperatures, thus, coincide with large amounts of ozone (see Allington, Boville, and Hare, 1960; Godson, 1960; Ohring and Muench, 1960). This may be easily understood by means of Figure 4.414.1. Because of sinking motions which appear indicated by regions of warm air, the equilibrium between ozone production and recombination is disturbed by an additional import from greater heights (Paetzold and Piscaler, 1959). Sometimes during balloon or rocket ascents several ozone maxima may appear on top of each other. This has to be due to an advective phenomenon (import of ozone with the upper current from lower latitudes). From such ozone measurements (Paetzold, 1956*b*) the conclusion can be drawn that vertical motions of the order of magnitude of 1 to 10 cm per second may exist at levels above 40 km. Such an intensive vertical circulation in the stratosphere, of course, will be in a position to transport atomic debris into the troposphere much faster than would be the case in a settling process due to pure gravitational forces. Turbulent mixing and other diabatic processes may play an important role in these transport considerations, which should not be overlooked.

With all that has been said so far, we are now in a position to supplement a picture of *the winter stratospheric circulation* as it has been designed by Kellogg (1956). The westerly ASJ draws its angular momentum—under the assumption of a motion which occurs with conservation of angular momentum—from lower latitudes. In order to maintain a jet stream of 200 knots at 54° N (Trout Lake [848]), the air would have to come from approximately 49.5° N according to Eq. 1.236 (14). Thus it needs only a small northward displacement to obtain a large zonal wind component. In Figure 4.414.1 the horizontal shear on the anticyclonic side of the ASJ amounts to about $0.9 \cdot 10^{-4}$ sec^{-1}. The Coriolis parameter has the magnitude of about $1.1 \cdot 10^{-4}$ sec^{-1}. Flow patterns with constant angular momentum ($Q = f$) therefore may well be possible in the influence region of the ASJ.

According to the customary picture of meridional stratospheric circulations as it has been designed by Kellogg (1956; and Schilling, 1951) from the results of balloon ascents, rocket and grenade observations, sound propagation measurements, and observations of noctilucent clouds and meteor trails, an ascending air motion prevails in the stratosphere over the summer hemisphere, and a descending motion is present over the winter hemisphere. From the slope of the isentropic surfaces Goldie (1952, 1953) concludes the existence of a stratospheric meridional circulation. A large part of the adiabatic warming (67 per cent during winter) is, however, lost by diabatic cooling due to outgoing radiation.

The meridional circulation manifests itself in an *ageostrophic* flow of mass from the summer toward the winter hemisphere, i.e., from higher to lower pressure. From the considerations made in Chapter 4.122 we may conclude that an ageostrophic component of flow oriented in such a manner would lead to an acceleration of the air masses. The reversal of the circulation from summer (50-knot easterlies) to winter (150-knot westerlies, see Fig. 4.211.4) would indicate an acceleration of more than one knot per day. Since, however, these accelerations are active only during a relatively short transition season, these values might at least be doubled or tripled. Furthermore, from Figure 4.414.1 one may conclude that the main portion of the stratospheric vertical circulation occurs in the region of the ASJ. This becomes apparent from the temperature distribution. In analogy to the conditions near the upper tropospheric jet streams one may assume that the *main transport of momentum* also occurs in the region of the stratospheric jet stream. A part of this momentum transport will be maintained by the *meridional circulation* mentioned earlier. It is, however, very likely that the larger part of the angular momentum will be transported by horizontal large-scale exchange processes in the region of planetary long waves, as is the case in the lower layers of the atmosphere.

The topography of the 10-mb surface of 15 November, 1957 (Fig. 4.414.3), shows that the stratospheric circulation during the winter season is not strictly zonal (Hovmöller, 1950; Kochanski, 1955; Moreland, 1956; Panofsky, 1956). In this diagram one may clearly discern the slope of the trough axis from southwest to northeast. This is the same orientation that is characteristic for an increased transport of momentum toward the north in the influence region of tropospheric long waves: On the leading side of the troughs westerly angular momentum flows northward in a current coming from the west-southwest; in the rear of the troughs, however, only little westerly momentum is carried southward in an almost northerly upper current. The *horizontal large-scale eddy-exchange* thus may transport considerable amounts of momentum in troughs oriented in such a fashion. Large-scale eddies in horizontal planes may even be observed in the tropical regions (Riehl and Higgs, 1960).

In Figure 4.414.3 the northernmost part of the upper trough lies over the North American cold pole in the lee of the Rocky Mountains, while a second trough is indicated over the Asiatic east coast. These trough positions are typical for the winter

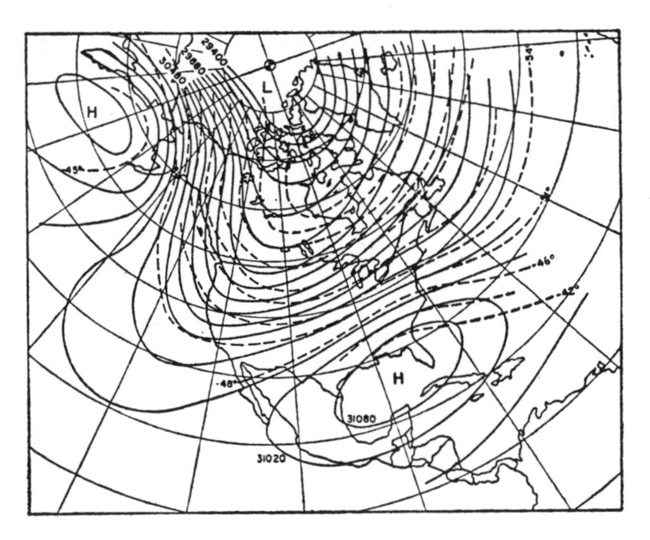

FIG. 4.414.3.—10-mb topography (m, solid lines) and isotherms (° C, dashed), 15 November, 1957. (Teweles 1959.)

stratospheric flow of the northern hemisphere (see Hare, 1960*a*; Palmer, 1959; Regula, 1949; Scherhag, 1948*b*, 1957; Wege, 1958). They are also present in the tropospheric circulation, and they prove that the effect of the high mountain ranges of the Himalayas and of the Rockies are felt even at these great altitudes and probably may extend their influence even higher (see sound propagation measurements in Alaska by Crary, 1953). This will be explained further in Chapter 7.

Although the difference in the radiation budget between the Aleutian Islands and the Greenland icecap agrees in sign with the position of the warm and cold centers of the stratosphere (Figure 4.414.3), it has to be assumed that the dynamic and orographic influences predominate (Teweles, 1958). Probably the colder winter temperatures of the Antarctic stratosphere as compared with the ones of the Arctic stratosphere also to a large part are due to the higher zonal index of the southern hemisphere, and not so much to the differences in the radiation effects and to the higher albedo (see literature in Chapter 4.212). The southern hemisphere does not have a prominent high mountain range like the Himalayas which would deflect the upper current meridionally to the same degree. A counterpart of the warm stratospheric high over the Aleutian Islands, therefore, is missing over Antarctica. Because a more intense meridional circulation causes a greater exchange of heat, it is easy to understand why

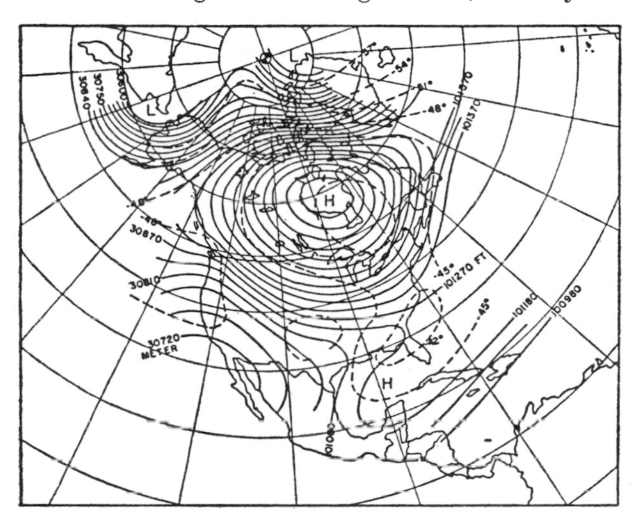

FIG. 4.414.4.—10-mb topography (m, solid lines) and isotherms (° C, dashed), 15 February, 1958. (Teweles, 1959.)

the Arctic stratosphere cools off less during winter than does the Antarctic stratosphere. A certain difference between Arctic and Antarctic conditions also seems to be present in the *yearly variation* of stratospheric temperatures (Bannon, 1958; Wexler, 1960*b*). Over most, not all (Goldie, Moore, and Austin, 1958), of the stations in the south polar region a rapid increase in stratospheric temperatures is observed during spring (September, October). Such an asymmetry does not seem to be present *on the average* over the Arctic. Furthermore, the variability of temperature in the Arctic stratosphere during the individual winter months seems to assume much higher values than in the Antarctic stratosphere. From a statistical investigation by McClain (1960) this becomes evident rather impressively. With increasing geographic latitude and with increasing height the January temperatures *of Arctic* stations show a tendency toward the formation of a *bimodal* frequency distribution. (Double frequency maxima are especially clearly established over Alert, 82° 33′ N, 62° 35′ W, at the 50-mb level.) It appears, therefore, that the occurrence of "abnormally" warm or "abnormally" cold temperatures over the north pole area is most likely—depending upon the magnitude of the meridional or zonal index of the winterly stratospheric circulation. The *mean* January temperature, expressed by the arithmetic mean of the sample of measurements, occurs relatively infrequently. This fact may serve to explain the discrepancies which occur between different meridional sections in the North Pole area (Hess, 1948; Kochanski, 1955; Wege *et al.*, 1958). *South polar stations on the other hand reveal only one frequency maximum in the temperature distribution* of the stratosphere, which may be regarded as a proof of the greater stability and of the predominantly *zonal* character of the stratospheric circulation in the southern hemisphere (Wexler, 1959; see also Moreland, 1960; and the frequencies of jet-stream directions in Astapenko, 1960*b*). The temperature conditions over the Arctic are mainly controlled dynamically because of the large meridional components of flow present there (Austin and Krawitz, 1956). Under these circumstances the *radiative warming* with the return of the sun above the horizon will predominate in the yearly variation of temperatures in ozonosphere and stratosphere over a *South Polar* station. At this time one may expect an *average* warming of more than one degree centigrade per day at the 50-mb level over the South Pole (Taylor, 1960). In an extreme case a temperature rise of 19° C within 12 hours at a height of 27 kilometers has been measured (Hanson, 1960; see also Flowers, 1960). The influence of large-scale vertical motion also plays an important role there (Palmer and Taylor, 1960). Over a North Polar station, however, one may expect a rather smooth *mean* variation of temperature because the various periods of warming produced by the passage of strongly meandering jet streams do not always occur close to the same date (see Fig. 4.414.5).

During the transition season the stratospheric flow reverses from a westerly into an easterly direction. Within a short time an enormous amount of angular momentum, therefore, will have to be transported into the other hemisphere. The mean meridional circulation will not be able to accomplish this, and we have to expect that especially during these transition months the stratospheric flow will have a strongly cellular "low index" character (see Behr *et al.*, 1960*a*, *b*, *c*; Mantis, 1959; Teweles, Rothenberg, and Finger, 1960; U.S. Weather Bureau, 1959). This is evident from Figure 4.414.4, which shows the topography of the 10-mb surface of 15 February, 1958. The slope of the ridge line in this diagram from northwest (north of Alaska) toward southeast (Hudson Bay) provides for more westerly angular momentum flow toward the south than toward the north. Not until summer is another zonal "high index" stage established in the easterly stratospheric flow. However, also during this season at times there may be large meridional components present (Kochanski and Wasko, 1956*a*, *b*).

The monsoonal character of the stratospheric circulation is interesting also in view of the vorticity transport. In Chapter 4.121 we have remarked that according to Rossby's mixing theory a continuous transport of positive vorticity from the northern into the southern hemisphere or of negative vorticity in the opposite direction occurs in the atmosphere (which has been assumed with a depth of 20 kilometers). Rossby (1947) considered these transports to be constant. If we include the circulation of the lower ozonosphere into these considerations, we are forced to the conclusion that this "constancy" may be assumed only for mean wind profiles measured over shorter periods of time and not, however, for seasonal fluctuations as they manifest themselves in the stratospheric circulation.

It may be seen from the isotherm pattern of Figure 4.414.3 that the wind velocities increase further beyond the 10-mb level during winter. The same holds for the summer conditions. This temperature distribution does not agree, however, with Figure 4.414.1. Investigations by Kellogg (1956) and Murgatroyd (1957) indicate that a level of maximum wind is present near the lower boundary of the ozonosphere also during winter as has been indicated by Godson and Lee (Fig. 4.414.1). According to Murgatroyd's model (Fig. 4.415.5), the level of maximum wind of the westerly stratospheric jet of winter lies close to a height of 60 kilometers. It shows, however, extensions down to about 25 to 30 kilometers height. It may, therefore, well be that, during special weather situations which are characterized by excessively strong vertical circulations, an upper wind maximum may already occur at lower levels as has been the case in Figure 4.414.1.

A third component of momentum transport finally occurs in the *vertical exchange*. With the sinking motions that are already indicated by the mean stratospheric meridional circulation and which are strongly expressed in the region of a jet stream (Fig. 4.414.1), this component may contribute—however little—toward the circulation of lower layers. A numerical estimate, like the one given by Palmén and Alaka (1952) for the STJ, is not yet possible with the sparse observational data.

Let us return once more to Figure 4.414.3. From the horizontal crowding of contour lines we may conclude that north of the Bering Strait a stratospheric jet maximum is present, whose delta region should be sought over the Northwest Territories. The same considerations with respect to divergence and vorticity distribution may be applied to this jet maximum as we have done with the PFJ and with the STJ [Eq. 1.233 (6)]. From the way in which the contour lines intersect the isotherms one finds the pattern of vertical circulation which has been derived for the PFJ corroborated qualitatively: ascending motion (cooling) in the left front quadrant, sinking motion (warming) in the right front quadrant. The inverse arrangement is called for in the rear quadrants. This, of course, is true only under the condition that the isotherms in Figure 4.414.3 move *more slowly* than the wind. This assumption, however, is not seriously restricting because the air moves relatively fast through the planetary wave pattern.

Since the same conditions with respect to vertical circulation are present in the ASJ that we have found in the PFJ, we may assume that the stratospheric "frontal zone" slowly intensifies itself in the delta region under adiabatic conditions of flow and slowly dissipates in the entrance area. Thereby the stratospheric jet maximum slowly propagates downstream as it does in the PFJ (see Chapter 4.221). Strong meandering of this jet stream has to be expected in a baroclinic stratosphere (Hare, 1960*a*). The wind shear on the anticyclonic side near the jet core of Figure 4.414.1 has the order of magnitude of about $0.9 \cdot 10^{-4}$; the dynamic stability, therefore, is not very large. Dynamically unstable conditions of flow which may lead to an amplification of disturbances and to the breakdown of the waves, thus, would not be impossible in the ASJ (see Behr *et al.*, 1960*a*, *b*, *c*). As could be shown by Palmer and Taylor (1960), the breakdown of the winterly stratospheric circulation of the southern hemisphere may be traced back to the amplification of such an unstable wave, which, in the case under consideration, appeared to the lee of Graham Land. From a paper by Fleagle (1958) one may conclude that especially the zone between the ozonospheric temperature maximum and the mesopause (also called the "mesodecline" because of the temperature decrease with height occurring here) is rather susceptible to disturbances during winter which magnify their amplitudes in temperate and high latitudes. Wexler and Moreland (1957) were able to show that the winter stratospheric circulation may change drastically within short periods of time. Even the possibility of the formation of stratospheric "blocking" anticyclones is considered similar to those which occur under the influence of the PFJ (see Chapter 6.125). This stratospheric "blocking" might explain the abnormally high amounts of ozone which have been observed over Tromsö during several years for extended periods of time (see Larsen, 1959). To the rear of such "blocks" ozone would be imported continuously from lower latitudes and then would gradually reach lower layers by sinking motion.

When a stratospheric jet maximum passes a radiosonde station, this becomes apparent in a very impressive manner from the variation of temperature on an isobaric level (Hare, 1960*a*; Lee and Godson, 1957; Namias, 1958; Teweles and Finger, 1958). Figure 4.414.5 shows overlapping 10-day averages of the temperature of the 100-mb surface for four stations of the North American Arctic. The sudden increase of temperature during January, 1955, and during February, 1957, is especially impressive (the latter probably occurred in connection with the jet stream shown in Fig. 4.414.1). On both occasions temperatures were reached in the middle of winter which otherwise are characteristic for these stations only for the summer months. This fact will have to overthrow our past opinions that the stratospheric temperature is controlled by radiation only. A sudden rise of temperature of about 30° C within a few days (the temperatures over Alert, February, 1957, appeared to be considerably smoothed by the calculation of overlapping means) cannot be explained by any radiation effects. The so-called "Berlin phenomenon" and the "Thule phenomenon," i.e., the "explosive" stratospheric warming which has been observed in January and February, 1952, over Berlin and Thule and which at that time was attributed to a solar outbreak (Scherhag, 1952, 1957) probably has its true cause in the passage of the stratospheric jet axis (Flohn, 1960*b*). As Scherhag (1952) himself indicated, large interdiurnal temperature variations occur in the stratosphere mainly during winter, especially late winter. Why would the effect of solar outbreaks be confined to the winter season and why would it be such a local phenomenon? The horizontal temperature gradient in a stratospheric frontal zone as shown in Figure 4.414.1, however, would suffice to explain interdiurnal temperature variations of more than 20° C in a plausible manner (Warnecke, 1956). Aside from horizontal advection, vertical motions will also play an important role in the temperature variations (Behr, 1960; Reinecke, 1952; Scherhag, 1960; U.S. Navy, 1960*b*; Wexler, 1958). The long-wave radiation from lower atmospheric layers also may influence the stratospheric temperatures during longer periods of time (Kraus, 1960*b*; Moreland, 1960). In the Antarctic stratosphere this effect even seems to dominate at times.

A certain solar influence may be present during periods of stratospheric warming in summer, as Scherhag (1960) found for the 20-mb level. A warm wave observed in July, 1958, proceeded at a very uniform speed from east to west, i.e., in the direction of the stratospheric easterlies, and circled the northern hemisphere within 12 days. For warm centers in winter at the 25-mb level Scherhag found retrograde motions—i.e., also from east to west—during January and February. The warming trend seems to reach to great altitudes because it was even evident from a distinct increase in the deceleration of Sputnik β1, 1957. Parallel to the braking action upon the satellite an increase in the emission of solar radio waves has been observed. It is, however, difficult to ascertain whether there is a causal relationship between these two phenomena, because the wave emission showed a distinct correlation only with the 25-mb temperature increase at 55° N and 10° E. In other sectors of the hemisphere such a correlation might be less distinct. Since the stratospheric disturbances travel only slowly, the probability is rather large that such a solar process will be coincident with high stratospheric temperatures on at least one place in the hemisphere. By this, however, a causal relationship is not necessarily proved (Teweles, Rothenberg, and Finger, 1960).

That such sudden warmings more commonly occur during the late winter might indicate that the increasing meridional temperature gradient, due to the outgoing

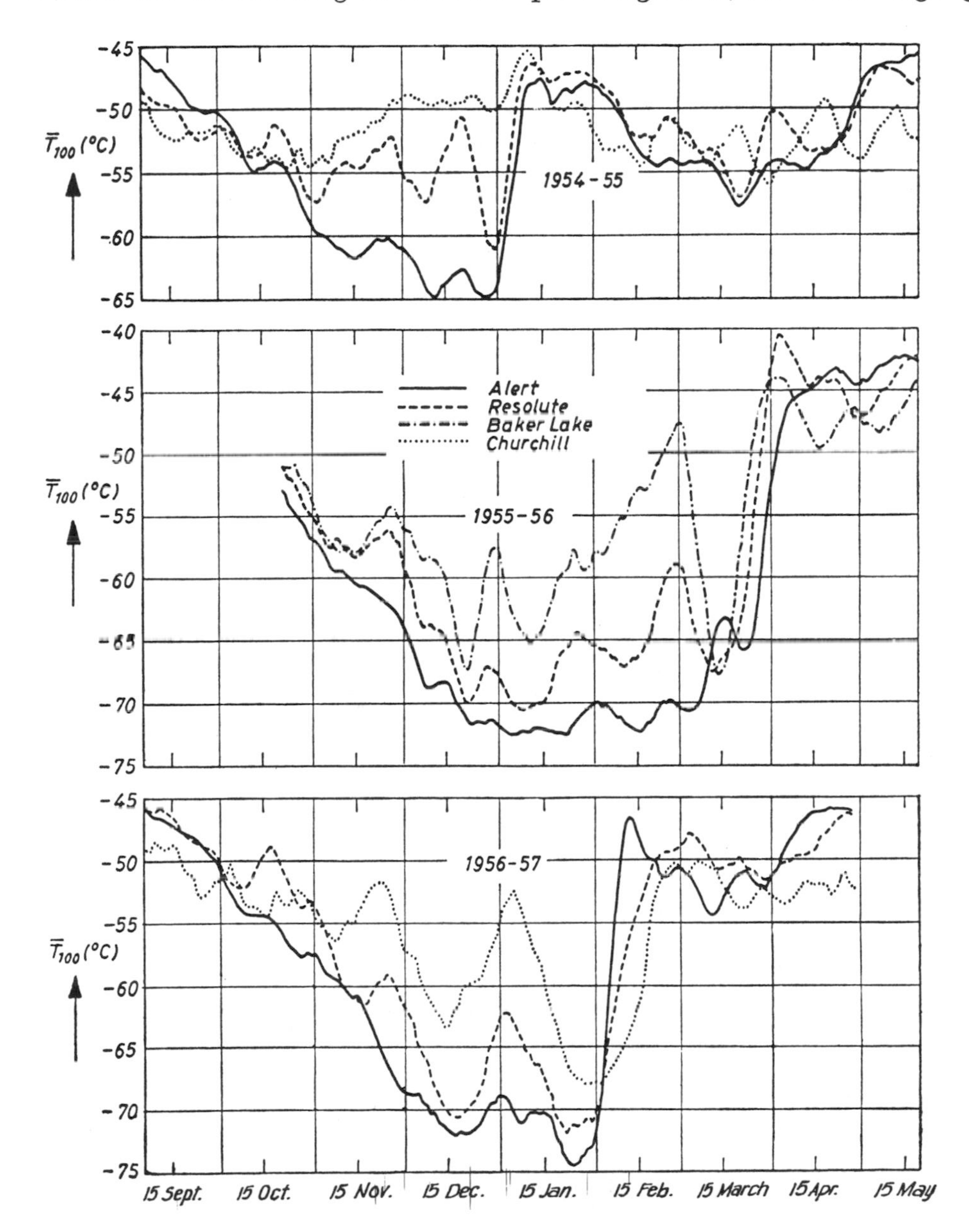

FIG. 4.414.5.—Overlapping 10-day averages of the 100-mb temperatures over four Arctic stations, which are approximately located along one meridian. (Godson and Lee, 1958.)

radiation during the polar night, finally leads to a breakdown of the zonal circulation. Kinetic perturbation energy is constantly fed into the upper current by the effect of high mountain ranges, especially of the Himalayas. These perturbations become evident from meridional components of flow. It may be assumed that these perturbations are unstable and increase their amplitudes rapidly as soon as a critical value of the zonal velocity is reached (see Palmer and Taylor, 1960). If the breakdown of the circulation occurs during late winter, a new, although weaker, cyclonic circumpolar vortex may establish itself. If, however, the circulation breakdown occurs during spring, it may initiate the development of the anticyclonic conditions of flow which prevail during summer. It has already been pointed out that the southern hemisphere lacks an orographic source the size of the Himalayas for kinetic energy of perturbation motions. This may be the reason why the "breakdowns" of the stratospheric zonal circulation over the southern hemisphere occur less frequently and later than they do over the North Polar areas. According to a study by Palmer (1959; see also Palmer and Taylor, 1960), the winter circulation of the southern hemisphere does not break down until after the spring equinox, while over the northern hemisphere the breakdown occurs during the winter night and is not bound to a certain date, as may be seen from Figure 4.414.5.

The strong temperature gradient which during winter appears between Alert and Churchill (Fig. 4.414.5) speaks for the presence of a powerful stratospheric jet. The rather regularly spaced maxima and minima of temperature indicate the transition of *wave disturbances* in this stratospheric jet stream. One will have to expect therefore that large *interdiurnal* changes of stratospheric winds may be possible.

Diurnal variations are to be expected, too, because the temperature conditions in the ozonosphere react rather sensitively upon the daily variation of radiation (Weeks, 1954). Kennedy and others (1954, 1955) could actually prove the existence of such fluctuations in the upper winds. According to Mantis (1960), the amplitude of the diurnal variations in the meridional component of the wind speed at 45° N and at the height of 29 km amounts to about 1 m/sec. Measurements in the Denver area showed that temperatures and high-level winds in the region between 30 to 60 km show a phase difference of 10 to 14 hours. Maximum speeds in the upper winds, thus, were to be expected during times of minimum temperatures (at about 10:00 A.M.). It might be possible, therefore, that these phase differences may be caused by inertial motions. The inertial semi-period in the Colorado region is about 9.5 hours. If, therefore, the meridional temperature gradient were increased by incoming radiation, and the geostrophic equilibrium were disturbed, one would have to expect maximum wind velocities to occur about 10 hours later. At this height one also would have to expect disturbing effects from solar and lunar tides (Haurwitz, 1950). This may be indicated from Kennedy's measurements in which the temperature minimum occurs some time *after* sunrise.

By means of radar wind measurements carried out with transponder equipment, Sawyer (1961) observed the existence of a vertical fine structure in the lower stratosphere (<20 km) which also may be due to inertial motions. It becomes apparent from the existence of layers of about 1 km thickness with different wind directions and wind speeds which retain their identity over several hours.

Shorter period oscillation with wave length of 30 to 200 km and amplitudes of 10 to

20 km within the easterlies of summer have been pointed out by Flohn, Holzapfel, and Oeckel (1959). These data have been obtained from transosonde measurements at heights above 20 km in the region of Sardinia. In the course of these measurements the stratospheric easterlies proved to be independent of the changing wind structure of

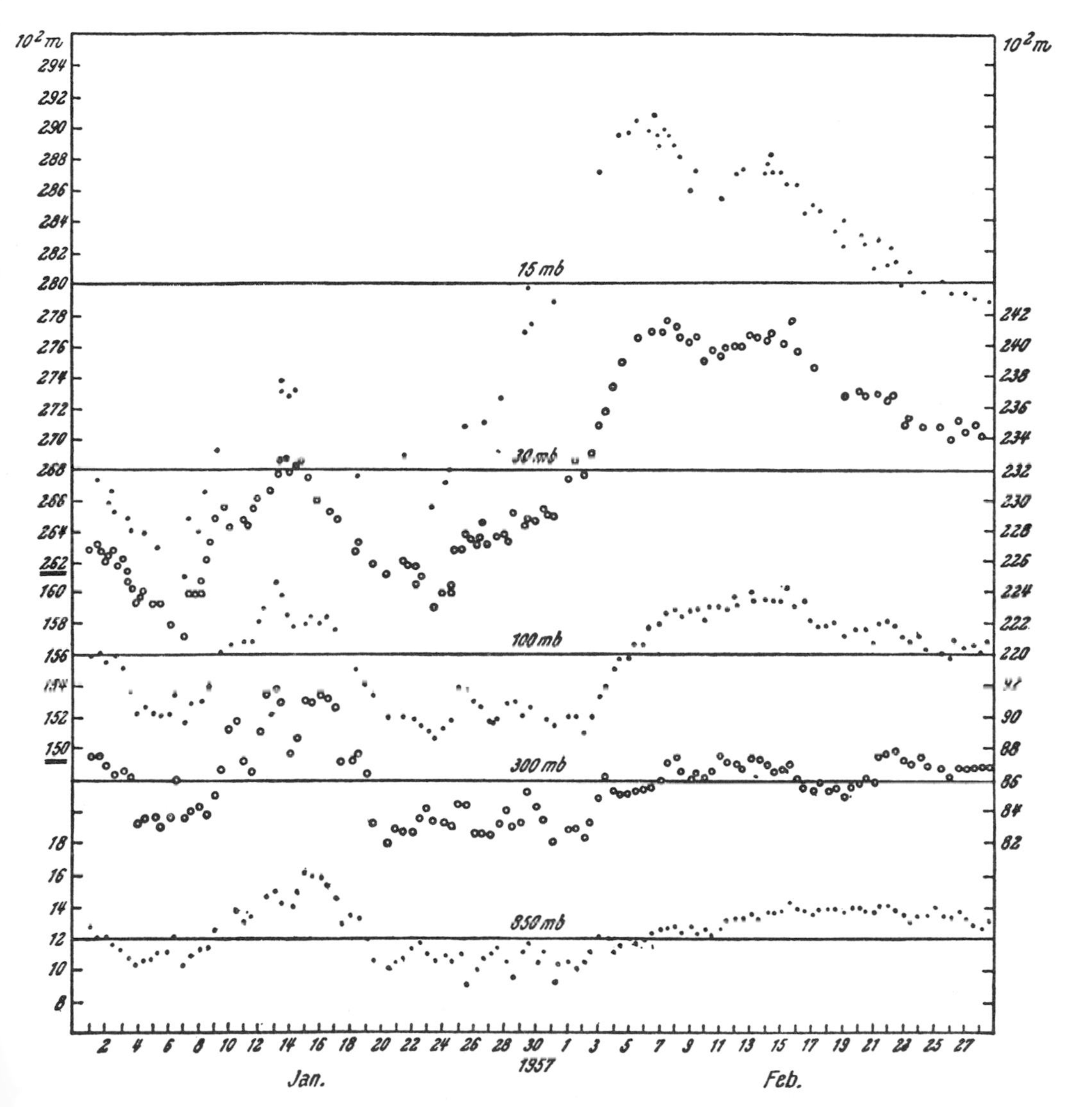

FIG. 4.414.6.—Height of the 850-, 300-, 100-, 30-, and 15-mb surfaces over Keflavik, Iceland, January and February, 1957. Height values for dots on left-hand margin, for circles on right-hand margin of diagram. Dates are given for 0000 GCT. (Teweles, 1958.)

the troposphere. It might be possible that such meso-meteorological fluctuations in the upper wind field might contribute toward the transport of momentum.

In the discussion of Figure 4.414.1 an apparent coupling between PFJ and ASJ has already been pointed out. Teweles (1958) found from an analysis of the same synoptic map time (1 February, 1957) that the jet maxima in the upper troposphere as well as at the 25- and 15-mb levels lay on the eastern edge of a well-defined long-wave trough which was formed by the cold pool over the northern Hudson Bay area. Three days before this map time similar conditions prevailed. The 300-mb jet appeared split into two "fingers": the southern branch followed a slightly anticyclonic curvature and apparently reflected the influence of subtropical air masses, while the northern branch followed in a very distinct manner the cyclonically curved stratospheric jet.

A time section containing the heights of individual standard isobaric surfaces over Keflavik, Iceland, for January and February, 1957 (Fig. 4.414.6) shows clearly the coupling between ASJ and PFJ. The change of circulation in this area seems to become evident first in the stratosphere and only several days later in the troposphere (see also Palmer, 1959). So, for instance, the transition from a trough to a ridge position, which occurred at the 300-mb level on 3 February, appears at the 15-mb level already between 24 and 26 January. If such relationships between stratospheric and tropospheric circulation were applicable on a global basis one would have won a powerful tool for medium-range forecasting.

Whether the time lag with which stratospheric warming and pressure rise proceed toward lower levels is caused by the slow action of turbulent vertical exchange (Fortak, 1959) is questionable. It rather seems that in this process the *dynamics* of the upper current are reflected, which, by virtue of pressure changes, cause the slow change of the large-scale flow patterns also at lower levels. Craig and Hering (1957) considered the same period from which Figure 4.414.1 had been taken, with respect to changes of the tropospheric circulation. They found that the stratospheric warming in high latitudes was followed by a rather conspicuous decrease in the tropospheric zonal index.

Naturally, intensive and short periodic tropospheric pressure systems will also cause a certain influence upon the stratospheric (50-mb) pressure and height tendencies of high latitudes. In this case the tendencies in the stratosphere will appear strongly damped. The statistical investigation by Austin and Krawitz (1956) shows that on the other hand, large-scale pressure systems at the 50-mb level are not without considerable influence upon the pressure tendencies—and therefore upon the weather processes—in the troposphere (see Barbé, 1959). Although the influence of the tropo-

TABLE 4.414.1. AVERAGE HEIGHT CHANGES (FEET) OF THE STANDARD ISOBARIC SURFACES IN HIGH LATITUDES (Austin and Krawitz, 1956)

	50 mb	100 mb	200 mb	300 mb	500 mb	700 mb	1000 mb
Average of all cases	−1670 (58) +1740 (51)	−1210 +1220	− 890 + 850	− 770 + 660	− 550 + 450	−370 +280	−160 +110
Predominantly stratospheric systems (50 mb)	−1950 (20) +2060 (25)	−1430 +1520	−1050 +1070	− 920 + 910	− 640 + 670	−410 +450	−140 +220
Predominantly tropospheric systems	−1140 (7) 0 (0)	−1310 0	−1750 0	−1800 0	−1280 0	−950 0	−540 0
Tropospheric and stratospheric systems 180° out of phase	−1600 (16) +1560 (13)	−1010 +1080	− 340 + 600	− 80 + 290	− 60 + 100	+ 50 − 80	+110 −220
Troposphere and stratosphere in phase	−1760 (12) +1310 (13)	−1150 + 790	− 930 + 570	− 870 + 530	− 670 + 370	−550 +290	−430 +270

Numbers of cases appear in parentheses.

sphere upon the surface pressure tendencies will prevail whenever there is a phase difference between tropospheric and stratospheric pressure fields, the development of surface low-pressure or high-pressure cells will be damped considerably as compared with the cases when tropospheric and stratospheric systems are in phase (Table 4.414.1).

One should not expect, however, the stratospheric jet of winter with its high wind velocities to regulate all processes in the region of the PFJ. In spite of its smaller wind velocities the latter contains much higher kinetic energies due to the greater air density. This becomes apparent from a table by Scherhag (1948*b*): This table contains as a measure of the zonal wind speed the height difference Δz (in dynamic decameters) for the months of January, 1942 to 1944 between Catania and Tromsö. $\rho(\Delta z)^2$, therefore, gives a means of comparison for the kinetic energy of the zonal current.

TABLE 4.414.2. COMPARISON OF THE KINETIC ENERGIES OF THE MEAN ZONAL CURRENT IN JANUARY BETWEEN CATANIA AND TROMSÖ

Isobaric surface	1000 mb	500 mb	225 mb	96 mb	41 mb
Air density ρ	1.250	0.738	0.360	0.165	0.065
Δz	8	31	50	62	71
Δz^2	64	961	2500	3844	5041
$\rho(\Delta z)^2$	80	709	900	634	328

4.415. Wind Systems of the High Atmosphere

The jet-stream systems discussed so far can be analyzed synoptically with our present techniques of meteorological measurement. Beyond this, however, there are current systems in the upper atmosphere of whose existence we know only by various means of direct and indirect measurement. These observations, however, are not dense enough in space and time to indicate the exact pattern of these wind systems.

Let us first consider the *stratosphere* and *mesosphere*. According to a definition by Chapman (1950), the former constitutes the nearly isothermal region above the *troposphere*. The *mesosphere* starts above the stratopause (*ca.* 30 km). (It constitutes the upper part of the ozonosphere. The portion with decreasing temperature between 60 and 100 km is also called chemosphere by Gerson and Kaplan [1951]). The mesosphere shows a temperature increase along the "mesoincline" up to the "mesopeak," which corresponds to the level of maximum temperature at about 50 to 60 km. Above this level the temperature decreases along the "mesodecline" until the "mesopause" is reached, i.e., the level with minimum temperature near 90 to 100 km height. This temperature distribution in the upper atmosphere will be further discussed below. As has been described in the preceding chapter the ASJ is a phenomenon which primarily is connected with the stratopause of the polar cap of winter. It therefore occurs near an altitude of 30 km (see Fig. 4.414.1).

With the aid of Figure 4.211.5 it could be shown that a belt of westerlies is embedded in the easterly current near the equator at a height of about 20 km. These are the so-called *Berson westerlies*.

They occur at about 50 mb, i.e., at a higher level than the easterly jet of the tropics

(100 mb) and they are confined to the equatorial stratosphere. Berson (1910) found these winds in 1908 during an expedition into the area around Lake Victoria in Central Africa (Sellick, 1950). Van Bemmelen (1924) also found a zone of very persistent westerlies at a height of about 20 km over Batavia. Radiosonde ascents which have been made in the course of atomic tests over several islands of the equatorial Pacific corroborated these results (Flohn, 1960*a*; Korshover, 1954*a*, *b*), so that Palmer (1954) arrived at the hitherto unproven conclusion that these Berson westerlies at 20 km height surround the whole globe. The transition to the Krakatoa easterlies above (see Fig. 4.211.5) varies from month to month and also from year to year as could be substantiated from the data series available over the Pacific. The Berson westerlies do not show, however, a seasonal reversal as is present in the stratospheric circulation of the temperate latitudes (Palmer, 1953).

These Berson westerlies are very steady. For February, 1954 Dean (1956) found a mean wind speed of 15 knots and a maximum steadiness of more than 80 per cent (defined as $\frac{\mathbf{v}}{c} \cdot 100$, where $\mathbf{v}$ is the mean resultant wind vector and c is the mean scalar wind speed) in the Berson winds over Kusaie (equatorial West Pacific) at a height of 65,000 ft (20 km) (Fig. 4.415.1). During some months the steadiness may reach values

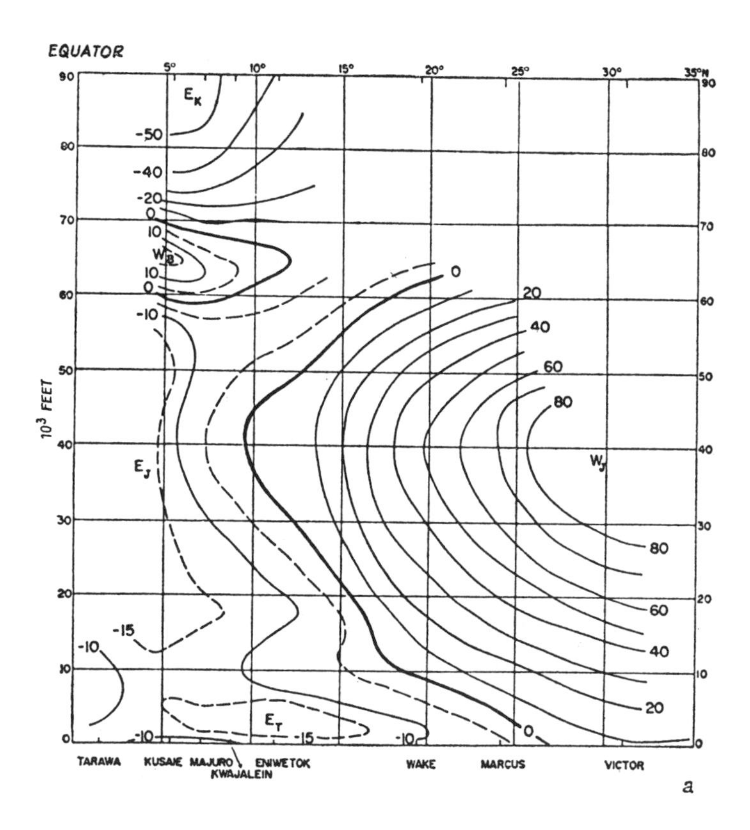

Fig. 4.415.1.—February, 1954: mean zonal wind component in knots (*a*), and steadiness of winds in per cent (*b*) along 167° E. (Dean, 1956.)

of 97 per cent (Flohn, 1960*a*; Palmer, 1954). A minimum of steadiness is found in the transition zone between Berson westerlies and other wind systems. Thus, these transition zones show rather large fluctuations in time.

A recent investigation by Ebdon (1960) indicates that the Berson westerlies do not seem to be present in every year. So for instance, the mean wind vectors at all available equatorial stations (Singapore; Philippines; equatorial Pacific; Albrook Field, Panama Canal Zone; Central Africa) showed easterly winds at the 50-mb level (21 km) during January, 1957. During this year the easterlies appeared as a continuous band between 20° S and 20° N. The mean wind vector at the equator reached maximum values of up to 50 knots over the Pacific.

During January, 1958 the same equatorial stations showed westerlies with average maximum velocities of 25 to 35 knots near 5° N.

Observations over Canton Island (02° 46′ S, 171° 43′ W) show a rather peculiar periodicity of two years in the appearance of the Berson winds, as may be seen from Table 4.415. This periodicity seems to occur also over the Christmas Islands farther to the east (02° 00′ N, 157° 23′ W), where the following mean wind vectors have been measured at the 50-mb level:

1957: 091°, 40 knots (52 observations),
1958: 271°, 27 knots (29 observations),
1959: 091°, 31 knots (3 observations).

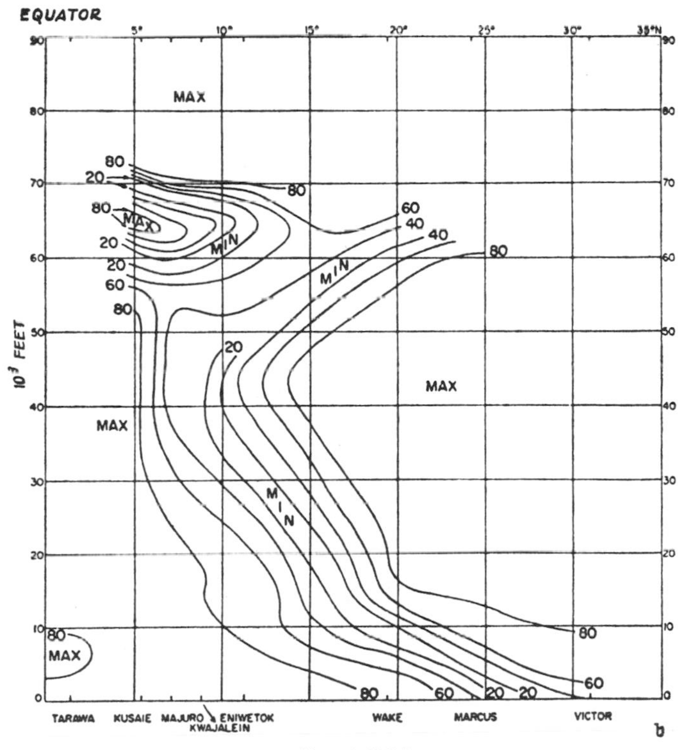

b

Fig. 4·415.1.

TABLE 4.415. MEAN AND MAXIMUM VALUES OF WINDS, CANTON ISLAND (02° 46′ S, 171° 43′ W)

JANUARY OF THE YEAR	LEVEL	Number of days with observations	Number of ascents	NUMBER OF CASES WITH ZONAL COMPONENTS FROM		MEAN WIND VECTOR		MAXIMUM WINDS	
				EAST	WEST	DEGREES	KNOTS	DEGREES	KNOTS
1954	65,000 ft	10	10	0	10	270	14	290	46
1955	65,000 ft	11	11	10	1	091	25	090	38
1956	50 mb	20	26	1	25	275	12	260	30
1957	50 mb	27	36	36	0	090	44	088	68
1958	50 mb	24	30	0	30	270	18	264	36
1959	50 mb	31	51	48	3	095	22	282 085	36 56

The velocity of the Berson westerlies hardly ever reaches the lowest threshold value proposed by WMO. However, since it is a rather narrow current which is embedded into easterlies, we shall discuss it in the following at least as a jet-stream-*like* phenomenon.

A zone of equatorial westerlies in the upper atmosphere also seems to be present on other celestial bodies, as for instance on the sun (Quiring, 1953). The appearance of such westerlies on the equator is rather difficult to understand from the point of view of conservation of angular momentum. Even air masses which are imported from the other hemisphere (Hubert, 1949) cannot carry along an angular momentum which is larger than the one of the earth at the equator. Which circumstances generate these winds and what keeps them alive in a surrounding of oppositely directed easterlies? Lettau (1956) tried to find a theoretical answer to these questions. He started from an *idealized* vertical wind profile which he assumed to be characteristic for the mean conditions of flow at the equator for a large range of geographic longitudes. Furthermore, he assumed these Berson winds to be symmetrical about the equator in their horizontal shear configurations. The latter assumption, however, does not seem to be quite justified according to the investigations by Ebdon (1960).

Order of magnitude estimates from this idealized wind profile and from the thermal stratification of the equatorial atmosphere lead Lettau to the conclusion that in the region of the Berson westerlies—similar to the nighttime inversion wind maxima—the turbulent viscosity assumes very small values and thereby supports the great steadiness of this wind system. In the Krakatoa easterlies above, the turbulent viscosity again increases strongly. The transport of westerly angular momentum out of the core of the Berson westerlies by means of turbulent exchange also appears to be rather small.

Lettau proposes the following solution for the distribution of vertical velocities over the equator: Near the tropical tropopause there are weak ascending motions; within the Krakatoa easterlies there are strong upward motions. The Berson westerlies in between have hardly any vertical motions in their upper part, while the lower part of this west wind zone is characterized by sinking motions (maximum -0.7 cm per second at about 21 km height). This has been corroborated by the drift of the Krakatoa ashes: within the belt of easterlies the ashes sank only slowly due to the ascending air motion (*ca.* 3 km per month). Furthermore, due to the horizontal convergence in this region the ashes did not spread much laterally. Only when the divergent zone of the Berson winds had been reached, the cloud of ashes spread out rapidly and during November, 1883, the turbidity reached temperate latitudes. This slight sinking motion may be the cause of the layered structure of the lower parts of the tropical stratosphere (Flohn, 1960*a*).

Energy considerations led Lettau to the conclusion that the *upper part* of the Berson westerlies is maintained by friction, i.e., here the current draws its kinetic energy mainly from turbulent exchange processes. The following computation shows that the equatorial Berson westerlies cannot maintain themselves by conservation of angular momentum without other processes being present at the same time: If an air particle were to sink over the equator from an altitude of 28 km down to 18 km under conservation of angular momentum, according to equation 1.236 (9) a westerly velocity of about 1.5 m per second would result. A velocity of about 10 m per second as it is observed in the Berson west wind zone could not be explained by this.

Flohn and Hinkelmann (1952) considered a simplified version of the equations of motions which led them to the conclusion that the observed westerlies in the friction layer of the atmosphere are *subgeostrophic* and are associated with rising motion w. Hollmann (1955*a*) reasoned that a westerly current which flows into lower latitudes under conservation of the pressure gradient would have to acquire kinetic energy because of the decreasing Coriolis parameter, which is accomplished by a departure toward lower pressures. By this latitudinal adaptation, a westerly current near the equator would be *ageostrophic*. Exner's (1925) assumption that these westerlies constitute a Eulerian flow, which obeys the equation $\frac{\partial \bar{u}}{\partial t} = -\bar{\alpha}\frac{\partial \bar{p}}{\partial x}$, seems to be inadequate to explain the great steadiness and the global extent of the Berson westerlies.

Lettau considers the possibility that the Berson westerlies are *geostrophic*. Since Eq. 1.222 (7) fails at the equator, we may differentiate again after y (Hollmann, 1955*a*). Because of

$$\frac{\partial f u_g}{\partial y} = \beta u_g + f\frac{\partial u_g}{\partial y}$$

and since $f = 0$, we obtain

$$u_g = -\frac{1}{\beta}\frac{\partial\left(\alpha\frac{\partial p}{\partial y}\right)}{\partial y}. \qquad 4.415\ (1)$$

This form of the geostrophic wind equation is valid also at the equator for $\varphi = 0$.

From the approximate form of the thermal wind equation 3.212 (2) we obtain by analogous differentiation after y an expression which may be used at the equator:

$$\frac{\Delta u_g}{\Delta z} = -\frac{g}{\beta}\frac{\partial^2 \ln T}{\partial y^2}. \qquad 4.415\ (2)$$

(A term $(u_p/T)(\partial T/\partial z)$ has been neglected in this equation because of its smallness.) Thus the zonal geostrophic winds over the equator will increase with height if the meridional temperature profile shows a negative curvature.

Palmer (1954) was able to show that the curvature $\partial^2 \ln T/\partial y^2$ at a height of 20 km at 0° of latitude has the order of magnitude of -10^{-18} cm^{-2} because of the presence of one cold tongue each at about 18 km height and several degrees to the north and to the south of the equator. According to Eq. 4.415 (2), we have $\Delta u_g/\Delta z = 40 \cdot 10^{-4}$ sec^{-1}, which is in excellent agreement with the values assumed by Lettau. The curvature of the temperature profile and the relatively warm tongue over the equator might be explained by adiabatic warming in the sinking motion within the Berson region mentioned earlier (see also meridional sections by Taylor, 1960).

From the investigations by Lettau one may conclude that the Berson winds are a phenomenon which draws energy of motion mainly from the turbulent exchange with the layers above and below and by creating a horizontal temperature field by means of the apparent vertical motions. With this temperature field the flow is in geostrophic equilibrium. Whether this hypothesis corresponds to the actual conditions is hard to prove from the scanty observational material presently available.

Above the Berson layer there is the zone of the easterly *Krakatoa* winds.

They became evident from the spreading of the ashes after the eruption of Krakatoa in August, 1883 (Krakatoa, Committee of the Royal Society of London, 1888; Pernter, 1889; Wexler, 1951). Figure 4.211.5 indicates a mean velocity of more than 60 knots (see Clarkson and Littlejohns, 1958). The steadiness of this wind system is rather great (Dean, 1956; Palmer, 1954). It does not seem to suffer any seasonal reversal. Only the transition zone which it shares with the Berson westerlies is subject to relatively large fluctuations.

According to Lettau's studies, an ascending motion increasing with height predominates on the average. The resulting convergence of the Krakatoa current helps to explain the fact that the cloud of ashes drifted westward for a long time without appreciable lateral diffusion. The explanation of equatorial easterlies offers no difficulties. Apparently they incorporate air masses coming from higher latitudes. If under conservation of angular momentum a velocity of 30 m/sec should be reached at the equator, according to Eq. 1.236 (14), the air particles would have to come from approximately 14° north or south. In looking at Figure 4.211.5 this appears to be possible by all means.

It is worth mentioning that the Krakatoa easterlies attain their greatest intensity over the equator. Considering the stratospheric circulation mentioned in Chapter 4.414, this suggests, that these winds result from the monsoonal interhemispheric mass exchange. No matter in which direction the stratospheric meridional circulation flowed, from the south to the north hemisphere or in opposite direction, each time the flow toward the equator under conservation of angular momentum would generate an easterly maximum over the equator which would show approximately symmetric conditions of horizontal shear, both to the north and to the south. Only at some distance from the equator the easterlies would give way to stratospheric west winds on the winter hemisphere, while on the summer hemisphere the Krakatoa easterlies would be connected with the easterly jet stream of the tropics and with the stratospheric circulation, which also is easterly.

A reversal of the meridional circulation would leave the Krakatoa current undisturbed over the equator for reasons of symmetry. This may explain the observed great steadiness of this wind system. As already mentioned, fluctuations are only observed in the transition zone with the Berson westerlies. They may be connected with changes in the structure and intensity of the divergence and convergence field in this altitude range.

Thus we are faced with the interesting fact that the reversal of the stratospheric circulation observed over temperate and polar latitudes does *not* hold for the equatorial atmosphere up to a height of about 60 km. Here extremely steady wind systems are

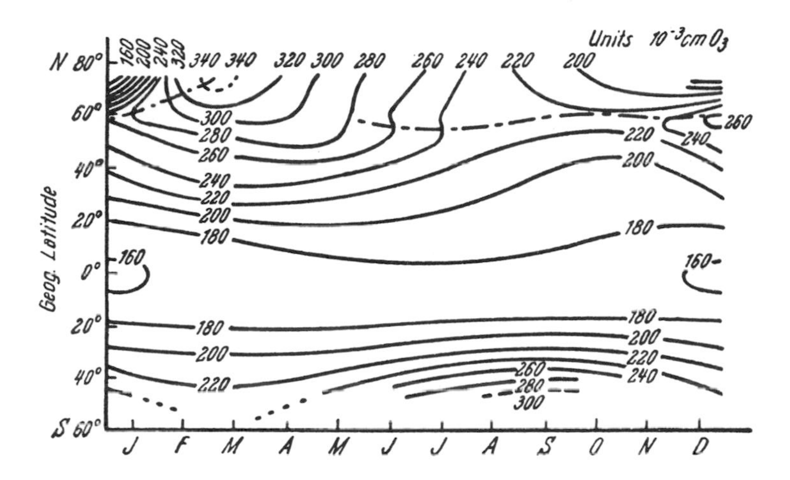

FIG. 4.415.2.—Isolines of total ozone distribution. (Götz, 1949.)

prevailing which are not even influenced in their persistence by the monsoonal changes of flow in extratropical latitudes. From Figure 4.415.5 it may furthermore be seen that the Krakatoa easterlies as well as the subtropical easterly jet of summer constitute only an extension of the mesospheric planetary easterly circulation of the summer hemisphere which attains its velocity maximum at the level of the temperature maximum in the mesosphere at about 55 km height (Flohn, Holzapfel, and Oeckel, 1959).

It may be seen from Figure 4.211.5 that the Krakatoa easterlies already belong to the ozonosphere. The circulation at these heights, therefore, should be reflected in the global ozone distribution (Craig, 1950; Götz, 1931, 1938, 1949; Goody, 1954). This is actually the case as may be seen from Figure 4.415.2, whose details are produced on the one hand by the intensity of incoming short-wave radiation and the resulting *production* and *decay* of ozone but on the other hand by *horizontal* and *vertical ozone transports* (see also Ramanathan and Kulkarni, 1960; U.S. Navy, 1958).

Let us first consider the influence of radiation absorption. Wave lengths smaller than 1800 Å are absorbed above 100 km, with the exception of a few "windows" in the absorption spectrum between 1000 to 1300 Å. These remnants of the short wave radiation may penetrate down to heights of about 80 km. At 100 km height molecular oxygen absorbs in the region of about 1300 to 2000 Å. Below 70 km the absorption by ozone predominates between 2000 and 2900 Å. These absorption coefficients are so large that the main ozone layer (15 to 35 km) absorbs energies only in relatively weak bands in the near ultraviolet. (The numerous literature on this problem cannot be discussed here. See the lucid resumé by Murgatroyd [1957].) The temperature changes because of radiation absorption may be computed from the expression:

$$\frac{dH}{dt} = c_p \rho \frac{dT}{dt} = - \int \frac{d\Phi_\lambda}{dt} d\lambda. \qquad 4.415\ (3)$$

H is the amount of heat added and $\Phi_\lambda\, d\lambda$ is the vertical influx of radiation energy at the level z and within the considered range of wave length $d\lambda$.

Figure 4.415.3 shows the heating effect produced by incoming radiation. Thus we have to expect maximum heating by radiation in the ozone layer over the pole in summer at a height of about 50 km. Over the equator the level of maximum heating lies somewhat lower (at about 47 km). In the winter hemisphere this level rises rapidly to great heights because of the tangential direction of incoming radiation. The absorption assumes correspondingly low values. Little is known about the long wave outgoing radiation of high atmospheric layers so that no total heat budget can be given as yet.

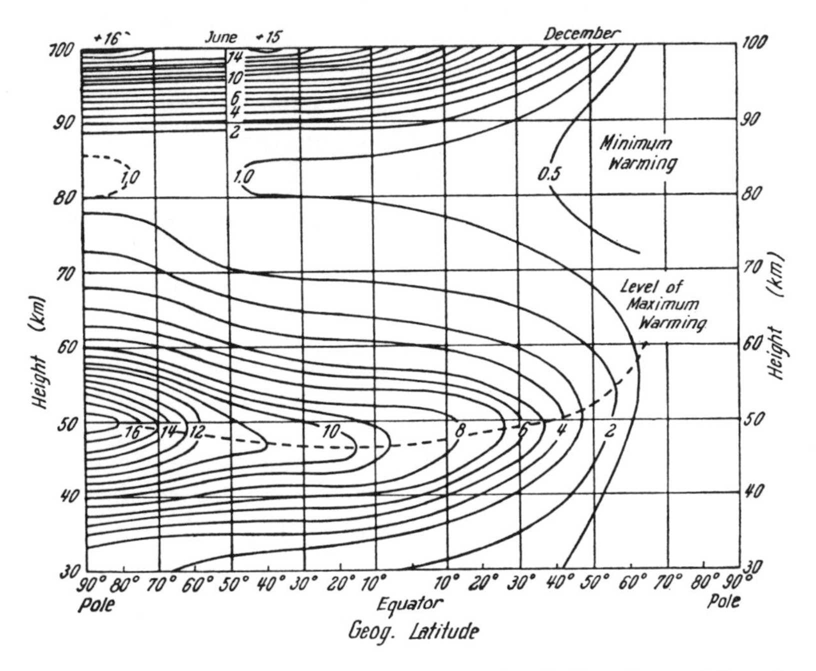

FIG. 4.415.3.—Heating due to incoming solar radiation at various heights, June and December, in units of ° C/day. (Murgatroyd, 1957.)

From the absorption conditions of Figure 4.415.3, we have to conclude that the ozone content of the atmosphere should show a similar meridional distribution as does the warming in the mesosphere. The deviations from this concept which clearly appear in Figure 4.415.2, therefore, should be caused by *ozone advection*, which disturbs the photochemical equilibrium between production and decay of ozone that would otherwise exist. The Arctic ozone minimum during winter agrees well with Murgatroyd's distribution of radiative warming, and also the ozone gradient directed toward the south over the North Polar area during summer. The secondary ozone maximum north of 60° N, which occurs during winter, as well as the equatorial ozone minimum cannot be explained by radiation. The latter may, however, be readily understood if in the lower regions of the Krakatoa easterlies there is convergence and upward motion. By this, air masses of low ozone content would be carried upward from below and air which is rich in ozone would be transported toward the winter hemisphere by the prevailing meridional circulation (see, for example, the yearly variation of the $180 \cdot 10^{-3}$ cm isopleth of ozone in the subtropical and tropical latitudes of the northern and southern hemisphere).

The ozone maximum in subpolar latitudes apparently depends on the import of air masses rich in ozone within the influence region of the Arctic and Antarctic stratospheric jet stream (see Brewer, 1949). We may assume, therefore, that in the region of this jet stream not only the meridional momentum transport attains a maximum as it does in the PFJ, but the ozone transport reaches a maximum, too. The deviations from an average ozone distribution may be intensified by vertical motions (see Fig. 4.414.2). Thus, the upward mean vertical motion in the stratosphere over the summer pole may be the reason that the ozone maximum over the North Polar areas is established already in March, i.e., at a time when the radiation influence just begins to become significant, without the ozone-reducing vertical circulation being established yet. Similarly, the polar ozone minimum of winter is established already in November. By the time the meridional temperature gradient reaches its maximum during January and February due to continuous outgoing radiation, a "turbulent and mean" meridional import of ozone from temperate latitudes already causes an increase of ozone in the Arctic region.

The rather simple scheme of meridional circulations devised by Palmén and reproduced in Figure 4.412.1 thus stands only for a small section of the total atmospheric circulation. The easterly tropospheric jet and the stratospheric jet streams are not considered in it. The measurements available so far do not suffice as yet to allow an incorporation of these new upper flow systems into vertical circulation wheels similar to the ones shown in Figure 4.412.1.

If we want to include the ionosphere into this short summary, a whole new complex of questions is laid open, which, however, would lead far beyond the scope of this book. Murgatroyd (1957) constructed the temperature and wind distribution up to a height of about 120 km, as shown in Figure 4.415.4 and .5. His data have been taken from an extensive study of literature. (See also Berg, 1956; Chapter 7 in Beynon, 1960; Gerson, 1952; Hulburt, 1952; Jenkins, 1952*a*; La Gow, Horowitz, and Ainsworth, 1958; Sprenger, 1960; U.S. Navy, 1958.) The upper wind field seems to agree well with the conditions to be expected from the horizontal temperature gradients (Pant, 1955, 1956). Because of possible errors in measurements it is, however, more reliable to compute the temperature distributions from the observed winds, rather than to proceed in the opposite way (Murgatroyd, 1957). According to the observations used here it seems that there was a reversal of zonal motions between ozonosphere and ionosphere. Effects of absorption of short wave radiation, therefore, do not suffice for the explanation of the observed ionospheric drifts. Is this reversal of the meridional temperature gradient, which has to be expected from the reversed motions of the atmosphere, nothing else but a compensating effect which might be caused by adiabatic warming or cooling due to the dynamics of atmospheric layers further below (Kellogg, 1956)? Does the high atmosphere in the polar night of winter have additional sources

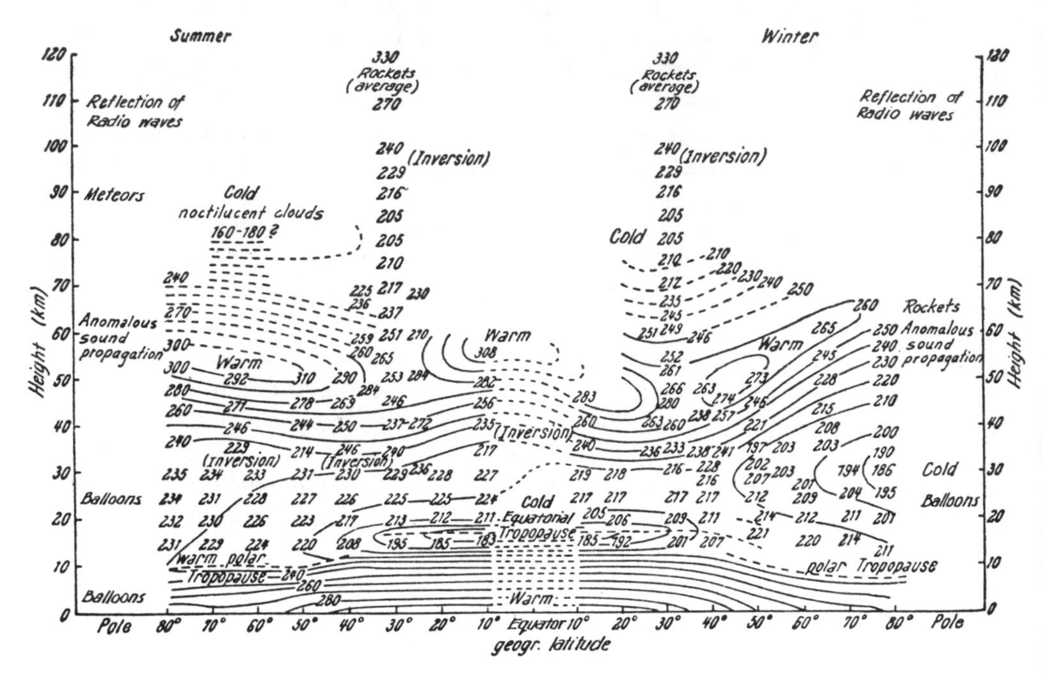

Fig. 4.415.4.—Observed temperature distribution (° K). (Murgatroyd, 1957.)

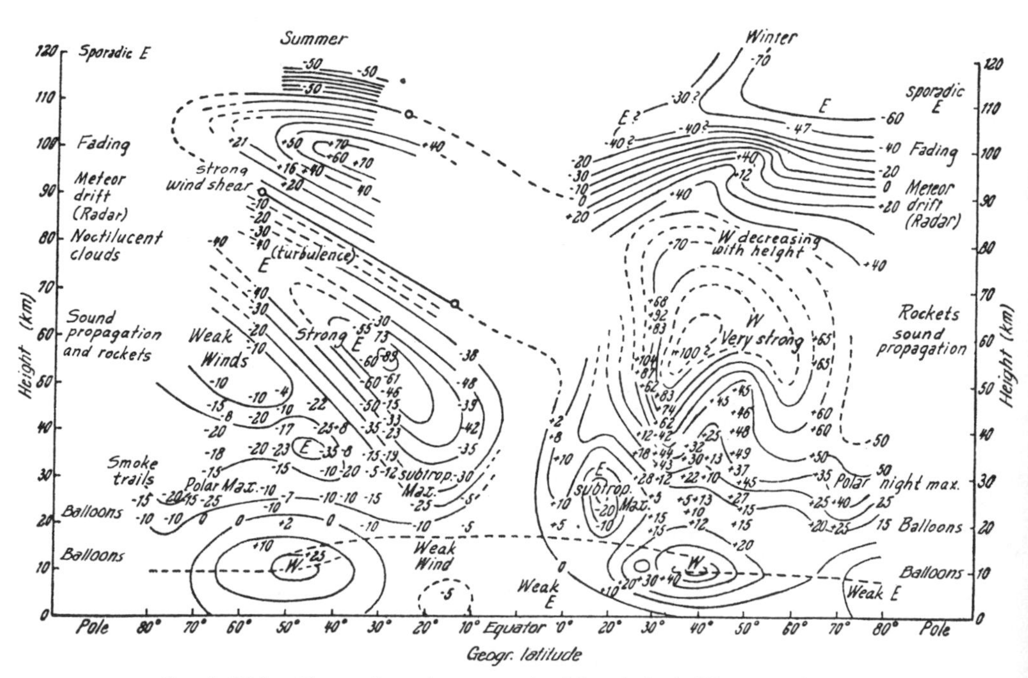

Fig. 4.415.5.—Observed zonal components of flow (m/sec). (Murgatroyd, 1957.)

of energy available such as corpuscular radiation or chemical processes? Since the flow at 100 km and above incorporates ionized matter, the forces of the earth's magnetic field would have to be considered in the equations of motion, together with the force of pressure gradients (Booker, 1959). At these levels large diurnal fluctuations have to be expected in the temperature field as well as in the wind field because of the thermal effect of incoming solar radiation and of the tidal effect (order of magnitude 50 to 100 m/sec at 100 km height [Greenhow, 1959; Greenhow and Neufeld, 1956; Stolov, 1955]). These effects cannot always be separated from the mean conditions of flow because of the sparse observational data.

A comparison of the observed wind speeds (Fig. 4.415.5) with the temperature determinations (Fig. 4.415.4—the latter usually are less reliable in the upper atmosphere than the former) shows that PFJ and STJ, and perhaps also the TJ, are in a close connection with the tropopause. The westerly wind maximum of the polar night and the easterly maximum of the polar day seem to form near the inversion above a nearly isothermal stratosphere (i.e., at the "stratopause"). The ozonospheric west wind and east wind maxima at about 60 km, which may be described as *ozonospheric jets*, also lie in a region of a marked change of vertical temperature lapse rate, i.e., at the mesospheric temperature maximum (mesopeak). Above this, there is a zone of temperature decrease with height up to the mesopause (at about 80 km) which shows strong convective currents and turbulent mixing according to meteor trail observations (University of California, 1950). The westerly wind maximum at about 90 km height seems to establish itself at the upper boundary of the mesosphere (i.e., at the mesopause).

The relationship between levels of maximum wind and surfaces at which the vertical temperature lapse rate undergoes marked changes is easy to understand. If the latter are not horizontal the baroclinicity which in the lower layer has contributed to the formation of high wind speeds will reverse its sign in the upper layer and thereby according to the thermal wind equation reduce the wind speeds. The actually observed height differences between tropopause and level of maximum wind in the regions of the PFJ and the STJ are details of secondary importance and are probably brought about by the effect of vertical circulation and therefore by the dynamics of the jet streams. Nothing more definitive can be said at this time about ozonospheric and ionospheric jet streams ("electro jets"). Only recently has research opened up a new field of investigation in these areas.

4.416. Low-Level Jet Streams (LLJ)

In meteorological literature the existence of a jet stream has been pointed out which attains maximum wind speeds in the lower parts of the troposphere, sometimes even below the 500-mb surface, and which seems to have some kind of relationship with the formation of squall lines and tornadoes.

Before we discuss this LLJ, however, we will re-define the term "jet stream" as it will be used in the following. The WMO specification of a minimum velocity of 60 knots will be abandoned, but we will still consider the existence of marked horizontal and vertical gradients of wind speed as an essential feature.

We will further neglect small-scale processes of motion, in which the rotation of the earth is not to be taken into account. Eulerian $\left(\frac{\partial u}{\partial t} = -\alpha \frac{\partial p}{\partial x}\right)$ and antitriptic winds $\left(\nu \frac{\partial^2 u}{\partial z^2} = \alpha \frac{\partial p}{\partial x}\right)$ will not be discussed, either (Brunt, 1944). Mountain and valley breezes, therefore, will be eliminated from our consideration. Even though they might show jet-stream-like characteristics in a cross section, they are mainly formed by frictional influences of the ground and of the slopes of the valley, and by micrometeorological effects. Vertical "jets," as they occur in convective currents and clouds, will also be disregarded.

An extensive study of wind maxima at nocturnal inversions has been made by Blackadar (1957). Although these wind maxima have also been called "low-level jet streams," there is a marked difference from the jet stream which sometimes is observed in the lower troposphere (at about 850-mb). While the latter has definite jet-stream characteristics in horizontal as well as vertical shears (although the minimum velocity of 60 knots may not always be reached), the phenomenon described by Blackadar is observed over wide areas especially over the American Middle West, and has only significant vertical shears but no appreciable horizontal shears. We will therefore differentiate between *inversion wind maxima* (IWM), i.e., maxima of wind speed at (nocturnal) inversions, and "low-level jets" (LLJ), a term we will reserve for genuine laterally confined jet streams.

The strong vertical shears in the region of an LLJ or IWM gave rise to several practical considerations. Byram (1954) was able to show that forest fires may spread rather suddenly (the so-called "blow-up" phenomenon) when an IWM wind profile is present: a convective "chimney," which apparently breaks through the inversion, causes a sudden intensification and spreading of the fire. Differential thermal advection within the influence region of such strong wind shears may contribute to the observed nocturnal maximum of thunderstorms over the American Middle West (Means, 1944, 1952).

The extremely strong decrease of wind speed near the ground (at times up to 3 knots per 10 m within the lowest 100 m) in the region of an IWM may lead to aircraft accidents during landing, because the head-wind component might be overestimated.

As Blackadar was able to show, the IWM contains *super-geostrophic* wind speeds in the early morning hours, which exceed the geostrophic wind *above* the level of maximum wind, just about by as much as they have been *subgeostrophic* during the preceding afternoon. The level of maximum wind usually coincides with the upper surface of the nocturnal inversion layer.

For the formation of a nocturnal inversions Blackadar derived the condition that Richardson's number (see Chapter 4.322) increases with increasing thickness h of the inversion layer, i.e., $\partial R_i/\partial h \geqq 0$. This may be expected whenever the wind maximum lies at the same height h as the upper surface of the inversion layer. If the wind speed increases further above the inversion, the latter will be dissipated by turbulent exchange.

During the daytime turbulent exchange processes are transporting momentum toward the ground. Near the ground subgeostrophic conditions of flow prevail. As soon as the nocturnal inversion begins to form—probably around sunset—these vertical mixing processes will largely die out.

Because of the increased vertical wind shear a certain residual value of turbulence will be maintained. By this, heat and momentum will still be transported toward the ground and will be consumed here by radiation and by friction. By this process the inversion layer is able to deepen in the course of the night.

Let us assume that the horizontal pressure gradients are constant with time and space. The ageostrophic component $\mathbf{v}^*$, which has been defined in Eq. 1.224 (2) will therefore vary only locally and not advectively. We obtain the equation of motion for *horizontal* flow above the inversion (neglecting frictional effects) by subtracting Eq. 1.222 (6) from Eq. 1.222 (1):

$$\frac{\partial \mathbf{v}}{\partial t}-\frac{\partial \mathbf{v}_g}{\partial t}=-\alpha\nabla p+f\mathbf{v}\times\mathbf{k}+\frac{\alpha}{f}\frac{\partial}{\partial t}\nabla p\times\mathbf{k}.$$

The last term vanishes because of the assumed constancy of the pressure gradient. Thus we arrive at

$$\frac{\partial \mathbf{v}^*}{\partial t}=f\mathbf{v}^*\times\mathbf{k} \qquad 4.416\ (1)$$

or in component form

$$\frac{\partial u^*}{\partial t}=fv^*$$
$$\frac{\partial v^*}{\partial t}=-fu^*, \qquad 4.416\ (2)$$

where $u^*=u-u_g$ and $v^*=v-v_g$ are the components of the "geostrophic departure" [see Eq. 1.224 (2)]. If in analogy to the vector $\mathbf{v}^*$ we define $V^*=u^*+iv^*$ in the plane of complex numbers, we obtain from Eq. 4.416 (2)

$$\frac{\partial V^*}{\partial t}=-ifV^*. \qquad 4.416\ (3)$$

Integration of this differential equation renders

$$V^*=V_0{}^*e^{-ift}. \qquad 4.416\ (4)$$

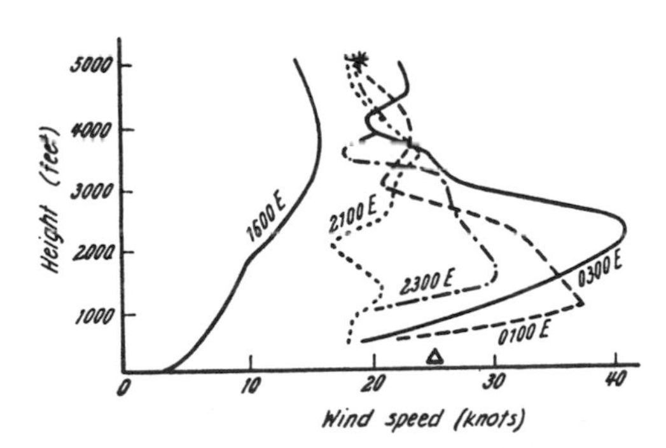

FIG. 4.416.1.—Formation of an inversion wind maximum, Silver Hill, Maryland, during the night of 30 to 31 October, 1950. * = mean gradient wind, 31 October, 0300 to 1500 GCT. Δ = geostrophic wind at surface, 30 October, 2130 GCT, to 31 October, 1530 GCT. (After Gifford, 1952; Blackadar, 1957.)

The "geostrophic departure" remains constant under the above assumptions; it rotates, however, in a clockwise sense and executes a complete revolution during one-half pendulum day. It, therefore, has the period of inertia motions [see Eq. 4.123 (1)]. If $V_0{}^*$ is the geostrophic departure at sunset, which led to subgeostrophic conditions of flow, one may expect a supergeostrophic wind maximum six pendulum hours later (this corresponds to about 8¾ hours at 45° latitude). If the vector $\mathbf{v}^*$ does not point exactly in the opposite direction of the vector $\mathbf{v}_g$ at sunset, the wind maximum may occur at a correspondingly different time. The maximum supergeostrophic departures also need not occur simultaneously at all levels.

V_0^* is a function of height. Correspondingly also V_t^* is a function of height. The upper surface of the inversion in the end is determined by the turbulence conditions within the strong wind shear above the inversion layer. If the *geostrophic* wind speed decreases with height, the jet-like vertical wind profile will appear more pronounced and may also occur, under favorable conditions, during daytime. If, however, the geostrophic wind increases strongly with height, the formation of a wind maximum will be suppressed also during the night.

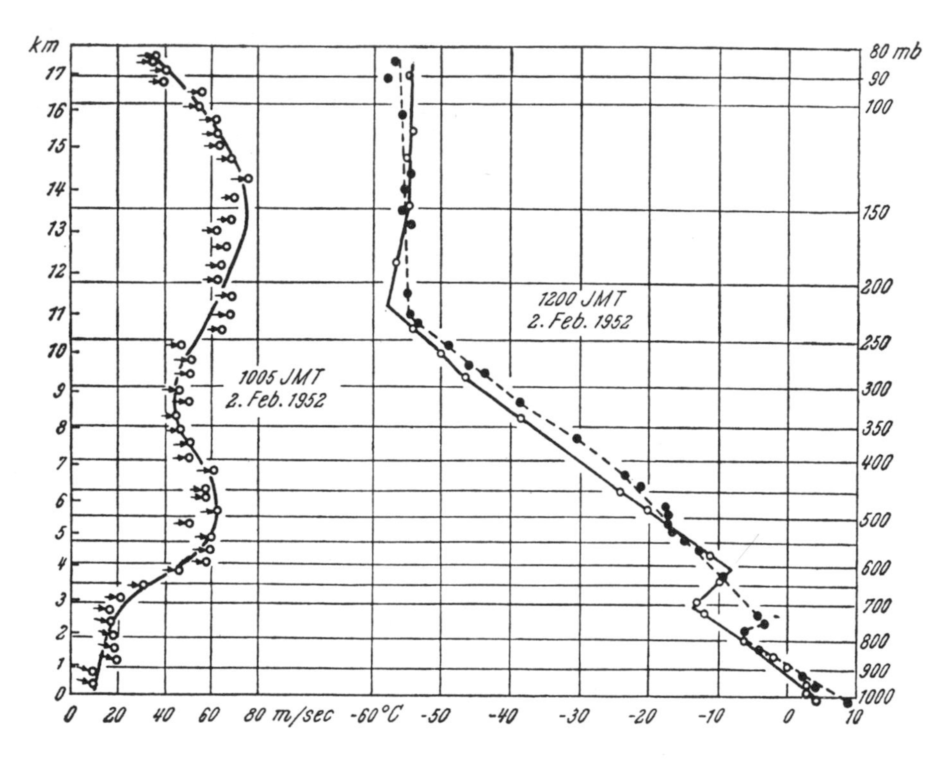

FIG. 4.416.2.—Left, upper winds over Tateno, 2 February, 1005 JMT (arrows are "flying" with the wind); right, radiosondes of Tateno (solid line) and Shinomisaki (dashed) at 1200 JMT. (Arakawa, 1956b.)

An investigation by Gifford (1952) seems to corroborate Blackadar's theoretical considerations. In Figure 4.416.1 the variation of wind with height during the night of 30 to 31 October, 1952, over Silver Hill, Maryland, has been plotted. If one were to consider the axis between the mean gradient wind (*) at 5000 ft (1524 m) height and the geostrophic wind at the ground (Δ) as characteristic for the quasi-stationary pressure conditions, the wind profile which establishes itself until 0300 hours Eastern Standard Time apparently emerged from the 1600 hour profile by superposition of the inertia period. Only at 4000 ft (1219 m) there is a departure. Here, however, a wind maximum has already been found at an earlier time (0100 hours), which also corresponded approximately to the geostrophic departure at this level.

After all that has been said here, the IWM cannot be considered a genuine jet-stream phenomenon. It results from a superposition of inertial and frictional effects and does not have much to do with any genuine baroclinicity in the lower troposphere.

Arakawa (1956*b*) on the other hand described a true jet-stream phenomenon which deserves the name "low-level jet": This low-level wind maximum occurred over Japan and satisfied the conditions of the thermal wind equation, and therefore coincided with an isopycnic level. All this was caused by the slope and by the structure of a frontal inversion, as may be seen in Figure 4.416.2, which shows the ascents of Tateno and Shinomisaki of 2 February, 1952 (right-hand portion of the diagram). In the left-hand part of this figure the vertical wind profile over Tateno has been plotted. According to Arakawa such an LLJ over Japan is usually connected with precipitation. This may not surprise, because along a frontal zone with such a slope well-pronounced ascending motions usually take place.

Studies by Fay (1958) over the United States confirmed the existence of relatively small thermal gradients in the lower troposphere (frequency maximum around 5 km height) which may lead to the formation of a wind maximum. These gradients, however, do not necessarily have to show a frontal character as is the case in Figure 4.416.2. Blackadar and Fay were able to show that wind maxima in the middle and lower troposphere are by no means seldom. So for instance 27.3 per cent of all ascents over the United States between August, 1955 and August, 1956 showed such maxima. A large part of these probably was constituted by Blackadar's inversion wind phenomenon.

Studies from Equatorial Africa showed that also the flow of the easterly trades may sometimes assume a jet-stream-like character, with maximum wind speeds at about 3 to 4 km height, and with marked horizontal and vertical shears. A certain relationship with the weather sequence seems to exist (Nevière, 1959).

In a true LLJ the same considerations with respect to vorticity and divergence will hold as we have found for the high tropospheric PFJ and STJ (Beebe and Bates, 1955; see Fig. 4.122.3)—provided that the wind speed is greater than the rate of propagation of the jet-stream maximum, the air thus being forced to travel through the wind maximum. In the left rear quadrant we have to expect convergence; in the left front quadrant, however, divergence can be expected if the flow is straight or cyclonically curved. The conditions in the other quadrants and with anticyclonic curvature may easily be derived from Eq. 1.233 (6) ($\frac{\partial Q}{\partial t}$ usually may be neglected against $\mathbf{v} \cdot \nabla Q$).

The LLJ may be of some importance in the formation of severe thunderstorms, squall lines, and tornadoes. For these weather situations a tongue of moist air seems to be characteristic which is conditionally and latently unstable, whereby the level of free convection in general lies lower than 650 mb. Above the inversion, which strongly impedes the convective activity, lies a deep, extremely dry layer which also is unstable with respect to moist adiabatic lifting (Breiland, 1958; Showalter, 1943; and Fulks, 1943). The instability apparent from thunderstorms and tornadoes is released only if the lower moist layer experiences some lifting, so that the air masses are allowed to reach the level of free convection. This lifting might be caused by an approaching cold front. Frequently, however, squall lines form many miles ahead of the front. Thus, one will have to search for another mechanism which will explain their formation. Showalter (1943) lists as a further criterion for the formation of tornadoes the existence of a narrow band of strong westerlies (35 knots at 600 mb; see Conner, 1956), which intersects the axis of the moist-air tongue at an oblique angle (Godske *et al.*, 1957). Other cases have been observed, however, in which the LLJ coming from a southerly direction flows parallel to the tongue of warm air near the leading edge of a trough (Breiland, 1958). Such weather situations may lead to widespread precipitation over the central United States, because of the import of moist air in the lower layers (Means, 1954). Some of the wind speed maxima observed in the lower troposphere (850 mb) to the lee of the Rocky Mountains (especially over Colorado), and flowing from a southerly direction, may be of considerable influence on the generation of cyclonic vorticity and thereby on cyclogenesis in this area due to the frictional forces, which are acting on their left side along the slope of the mountains (Newton, 1956*a*).

From the vorticity distribution one may under favorable circumstances expect intensive convergence within the moist air masses. Showalter indicates the anticyclonic (right) front quadrant of this LLJ as an area of convergence, which stands in good agreement with the results from vorticity advection considerations. If the inversion layer which separates the moist from the dry air masses is penetrated because of the convergence acting in a small area, and due to the resulting lifting motion, the conditional instability of the deep upper layer may contribute to the rapid formation of large cumulo-nimbi (Breiland, 1958; House, 1959).

Beebe and Bates (1955) consider this forced lifting process especially effective, if a high tropospheric jet stream is superimposed upon the LLJ (maybe even with different wind direction), in such a manner that the convergent quadrant of the latter comes to lie underneath the divergent quadrant of the former. This seems to be evident also from an investigation by Newton and Newton (1959) in which the *left front* quadrant of the wind maximum at the 500-mb level (which characterizes already the high tropospheric conditions of flow) is characterized by maximum frequency of tornadoes and severe thunderstorms.

It is hard to estimate from the presently available analyses to which circumstances the LLJ owes its existence in individual cases. Is it a relatively small irregularity in the thermal structure of the lower troposphere, i.e., is the wind maximum quasi-geostrophic, or is it a vertical transport of momentum whereby kinetic energy is imported from greater heights due to strong sinking motion thus giving rise to abnormally high wind speeds in a small area near the ground? Newton's (1950) study of a prefrontal squall line seems to give some indications in this direction. In the cases investigated by him the squall line preceded the cold front, steadily increasing the distance in between. In Chapter 6 it will be shown from moisture and cloud distributions and ozone measurements that strong sinking motions may be present near well-developed frontal zones. Thus, a mechanism would be given for the transport of kinetic energy into lower layers within a confined area. This might offer one explanation for the formation of an LLJ. As soon as a convective motion to great height is established by the convergence near the ground within a forming squall line, new momentum is steadily transported toward the ground (Fig. 6.121). Since the squall line draws its momentum from more rapidly flowing layers at greater heights, it will readily be understood that it moves faster than the subsequent front (Newton, 1956*b*). Thus, the vertical wind shear constitutes an additional source of energy which supports the formation of vertical convective currents (Newton and Newton, 1959).

Formation of squall lines has, however, been reported also in the absence of fronts. In these cases, too, a powerful vertical wind shear has been present, indicating the existence of an LLJ. As soon as the first cumulo-nimbi form in this shearing current, the mechanism of regeneration outlined in Figure 6.121 will become effective. It would go far beyond the scope of this book if we entered any further into the theories and investigations on squall lines. We may, however, point out some of the research work by Tepper (1950; *et al.*, 1954) and Fujita (1955; Fujita, Newstein, and Tepper, 1956), which makes a pressure jump that travels as a gravity wave along the inversion between moist and dry air responsible for the formation of squall lines and tornadoes.

4.42. Jet Streams in the Oceans

We have found the large-scale atmospheric motions to be brought about by the horizontal temperature gradients which in the end are produced by the radiation budget being a function of geographic latitude and season. The momentum budget is controlled by the frictional conditions at the earth's surface.

In the oceans the situation is somewhat more complicated. Horizontal density gradients are determined here by temperature and salinity of the ocean water. The latter is controlled by supply (precipitation, water discharge from the continents in the form of liquid and ice) and loss (evaporation) of fresh water. These density gradients determine the thermohaline circulations which are not very intensive. The large oceanic circulation systems have an additional source of energy, namely the stresses which the winds exert upon the ocean surface. Thus, the large ocean currents near the surface are mainly wind driven.

Since these are large-scale and long-lived current systems, the Coriolis force plays the same important role in the equations of motion there as it does in the atmosphere. It would lead too far to enter into these problems in more detail. Reference is made to the oceanographic literature (Dietrich, 1957; Proudman, 1953; Sverdrup, 1952). Since the motions in the atmosphere as well as in the oceans are confined to a relatively thin layer with meridional density gradients, proceeding in a rotating "container," we will have to expect certain parallels (Iselin, 1950).

On the western sides of the oceans a strong gradient current develops, which responds to similar laws of motion, as does the gradient wind in the atmosphere. This flow transports the water masses poleward which have been flowing westward in the trade wind region (Munk, 1950; Munk, Groves, and Carrier, 1950). The current does not spread out, however, in the subtropical belt of weak winds, but it remains concentrated in a narrow band of high velocities—the *oceanic jet stream*. Most strongly developed—and also most thoroughly investigated—are the Gulf Stream and the Kuroshio. Analogous current systems exist also in the southern hemisphere (Brazil current, East Australian current, Agulhas current).

The seasonal fluctuations of the surface velocities of the current in the Florida Strait, which may be either measured directly or computed from differences in sea level between Florida and the Bahama Islands, show that the Gulf Stream is closely related with the water transport in the trade wind region. The mean speed of the current in November is about 105 cm/sec, in July and August, however, 140 cm/sec. An analogous fluctuation occurs one month earlier in the mean wind speed of the trade wind region. The phase lack may be understood easily because the Florida Strait lies already outside of the trade wind region.

Near Cape Hatteras the Gulf Stream leaves the continental shelf. It retains, however, its jet-stream-like character: Figure 4.42 shows a cross section through the Gulf Stream along the direction Chesapeake Bay-Bermuda (see theory by Ichiye, 1960). From a comparison of isotachs with isotherms, it becomes apparent that the Gulf Stream not only transports warm but also cold water masses. Similar to the atmospheric jet stream the Gulf Stream, too, lies above a strongly baroclinic zone.

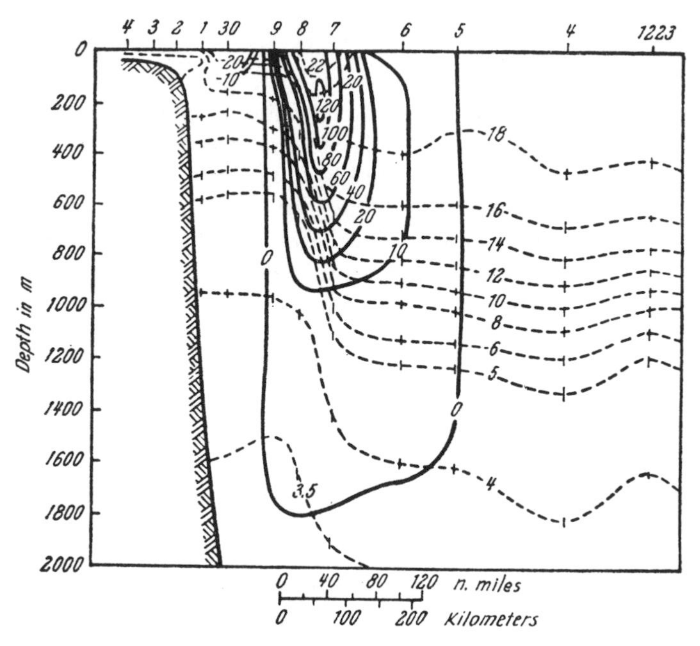

FIG. 4.42.—Cross section through the Gulf Stream off Chesapeake Bay. The oceanographic stations have been entered along the upper margin of the diagram. Isotherms (° C), dashed lines; isotachs (cm/sec), solid lines. (After Iselin, 1936; Newton, 1959b.)

The isotherm pattern, which in essence determines the density distribution, also is in agreement with weak counter-currents which may be recognized on both sides of the Gulf Stream. On the left side of the Gulf Stream the horizontal temperature and density gradients are so strongly developed that they almost correspond to a discontinuity which is called the "cold wall." By means of this discontinuity the Gulf Stream may easily be mapped on a synoptic basis by measuring from an airplane the long-wave outgoing radiation of the sea surface.

From Figure 4.42 maximum shears on the anticyclonic side may be computed to be of the order of magnitude of $0.3 \cdot 10^{-4}$ sec^{-1} (see Nan'niti, 1958). Although this does not yet correspond to dynamic instability as we have found it in the influence region of strongly developed atmospheric jet streams, much higher current velocities may be present and have been measured by means of positioning of ships (*ca.* 3 m/sec). It might therefore well be possible that also the oceanic currents, as Gulf Stream or Kuroshio, may show confined areas with dynamic instability.

A further analogy with atmospheric jet streams is offered by the velocity fluctuations that have been measured in the Florida Strait (O'Hare, Carlson, and Tamblyn, 1954), and according to which the water transport may double within 10 days (Stommel, 1954). This seems to be a phenomenon similar to the atmospheric "jet maxima."

As soon as the Gulf Stream abandons the guiding influence of the continental shelf it starts forming meanders, which may eventually lead to cut-off processes and closed cyclonic vortices. These meanders contribute substantially to the turbulent exchange in a horizontal plane (Stommel, 1951). (An atmospheric analogy might be found in the subtropical jet of winter over northern India, which is also "channeled" by the Himalayas, and which is characterized by its extraordinary steadiness; it breaks down into meanders as soon as it leaves the "guiding" influence of the high mountains. Another example is given by the LLJ, which sometimes blows from a southerly direction along the eastern slopes of the Rocky Mountains, and which, too, is bounded by the mountain ranges on one side [Newton, 1959*b*].) In the cross section shown in Figure 4.42 the core of the Gulf Stream has a width of about 50 km; its horizontal oscillations, however, have an amplitude of about 150 km.

Studies of the detailed structure of the Gulf Stream in 1950 during a Multiple Ship Survey (Operation Cabot) (Fuglister and Worthington, 1951) revealed the formation of such meanders rather clearly: waves with a length of 200 to 300 km propagate downstream at a rate of about 11 nautical miles per day. Similar displacements of the current have been observed in the Kuroshio (Fukuoka, 1958; Masuzawa, 1960). Wave lengths and amplitudes are considerably smaller than in the analogous atmospheric jet streams. From Eq. 3.251 (5) it should be expected that the stationary wave lengths in ocean (oc) and atmosphere (at) are related in the following manner (Rossby, 1951*a*)

$$\frac{L_{oc}}{L_{at}} = \sqrt{\frac{u_{oc}}{u_{at}}}. \qquad 4.42\ (1)$$

These meanders, in part, have an unstable character (Haurwitz and Panofsky, 1950), i.e., they magnify their amplitude and finally may form a "cut-off" vortex. The flow observed in these vortices approximately follows the isotherms; thus, it is quasi-geostrophic. This amplification process is similar to the one leading to the formation of an upper cyclone (see literature given by Newton, 1959*b*).

There is a marked difference in color between the warm Sargasso waters and the cold water near the continental shelf, which may be seen distinctly from an aircraft. The cold water coming from lower levels is of green-blue color, while the warm water to the right of the current is deep blue (Dietrich, 1957). As the observation of color spots during "Operation Cabot" revealed, the visually observed boundary line between the two water masses constitutes at the same time a velocity discontinuity and a convergence line. Warm surface water with high salinity is flowing in from the right-hand side, while to the left of the Gulf Stream cold water rich in plankton wells up from deeper levels. Thus, we have an indirect circulation which runs opposite to the sense of rotation of the isobaric-isosteric solenoids, i.e., which generates potential energy at the expense of kinetic energy. The latter is drawn from the atmosphere, since the Gulf Stream is a wind-driven circulation system.

As has been established during the "Multiple Ship Survey," the Gulf Stream near the Newfoundland Grand Banks shows several separate bands of high speed, each of which is attached to its own baroclinic zone. In between there are relatively weak counter-currents (Fuglister, 1951). In the region of atmospheric PFJ and STJ we frequently observe a multiple structure, too; there are, however, no easterly counter-currents in between (Rossby, 1953).

4.43. Jet Streams in Geophysical Model Experiments

Although atmospheric weather patterns yield an abundance of data which may be sorted and combined according to a multitude of physical and statistical principles, the sequence of events cannot be controlled by the observer, and therefore one of the basic characteristics of an "experiment" is lost: the possibility of repeating it. It has long been the effort of meteorologists, therefore, to create "quasi-atmospheric" conditions in a suitable experimental setup and to study the influence of certain factors upon atmospheric flow patterns by varying different elements in this experiment.

All the early experiments (see Fultz, 1951*a*) cannot be described here, but it should be mentioned that F. Vettin pointed out an experimental arrangement already in the eighties of last century which makes use of a rotating cylindrical vessel, at whose center a piece of ice serves as coolant (Vettin, 1884–85). Ascending motion was assumed along the periphery of the vessel, descending air motion over the center. Between this simple arrangement and the modern "dish-pan" experiments (so-called because of the rather simple form of the rotating water tank), technology has advanced very far; the principle, however, remained unchanged. Fultz and his collaborators (Fultz *et al.*, 1956) have compiled an extensive bibliography containing about 350 references on model experiments imitating atmospheric circulations and their results. In the following a few more recent experiments will be discussed, which might contribute toward the understanding of the structure and the mechanisms involved in atmospheric jet streams.

4.431. Spherical Models

The experimental arrangement consists of two hemispherical glass shells with different diameters, which are fitted together, leaving a space in between them, which is filled with water (Fultz, 1949). These spherical "cups" are heated at the *pole*, and rotated at the same time. In order to make the circulation generated in the water visible, organic colors or ink are introduced into the cup at certain meridians. Tobacco mosaic virus also serves this purpose, because its oblong particles orient themselves parallel to the stretching axis of the deformation field in a shearing current. In polarizing the light which passes through the liquid, a difference in brightness may be observed against the isotropic orientation of the particles in non-shearing areas.

These experiments yielded the remarkable result that easterlies established themselves in this cup equatorward of 30° latitude resembling the atmospheric trade wind region. North of this zone there were westerlies which showed speeds similar to what is observed in the atmosphere. With increasing heat input at the pole and with constant rate of rotation the circulation intensified. At the same time the scattering of the observed velocities about a mean meridional "wind" profile increased appreciably, which indicates an increase of the non-stationary character and of the turbulence of the circulation. The rate of rotation does not seem to have a large influence upon the formation of the *mean* "wind" profiles in this experimental setup. Remarkably enough, conditions like those we have met in Figure 4.121.6 prevail: along the polar side of the zone of westerlies *mean* wind profiles with constant absolute vorticity corresponding to what is prescribed by the angular velocity Ω of the rotating vessel establish themselves, while on the equatorial side a mean profile is found which corresponds to constant vorticity transfer southward of 62° or 63° latitude. (Individual profiles may show large departures from this mean profile, as they do in the atmosphere). The average conditions of flow, thus, seem to agree in this experiment with Rossby's mixing theory described in Chapter 4.121.

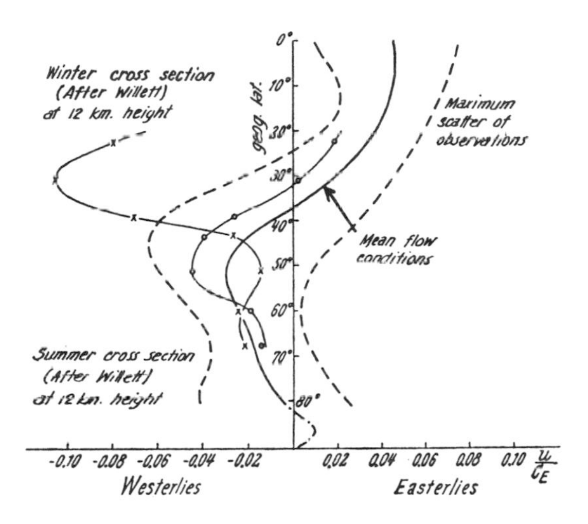

FIG. 4.431.1.—Mean velocity distribution and its scatter in a rotating hemisphere, expressed in units of u/C_E, for 16.27 revolutions per minute and 30 volts heating current. For comparison also, mean zonal wind speeds of the atmosphere at 12 km during winter and summer. (Fultz, 1949.)

In the experimental setup described above, the Coriolis parameter is $2\Omega \sin \varphi$, as it is on the rotating earth. The design of the experiment permits a variation in the rate of rotation and in the heat input. It is surprising that a *heat source* at the pole is able to produce a westerly circulation as it appears on the earth. Thus, the flow processes in the water in between the two hemispherical shells resemble the summer circulation of the atmosphere, which, too, has a stratospherical heat source at the pole due to the continuous exposure to incoming radiation.

If we regard the outer shell of this model as the tropopause, there is, again, a parallel connection with the atmospheric tropopause, which is warm over polar areas and cold over the equator.

In Figure 4.431.1 the mean "wind" profile (heavy solid line) for 16.27 revolutions per minute and 30 volts heating current is plotted together with the scattering of the observed speeds (dashed lines). The distribution of the mean zonal wind speed in winter and summer at 12 km height between Havana and Thule as published by Willett (1944) has also been entered into this diagram. The *summer distribution* fits remarkably well into the experimental circulation pattern of maximum speeds as well as meridional shears. More recent cross sections by Hess (1948) may show a few departures from the data used by Willett; these, however, are irrelevant with respect to the comparison made in Figure 4.431.1.

In this representation, as in Figure 4.121.5, $(u/C_E) = Ro$ has been entered along the abscissa. This non-dimensional form of speed allows a comparison of data from various rotating bodies. Fultz (1951*c*) termed this expression "*Rossby number.*"

Because of the good agreement with the actual flow distribution in the atmosphere, one may draw the conclusion from Figure 4.431.1 that the present experimental setup is capable of imitating the basic causes of the general circulation of the atmosphere. This agreement may have been influenced in part by the dimensions of the apparatus, and by the variability of rotation rate and heat input (University of Chicago, 1947); the stunning agreement in the magnitudes of the non-dimensional speed u/C_E and in the boundary between easterlies and westerlies at tropopause level is, however, based upon three factors which are inherent in the atmosphere as well as in the geophysical model:

1. The latitude dependency of the Coriolis parameter has been truly transferred to the model. We shall see, however, that this is not a necessary condition for the formation of jet streams. These may also be observed in flat, rotating pans of water, in which the Coriolis parameter is a constant $(=2\Omega)$.

2. The circulation is confined to a shallow layer in the atmosphere as well as in the model.

3. In the atmosphere as well as in the geophysical model there are mixing processes which act across latitude circles and which have a tendency to let horizontal "physical" area elements remain horizontal, i.e., the exchange processes act primarily in a horizontal direction.

If a model experiment should be compared with conditions in the free atmosphere, one may make use of the similarity principle which is also applied in testing aircraft and other models in the wind tunnel. From this comparison between flow characteristics in model and in reality, non-dimensional relationships, expressing the similarity, are derived, which serve as a basis for modification of the experimental setup. The similarity principle has been treated in earlier meteorological literature by combining the variables A_{im} in the model with the corresponding variables A_{ip} of the prototype (in our case the atmosphere) by the relationship

$$A_{im} = \alpha_i A_{ip} \qquad 4.431\ (1)$$

(Abbè, 1907; Helmholtz, 1873; Weickmann and Haurwitz, 1929). These transformations now are introduced systematically into all differential equations and their boundary conditions. From the condition that all terms have to be numerically equal for model and prototype, one arrives at a series of similarity conditions for the factors α_i. A study by Rossby (1926) which aims in this direction is quite remarkable. It considers the conditions under which the vertical scale of a layer of liquid used in the model may be reduced in comparison to the prototype by a smaller factor than the horizontal scale. This consideration is of importance because if a layer of liquid were reduced strictly by *geometric* similarity with the atmosphere, this layer would become so thin that the effects of molecular viscosity would predominate.

Into the simplified equation of motion of the prototype (subscript p)

$$\rho_p \frac{du_p}{dt_p} = -\frac{\partial p_p}{\partial x_p} \qquad 4.431\ (2)$$

and into the hydrostatic equation

$$\rho_p g = -\frac{\partial p_p}{\partial z_p} \qquad 4.431\ (3)$$

one may introduce the transformation equation

$$dx_p = L\, dx_m, \quad dy_p = L\, dy_m, \quad dz_p = l\, dz_m, \quad dt_p = T\, dt_m. \qquad 4.431\ (4)$$

L is the reduction factor for the horizontal, l for the vertical, and T for time.

One arrives at

$$\frac{L}{T^2} \frac{\rho_p}{\rho_m} \rho_m \frac{du_m}{dt_m} = -\frac{1}{L} \left(\frac{\partial p_p}{\partial p_m}\right)_{\text{horizontal}} \cdot \frac{\partial p_m}{\partial x_m} \qquad 4.431\ (5)$$

and

$$\frac{\rho_p}{\rho_m} \rho_m g = -\frac{1}{l} \left(\frac{\partial p_p}{\partial p_m}\right)_{\text{vertical}} \cdot \frac{\partial p_m}{\partial z_m}. \qquad 4.431\ (6)$$

If we substitute from the equations valid in the model experiment (subscript m)

$$\rho_m \frac{du_m}{dt_m} = -\frac{\partial p_m}{\partial x_m} \qquad 4.431\ (7)$$

and

$$\rho_m g = -\frac{\partial p_m}{\partial z_m} \qquad 4.431\ (8)$$

for $\partial p_m/\partial x_m$ and $\partial p_m/\partial z_m$, we obtain

$$\left(\frac{dp_p}{dp_m}\right)_{\text{horizontal}} = \frac{\rho_p}{\rho_m} \frac{L^2}{T^2} \qquad 4.431\ (9)$$

and

$$\left(\frac{dp_p}{dp_m}\right)_{\text{vertical}} = \frac{\rho_p}{\rho_m} l. \qquad 4.431\ (10)$$

Because 4.431 (9 and 10) have to be equal for reasons of dynamic similarity, we have

$$l = \frac{L^2}{T^2}. \qquad 4.431\ (11)$$

This relationship has been derived without considering the effects of molecular viscosity.

Another possibility of comparing model with prototype consists in dividing all equations of motion and their boundary conditions by certain *comparative quantities* B_j, so that all variables appear in a *non-dimensional* form (expressed by prime): A'_{ip} and A'_{im}. The resulting equations consist of the non-dimensional variables A'_i and of certain parameters Π_{km} and Π_{kp}, which are also non-dimensional and are produced by combinations of the B_j. They are constant for the system under consideration, model as well as prototype (Fultz, 1951*c*; see Rouse, 1951). The similarity conditions have the form

$$A'_{im} \equiv A'_{ip} \quad \text{and} \quad \Pi_{km} \equiv \Pi_{kp}. \qquad 4.431\ (12)$$

In general the Π_k may be regarded as orders of magnitude of the various terms with which they occur in the equations.

This method of comparison has the advantage that the experimental results may be given easily in terms of A'_i, and that the Π_{km} and Π_{kp} appear in those places of the equations where they influence the fundamental relationships between model and prototype.

For practical purposes it may not always be possible to equalize all of the Π_k in the model with those in the prototype. In many cases experience will have to decide which of the Π_k may be neglected or may be given only in approximation, after the *dominant* variables A'_i and the parameters Π_k have been made to agree in model and prototype.

Let us consider the equations of motion in the following form:

$$\frac{\partial \mathbf{v}}{\partial t} + \mathbf{v} \cdot \nabla \mathbf{v} + 2\mathbf{\Omega} \times \mathbf{v} = -\alpha \nabla p - g\mathbf{r} + \nu[\nabla^2 \mathbf{v} + \tfrac{1}{3}\nabla(\nabla \cdot \mathbf{v})]. \qquad 4.431\ (13)$$

$\mathbf{r}$ is a unit vector, pointing upward, and being perpendicular to the level surfaces; ν is the coefficient of kinematic viscosity.

The variables A'_i will be defined in the following fashion:

$$\mathbf{v}' = \frac{\mathbf{v}}{R\Omega} \qquad t' = \Omega t \qquad p' = \frac{p}{DR^2\Omega^2}$$
$$\alpha' = \alpha D \qquad \nabla' = R\nabla \qquad \nabla'^2 = R^2 \nabla^2. \qquad 4.431\ (14)$$

R is the radius of the sphere (earth or model), Ω the magnitude of the angular velocity of the moving (relative) co-ordinate system, D is a reference density, and U a speed relative to the rotating sphere. We may define the Rossby number

$$Ro = \frac{U}{R\Omega}, \qquad 4.431\ (15)$$

a Reynolds number

$$Re = \frac{UR}{\nu}, \qquad 4.431\ (16)$$

and a Froude number

$$F = \frac{U^2}{gR} \qquad 4.431\ (17)$$

(see also Raethjen, 1958*b*). We obtain the equations of motion in non-dimensional form as a combination of A'_i and Π_k,

$$\frac{\partial \mathbf{v}'}{\partial t'} + \mathbf{v}' \cdot \nabla' \mathbf{v}' + 2\mathbf{\Omega}' \times \mathbf{v}' + \alpha' \nabla' p' = -\frac{\mathbf{r}'(Ro)^2}{F} + [\nabla'^2 \mathbf{v}' + \tfrac{1}{3}\nabla'(\nabla' \cdot \mathbf{v}')]\frac{Ro}{Re}. \qquad 4.431\ (18)$$

$\mathbf{\Omega}'$ is a non-dimensional unit vector parallel to the vector of rotation of the system (earth or model), and $\mathbf{r}'$ is a non-dimensional unit vector normal to the equipotential surfaces.

The definitions given in 4.431 (14) are not the only possible ones to obtain non-dimensional expressions. They may suffice, however, as an illustration. With other definitions of the variables A'_i, too, only three parameters Π_k will be retained in 4.431 (18), which cause the dynamic as well as the geometric similarities, irrespective of the size of the systems under consideration. These are the numbers Ro, Re, and F. The *condition of similarity* simply consists of the *identity* of these three parameters in prototype and model; this condition may be checked very easily.

Reynolds' number Re may be regarded as the ratio of the characteristic viscous forces to the characteristic inertia forces of the system. Rossby's number Ro in the form $\frac{U^2/R}{\Omega U}$ indicates an estimate of the orders of magnitude of characteristic inertia forces (see Charney, 1948) or centrifugal forces as compared with the characteristic Coriolis force. *The smaller the Rossby number, the better the motion corresponds to geostrophic conditions.* In the form $\Omega U/R\Omega^2$ Rossby's number constitutes the ratio between a Coriolis force and a centrifugal force. In $(2U/R)/2\Omega$ we find the ratio of a characteristic relative vorticity to the absolute vorticity of the rotation of the system.

Froude's number may be interpreted as the ratio of the square of a characteristic flow velocity U to the speed of long water waves (gR), where R is the depth of the water.

By including thermodynamics in the similarity considerations between model and prototype, new parameters Π_k will be introduced. Considerable difficulties will have to be met, because the various diffusion and conduction terms of the earth's heat budget are not easily determined. Let us assume that the equation of state in model and prototype is given to a sufficient degree of accuracy by the expansion equation

$$\alpha = \alpha_0(1 + \varepsilon T). \qquad 4.431\ (19)$$

ε is the coefficient of cubic expansion. α_0 is the specific volume at temperature $T = 0$. If we take a characteristic temperature difference $\Delta\Theta$ between pole and equator as reference quantity, we obtain the non-dimensional form of temperature $T' = T/\Delta\Theta$ and, by utilizing the reference density D [see Eq. 4.431 (14)],

$$\alpha' = \alpha_0'[1 + (\varepsilon\Delta\Theta)T']. \qquad 4.431\ (20)$$

$\varepsilon\Delta\Theta$ constitutes a new, non-dimensional parameter Π_k, which enters into the equations of motion through the term $\alpha\nabla_p$.

One of the difficulties of model experiments with spherical shells, as they have been described in the first part of this chapter, lies in the fact that the non-dimensional unit vector $\mathbf{r}'$ of Eq. 4.431 (18) assumes a different direction in the model than it does on the earth, where it is parallel to the radius vector of the sphere. To obtain this effect, one would have to eliminate the earth's gravity during the model experiment. The disturbing term which contains gravity may be eliminated when considering the motion as two-dimensional, homogeneous, incompressible, and frictionless. In experiments with "flat" models (Chapter 4.432) this problem vanishes, too.

During the model experiments whose results have been shown in Figure 4.431.1, most of the Π_k were of the same order of magnitude in model and prototype, although not quite identical with the conditions on the earth. This, apparently, suffices to create circulation patterns similar to the ones on earth. The various parameters are compared in Table 4.431. δ stands for the depth of the liquid layer (1.6 cm) and of the atmosphere, which is considered up to the height of the tropopause (*ca.*, 12 km). This depth δ of the water is enough to permit vertical motions connected with a meridional circulation.

From this table it may be seen that the last two parameters either have no effect upon the observed circulation patterns, because of the large differences between model and atmosphere, or that they appear in a combination, as for instance Prandtl's number $\sigma = \mu/\rho\nu_c$, which is 0.7 for the earth, and *ca.* 3.6 for the particular model considered here. Thus, this model imitates with sufficient approximation the atmospheric conditions with respect to dimensions (δ/R), to the ratio of gravity to centrifugal force ($g/R\Omega^2$), to baroclinicity because of thermal expansion ($\varepsilon\,\Delta\,\Theta$), and to the ratio between thermometric conductivity and kinematic viscosity.

TABLE 4.431. COMPARISON OF THE NON-DIMENSIONAL BASIC PARAMETERS BETWEEN MODEL (hemispherical shell: 9.2 cm inner radius, 10.8 cm outer radius, 1.6 cm depth of liquid, 1050 cm³ volume of liquid, $\Delta\,\Theta = 2°$ C) AND PROTOTYPE (atmosphere: height of tropopause, *ca.* 12 km, $\Delta\,\Theta = 30°$ C)

	EARTH	MODEL
δ/R	$2.0 \cdot 10^{-3}$	$1.7 \cdot 10^{-1}$
$\frac{g}{R\Omega^2} = \frac{1}{F}$	$2.9 \cdot 10^2$	$3.4 \cdot 10$
$\varepsilon\,\Delta\,\Theta$	$1.2 \cdot 10^{-1}$	$1.0 \cdot 10^{-3}$
$R^2\Omega\frac{\rho}{\mu} = Re$*	$1.4 \cdot 10^{14}$	$3.4 \cdot 10^4$
$\frac{\nu_c}{R^2\Omega}$*	$5.5 \cdot 10^{-15}$	$8.2 \cdot 10^{-6}$

* $\nu = \frac{\mu}{\rho}$ kinematic viscosity, given by the acceleration due to friction $\frac{du}{dt} = \nu\frac{\partial^2 u}{\partial z^2}$.

μ = dynamic viscosity, given by the ratio of shearing stress τ to shear: $\tau = \mu\frac{\partial u}{\partial z}$.

ν_c = thermometric conductivity, given by the temperature increase due to a temperature distribution $\frac{dT}{dt} = \nu_c\frac{\partial^2 T}{\partial z^2}$ and by $\nu_c = \frac{k}{c_p\rho}$, where k is the thermal conductivity and c_p is the specific heat at constant pressure. k is given by the amount of heat H, which is conducted per unit of time and area, if $H = -k\frac{\partial T}{\partial z}$ (Hann and Süring, 1939, List; 1958).

The experimental setup which has been described at the beginning of this chapter may be changed in many ways. Fultz (1950*a*) and Long (1951*a*, *b*) describe an experiment in which the space between the hemispheric shells has been filled with two immiscible liquids of different densities. They were set in motion relative to the rotating shells by means of an agitating mechanism. In this way the influence of a latitude-dependent Coriolis parameter upon a symmetric vortex could be studied. Rossby (1948, 1949*b*) had pointed out that cold anticyclones have a tendency to migrate toward the equator, whereas cyclones show a tendency of displacement toward the poles. Sinking motion prevails in the anticyclones—in connection with a spreading-out of the air masses—which generates kinetic energy at the expense of potential energy. Cyclonic circumpolar vortices constitute a stable flow pattern and may only carry out a stable nutation movement with the period (in days)

$$T = \frac{R}{r}\sqrt{2d}, \qquad 4.431\ (21)$$

when displaced slightly from the pole of the rotating sphere (either by a small external impulse imparted to the model, or by the distribution of mountains on the earth). (R = earth's radius, r = radius of the vortex, and d = period (in days) of the vortex motion.)

Anticyclonic circumpolar vortices, on the other hand, are unstable and will be transported toward lower latitudes where their potential energy is transformed into kinetic energy.

In the experimental setup with two liquid layers of different densities on top of each other, contained between two rotating hemispherical shells as described above, a certain static stability is introduced by the stratification, which has no analogue in the atmosphere. Furthermore, the motion of the liquid relative to the rotating shells contains a centrifugal force, which is not present in the meteorological equations of motion. This centrifugal force could be eliminated by using parabolic containers.

In spite of these deficiencies of the experimental setup used by Fultz and Long, Rossby's theoretical results were quite remarkably corroborated. If the stirring mechanism rotates cyclonically with respect to the hemispherical shells, slow stirring produces a stationary three-wave system (three long waves with a distance of 120°), faster stirring results in a two-wave system (hemispheric wave number = 2); in both systems the wave pattern is symmetric with respect to the pole. If the cyclonic speed of rotation of the stirring mechanism relative to the shells increases further, the two-wave pattern becomes less distinct; it still remains symmetric, although due to the centrifugal force the denser liquid may be completely ejected from the polar regions.

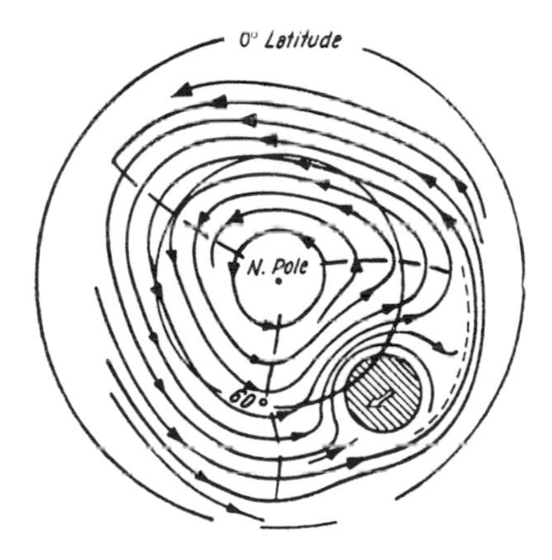

FIG. 4.431.2.— Streamlines during westward displacement of an obstacle in a rotating hemisphere. $\omega_r/\Omega = -0.10$. (Fultz, 1956b.)

If the stirring mechanism rotates anticyclonically with respect to the shells, the wave pattern will be similar to the cyclonic case for a slow rate of relative rotation. But if the rotation speed of the stirring mechanism is increased, the center of gravity of the denser liquid suddenly departs from the rotation pole, and a more or less well-defined single wave forms (hemispheric wave number = 1).

Another very interesting series of experiments conducted at the University of Chicago dealt with the influence of mountain barriers upon the general circulation (Frenzen, 1955; and La Seur, 1956; Fultz, 1950b; and Long, 1951; Long, 1952). In

Chapter 7 this influence of high mountains upon large-scale atmospheric flow patterns will be discussed in more detail. Here, however, we will anticipate several experimental results which prove rather conclusively the usefulness of geophysical model experiments.

A disk-shaped barrier is introduced into the hemispherical shells described earlier. The container, then, is rotated until the liquid moves with the same constant angular velocity as does the vessel. The obstacle may be moved eastward or westward with arbitrary speed relative to the hemispherical shell. Thus, instead of the "atmosphere," the "mountain" is moved. The obstacle fills the whole height of the "atmosphere." Besides this, a "mountain barrier" has also been used which reached from the pole to the equator, and which measured only half the height of the "atmosphere." The former obstacle may be regarded as a model of the Himalayas, the latter resembles the North American Rockies and South American Andes.

This experiment, which is of a purely mechanical nature, i.e., without any temperature gradient worth mentioning within the liquid, shows rather remarkable results, if the obstacle is moved westward relative to the container (Fig. 4.431.2). In this diagram the direction of the streamlines has been reversed by 180° in order to render the flow conditions in the northern hemisphere.

An undisturbed observation of the flow conditions has been made possible by the *rotoscope*. It consists essentially of a prism whose rotation is synchronized with the rotation of the dishpan, and whose optical axis is exactly parallel to the axis of rotation. Through a telescope an apparently *motionless* image of the dishpan is obtained, while the flow of the liquid *relative* to the dishpan is clearly visible (Frenzen, Kaylor, *et al.*, 1956). The decisive advantage of this setup as compared with the experiments in Göttingen (Fette, 1933; Prandtl, 1926)[3] during which the whole laboratory including the observer was rotated, is rather obvious.

In the case of a westward displacement $(\omega_r/\Omega) = -0.10$, where ω_r is the angular velocity of the obstacle relative to the hemispherical shell, and Ω is the angular velocity of the dishpan itself, a pronounced anticyclonic circulation may be observed around the "mountain." Well-marked troughs and ridges appear in the zonal current that covers the rest of the hemisphere.

This flow pattern is very similar to the one found at jet-stream level near the Himalayas (see Chapter 7.413). Blocking high-pressure cells show a similar arrangement in the upper flow.

Variations in the height of the obstacle showed that, as long as the barrier is at least half as high as the "atmosphere," the amplitudes of the planetary waves in the case of "westerlies" (obstacle is moved toward the west) are larger than in the case when the obstacle fills the distance between the two spherical shells completely. This is due to the effect of overflow across the obstacle and the resulting divergence pattern. Even if the barrier measures only one quarter of the height of the atmosphere, a marked wave formation may be observed (Long, 1952). A decrease in the rate of rotation of the container (equivalent to a slowing down of the zonal wind speed) leads to an increase in the wave amplitudes, while a reduction of the diameter of the obstacle produces the opposite effect.

[3] The experimental machinery may be found in the Max-Planck-Institut für Strömungsforschung (formerly Kaiser-Wilhelm-Institut für Strömungsforschung).

The number s of the planetary waves excited by the obstacle is determined by the Rossby number, i.e., by the "wind" speed and by the Coriolis parameter. Long (1952) finds the following relationship:

$$Ro = \frac{2}{(s+1)(s+2)}. \qquad 4.431\ (22)$$

Thus, for wave numbers 1, 2, 3, and 4, Rossby numbers of $Ro = 0.333$, 0.167, 0.100, and 0.067 would have to be present.

If a "mountain range" extending from the pole to the equator and measuring half the height of the "atmosphere," so it can be traversed by the flow, is introduced into a spherical shell with "westerlies," much the same circulation pattern is obtained as corresponds to the mean upper-flow conditions over the United States (see Chapter 7.3). To the lee of the mountains a strongly developed jet stream forms in rather low latitudes (Fultz and Frenzen, 1955).

This flow pattern leads Long to the conclusion that the intense jet streams observed along the southeastern slopes of polar cold domes are caused by a similar "barrier effect": A westerly jet stream tries to flow across the cold-air barrier, shallow as it may be.

Frenzen (and La Seur, 1956) points out that the eccentricity of the circumpolar vortex observed by La Seur (1954) may be interpreted as an effect of the mountain obstacle of the Himalayas. According to Eq. 4.431 (22) the transition from wave number 2 to wave number 1 should take place at Rossby numbers between 0.2 and 0.3, which corresponds to 150 to 225 knots at 35° N (southern slopes of the Himalayas), and to 130 to 195 knots at 45° N (northern slopes of the plateau of Tibet). During this transition state a single, strongly eccentric vortex is observed in the model experiment approximately 100° longitude downstream from the mountain obstacle. In the atmosphere the center of this eccentric vortex in fact may be found 100° longitude downstream from the Himalayas. The mean wind speeds in the atmosphere, however, do not necessarily reach almost 200 knots, as has been calculated by Frenzen. This may have its reason in the fact that the atmospheric conditions express a certain resonance between Himalayas and Rocky Mountains, which has not been taken into account in the model experiment described above. Furthermore, the position of the heat sources over the western parts of the oceans during winter may contribute to the intensification of the orographically induced wave amplitudes (Smagorinsky, 1953).

4.432. Flat Models

Based upon experiments by Taylor (1921, 1924), *flat* rotating "dishpans" have been used with great success at the Hydrodynamics Laboratory of the University of Chicago for studies of flow patterns similar to the ones prevailing in the atmosphere (Fultz, 1951*b*). First of all two liquids of different densities were rotated in this pan. During the rotation, the denser of the two liquids bulged upward over the pole, similar to the cold air in the atmosphere (Fultz, 1952). Where the boundary surface between the denser and the less dense medium showed maximum inclination, a westerly jet stream was observed, corresponding to Margules' equation [6.11 (1)]. The "cold dome" of this experiment at first had a circular border. Soon, however, a certain de-stabilization was observed, and at the boundary between warm and cold "air" a train of waves formed which migrated eastward and which was subject to occlusion processes very similar to those in the atmosphere.

In a more recent experimental setup, which has also been described by Hide (1953, 1956) and others (Davies, 1952; Faller, 1956), the two liquids of different densities were replaced by a single liquid (water, 2 to 15 cm deep), which was heated at the rim of the dishpan (a spiral heater runs around the metal pan; the bottom of the pan may, however, be insulated, so that the heating is effective at the rim only) and cooled at the center (a small metal cylinder may be placed in the rotation pole of the pan; it is constantly fed with cooling water). Heat input and output may be measured and regulated accurately. The movement of the water in the pan is made visible by aluminum powder, which floats on the surface, or by crystals of malachite green, which submerge slowly, leaving a color streak in the clear water. From these streaks, "winds" and "wind shears" may be evaluated.

As compared with the rotating hemispheric shells, these experiments are easier to evaluate. Because of the simpler basic apparatus, the motions may be more readily observed. With the aid of the rotoscope, mentioned earlier, the relative movements of the liquid may be studied in a comparatively simple way. Photographs of the floating aluminum powder, taken with time exposure through the rotoscope, give a lucid easy-to-evaluate pattern of the relative "wind" vectors at the surface of the rotating water annulus contained between outer and inner rim of the dishpan. Synoptic studies based upon these photographs under certain experimental conditions have a striking resemblance to atmospheric weather patterns (Corn and Fultz, 1955). Quantitative calculations of momentum transport, etc., are possible, too (Starr and Long, 1953). To these experiments we owe a number of stunning results which shed some light upon the structure and mechanism of the jet stream and of the general circulation (Hide, 1953; Fultz, 1956*a*, *b*; Fultz, Long, *et al.*, 1959; Riehl and Fultz, 1957, 1958).

In the preceding chapter it has already been pointed out that motions in a model experiment are most suitably described by non-dimensional quantities, which allow a comparison with other systems. Three parameters have been introduced which characterize the motions: the Rossby number [Eq. 4.431 (15)], the Reynolds number [Eq. 4.431 (16)], and the Froude number [Eq. 4.431 (17)]. The latter is mostly used in the form of its reciprocal value, which we may denote as

$$G^* = \frac{1}{F} = g/R\Omega^2. \qquad 4.432\ (1)$$

R is a characteristic length, as, for instance, the radius of the dishpan or of the earth. The Rossby number may be expressed in different ways. In the form

$$Ro_T{}^* = \frac{u_T}{R\Omega} \qquad 4.432\ (2)$$

it is the so-called "thermal Rossby number." u_T is the thermal wind in the layer with the thickness δ. The thermal Rossby number in the form chosen by Kuo (1954*b*) reads:

$$Ro_T{}^* = \frac{g\varepsilon(\Delta_r\Theta)\delta}{2\Omega(R\Omega)(\Delta r)}. \qquad 4.432\ (3)$$

$\Delta_r \Theta$ is the temperature difference measured over the distance Δr and 2Ω is the Coriolis parameter, which, as a noteworthy fact, is constant in the flat model and thus is independent of "geographic latitude." Thus, the temperature gradient maintained by warming at the "equator" and by cooling at the "pole" enters into the Rossby number.

As a second parameter in characterizing the experimental setup, the ratio between the force of gravity and the centrifugal force may be taken. This number is exclusively controlled by the rate of rotation and not by the temperature conditions. Finally we may introduce Taylor's number,

$$T^* = 4\Omega^2 \delta^4/\nu^2 \qquad 4.432\ (4)$$

which emerges from Reynolds' number [Eq. 4.431 (16)] and which also depends on rotation.

By varying the temperature gradient $\Delta_r \Theta$ (this may be accomplished by varying the heat input or the effective cooling) and the rate of rotation Ω, the two parameters Ro_T^* and G^* may be varied arbitrarily between wide limits (Long, 1955). In doing so, it appears that, depending on the magnitude of these parameters, with small rates of rotation a trade wind cell develops, which at a critical Rossby number breaks down into a westerly circulation with planetary long waves, whose number again depends on the magnitude of the meridional temperature gradient and on the rate of rotation (see Brindley, 1960).

1. *The Hadley Regime.*—The heated water ascends over the heat source (at the rim of the rotating cylinder), then flows toward the north and is deflected eastward in an antitrade circulation. In polar latitudes the westerlies sink toward the bottom of the vessel and finally flow into a northeasterly trade. Early experiments by Vettin 1884–85) have already been pointed out. The first theoretical treatment of this flow was made by Oberbeck (1877).

A Hadley regime is established if the characteristic parameters assume low values of approximately the following orders of magnitude:

$(G^*)^{-1}$	$\simeq 10^{-6}$	to 10^{-3}	see 4.432 (1)
Re^*	$\simeq 10$	to $5 \cdot 10^3$	see 4.431 (16)
T^*	$\simeq 10$	to $5 \cdot 10^5$	see 4.432 (4)
Ro_T^*	> 0.2	to 0.6	see 4.432 (2).

The non-dimensional velocity in the jet stream, $Ro_j^* = \mathbf{v}'_{max}$, is smaller than Ro_T^* because of the curvature effect of the strongly cyclonic flow. Thus *strongly ageostrophic* conditions of flow prevail. A Hadley cell which is asymmetric with respect to the pole of rotation will be observed in all experiments in which the cooling is accomplished, not by a small cold-water cylinder placed at the pole, but by a cold-water jet hitting the bottom of the rotating tank from underneath; in this experimental setup the water in the dishpan may flow freely across the pole. This wave number 1 does not even disappear if the rate of rotation (and thereby also Re^* and T^*) are reduced to a minimum value.

Figure 4.432.1 shows the mean meridional speed profile at the surface for a Hadley regime (see also Kuo, 1954*b*). The ordinate indicates the relative speed of the water in cm/sec. The non-dimensional speed $\mathbf{v}'$ may be obtained from these values by division through $C_E = 0.320$ cm/sec.

This experiment reveals the following:

1. A strong west wind maximum with jet-stream character (Ro_j* of the order of magnitude of 4.2 in C_E units) develops at a short distance from the pole ($r' = r/R$ about 0.1 to 0.2). The higher the speed of the jet stream, the more it approaches the axis of rotation.

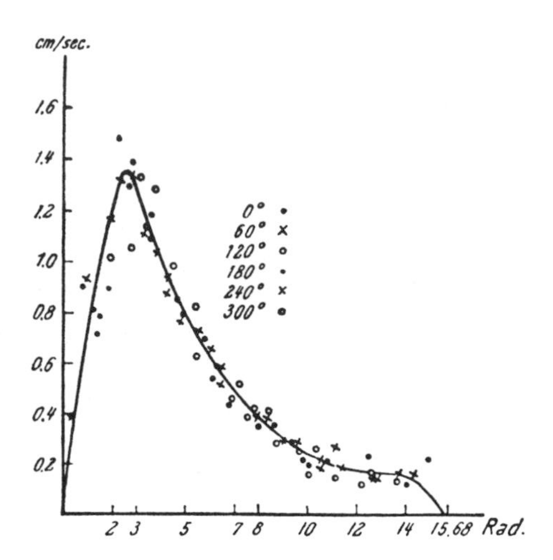

FIG. 4.432.1.—Hadley-regime: mean velocity distribution at water surface, constructed from observed speeds (ordinate, cm/sec) at various degrees of longitude. *Rad* = radius of rotating dishpan (cm). (Experimental conditions: $2\Omega = 0.0408$ sec^{-1}, $C_E = 0.320$ cm sec^{-1}, heat input at equator 6 cal. sec^{-1}.) (Fultz *et al.*, 1956.)

2. On the anticyclonic side of this jet stream the wind profile approaches a *constant* value of *absolute angular momentum*. With still stronger heating at the "equator" ($r' = 1$) this approximation is even better than in the case shown in Figure 4.432.1.

3. If the cooling is accomplished by a cold-water jet which is directed against the bottom of the tank from underneath, easterlies are established near the bottom of the dishpan only beyond a radius of r' of about 0.7 to 0.8. If, however, a cylinder containing cold water is used as heat sink at the pole, easterlies appear over the whole bottom surface of the vessel. These differences have their reason in the angular momentum budget: if there is no inner cylinder, the outer rim of the dishpan and the relatively narrow zone of northeasterly trades act as a source for westerly momentum. The westerlies near the bottom surface in polar and temperate latitudes, however, act as momentum sinks. If a cold-water cylinder is present at the pole, its surface constitutes an additional momentum sink because of its frictional effects. The whole bottom surface of the dishpan now becomes a momentum source.

If the rotation is increased beyond the orders of magnitude given above (Re* and T* increased, Ro_T* and Ro_j* are decreased), the Hadley regime becomes unstable. Long-wave troughs with axes showing a strong inclination toward southwest appear. Such an inclination of the trough axes permits a pronounced poleward transport of momentum (Arakawa, 1953*b*). At the same time the axis of maximum westerly velocities shifts rapidly toward temperate latitudes. Now, under *quasi-geostrophic* conditions, the flow assumes a narrower jet-stream-like character. Asymmetries in the flow pattern disappear as soon as a cooling cylinder—as small as it may be—is used at the pole.

2. *The Rossby Regime.*—If the rate of rotation is increased (Ro_T* and Ro_j* decreased) until quasi-geostrophic values are established, a pattern of 2, 3, 4, or more Rossby waves emerges from the symmetric Hadley regime (Davies, 1956). These waves are extremely stationary and remain present during thousands of revolutions of the dishpan (see Chapter 4.433; Fultz *et al.*, 1956). A continuous, narrow jet stream surrounds the whole hemisphere. The waves slowly propagate eastward with a velocity of the order of magnitude of $\frac{1}{10}Ro_j$*. The wave number increases with increasing η and decreasing Ro_T*. η is the ratio of the radius of the polar cooling cylinder to the total radius of the dishpan. If the Rossby number is decreased further the regime of stationary waves breaks down (under otherwise equal conditions for η and depth of

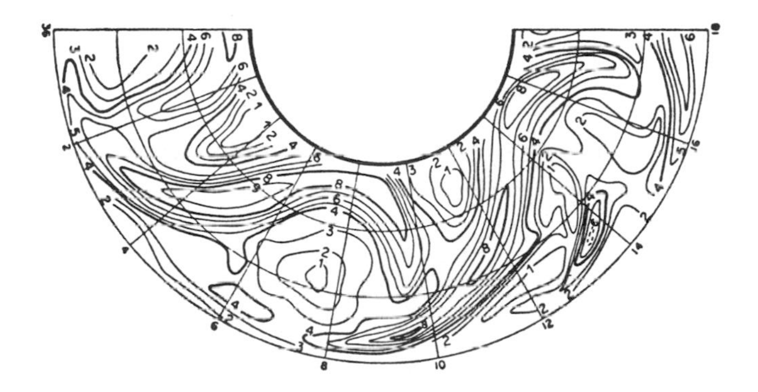

FIG. 4.432.2.—Isotachs ($10^{-2}C_E$) in a non-stationary five-wave pattern in a flat dishpan with cooling cylinder at the pole. (Fultz *et al.*, 1956.)

water). Waves form which show a strong inclination of the trough axes toward the southwest, and which constantly change, at times going through a regular index cycle and dissipating into closed cyclonic and anticyclonic vortices.[4] For Ro_T* approximately 0.01 the wave number lies between 5 and 6. Figure 4.432.2 shows an isotach analysis of a non-stationary 5-wave pattern (speeds given in units $C_E \cdot 10^{-2}$). During this experiment well-marked jet streams appeared, which, at times, formed shear lines and vortices such as we are accustomed to see in analyses of the atmospheric upper-wind field. If the cooling is done *without* the cylinder at the pole, the transition toward unstable wave patterns occurs already at somewhat higher Rossby numbers. Here the similarity with atmospheric circulation is especially striking (Fig. 4.432.3). As we have seen in the discussion of the Hadley regime, the cooling cylinder exerts a stabilizing influence upon the general circulation in the dishpan.

The analogy of these irregular waves to the atmospheric weather pattern is also valid for the conditions of flow near the surface: The position of cyclones and anticyclones at the ground is displaced slightly toward the east with respect to the

[4] Index cycles are also observed during stationary wave patterns, if the dishpan is considerably deeper at the equator than at the pole (Fultz and Kaylor, 1959).

position of the troughs and ridges, as is the case with migrating atmospheric wave disturbances. With the aid of thermo-couples, frontal passages could be observed in the case of stationary as well as of non-stationary waves. These fronts seem to be more sharply pronounced during the regime of irregular Rossby waves than with stationary waves.

Some of the frontal passages showed temperature drops of the full magnitude of the temperature difference between pole and equator. Thus, in these fronts water masses are brought together which have experienced hardly any heat exchange or turbulent mixing with the surroundings. The baroclinicity which leads to the formation of jet streams is correspondingly large.

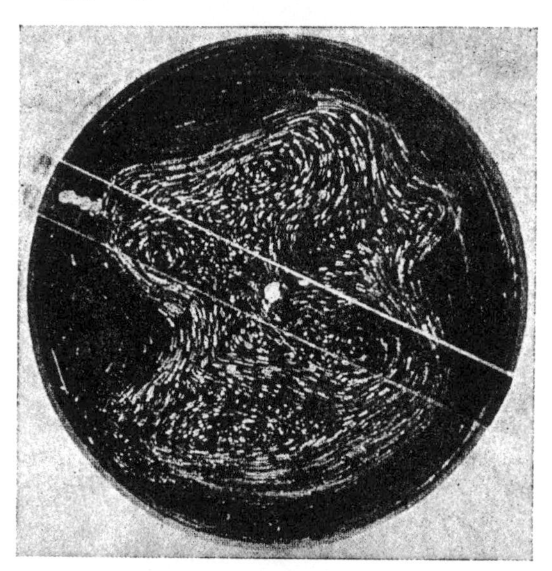

FIG. 4.432.3.—Time exposure of floating aluminium particles in a rotating dishpan, the "pole" of which is cooled by a cold-water jet from below. Rotational conditions correspond to the Rossby regime. (Photo: Hydrodynamics Laboratory, Department of Meteorology, University of Chicago; by courtesy of Dr. D. Fultz.)

The horizontal shears in the dishpan jets are by all means comparable with those experienced in atmospheric jet streams. In spite of these apparent analogies between atmosphere and model there are several noteworthy differences. So, for instance, the turbulent momentum transport in non-dimensional form (uv/C_E^2) shows magnitudes in the dishpan which are larger by a factor of 3 to 4 than in the atmosphere. This is probably caused by additional momentum sources and sinks at the inner and outer border of the dishpan. This will be discussed further in Chapter 4.433.

Figure 4.432.4 gives a comprehensive view of the spectrum of different circulation regimes of symmetric waves in a relatively deep, rotating annulus (cold source active at the inner radius, heat source active at the outer radius) as a function of the thermal Rossby number [see 4.432 (3)] and of the parameter $(G^*)^{-1}$ [see 4.432 (1)]. These observations agree well with the theory developed by Kuo (1954*a*, 1955, 1956*b*, 1957, 1960) whereby in the Hadley regime the meridional circulation assumes the total production of kinetic energy; in the Rossby regime, however, with increasing rate of rotation and wave number the horizontal vortices take over part of this task.

The heavy lines indicate transition zones between the various wave regimes (see Fultz, 1960). With very low Ro_T^* numbers ($\Delta_r \Theta$ small) a trade wind circulation exists with only slow motions. This regime with slow symmetric flow is connected on the *left-hand side* of the diagram with the region of rapid Hadley circulation ($\Delta_r \Theta$ relatively large) which also is symmetric. If, therefore, with a small rate of rotation [$(G^*)^{-1}$ about $2 \cdot 10^{-3}$] the temperature gradient $\Delta_r \Theta$ is increased from zero to rather considerable values, the resulting circulation will always be axially symmetric.

With a somewhat faster rotation [$(G^*)^{-1}$ smaller than $2 \cdot 10^{-2}$], a critical value of temperature gradients will be reached at which the symmetric circulation suddenly breaks down and gives room to a regime of Rossby waves. According to Figure 4.432.4 the wave number may be 4, 5, or 6 depending on the magnitude of the parameter of $(G^*)^{-1}$. Instead of the wave number 6, at times also a 7-wave pattern will be observed which is indicated in Figure 4.432.4 by a dotted line. With even faster rotation [$(G^*)^{-1} > 2 \cdot 10^{-2}$] either alternating closed vortices appear which form out of waves, or a new kind of retrograde wave may be observed which proceeds from east toward west.

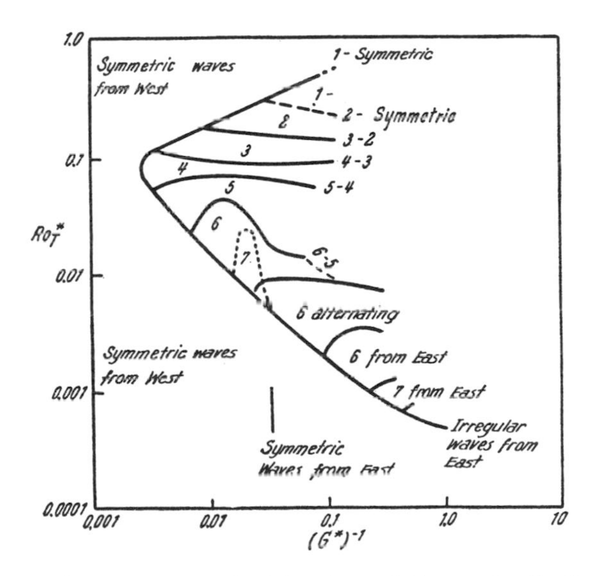

FIG. 4.432.4.—Spectrum of waves (wave numbers) in a deep, rotating annulus (depth 13 cm, radius of cooling cylinder 2.5 cm, equatorial radius 4.95 cm). These waves form when, with constant rate of rotation, the temperature difference between pole and equator is slowly increased. The co-ordinates are $(G^*)^{-1} = R\Omega^2/g$ and Ro_T^*. (Fultz, 1960.)

This diagram also permits several conclusions with respect to atmospheric conditions of flow. If, with constant rate of rotation ($G^* = \text{constant}$), the temperature contrast between pole and equator increases, we have to expect a decrease of the wave number (see Winston, 1960). This is actually evident from a comparison of the mean topographies of the 700-mb surface for winter and summer. During winter the mean charts show a wave number $n=3$; during summer, however, $n=4$ appears indicated. The wave numbers on the daily synoptic upper weather charts, however, may show considerable departures from these mean values.

Naturally the atmospheric conditions may not be transferred directly into the pattern of Figure 4.432.4. The disturbing influence of high mountain ranges allows one to expect a strong modification of the wave numbers as compared with the free Rossby regime.

The dishpan experiments presented here indicate that the planetary long-wave pattern and therefore also the magnitude of the turbulent meridional transport of heat and momentum will react sensitively to the meridional temperature gradient.

4.433. The Jet Stream in a Stationary Three-Wave Pattern

Riehl and Fultz (1957, 1958) have analyzed in detail circulation patterns which are established in the case of stationary Rossby waves with the wave number 3 in an annulus filled with water which is warmed at the equator and cooled at the pole by means of a cooling cylinder flushed with cold water. Since these studies are very informative from the point of view of the dynamics of jet streams they will be discussed in detail in the following.

Since, during this experiment (depth of water 4 cm, inner radius 6.5 cm, outer radius 15.6 cm), the three waves were arranged symmetrically, it suffices if only one wave is analyzed. (A certain micro-structure of the wind field has been eliminated by averaging the velocity and temperature distribution over the three waves.)

The co-ordinate system is rotated with the water tank, following the custom of analysis of atmospheric flow patterns. The waves are moving with the speed of 25° longitude per rotation of the tank (=per "day") toward the east. If this wave speed is subtracted vectorially from the measured "wind" speeds, which are shown in Figure 4.433.1, one obtains the motion *relative* to the migrating waves. The existence of a cross-stream circulation (which could also be made visible by traces of color particles) becomes evident from the *relative* streamlines (arrows in Fig. 4.433.1) which at the

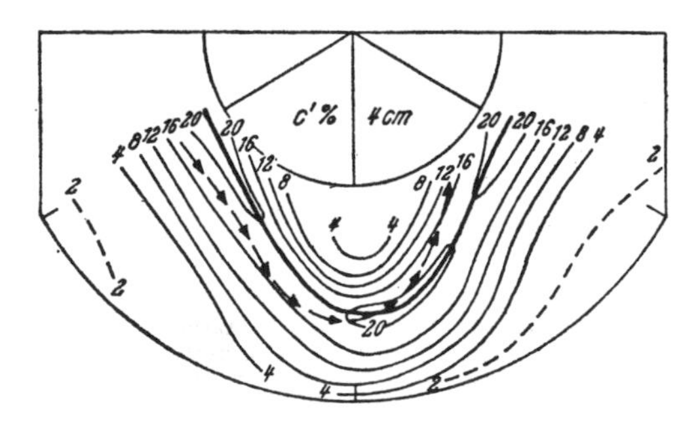

FIG. 4.433.1.—Isotachs of speed at water surface (in per cent of C_E). The heavy line indicates the position of the jet axis. A *relative* streamline is represented by arrows. (Riehl and Fultz, 1957.)

surface emerge from the warm rim of the dishpan and subsequently cross the jet axis toward the low-pressure side; they follow through all three waves and finally end in the sink of a polar low-pressure vortex. Thus, this relative streamline pattern already indicates a *direct* circulation (rising of warm air, sinking of cold air) which maintains the jet stream. This is in agreement with the circulation scheme devised by Palmén and shown in Figure 4.412.1. The "zero-layer effect" (supergradient winds in the upper troposphere in the region of wind maxima showing a mass flow toward higher pressure), which has been found by Faust (1954*a*) and Hollman (1954) in jet-stream weather situations and which has been explained by a transport of kinetic energy directed upward in cyclones in connection with the positive vertical motion present there, could not be verified by these dishpan experiments (see Chapter 4.122).

Supergradient winds and zero-layer effect seem to be tied to circulations with well-defined velocity maxima. The isotachs shown in Figure 4.433.1 reveal, however, an almost homogeneous distribution of wind speeds along the jet axis (the two wind maxima $V' > 20$ per cent are of hardly any significance). Thus, the water masses flowing through this wave pattern are subject to relatively smaller accelerations and decelerations than the air masses in the region of an atmospheric jet maximum.

The discrepancy between dishpan circulation and results from Faust's investigations will have to be expected also from reasons of continuity: Well-pronounced wind maxima at the 225-mb level, which on the average may show supergradient conditions of flow, in general are connected with active cyclones or even with cyclogenesis. In these cyclones a strong convergence prevails near the ground which has to be compensated at high levels by divergence and by mass flow toward higher pressure if the cyclone should not be filled up immediately.

The flow pattern shown in Figure 4.433.1, however, conforms to *stationary* conditions without cyclogenesis. The cold water flows out toward the equator near the surface; thus, in the upper layers one will have to expect a compensating mass flow toward the pole. This ageostrophic component of flow toward lower pressure is, *nota bene*, also found by Faust well established in weather situations *without* wind maxima between 300 and 175 mb, which most likely reflect quasi-stationary conditions.

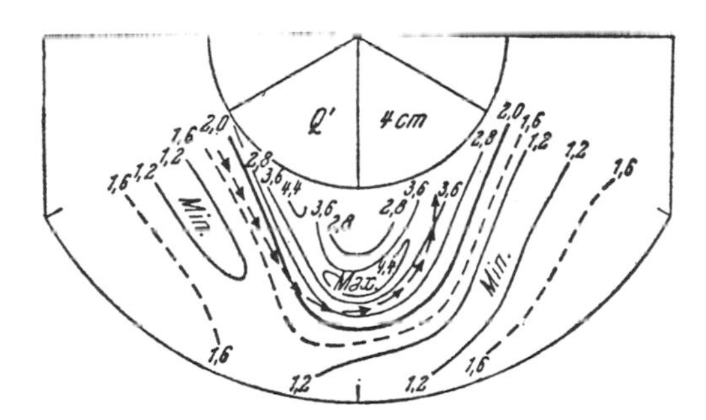

FIG. 4.433.2.—Absolute vorticity and relative streamline (arrows) at water surface. (Riehl and Fultz, 1957.)

The vorticity distribution at the surface of the rotating dishpan (Fig. 4.433.2) shows that the horizontal shears are less in the model experiment than in the atmosphere; however, the cyclonic shear exceeds the anticyclonic one as it does in atmospheric jet streams. The vorticity is obtained in a non-dimensional form Q', by dividing through the angular velocity of the rotating container,

$$Q = 2\Omega + q,$$

$$Q' = 2 + q'. \qquad 4.433\ (1)$$

The curve $Q=2$ or ($q=0$) runs very close to the jet axis but it has a slightly larger amplitude than the latter, which is caused by the change of streamline curvature along the jet axis. A vorticity minimum extends along the anticyclonic side of the jet stream. The magnitude of relative vorticity amounts to only 40 per cent of the Coriolis parameter, however. Thus, the absolute vorticity nowhere reaches the value zero. Only with a higher rate of rotation of the dishpan are meridional wind profiles and vorticity distributions produced which correspond to actual atmospheric conditions. In the regions of the long waves near the upper surface, conditions of approximately constant absolute vorticity are maintained because of only small values of divergence. With a Coriolis parameter *independent of latitude* this is accomplished by different horizontal shears in troughs and ridges. At lower levels the *potential vorticity* seems to be conserved approximately.

From the temperature distribution in meridional cross sections it follows that the horizontal temperature gradient at the surface of the dishpan is still directed toward the north as it is at the bottom, although the magnitude of the gradient is only about half what it is at the bottom of the pan. (Some indications of a cooling at the surface are due to evaporation.) The jet-stream level therefore is *not* an isopycnic level. Neither is there any *tropopause* or *stratosphere* present in this experiment. The characteristics of an atmospheric vertical temperature distribution, thus, *do not seem to be the necessary condition for the formation of jet streams*. There is, however, a marked difference between model and prototype: The model has—as a difference from the atmosphere—a free surface, which shapes the *vertical* wind profiles at jet-stream level very much like the tropopause or other levels with marked discontinuity in the vertical temperature gradient do (see Chapter 4.415).

By comparing the pattern of relative streamlines with the analysis of upper-surface temperatures in the dishpan, a marked warm advection is revealed. If a stationary temperature field is nevertheless maintained, this will have to be attributed to the effect of evaporation and of a certain turbulent exchange in the unstable layer near the upper surface.

The pressure distribution at arbitrary lower levels may be computed from the three-dimensional thermal structure of the dishpan circulation and from the "wind" velocities at the upper surface by means of the geostrophic wind equation in non-dimensional form

$$V_g' = \frac{1}{2} \frac{\partial D'}{\partial n'} \qquad 4.433\ (2)$$

(D' is the non-dimensional altimeter correction, and n' is the horizontal scale in units of $R \equiv r_0$, the dishpan radius). Figure 4.433.3 shows the analysis of the geostrophic stream function D' on selected isobaric surfaces.

The jet stream rapidly loses its intensity with increasing depth. Below the 2-cm level the circulation breaks down into closed vortices which especially at the 1-cm level reveal an analogy to the atmospheric circulation near the ground. (The jet-stream axis has been entered in Figure 4.433.4*c* for purposes of comparison. It runs across the centers of the high- and low-pressure cells.) Slightly to the east of the upper trough a cold front seems to be indicated in the circulation of the 1-cm surface (and also in the temperature distribution which is not shown here) behind which weak northwesterly winds prevail. The horizontal temperature discontinuity is rather shallow (it hardly reaches the 1-cm level) and seems to be maintained by advective processes. Since this experiment describes stationary conditions of flow, the wave indicated by this "front" is *not* subject to an occlusion process. It may well be that the advective processes along this front are closely connected with the mechanism of propagation of the planetary jet-stream waves located above.

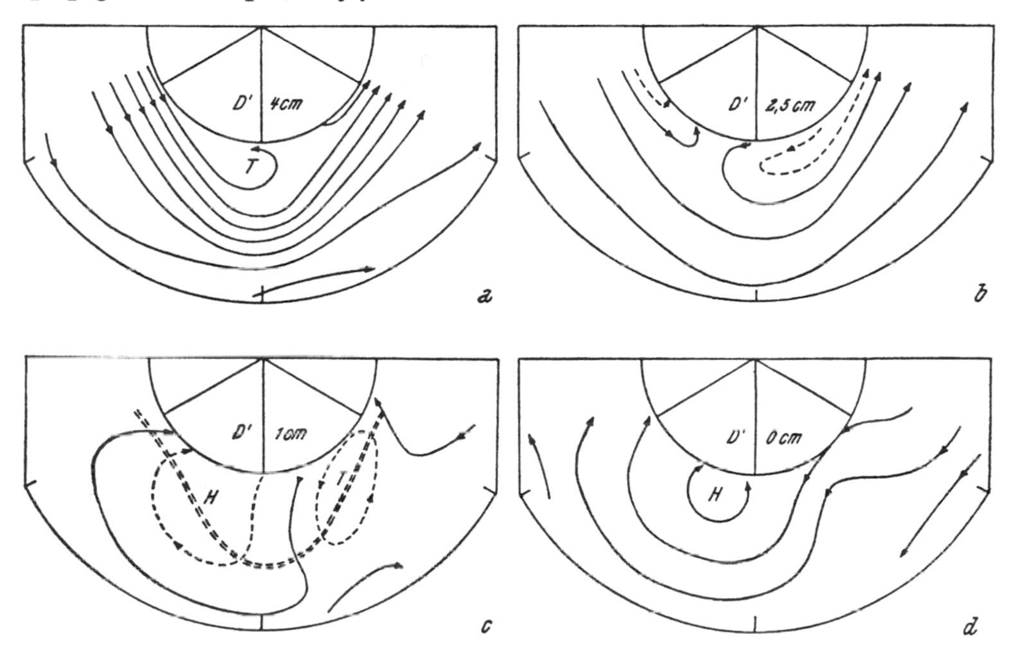

FIG. 4.433.3.—Stream function of the geostrophic "wind" speed on four isobaric surfaces. The double dashed line corresponds to the jet axis at the water surface. (Riehl and Fultz, 1957.)

The easterly flow near the bottom surface of the dishpan has no parallel in the atmosphere. Apparently the changed conditions in the momentum budget are decidedly responsible for the maintenance of these easterlies which are due to an additional westerly momentum sink on the inner wall of the rotating tank. Under the influence of these easterlies the whole bottom surface of the dishpan becomes a momentum source.

Vertical motions may be calculated by means of the adiabatic method. Since in the incompressible model "atmosphere" adiabatic is synonymous with isothermal, and since because of the stationary conditions the derivative $\partial/\partial t$ may be neglected, Eq. 3.248 (16) reduces to

$$w=\frac{dz}{dt}=V_{rg}\frac{\partial z_T}{\partial s_r}$$

(V_{rg} is the geostrophic speed *relative* to the migrating wave, z_T is the height of the isothermal surface, and s_r is an element of the three-dimensional relative streamline). In non-dimensional form (division by $C_E=r_0\Omega$) this expression reads

$$w'=V_{rg}'\frac{\partial z_T'}{\partial s_r'}. \qquad 4.433\ (3)$$

Figure 4.433.4 shows cross sections of the vertical motion (in per thousand of C_E) for the ridge (R), the inflection point between ridge and trough ($I-NW$), the trough (T), and the inflection point between trough and ridge ($I-SW$). In this representation 5 per thousand are equivalent to 1 cm/sec in the atmosphere, because of the 250-fold exaggeration of height in the model.

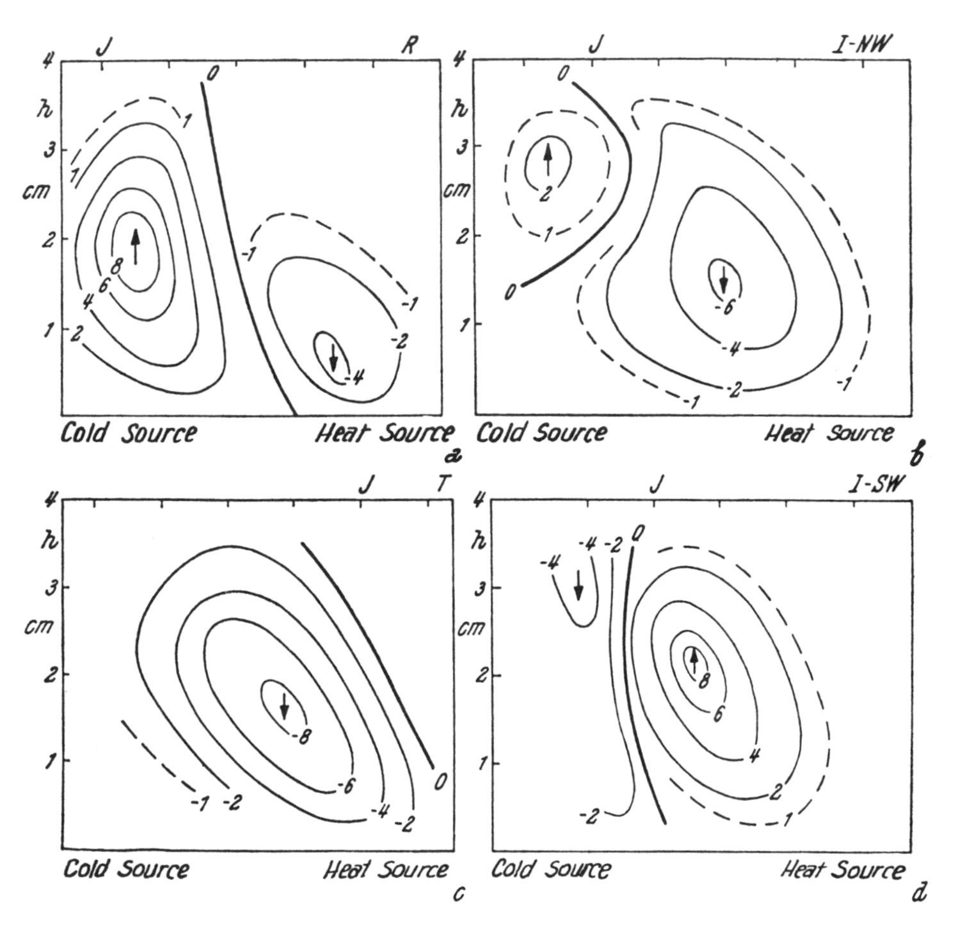

FIG. 4.433.4.—Vertical motion (in per thousand of C_E) along various cross sections (see text). (Riehl and Fultz, 1957.)

The results of these investigations confirm in a surprisingly clear way what has already been derived from studies of atmospheric frontal zones (Chapter 4.221): *The sense of the vertical circulation along the jet axis is not constant.* In the atmosphere entrainment and delta region of a jet maximum could mainly be distinguished by direct and indirect ("solenoidal" or "antisolenoidal") circulation.[5] Because of the much more uniform wind speeds along the jet axis in the model, it is the position of the wave troughs and ridges and their displacement which determines the sense of the circulation. At the ridge and at the northwestern inflection point "antisolenoidal"

[5] Circulation should be understood here in a thermodynamic sense.

circulation prevails with rising cold and sinking warm water. With respect to the *jet stream*, however, only the northwestern inflection point shows an indirect circulation, because in the ridge the center of ascending motion still lies to the *south* of the jet axis. The cross sections through trough and southwesterly inflection point indicate a direct circulation with respect to the jet axis as well as with respect to the sense of the solenoids. The direct circulation exceeds the indirect circulation if one integrates over the length of the whole planetary long wave.

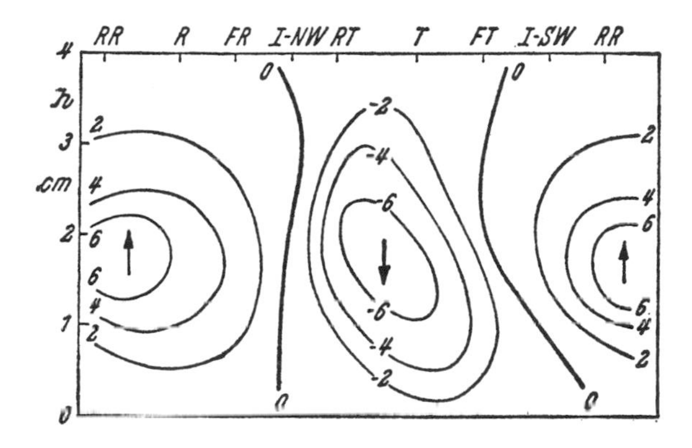

FIG. 4.433.5.—Vertical motion (in per thousand of C_E) in a vertical cross section along the jet axis (see text). (Riehl and Fultz, 1957.)

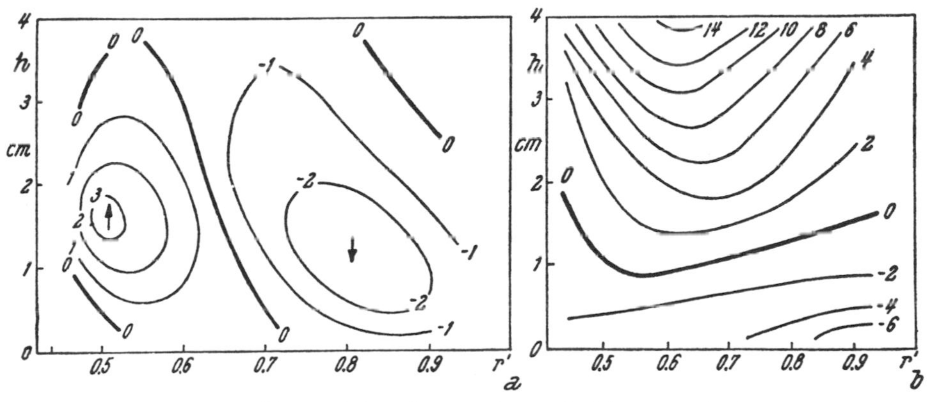

FIG. 4.433.6.—Zonal average of (*a*) vertical motion (per thousand of C_E), and (*b*) horizontal speed (per cent of C_E). (Riehl and Fultz, 1957.)

Figure 4.433.5 contains the vertical speeds in a section *along* the jet axis (RR=rear side of ridge, R=ridge, FR=front side of ridge, I-NW=northwesterly inflection point, RT=rear side of trough, T=trough, FT=front side of trough, I-SW= southwesterly inflection point). The strongest sinking motions are found in the middle troposphere to the rear of troughs, the strongest ascending motions are present between ridge and inflection point upstream from the ridge. Again the agreement with atmospheric conditions is very striking.

That a *zonal average* of the horizontal speed and of the vertical motion may under circumstances render a completely different picture of the meridional circulation pattern is evident from Figure 4.433.6. Here the impression is created that the jet stream on the average is connected with an antisolenoidal (indirect) circulation because in the north of the mean cross section (Fig. 4.433.6*a*) ascending motions are indicated, and in the south sinking motions prevail. Such a circulation would also correspond to Faust's "zero-layer effect." If we finally incorporate into this circulation pattern the ascending motion at the outer rim of the dishpan and the sinking water masses at the inner rim, we arrive at an atmospheric structure consisting of three cells, as it also appears in Figure 4.412.1. In reality, however, the "indirect" mean circulation wheel is simulated by the ascending motions in high-pressure ridges which have proceeded far to the north and by sinking motions in troughs which have been displaced to the south. Although an "indirect" circulation may exist in certain places in the dishpan as well as in the atmosphere, it could hardly be assumed as a mean

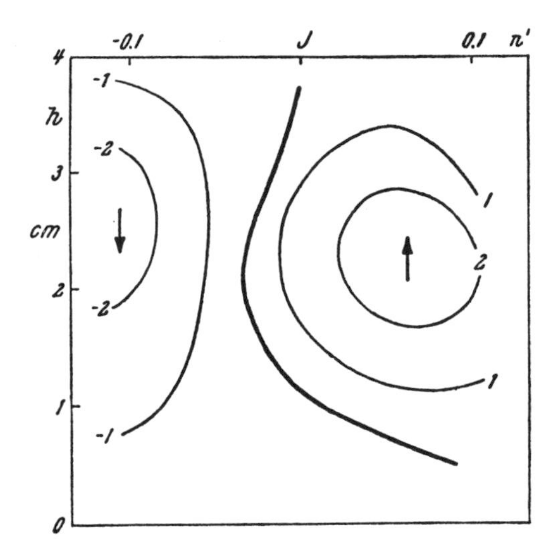

FIG. 4.433.7.—Vertical motion (per thousand of C_E) in a "curvilinear" co-ordinate system, which follows the jet axis. (Riehl and Fultz, 1957.)

condition, because it would constantly consume kinetic energy and thereby would lead to the dissipation of the jet stream. In mean cross sections these indirect circulation cells owe their existence to the fact that the rising motion over a warm front occurs to the north of the sinking motion behind the cold front.

If one averages, however, the vertical speeds with respect to the *jet axis* (curvilinear co-ordinate system) one obtains the meridional cross section shown in Figure 4.433.7, which contains only a single direct circulation wheel in its actual physical meaning as a driving mechanism of the jet stream. It might be that the discrepancy between Faust's investigations and the meridional water transport in the dishpan indicated above might be explained by the fact that the "zero-layer effect" was obtained from a co-ordinate system which was fixed to the rotating earth.

The remarkable fact that the mean distribution of vertical circulations in the jet-stream region depends on the choice of the co-ordinate system has a bearing also for heat and momentum transport considerations. The following problem, which time and again appears in meteorological literature, remains to be solved (Bjerknes, 1953*a*, *b*; Palmén and Alaka, 1952; Rossby, 1949*b*; Starr, 1948*a*): Is this transport accom-

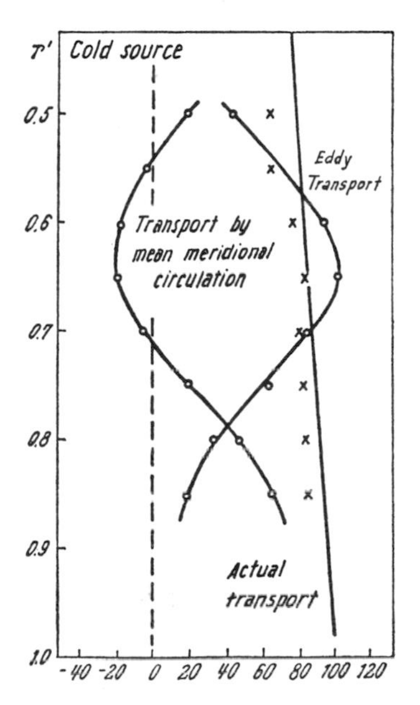

FIG. 4.433.8.—Mean meridional heat transport in a cylindrical co-ordinate system (in per cent of the equatorial heat source). The solid straight line indicates the actual heat transport, the crosses show the computed transport. (Riehl and Fultz, 1958.)

plished by quasi-geostrophic horizontal vortices with vertical axes or by ageostrophic components of flow which necessarily would manifest themselves in a vertical circulation? Let us first consider this problem in a cylindrical co-ordinate system. The heat transport H through a vertical surface is given by

$$\frac{H}{\rho c_w} = 2\pi r \int_0^D \bar{T}\bar{v}\,dz + 2\pi r \int_0^D \overline{T^* v_g}\,dz. \qquad 4.433\ (4)$$

c_w is the specific heat of water, r the radius at which the vertical control surface is placed, D is the depth of the water, $\bar{T}$ is the mean temperature at the latitude circle r and T^* is the deviation from this mean temperature, $\bar{v}$ is the mean meridional component of velocity (positive toward the north) and v_g is the geostrophic meridional component present at the individual points of observation. The amount of heat H is for practical purposes expressed non-dimensionally as per cent of the energy of the heat source. The first term on the right hand side of this equation constitutes the heat flow, which is caused by a *mean meridional circulation*; the second term gives the contribution of the *turbulent transport* which becomes effective if the departures of temperature from the mean and the geostrophic meridional components of flow are correlated with each other (if this correlation is positive there will be a heat transport toward the north). Figure 4.433.8 shows the results of the computations (the evaluation of v has been checked by various methods, so that the results may be considered reliable). Thus, the turbulent heat transport takes over the largest part of the total transport in temperate latitudes, i.e., in the immediate vicinity of the jet stream; it even transports too much in these regions, so that the meridional circulation in this latitude belt has to accomplish a transport in the opposite direction (toward the south). In lower latitudes the portion of the transport which is accomplished by the meridional circulation predominates. The sum of both processes renders the total transport (indicated by crosses in Fig. 4.433.8), which agrees well in order of magnitude with the actual conditions (indicated by the heavy straight line which has been computed under the assumption of a linear distribution of the heat loss due to evaporation).

Thus, the distribution of the meridional circulation indicates the existence of an *indirect* circulation wheel in temperate latitudes, which by means of ageostrophic components of flow transports heat energy toward the south. Since a *direct* circulation wheel has to be present at each, the heat source and the cold source, we arrive at the same structure of the circulation consisting of *three cells*, as we have derived it already from Figure 4.433.6.

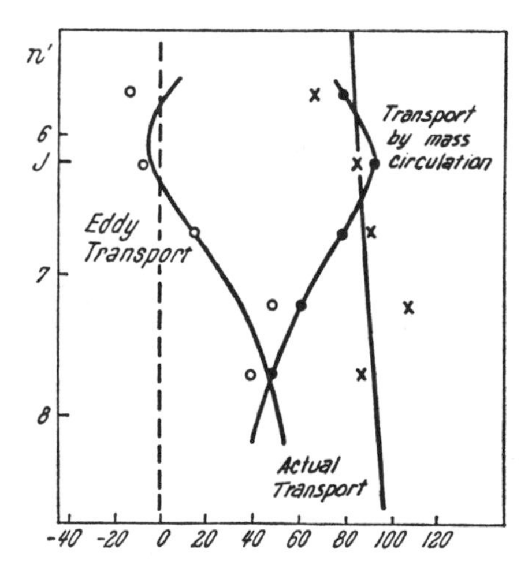

FIG. 4.433.9.—Heat transport in a "curvilinear" co-ordinate system; otherwise as Figure 4.433.8. (Riehl and Fultz, 1958.)

If, however, we make these computations in a "curvilinear" co-ordinate system, in which the averaging is done along the jet axis and normal to it, we arrive at the results presented in Figure 4.433.9. In this diagram the turbulent heat transport has to decrease toward the jet axis (J), approaching here the value zero, as far as the accuracy of the computations permits. The total *heat transport* in the jet-stream region of this model therefore will have to be accomplished by the *ageostrophic flow of mass.* The direct circulation wheel shown in Figure 4.433.7 is thus corroborated.

We, therefore, are faced with the fact that two—and maybe more—models of the atmospheric circulation may be established, each mathematically correct but with a different transport mechanism depending on the co-ordinate system we choose.

Thus, the controversial question whether the geostrophic (following a horizontal plane) or the ageostrophic (occurring in a vertical meridional plane) heat transport prevails must be attacked from a different line of thinking. The same holds for the problem of momentum transport. That these problems have been exposed in such a striking way seems to be one of the main merits of the dishpan experiments made by Riehl and Fultz and described here—even more than the very valuable quantitative results. This series of experiments may serve as a stimulus for placing more emphasis in the quantitative analysis of atmospheric flow patterns upon a "natural" co-ordinate system as it is offered for instance by the jet axis.

Let us finally consider the energy budget in the jet-stream region. Figure **4.433.10** shows the production of kinetic energy dK_r/dt of the *relative* motion whereby the summation is carried out over the total water depth in a curvilinear co-ordinate system. The energy production (positive sign) to the east of the trough exceeds the dissipation to the west of the trough. These results agree very well with Palmén's analysis of the weather situation over the United States, which will be described in detail in Chapter 6.122 (Palmén, 1958). From the present experiment it could be shown that the total transport of kinetic energy, which *everywhere* is directed *poleward* in a curvilinear system, is accomplished by the *ageostrophic mass circulation.* The transport appears to be largest in the region of the jet axis. Thus, the kinetic energy on the average is produced to the south of the jet axis and is dissipated on the

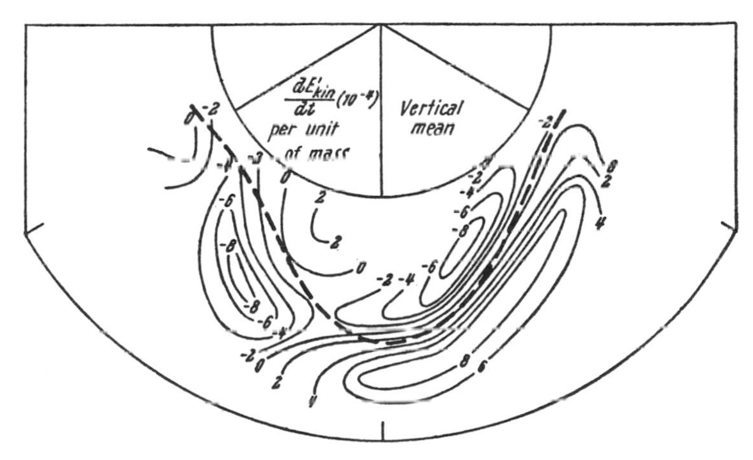

FIG. 4.433.10.—Distribution of the vertical mean of the gain and dissipation of kinetic energy (non-dimensional units). (Riehl and Fultz, 1958.)

polar side of the axis. *In the region of the jet axis itself no kinetic energy is either produced or dissipated* (frictional effects will be neglected here) (see Fig. 4.433.10). Thus, the jet stream itself is neither a place of *production of kinetic energy*, which then would be spread laterally in order to maintain the kinetic energy of the surroundings, nor is it a *sink* which would consume kinetic energy coming from other latitude belts.

Let us consider a volume τ, which comprises the total depth of water and which is confined in between two streamlines in a curvilinear co-ordinate system (subscript r), i.e., by two lines which run parallel to the jet axis and which surround the whole hemisphere. The equilibrium of the geostrophic kinetic energy K_{rg} within this volume will be given by

$$\int_\tau \frac{dK_{rg}}{dt}\,d\tau = \int_\sigma v_{rn}K_{rg}\,d\sigma = -f_r\int_\tau (u_{ra}v_{rg} - v_{ra}u_{rg})\,d\tau - \int_\tau FV_r\,d\tau \qquad 4.433\ (5)$$

because of the stationary condition ($\partial/\partial t = 0$). σ is the surface which surrounds the volume element τ, v_{rn} is the component of the wind speed V_r normal to the surface σ. The subscript a indicates quantities measured in an absolute system, the subscript g points to geostrophic speeds, and the subscript r to a curvilinear co-ordinate system which moves with the planetary wave pattern. The first term on the right-hand side of this equation gives the production of kinetic energy by pressure forces. It may be decomposed into an expression $f_r \int_\tau \bar{v}_{rna}\bar{v}_{rng}\,d\tau$ which is caused by the ageostrophic *mass circulation* and into the expression $-f_r \int_\tau (u_{ra}v_{rg} - v_{ra}u_{rg})\,d\tau$ $-f_r \int_\tau \bar{v}_{rna}\bar{u}_{rng}\,d\tau$ which is due to large-scale horizontal turbulence (long waves). The second term on the left-hand side of 4.433 (5) corresponds to the dissipation by frictional forces F. Figure 4.433.11 shows the results of the computations for 5 volumes, which are oriented along the curvilinear co-ordinate system.

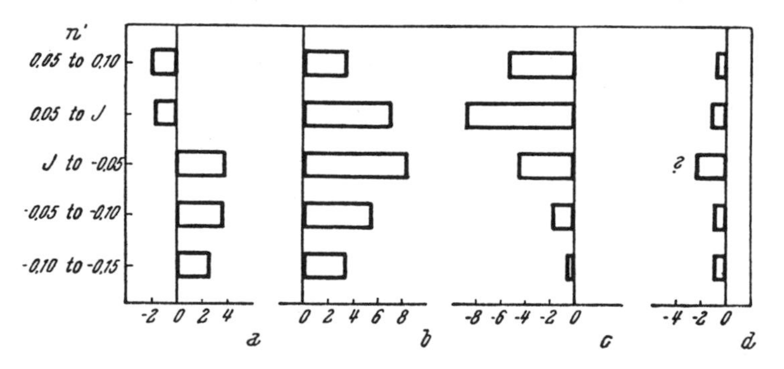

FIG. 4.433.11.—Production of kinetic energy within five volume elements of a curvilinear co-ordinate system (non-dimensional units), (*a*) by pressure forces, (*b*) by mass circulation, and (*c*) by eddies relative to the jet axis; (*d*) dissipation of kinetic energy by friction, computed as residual between actual production and divergence of transport. (Riehl and Fultz, 1958.)

The total production of kinetic energy from the effect of pressure forces—corresponding to the first term on the right-hand side of 4.433 (5)—is positive on the equatorial side of the jet axis and negative on the polar side (Fig. 4.433.11*a*). Diagram *b* contains the part of the production of kinetic energy which is due to the mass circulation. It is positive in all latitudes. Corresponding to the difference between *a* and *b*, the production by horizontal vortices has to be negative everywhere (diagram *c*) and has to show a maximum north of the jet axis. Here the braking mechanism is easy to understand: The amplitude of the isobars increases with depth (Fig. 4.433.3). Thus, if a water particle is sinking in the southwesterly current to the north of the jet axis, it will flow toward higher pressure and will be subject to a corresponding braking action if it tries to retain its relative momentum over a short distance.

Diagram *d* contains the frictional influence computed as a residual of 4.433 (5). Although the numerical results of this computation may not be considered very reliable, they still show the correct sign everywhere.

The source for the observed kinetic energy in the atmosphere as well as in the model experiment lies in the potential energy. In the dishpan the conditions are much simpler than in the prototype of the atmospheric circulation. We do not have to worry about the latent heat of condensation processes, which in some types of atmospheric circulations—as for instance in tropical hurricanes—plays a predominant role. Furthermore, if we assume adiabatic conditions, equivalent in the model experiment with isothermal conditions, the internal energy of a flowing water particle also will remain constant. Nevertheless, we will meet some difficulties here, as well as in the atmosphere: A particle rising under the prevailing vertical conditions of shear will be imparted potential as well as kinetic energy. A sinking particle however loses *both* forms of energy. *The principle of constancy of energy thus does not hold for individual liquid particles but only for the total closed system.* The difficulty in atmospheric analysis lies in the question how this "system" will have to be bounded in order to make it closed on the one hand but still not too large to lose a view of it. In the dishpan, the conditions are also simplified with this respect: The potential energy of the whole pan must remain constant. Because of the stationary condition this holds also for each volume element fixed in the curvilinear co-ordinate system:

$$\int_\tau g\rho z \, d\tau = \text{const.} \qquad 4.433\ (6)$$

By introducing the continuity equation 1.221 (2) and the departure T of the temperature from standard conditions (indicated by index s) and of the coefficient of expansion ε [equation 4.431 (19)], we obtain

$$g\rho_s\varepsilon \int_\sigma T v_{\tau n} z \, d\sigma = g\rho_s\varepsilon \int_\tau T w \, d\tau. \qquad 4.433\ (7)$$

The expression on the right-hand side indicates the amount of potential energy which is released in the volume element τ under consideration, the left-hand side of 4.433 (7) gives the export through the boundary surfaces of this volume element.

Corresponding to a notation used earlier [see 4.433 (4)] we may write

$$Tw = \bar{T}\bar{w} + \overline{T^* w^*}, \qquad 4.433\ (8)$$

where the quantities marked with an asterisk indicate departures from the mean value. The first term on the right-hand side represents the release of potential energy by the mean meridional mass circulation, and the second term indicates the share of vortices along the jet axis. The evaluation of 4.433 (8) is made in a curvilinear co-ordinate system. In the individual volume bands τ, which in this co-ordinate system are oriented parallel to the jet axis, $\bar{T}\bar{w}$ may be large or small, depending on $\bar{w}$ being large or small in this respective band, without the inclination of isothermal surfaces, which is reponsible for the release of potential energy, being considered adequately. Therefore again averages and departures along the *perpendicular direction n* in this curvilinear co-ordinate system have been computed and have been indicated by $\sim$ and ^{0}:

$$\bar{T}\bar{w} = \tilde{\bar{T}}\tilde{\bar{w}} + \widetilde{\bar{T}^0\bar{w}^0}. \qquad 4.433\ (9)$$

Thus, the release of free potential energy is given by

$$P = g\rho_s\varepsilon \int \left(\overline{T^* w^*} + \widetilde{\overline{T}^0 \overline{w}^0}\right) d\tau. \qquad 4.433\ (10)$$

The first term under the integral sign contains the influence of vortices, and the second term gives the contribution from the mass circulation.

The results of these computations are shown in Figure 4.433.12 in terms of non-dimensional quantities. The contribution from vortices could not be computed for the region between the inner rim of the vessel (cold source) to the distance $n=0.10$ from the jet axis. According to these findings, the meridional circulation tends to orient the isothermal surfaces into horizontal planes, whereby the axis of this rotation (which, however, is not carried out because of the stationary state of the experiment) coincides with the jet axis. Correspondingly, here the share of the mass circulation in the release of potential energy shows a *minimum*. Again the *total* release of potential energy is

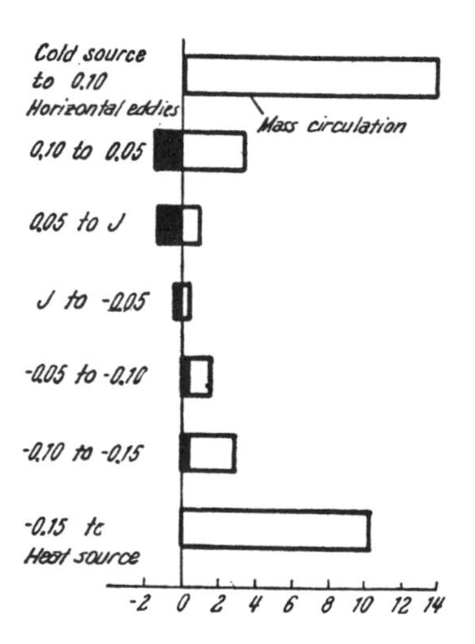

FIG. 4.433.12.—Release of potential energy by mass circulation (white areas) and by eddies relative to the jet axis (black areas) in a curvilinear co-ordinate system. (Riehl and Fultz, 1958.)

managed by the *meridional mass circulation* (see also Kuo, 1954*a*). The vortices, however, have a tendency to store potential energy, especially to the north of the jet axis. This is accomplished by rising of relatively cold water masses in the ridges and by sinking of warm masses in the northwesterly current (Fig. 4.433.4, cross section *R* and *I-NW*).

If we compare this figure with Figure 4.433.11*b*, we may see the remarkable fact that the release of potential energy by the mass circulation has a maximum in polar and equatorial dishpan latitudes, i.e., far from the jet stream. *This mass circulation, however, transforms the kinetic energy within the jet-stream region.* The mean circulation in a curvilinear co-ordinate system thus represents a simple heat engine, with warming at the equator and cooling at the pole.

We finally arrive at the important question to which kind of circulation the jet stream owes its existence. From the well-pronounced horizontal temperature gradients, we have concluded the existence of an indirect circulation, while on the other hand the existing kinetic energy indicates the presence of a *direct* circulation. Because of the prevailing vertical motions the latter would decrease the existing horizontal temperature gradient.

By assuming the potential vorticity to be conserved (this condition is not exactly valid at the surface of the dishpan because of the modifying influence of evaporation), the velocity distribution has been computed which would result from a mass circulation exclusively responsible for the formation of the jet stream. On the anticyclonic side of the jet stream, theory and observations are in good agreement. The mass circulation would, however, establish the jet stream much closer to the cold source and would also cause much higher velocities than are observed in reality. We would obtain a velocity distribution characteristic for the Hadley regime (see Fig. 4.432.1), which, as we have pointed out, is maintained by the meridional circulation only without the existence of any horizontal vortices.

The *cyclonic* shears observed in the jet stream cannot be explained by a mass circulation. Furthermore, the *direct* meridional circulation would diminish the horizontal temperature gradient, as has been mentioned earlier, thus causing a weakening of the jet stream. This tendency apparently is counteracted by horizontal large-scale vortices. They, therefore, are responsible for the *maintenance of the horizontal temperature field* and for a certain *reduction in speeds* in the jet axis and on its cyclonic side.

If the vorticity theorem is written in the form of a continuity equation [Eq. 1.234 (4)], we obtain the following expression valid in the curvilinear system

$$\frac{\partial}{\partial n} \oint_s \int_0^D v_{rn} Q_r \, ds \, dz = 0. \qquad 4.433\ (11)$$

Q_r is the absolute vorticity in this system. According to 4.433 (11), in which several terms of the complete vorticity equation which proved to be irrelevant have been neglected, we may count on a constant vorticity transport $\bar{v}_{rn} Q_r \cdot s$. If we consider the share of the mass circulation [first term on the right-hand side of 4.433 (12)] and the share of large-scale vortices (second term) separately, we arrive at

$$v_{rn} Q_r \cdot s = \overline{v_{rna}} \cdot \overline{Q}_r \cdot s + \overline{v_{rng} Q_r{}^* \cdot s}. \qquad 4.433\ (12)$$

These quantities have been entered in Figure 4.433.13 in a non-dimensional form (subscript g indicates "geostrophic," $c \equiv v$). The dashed line indicates the total constant vorticity transport according to 4.433 (11). The vorticity transport by the mass circulation is too large north of the jet axis. Here it is opposed by the transport due to horizontal vortices of the planetary long waves. This transport is brought about by the fact that in the northwesterly current to the rear of the troughs, with its indirect circulation (see Fig. 4.433.4), the cyclonic shear is larger than on the leading side of the troughs within the southwesterly current.

By the dishpan experiments described above, a whole new complex of questions has been touched and although not solved, they have been presented under a completely new view. Above all, we are confronted with the Socratic realization that we cannot make any definite statement on the mechanism of the general circulation, as long as the result will be influenced by the choice of co-ordinate system. Phillips (1956) carried out a numerical experiment in computing the resulting circulation in a Cartesian co-ordinate system, which in the interpretation of the various terms corresponds to a polar co-ordinate system, by considering also friction and non-adiabatic effects (heating). He arrived at the same conclusions as several authors before him,

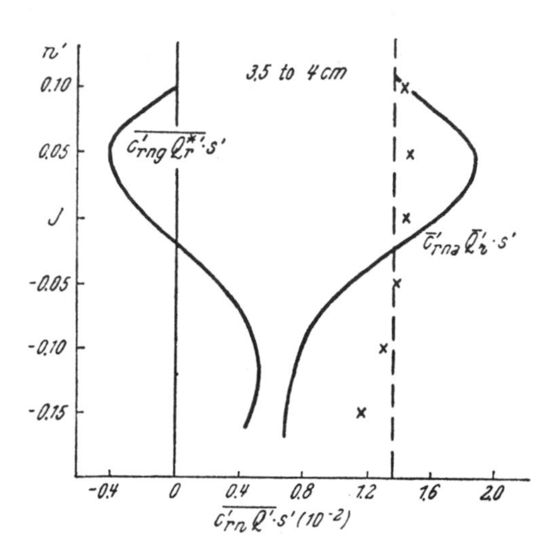

FIG. 4.433.13.—Vorticity transport (in non-dimensional units) by mass circulation and by eddies along the jet axis, in a curvilinear co-ordinate system. The dashed line indicates the transport according to Eq. 4.433 (11), the crosses represent the observed total transport. (Riehl and Fultz, 1958.)

that the energy of the general circulation stems from horizontal large-scale and quasi-geostrophic vortices. *The meridional circulation, however, exerts only a "braking" action upon this energy generation.* On the other hand, however, the dishpan experiments show that, in a curvilinear co-ordinate system based upon the jet axis, the conditions are exactly reversed: *The total kinetic energy stems from the meridional mass circulation,* while the horizontal vortices act as brakes (see Fig. 4.433.11). (Numerical values will not be discussed here any further, since model and prototype cannot be brought into exact agreement because of the differences in the thermodynamic effectiveness of the "circulation machine.")

Thus, the mechanism which drives the jet stream depends upon the point of view from which we consider it. Therefore, the quest for the origin of the jet stream becomes a philosophical question. If we base our computations upon a polar co-ordinate system in the departures from zonal mean values, the influence of wave motions of the current in a horizontal plane will be stressed, while vertical circulations, which are caused by the jet stream itself, will be grossly reduced and distorted by this kind of averaging process. The influence of these vertical circulations upon the transport of various quantities will have to be interpreted as correlation of the mass circulation with the phase of the long waves.

If, however, we follow the jet axis in our computations, the influence of its meanderings will be reduced, and the effect of vertical circulations will be stressed. The share of horizontal vortices in the transport of various quantities (heat, kinetic energy, etc.) again will have to be considered as a correlation with the *phase* of the long waves in this co-ordinate system.

Probably the importance of meridional circulations is strongly reduced in the customary meteorological treatments by polar co-ordinates. If we consider the circulations in the Hadley regime, the mass circulation appears as the only carrier of the various quantities, as for instance heat, momentum, etc. This Hadley circulation cell will remain stable only as long as the release of potential energy is caused directly by diabatic processes at the heat and cold source.

If, however, waves contained in horizontal surfaces appear within this circulation, the areas of main rising and sinking motion will not be found any longer along the rim of the vessel but within the liquid itself (Figs. 4.433.4 and .7), where heat and cold source are no longer *immediately* active. Should a stationary state be maintained, certain asymmetries, which constitute the *main properties of planetary waves* in view of the general circulation of the atmosphere, will have to be present to show the correlations mentioned above. In the dishpan experiments this is accomplished by the indirect circulation in the northwesterly current and by the direct circulation in the southwesterly current (Fig. 4.433.4).

If we integrate over the total depth of the water the rear side of the troughs will be cold, the leading side will be warm—in analogy to the atmosphere. By this distribution heat will constantly be transported toward the north by the horizontal waves and thus the stationary temperature gradient, which would be eliminated by the action of the meridional circulation, will be maintained.

The studies by Riehl and Fultz described here in great detail indicate only a beginning which allows us to place great expectations in the continuance of other modified model experiments.

5

JET-STREAM FORECASTING

5.1. GENERAL REMARKS

At an arbitrary point in space the wind vector is determined by wind direction and wind speed. Since both quantities are subject to changes with time, the forecasting of the upper-wind field is of a rather complex nature. It has been pointed out already in the preceding chapter that at jet-stream level ageostrophic components of flow play an important role in development processes. The determination of the geostrophic wind field from the topography of a prognostic chart, therefore, may be regarded only as a first approximation (Anonymous, 1952). Experiments over England resulted in forecasting errors of up to 26 knots during a time interval of 24 hours, due to ageostrophic departures (Murray, 1954). The quality of approximation is different for wind direction and wind speed. An inspection of upper-wind charts shows that the angle of deviation between actually observed and geostrophic winds hardly ever exceeds the order of magnitude of 10° (Reiter and Danielsen, 1960). Relatively large deviations in direction are observed only in areas of weak winds—in the centers of low- and high-pressure regions—where the angle between streamlines and trajectories is large due to the rate of propagation of the systems. These areas of weak winds, however, are only of minor importance to navigation. Notable departures in direction occur, furthermore, in the entrance and delta regions of frontal zones, where positive and negative accelerations may be sizable (Riehl, 1954*b*; see Chapter 4.122). In most instances, however, the *direction* of the geostrophic wind will agree well with the actually present streamline configuration, and a forecast from the contour pattern of a topography, therefore, will produce usable results.

Different considerations will have to be made with wind speed, i.e., when forecasting the position of isotachs. Because of the strong horizontal wind shears near the jet axis, especially on its cyclonic side, the quality of the wind-speed forecasts mainly depends upon the accuracy of the forecast of the position of the jet axis. From the geostrophic wind field of a prognostic chart of the 300-mb topography the jet axis may be determined only inadequately, however, first, because the horizontal wind profile is subject to various smoothing processes in analysis and forecast (Estoque, 1956, 1957*a*, *b*; Fjørtoft, 1952), and second, because the formation of jet streams incorporates ageostrophic processes (Kochanski, 1958).

In general, spot-wind forecasts, which are valid only for a certain point in the atmosphere, are subject to larger errors than mean winds along a flight route. According to Kochanski the error of the former amounts to 34 knots, on the average, with 36-hour forecasts at the 300- and 200-mb levels over the United States (see also Elsaesser, 1957; Garriock, 1957). The same data showed a mean error in the forecasts over 1900 nautical miles of only 17 knots. According to O'Carroll (1955), 92 per cent of the forecasts at the 700- and 500-mb levels along the flight route Shannon–Gander are within an error limit of 12 knots. Results from the Transatlantic route

Idlewild–Frankfurt showed, that in 60 per cent of the flights of the Boeing 707 the actual flying time was within ± 10 minutes of the forecast time (Bundesanstalt für Flugsicherung, 1959).

The prognosis of the time variation of the *three-dimensional* wind field creates further problems: Although the baroclinicity, on which the existence of the jet stream hinges, is no serious obstacle for objective, numerical forecasting (Nabeshima, 1957), the thermal wind equation which rests upon the geostrophic assumption, is only valid *approximately* in the jet-stream zone (see Chapter 4.232). Therefore, especially in the jet-stream region, we will have to expect maximum errors in numerical forecasts (Saucier, 1958*d*). For a reliable prognosis the atmospheric model in use would have to incorporate ageostrophic components of flow (Bundgaard, 1956*b*). Kinematic extrapolation of the parameters obtained from an LMW analysis constitutes a possibility of avoiding the geostrophic approximation. These extrapolation techniques, however, again are subject to serious restrictions in their dependability.

Over oceans, and over continents where the aerological observation network is not dense enough for quantitative prediction, some qualitative conclusions may be drawn on the displacement tendency of jet streams (Dickson, 1955*b*). So, e.g., it had been shown by Sawyer (1950*b*) that a line through the center of a hodograph, which runs *perpendicular* to the tangent at the part of the hodograph that runs approximately straight, giving the upper-flow conditions, indicates roughly the rate and direction of displacement of the jet axis.

Statistical correlations between position of the jet axis, height of the isobaric surface, and geographic latitude may sometimes be utilized (Fletcher, 1953); such correlations, however, should not be considered too significant. More promising are experiments which try to extrapolate in space and time the wind conditions at a higher level (e.g., 100 or 150 mb) from those at a lower level (e.g., 400 or 500 mb) by means of regression equations (Charles, 1959*b*; Ellison and Walshaw, 1955; Graystone, 1954; Johnson, 1955; Julian, Krawitz, and Panofsky, 1959; see also Brooks *et al.*, 1950; Knighting, 1954; U.S. Navy, 1960*a*; Weyant, 1960). Vederman and Dubofski (1959) report on a method which allows a construction of the 200- and 300-mb maps from a 500-mb prognostic chart. This method is based in part upon the correlations between the heights of the respective isobaric surfaces and in part upon the position of the tropopause, which influences especially the relative topography 200 to 300 mb and which is taken into account by a correlation with the relative geostrophic vorticity at the 500-mb level. Meyer (1957) finds the following statistical relationship between the relative topographies 300/500 mb and 500/1000 mb:

$$\Delta Z(300/500) = 0.53\Delta Z(500/1000) + 70 \qquad 5.1\ (1)$$

if the data for ΔZ are given in decameters. This relationship may be utilized for the extrapolation of the pressure field with height by re-labelling the isohypses of the relative topography $Z(500/1000)$ accordingly and by adding the resultant values to the absolute topography of the 500-mb surface (see Bundesanstalt für Flugsicherung, 1959).

Predictions at higher levels, based upon the *persistence* of the wind field, seem to be superior to climatological forecasts (Charles, 1959*a*; see also Kochanski, 1957).

Already a medium-range forecast, and even more so a long-range forecast of the

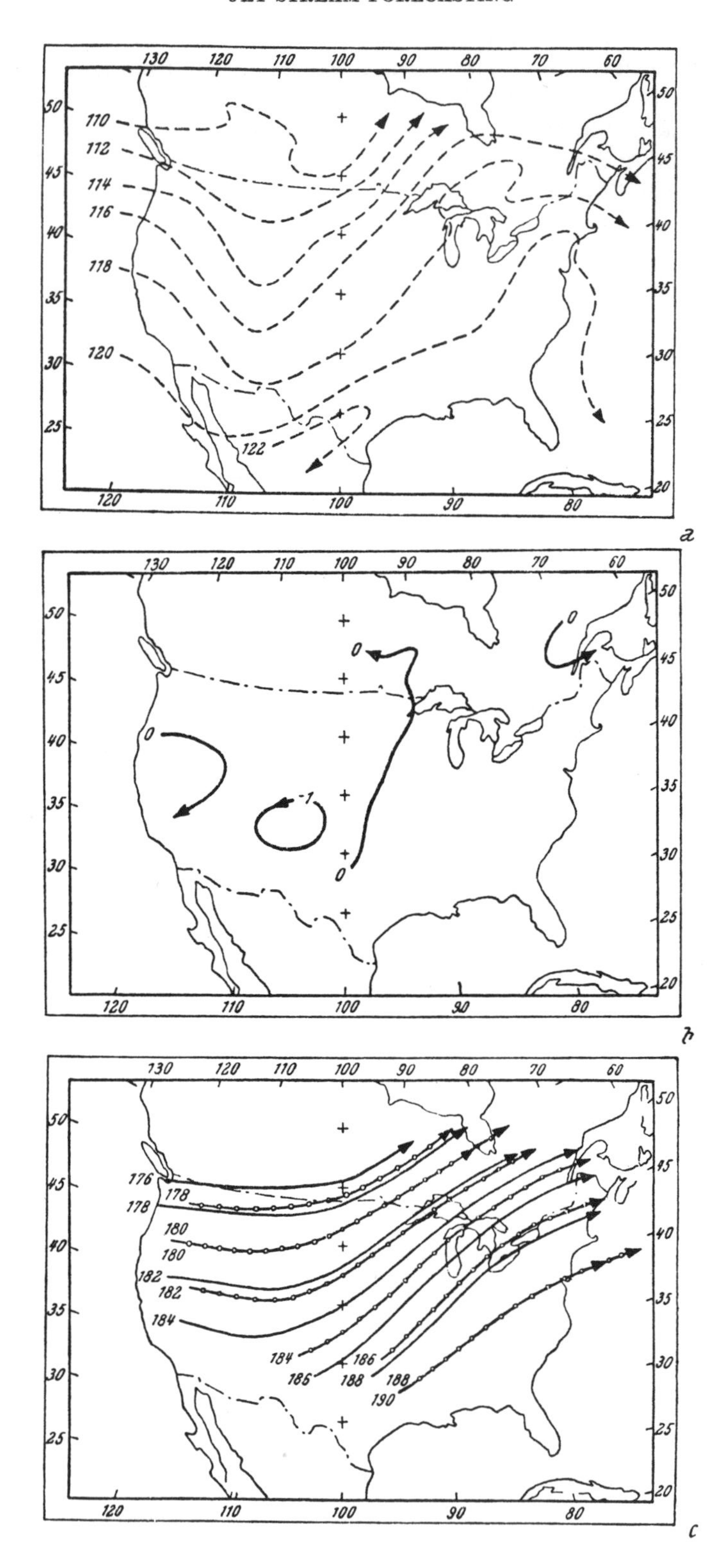
130 120 110 100 90 80 70 60
50 45 40 35 30 25 20
110
112
114
116
118
120
122
120 110 100 90 80
a
130 120 110 100 90 80 70 60
50 45 40 35 30 25 20
0
0
0
-1
0
120 110 100 90 80
b
130 120 110 100 90 80 70 60
50 45 40 35 30 25 20
176
178
178
180
180
182
182
184
184
186
186
188
188
190
120 110 100 90 80
c

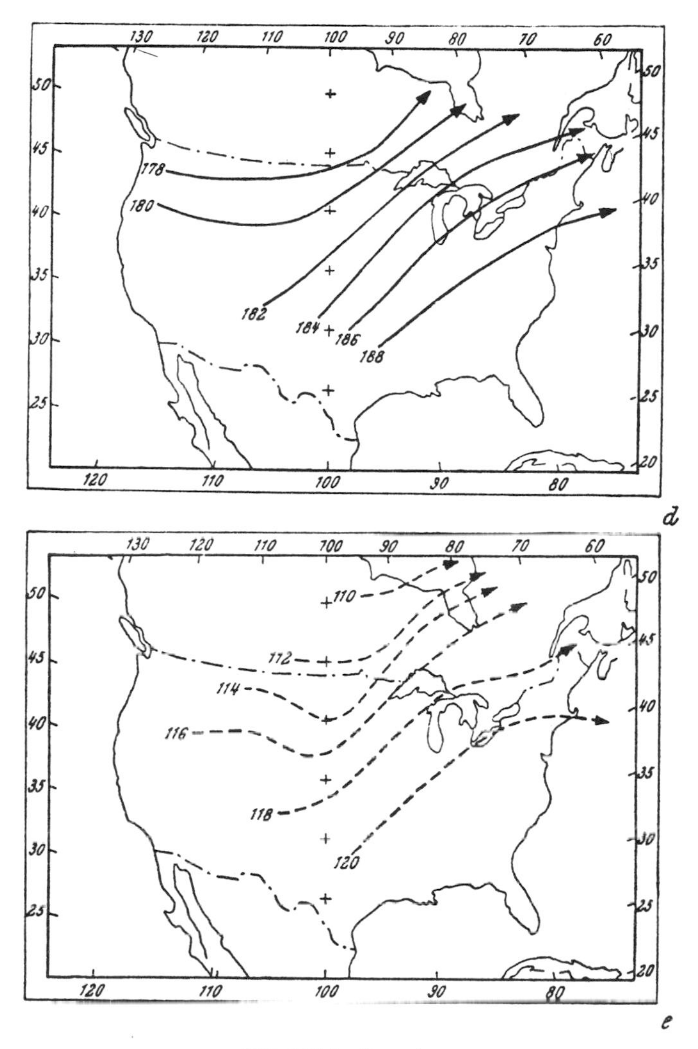

FIG. 5.21.1*a* through *e*.

FIG. 5.21.1.—Forecasting the 300-mb topography: (*a*) relative topography 300/500 mb, 15 February, 1954, 1500 GCT; (*b*) $\frac{1}{2}(z-\bar{z})$-field of 500 mb, 15 February, 1954, 1500 GCT; (*c*) $\bar{z}$-field and $\frac{4}{5}\ \bar{z}$-field, 500 mb, 15 February, 1954, 1500 GCT; (*d*) $\bar{F}$-field of the 500-mb surface, 15 February, 1954, 1500 GCT; (*e*) prognostic chart of the relative topography 300/500 mb, 16 February, 1954, 1500 GCT. (U.S. Air Weather Service, 1956*d*.)

jet streams, such as would be necessary for planning large-scale airborne operations, meet with considerable difficulties due to the complex structure of the jet stream. A detailed prediction to be utilized by the air weather services, and accurate for several days cannot be obtained by the means presently available to meteorological research, not even over continental areas. In the estimate of hemispheric mean values, the situation is a little more favorable, but even here the scientist still finds a large field for improvement.

In the following a few objective prediction methods will be discussed briefly.

5.2. THE PREDICTION OF THE WIND DIRECTION

If we accept the geostrophic approximation at least for the wind direction, the problem of forecasting the upper-level streamlines is reduced to the prediction of the absolute topography of constant pressure surfaces.

5.21. Numerical Prediction

It would be far beyond the scope of this book to attempt a survey, or even a summary, of the methods and problems of numerical weather prediction. Reference will be made, however, to treatises in various meteorological textbooks (Defant and Defant, 1958, Haltiner and Martin, 1957; Petterssen, 1956; Reuter, 1954) and to basic articles by Charney (1948; and Eliassen, 1949; Charney, Gilchrist, and Schuman, 1956), Fjørtoft (1952), Estoque (1956, 1957*a*, *b*), and other authors (Bolin and Newton, 1952; Deutscher Wetterdienst, 1957, Petterssen, Estoque, and Hughes, 1957.)

In several forecasting centers, as, for instance, in Washington, D.C., and in Offenbach/Maine (Germany), numerical forecasts are utilized in the routine synoptic service. Forecasts of the absolute topography of the 500-mb surface are prepared regularly.

Since the quality of the numerical predictions to a certain measure depends on the accuracy of the analysis of the diagnostic charts, efforts have been undertaken to make objective analyses, too (Bergthorsson, and Döös, 1955; Corby, 1961; Cressman, 1959; Döös, 1956; and Eaton, 1957). As far as the analysis of a topography and the geostrophic vorticity and its time variation computed from this topography are concerned, objective analysis methods computing the value at a grid point of the prediction area from a correlation with the values at surrounding stations proved to be feasible. If, however, the horizontal wind shear were to be considered in the contour distance by making a quasi-geostrophic approximation, the process of objective analysis becomes substantially more complicated. First one would have to determine the position of the jet axis, and, second, the contour distances would have to be modified according to the statistical results on horizontal wind shear (Chapter 4.122).

The present state of forecasting techniques justifies the assumption that, for the 500-mb surface which lies close to the level of non-divergence, reliable 24- and 48-hour forecasts are available. The problem of predicting the wind direction at jet-stream level reduces to the task of constructing a usable forecast of the 300-mb topography from an available forecast of the 500-mb level.

The prediction equations for a barotropic model atmosphere may be integrated graphically using a method developed by Fjørtoft (1952). Estoque (1956) extended this method to baroclinic models. A technique developed by the U.S. Air Weather Service (1956*d*) permits one to obtain an objective forecast of the 300-mb topography from the advection of the 300/500-mb thickness field, by adopting the Fjørtoft method.

For non-divergent isobaric motions the absolute geostrophic vorticity is a conservative quantity, which means

$$\partial Q_g/\partial t = -\mathbf{v}_g \cdot \nabla Q_g. \qquad 5.21\ (1)$$

Replacing the differential operator ∇ by a difference operator [see Eq. 3.247 (6)], one obtains

$$Q_g = -(4gm^2/fh'^2)(z-\bar{z})+f, \qquad 5.21\ (2)$$

where $\bar{z}=\frac{1}{4}(z_1+z_2+z_3+z_4)$ is the mean value of the geopotential heights at the surrounding four grid points, and z is the value at the center point.

According to the geostrophic wind equation, the 500-mb topography gives a measure of the geostrophic wind vector $\mathbf{v}_g$, a certain fraction of which is steering the wave disturbances in the upper troposphere, which show up in the relative topography 300/500 mb. Instead of the z-field, one uses the $\bar{z}$-field, however, in the computation of the geostrophic advection, because practical experience proved that the latter is more conservative than the former and thereby renders better results in the forecasts, due to the smoothing process to which it has been subjected in its calculation (Sanders and Kessler, 1955).

The field $(z-\bar{z})$ constitutes a measure of the rotation of the wind field, which (during non-divergent motions) also is a conservative quantity.

The $\bar{z}$-field may be most easily determined, by first adding graphically two copies, A and B, of the same 500-mb topography, one of which has been displaced by the distance $2h$ along the x-axis, thus obtaining $\frac{1}{2}(z_1+z_3)$. Then, the same chart is displaced along the y-direction by the distance $2h$, and by graphical addition to the other chart one arrives at $\frac{1}{2}(z_2+z_4)$. By graphical addition (and division by 2) of the two resulting charts one obtains the field $\bar{z}$. Graphical subtraction from z renders the field $(z-\bar{z})$.

During his first experiments Fjørtoft used a grid distance $h=600$ km. A larger grid distance of $h=1000$ km proved to give better results, however.

Experiments at the U.S. Air Weather Service (1956*d*) showed that one obtains usable 300-mb forecasts by advecting the relative topography 300/500 mb with 80 per cent of the $\bar{z}$-field obtained from the 500-mb surface, and by 50 per cent of the $(z-\bar{z})$-field of the same surface. These per cent values have been found empirically. They correspond to the experience that only a certain fraction of the thickness change is caused by purely advective processes. Nyberg (1949) finds, e.g., that the displacement rates of the 500-mb contour lines correspond to about 60 per cent of the wind velocities at this level. Part of the thickness change is caused by dynamic developments, i.e., by vertical motions and associated stretching or shrinking, and is given by the geometry of the relative topography, which contains the vertical change of the vorticity transport. This part is accounted for by the $(z-\bar{z})$-field. Thickness changes caused by non-adiabatic processes may play a certain role, but they cannot be considered here (Sutcliffe and Forsdyke, 1950).

The relative topography 300/500 mb which has been displaced in this fashion is added to the 500-mb prognostic chart; the result gives the 300-mb prognostic map. Figure 5.21.1 shows this process by means of an example. Figure 5.21.1*a* contains the relative topography 300/500 mb. As a first step the field $(z-\bar{z})$ is constructed in the manner described above; the contour lines are labeled, however, only with half their value (50 per cent). Figure 5.21.1*b* shows the resulting field $\frac{1}{2}(z-\bar{z})$. As a next step the $\bar{z}$-field of the 500-mb surface is analyzed in 250-ft intervals or in 125-m intervals; the contour lines, however, are labeled in 200-foot (100-m) intervals. Thereby a multiplication by $\frac{4}{5}$ (=80 per cent) is accomplished (Fig. 5.21.1*c*). Now one adds $\frac{1}{2}(z-\bar{z}) + (\frac{4}{5})\bar{z}=\bar{F}$; $\bar{F}$ is the field which describes the geostrophic advection of the relative topography 300/500 mb (Fig. 5.21.1*d*). The result of this advection process is shown in Figure 5.21.1*e*.

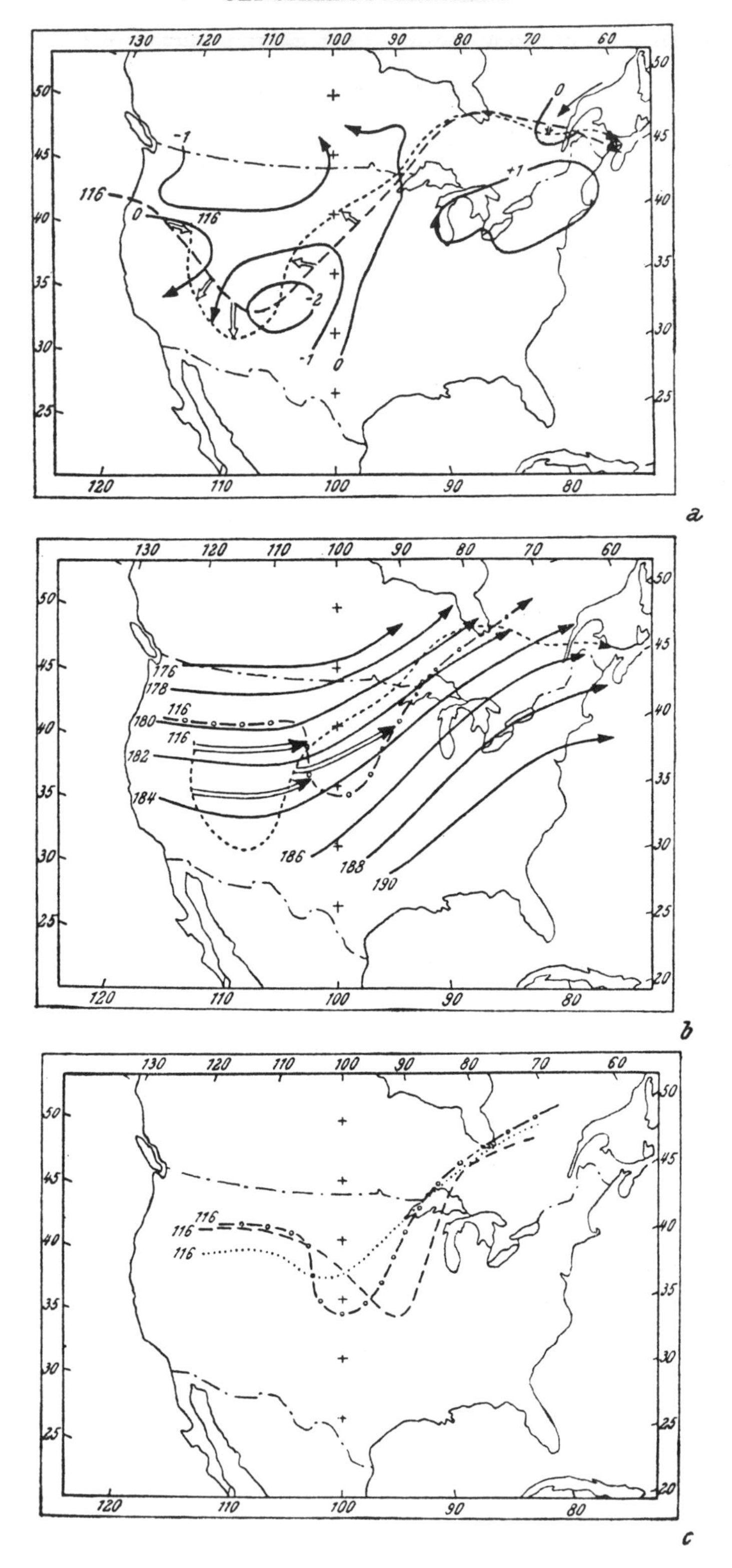
130 120 110 100 90 80 70 60
50 45 40 35 30 25
120 110 100 90 80
-1
116
0
116
0
-2
-1
0
+1
a
130 120 110 100 90 80 70 60
50 45 40 35 30 25 20
176
178
116
180
116
182
184
186
188
190
120 110 100 90 80
b
130 120 110 100 90 80 70 60
50 45 40 35 30 25 20
116
116
116
120 110 100 90 80
c

A somewhat better result is obtained when the $(z-\bar{z})$- and $\bar{z}$-advections are carried out separately in the sequence stated here, because the former of the two fields is more conservative than the latter. In Figure 5.21.2*a* the displacement of a contour line of the relative topography 300/500 mb in the field $(z-\bar{z})$ is indicated. In Figure 5.21.2*b* the contour line thus obtained is advected with $\frac{4}{5}$ of the geostrophic wind velocity of the 500-mb $\bar{z}$-field. Figure 5.21.2*c* finally, contains a comparison of the two methods of advection with the actually observed pattern of the relative topography.

Experiments with these two prediction methods rendered satisfactory results as long as the 500-mb forecast on which the 300-mb forecast had to be based was not erroneous itself.

5.22. Kinematic Extrapolation Techniques

5.221. Control-Line Method

F. Defant (1952; see Riehl, La Seur, *et al.*, 1952) and Wasko (1952) describe a method which allows one to extrapolate in time the change of an absolute topography on the basis of preceding changes that have taken place. The two authors have tested this method mainly with contour lines of the 500-mb surface; the technique may be adopted, however, for other quantities and fields, as for instance for the 300-mb surface and the layer of maximum wind (Reiter, 1957*c*, 1958*c*; Sherman, 1954).

In essence, the technique consists in following the movement, and change of movement, of characteristic points in the topography or in the LMW analysis from one map to the next. The movement of these points is traced by so-called control lines. The displacement $\Delta \mathbf{s}$ of the characteristic points from one map to the next is given by $\mathbf{C}\cdot\Delta t$, where $\mathbf{C}$ is the rate of displacement of the system, and Δt is the time interval between consecutive charts. If there are only two maps available for the extrapolation, one necessarily will have to assume that $\mathbf{C}$ will be constant during the whole time interval. This may, at times, lead to considerable errors in the forecast of speed and direction of motion of the characteristic point.

If three charts are available for the preparation of the prediction, one has to assume $\Delta\mathbf{C}/\Delta t$ to be constant; $\mathbf{C}$, however, may be variable. This assumption, too, may lead to erroneous forecasts (see Fig. 5.221). The quality of the forecast usually is not improved by considering synoptic analyses still farther back in time. Experience shows that the changes in acceleration of an isobar or contour pattern occur rather suddenly, perhaps between synoptic observation times. Because the interpolation between two observation times allows only the calculation of differences, and not of differentials, the changes of acceleration are expressed only as an average over the time interval Δt. This may, at times, lead to a wrong estimate of their true magnitude. This drawback cannot be remedied by consulting observations still farther back in time, because the changes of accelerations might not have been active then.

Fig. 5.21.2.—Forecasting the 300-mb topography: (*a*) $(z-\bar{z})$-field of the 500-mb surface (solid lines) and one isoline of the relative topography 300/500 mb, 15 February 1954, 1500 GCT (dashed) (the displacement of the latter during the 24-hour forecasting period results in the dotted line); (*b*) the dotted line of (*a*) is advected by the 500-mb $\bar{z}$-field (solid lines) at $\frac{4}{5}$ of its geostrophic value (dashed-dotted line); (*c*) comparison between the forecasting method given in Figure 5.21.1 (dotted) with the one described in Figure 5.21.2*b* (dashed-dotted), and with the actually observed relative topography 300/500 mb (dashed). (U.S. Air Weather Service, 1956*d*.)

More likely an improvement would be obtained if the last intermediate six-hour observation time were incorporated into the prediction, at least for a few stations, which take these observations. The inferiority of differences versus differentials cannot be eliminated completely, however.

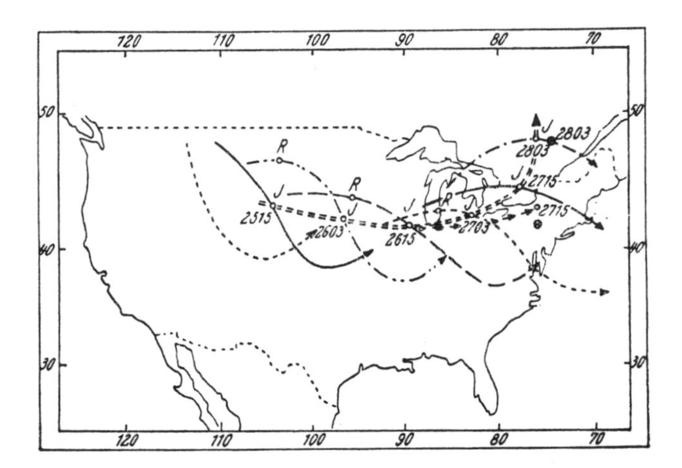

FIG. 5.221.—Control-line method of forecasting, 25 to 28 February, 1954: the track of the jet maximum is indicated by a double dashed line. The arrows and black dot give a 24-hour forecast by means of the control-line method, the crossed circles mark forecasts obtained with the "box" method. R = ridge.

A second limitation of the applicability of kinematic forecasts is already implicitly contained in the above: Although one may be able to forecast the dissolution of certain characteristic features of the pressure and flow pattern, a new formation of such features cannot be obtained from this method. So, e.g., from an originally straight flow this method cannot predict the formation of a wave, because if the velocity **C** of a characteristic point is indeterminate, the differences of **C** are indeterminate, too, and cannot suddenly assume real values.

For shorter periods of time, as are involved, e.g., in flight briefing, this method may, however, produce reasonably usable results. Naturally, for longer intervals of extrapolation the uncertainties in the forecast increase, because the assumption of a constant acceleration of the system becomes more unrealistic the longer the interval over which the forecast is to be made.

Figure 5.221 contains the example of a 24-hour forecast of the jet maximum by means of the control-line method (dashed line with arrows). In comparison with the actual position (displacement indicated by double dashed line), there is a discrepancy of about 200 km caused by a sudden change in the direction of the displacement, which became apparent between 26 February, 1500 GCT, and 27 February, 0300 GCT, which, however, had not been expressed in the prediction.

5.222. Kinematic Extrapolation Formulas

The variation of a quantity with time in a co-ordinate system fixed to the rotating earth is given by the operator

$$d/dt = \partial/\partial t + \mathbf{v}\cdot\nabla. \qquad 5.222\ (1)$$

With respect to a co-ordinate system moving with the velocity **C** we obtain

$$d/dt = \delta/\delta t + (\mathbf{v} - \mathbf{C}) \cdot \nabla. \qquad 5.222\ (2)$$

$\delta/\delta t$ indicates the local change in the moving co-ordinate system. Subtraction of the two equations from each other renders the operator

$$\delta/\delta t = \partial/\partial t + \mathbf{C} \cdot \nabla. \qquad 5.222\ (3)$$

This operator may be applied to the equations of contour lines and characteristic points of a topography, and, in doing so, one obtains expressions which give the rate of displacement **C** (Petterssen, 1956). Eq. 5.222 (3) may be simplified by assuming the x-direction to be parallel to the direction of displacement (which, of course, may be arbitrary). If the motion of a characteristic point is to be investigated, one equates $\delta/\delta t = 0$.

For a contour line ($z = \text{const}$) we obtain

$$C = -(\partial z/\partial t)/(\partial z/\partial x), \qquad 5.222\ (4)$$

for an isallohypse (line of equal height change, $\partial z/\partial t = \text{const}$)

$$C = -(\partial^2 z/\partial t^2)/(\partial^2 z/\partial x\, \partial t), \qquad 5.222\ (5)$$

for a trough or ridge ($\partial z/\partial x = 0$)

$$C = -(\partial^2 z/\partial x\, \partial t)/(\partial^2 z/\partial x^2), \qquad 5.222\ (6)$$

where $\partial^2 z/\partial x^2 > 0$ in troughs, and < 0 in ridges.

Substituting $\partial z/\partial x$ by the geostrophic wind component v_g one obtains analogous extrapolation equations, which now are based only on the first derivative of the wind velocity, and which are less sensitive to details in the analysis when used with a *dependable* wind analysis (Mulky, 1955).

For centers of high- and low-pressure areas one obtains

$$\begin{aligned} C_x &= -(\partial^2 z/\partial x\, \partial t)/(\partial^2 z/\partial x^2) \\ C_y &= -(\partial^2 z/\partial y\, \partial t)/(\partial^2 z/\partial y^2) \end{aligned} \qquad 5.222\ (7)$$

$\partial^2 z/\partial x^2 > 0$, $\partial^2 z/\partial y^2 > 0$ in cyclones, < 0 in anticyclones. x- and y-axes do not necessarily have to be orthogonal.

Because of the 12-hour intervals between synoptic map times of upper-air charts, the tendencies $\partial/\partial t$ may be determined not very adequately. The practical applicability of these extrapolation formulas, therefore, remains limited. Surface charts with their three-hour tendencies render more favorable results. Furthermore one has to consider that the *instantaneous* tendencies enter into the above equations. Because the changes of geopotential heights are available only as mean values over the last 12 hours, the rate of displacement **C** can be determined only for the center point of this time interval, i.e., 6 hours prior to the last upper-air map. Thus, much of its prognostic value is lost.

Several methods of forecasting the rate of displacement of troughs and ridges at the 500-mb level have been tested critically at the University of Chicago (1955, 1956). It is apparent that this level reflects the steering current better than does the 300-mb level (Johannessen and Cressman, 1952; California Institute of Technology, 1948). The best results, especially for the movement of troughs, are obtained from Petterssen's wave Eq. 3.251 (8) (Johannessen and Cressman, 1952). Next in quality of forecasting accuracy follow: Rossby's wave Eq. 3.251 (4) (Clapp, 1944; Cressman, 1949), the "box" method of geostrophic advection (see Chapter 5.32), and the kinematic extrapolation Eq. 5.222 (6). Each of these methods renders better results than linear extrapolation and, therefore, is of advantage in predicting the motion of waves in the upper-flow pattern. CAV trajectories and Fjørtoft's method of graphical integration fell behind in quality when compared with the above methods; for CAV trajectories the cause for this may be sought in the fact that $Q = \text{const}$ is valid on isentropic surfaces rather than on isobaric surfaces (Calstead, 1953).

Forecasting experiments in Norway (Breistein and Smebye, 1952) utilizing an extrapolation equation which considers the conservation of vorticity produced an average prediction error of 4° of longitude at 52° latitude. On the average, the result was better for troughs than for ridges.

5.223. Anomalous Changes of the Relative Topography 300/500 mb

In the U.S. Air Weather Service (1956*d*) a forecasting procedure has been tried for the 300-mb topography which takes into account the non-advective thickness changes between 300 and 500 mb, which are caused by warming or cooling. Experiments with this method gave satisfactory results.

First the relative topography 300/500 mb is advected with 50 per cent of the geostrophic wind speed at the 500-mb level. That only a fraction of the geostrophic wind is used for this advection corresponds to the tendency of the atmosphere to compensate part of the advective temperature changes by non-advective warming or cooling, mainly brought about by vertical motions. A systematic deviation of the forecast thicknesses from the observed values appears especially in areas with a southerly component of flow: here, the predicted thickness change may be too large by up to 250 ft. In these areas strong ascending motions are responsible for excessive cooling. Anomalies of the opposite sign—up to 300 ft—are mostly associated with northerly components of flow and indicate sinking motions. If these anomalous thickness changes (*ca.* +200 ft in areas with flow from the north, −200 ft in areas with flow from the south) are added to the ones obtained from geostrophic advection, one usually obtains better agreement with the actual changes of the relative topography than by using geostrophic advection only.

5.224. Extrapolation by Geometric Relationships

The following method for predicting the relative topography 300/500 mb has also been developed by the U.S. Air Weather Service (1956*d*): The relative topography is superimposed upon the absolute topography of the 500-mb surface of the same synoptic map time. Corresponding intersections of relative with absolute contour lines at *characteristic points* of the absolute topography (e.g., in troughs and ridges) are transferred to the 500-mb prognostic chart. From these points, then, the forecast relative topography is constructed. The line of equal thickness, which intersects a certain contour line of the 500-mb surface in a trough, will, therefore, intersect the same contour line in the new trough position on the prognostic chart. The relative topography 300/500 mb, thus obtained, may be added graphically to the 500-mb prognostic chart to obtain the 300-mb forecast.

None of the forecasting methods given above for the 300-mb surface will be reliable under all circumstances. The value of the forecast will be questionable especially when strong developments, e.g., intensification or filling of cyclones, are to be expected during the forecast interval. Each prediction deteriorates in dependability with increasing time interval over which the forecast has to be made. In the air weather services usually 12-hour upper-air maps are available, so that the extrapolation period hardly ever exceeds 20 hours, except for intercontinental flights over areas with scarce observations and, therefore, with poor forecasts. For shorter time intervals the methods described above should give usable estimates of the upper-flow patterns to be expected.

5.23. The Use of Continuity Diagrams

The kind of continuity diagrams described in Chapter 3.26 permits an extrapolation of trough and ridge positions. Although a complete picture of the respective topography (500 or 300 mb) cannot be obtained from this, they give valuable indications in areas of sparse observations and thus help to bridge the gap, at least to a certain extent, which is left by the uncertainties in these regions of the methods described in Chapter 5.22.

The extrapolation of the wave positions in the continuity diagrams is done after climatological mean values. In this, the group velocity effect will have to be considered especially. The meridional circulation diagram (Reiter, 1958*a*) gives useful indications of the mean wind speed components in a south-north direction, which are particularly valuable for Transatlantic and Transpacific flight planning. It may be used, therefore, as an aid in calculating optimum flight tracks. Unfortunately, the magnitude of the zonal wind component cannot be obtained from these diagrams. In order to estimate these over areas with sparse observations, one will have to consider time sections, as well as geostrophic and gradient wind computations.

5.3 PREDICTIONS OF THE VELOCITY FIELD

As has already been mentioned at the beginning of this section, geostrophic wind computations from the prognostic charts render rather unsatisfactory results because of certain smoothing tendencies and because of the important role of the ageostrophic components of flow. For these reasons no numerical prediction scheme could be developed so far for the wind velocity field which would match the quality of kinematic extrapolation techniques. In the following, several of these forecasting techniques will be discussed in detail.

5.31. Computation of the Rate of Displacement of Isotachs Using Kinematic Methods

Riehl and Jenista (1952; Riehl, La Seur, *et al.*, 1952; Sherman and Riehl, 1953) devised a method which seems suited to calculating the rate of displacement of an isotach field. It is essentially based upon the kinematic formulas given in Chapter 5.222.

Along the streamlines of a frictionless flow the expression

$$dV/dt = \partial V/\partial t + V\cdot\partial V/\partial s = -g(\partial z/\partial s)_p. \qquad 5.31\ (1)$$

is valid. The rate of displacement C of an isotach (V=const) is given according to Eq. 5.222 (3) by

$$C_i = -(\partial V/\partial t)/(\partial V/\partial s). \qquad 5.31\ (2)$$

Therefore,

$$(V - C_i)\ \partial V/\partial s = -g\ \partial z/\partial s$$

and

$$C_i = V + g[(\partial z/\partial s)/(\partial V/\partial s)] = V + g(\Delta z/\Delta V)_s. \qquad 5.31\ (3)$$

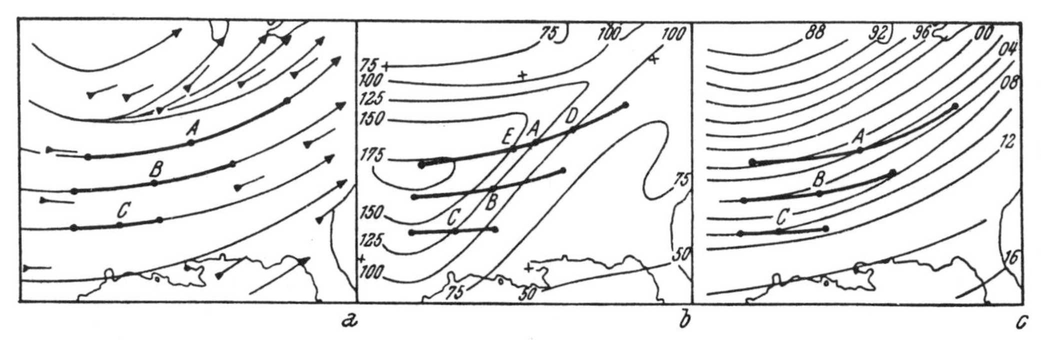

FIG. 5.31.—Computation of the rate of displacement of isotachs: (*a*) streamlines (300 mb), 2 November, 1951, 0400 GCT; (*b*) isotachs in knots (300 mb), same map time (superimposed are streamlines through points *A* to *E*); (*c*) 300-mb topography, analyzed in 200-ft contour intervals, with superimposed streamlines through points *A*, *B*, and *C*. (Riehl and Jenista, 1952.)

For a wind speed maximum or minimum we obtain, according to Eq. 5.222 (7),

$$C_m = -(\partial^2/\partial s\ \partial t)/(\partial^2/\partial s^2),$$

or,

$$C_m = V + g(\Delta^2 z/\Delta^2 V). \qquad 5.31\ (4)$$

Equation 5.31 (4) has not been tried by Riehl. Equation 5.31 (3) gave better results on the average than a geostrophic wind computation from the 300-mb prognostic chart.

The forecasting procedure is as follows: A streamline and isotach analysis of the 300-mb surface as well as the absolute topography of 300 mb, analyzed in 200-ft contour intervals, are assumed to be available (Fig. 5.31). The rate of isotach displacement will be calculated in the points *A* through *E*.

As an example, the calculations performed in point *A* will be discussed here: Let $\Delta s/2$ be the streamline segment between the point *A* on the 125-knot isotach and that point upstream of *A* in which streamlines and contour lines run parallel to each other (Fig. 5.31*c*). This point will be located in the jet maximum (Fig. 5.31*b*). A point of equal distance measured downstream renders the complete interval Δs. The decay of wind speed along Δs amounts to $\Delta V = 85 - 175 = -90$ knots. Δz measured over the same distance is $+350$ ft (Fig. 5.31*c*). Therefore $g \cdot \Delta z/\Delta V \cong -50$ knots and $C = 75$ knots. Analogously we obtain a speed $C = 95$ knots at point *B*, and 95 knots at point *C*, 55 knots at *D*, and 105 knots at *E*.

In the case presented here the isotach field will move faster in the north than in the south, and, furthermore, the gradient of wind speed will increase in the north.

A streamline prediction may be obtained from the forecast of the 300-mb topography (see Chapter 5.2). From the present and the predicted streamlines one may compute the trajectories. Petterssen (1956) gives a usable technique for this. The isotachs, then, are advected along these trajectories at a rate which is given by the above calculations. Thus, the prognostic chart of the wind velocity field is obtained and now has to be tested for its consistency with the 300-mb forecast chart.

Since the method described above is nothing but a kinematic extrapolation, no new formations of velocity maxima or of new isotachs can be forecast. If, however, the rear end of a jet maximum moves slower than the front end, one may assume in most cases an intensification of the maximum, and take this into consideration in the analysis.

Experiments showed that on the average the error was larger in the forecasts of wind speeds than of wind direction. In about 60 per cent of the cases the prognostic error in the speed was, however, smaller than 25 per cent. The larger errors in the speed forecasts stem from extrapolations on the cyclonic side of jet-stream maxima, where a small error in the position of the axis may lead to large differences between forecast and observed wind speeds, due to the large horizontal wind shears in this region.

5.32. Geostrophic Advection Technique ("Box" Method)

The "box" method, which has already been tested successfully in the prediction of hurricane tracks (Riehl, Haggard, and Sanborn, 1956) and of troughs in the upper westerlies (University of Chicago, 1956), is based upon the assumption—which also has been applied in some of the methods described above—that jet maxima are advected with a certain percentage of the mean geostrophic wind of their surrounding. This geostrophic steering current may be found by measuring the average pressure gradient along the sides of a rectangle ("box") whose center is located in the jet maximum.

For jet-stream forecasting a rectangle as shown in Figure 5.32.1 proved to be most appropriate (Reiter, 1957*c*, 1958*c*). The side lengths have been chosen empirically to be 15° of latitude and 20° of longitude (for forecasts over the United States) so that on the one hand the area of the "box" is large enough to eliminate the influence of the wave disturbance and of the jet maximum itself upon the steering current. On the other hand, however, the area should not be too large, so that the basic current which is effective for this region and this particular wave disturbance only is retained. In this forecasting technique the grid distance, therefore, is a function of the scale of the phenomenon to be predicted.

In Figure 5.32.2 the displacement of the jet maximum in a meridional direction has been correlated with the zonal differences in contour heights, measured along the sides of the "box." The ordinate contains

$$\Sigma \Delta_z h = (h_3 - h_1) + (h_5 - h_4) + (h_8 - h_6). \qquad 5.32\ (1)$$

The subscripts refer to the points in Figure 5.32.1. The abscissa of Figure 5.32.2 gives the rate of displacement of jet maxima in degrees of latitude per day. The regression equation for this displacement of the maxima in a meridional direction (in degrees of latitude per day) is

$$D_m = 0.1\ \Sigma \Delta_z h + 3. \qquad 5.32\ (2)$$

Analogously, for the displacement in a zonal direction a correlation with the meridional differences in contour heights

$$\Sigma \Delta_m h = (h_6 - h_1) + (h_7 - h_2) + (h_8 - h_3) \qquad 5.32\ (3)$$

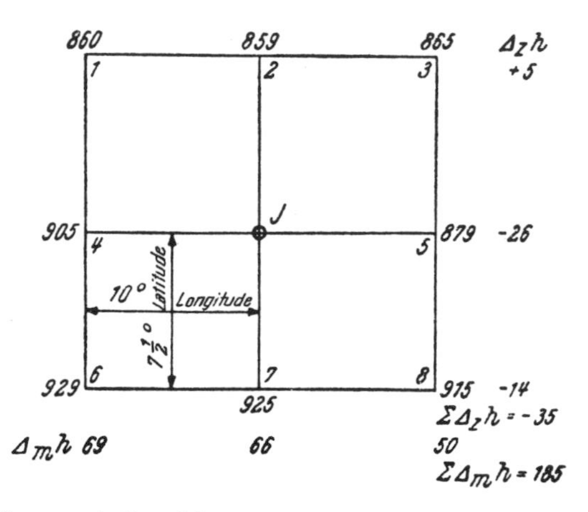

FIG. 5.32.1.—Grid for the computation of the geostrophic advection of jet maxima. The numbers along the margins of the rectangle represent heights of the 300-mb surface in decameters.

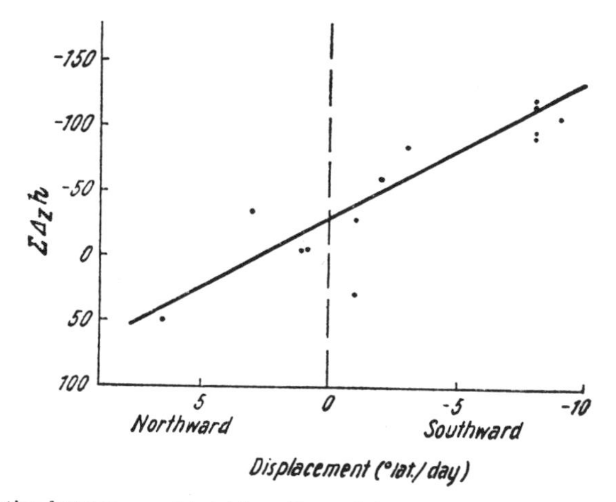

FIG. 5.32.2.—Correlation between zonal height gradient of the 300-mb topography and the displacement of jet maxima in a meridional direction during the subsequent 24 hours.

has been sought, but no significant relationship could be found. The cases which have been investigated only showed a scattering of $\pm 2°$ about the mean value of the speed of short waves given in Table 3.241 (*ca.* 12° of longitude per day). The climatological mean value of the eastward displacement, therefore, will in general give satisfactory forecasting results, because an error of 2° cannot be considered serious in view of the fact that the longitude of the position of a jet maximum cannot be determined exactly with the present-day observational methods. This error bears hardly any significance for the forecasting of zonally oriented jet streams, because $\partial u/\partial y \gg \partial u/\partial x$. During low-index stages, however, when the flow pattern shows great amplitudes, even $\partial u/\partial x$ may assume large values. Especially in these cases, the rate of eastward propagation of waves may deviate considerably from climatological mean values. Special treatment will have to be given to such weather situations when making an upper-wind forecast.

A noteworthy fact may be seen from Figure 5.32.3. Along the ordinate values of the ratio $\Sigma\Delta_z h/\Sigma\Delta_m h$ are plotted, the abscissa contains the total distance D of the displacement within 24 hours (in degrees of latitude per day), without regard to the direction of the movement. The scatter of the data points in this diagram is surprisingly small. For the United States, where 15° of latitude are approximately equivalent to 20° of longitude $\Sigma\Delta_z h/\Sigma\Delta_m h$ corresponds to the tangent of the direction of the geostrophic steering current. Jet maxima, therefore, migrate fastest when coming from the northwest ($\Sigma\Delta_z h/\Sigma\Delta_m h = -1$). They decrease their rate of propagation considerably when traveling around the long-wave trough. The observational data upon which Figure 5.32.3 is based, have not been very abundant. Further studies would be necessary to prove the general validity of these results

From a combination of D_m [Eq. 5.32 (2)] and D (Fig. 5.32.3), the position of the

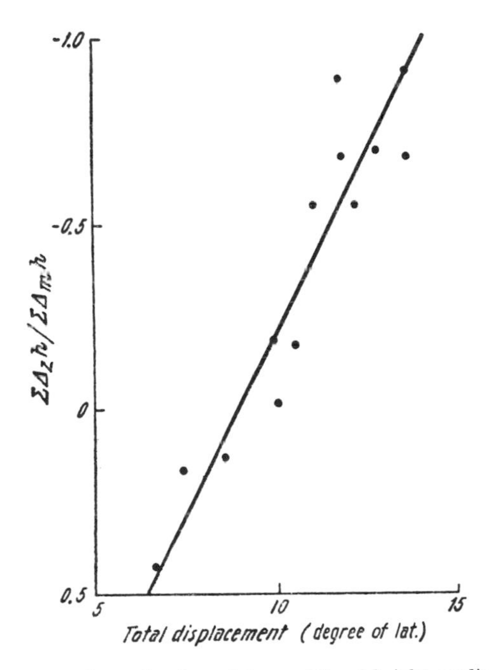

FIG. 5.32.3.—Correlation between the ratio of zonal to meridional height gradient and the total displacement of the jet maximum during the subsequent 24 hours, irrespective of the direction of this displacement.

jet maximum may be forecast for the next 24 hours: First a line parallel to latitude circles, giving the meridional displacement, is drawn at a distance D_m from the present position of the jet maximum. Then the distance D is measured off from the present jet maximum with the aid of a pair of dividers. The intersection with the D_m line gives the forecast position of the maximum.

This forecasting procedure fails whenever $D_m > 7.5°$ of latitude per day, because this would mean $D < D_m$. The occurrence of such cases will have to be expected.

Figure 5.221 shows two forecasts which have been made by means of the "box" method: on 26 February 1954, 1500 GCT, and on 27 February, 0300 GCT. Each prediction is indicated in the diagram by a circled cross. While the forecast for 27 February, 1500 GCT, turns out to be poorer than the one obtained from the control-line method, the prediction for 28 February, 0300 GCT, shows remarkable accuracy, even though during the 24 hours preceding the verification time the track of the jet maximum changed its curvature.

5.33. The Control-Line Method and the Prediction of the Layer of Maximum Wind

The main problem in a good jet-stream forecast rests with the reliable determination of the position of the jet axis. Relatively small displacements in the position of this axis may lead to large errors in the forecast of wind speeds, because of the large horizontal wind shears present in this region.

The basic principles of the control-line method have been discussed already in Chapter 5.221. Two examples of the displacement of jet maxima and of trough and ridge crests have also been given (Fig. 5.221). The deformation of the jet axis during the next 24 hours in general may be forecast rather satisfactorily by this method. An additional prediction of the intensity changes of the jet maximum and of the parameters determining the layer of maximum wind, therefore, would describe the three-dimensional wind field during the time interval of the forecast.

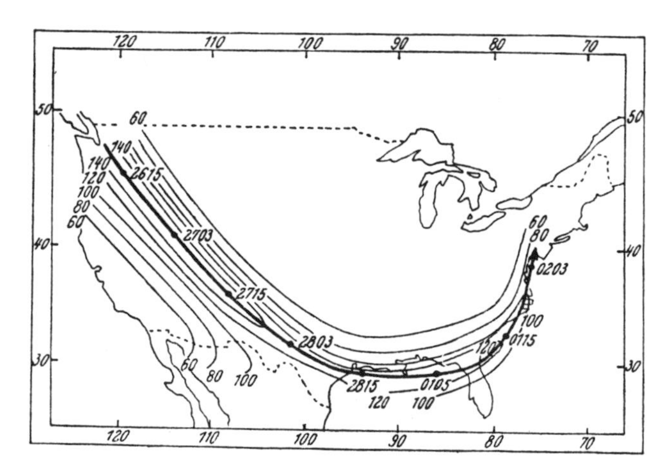

Fig. 5.33.—Space-time section of the isotachs of the LMW (knots). The heavy line indicates the track of the jet maximum between 26 February and 2 March, 1954. The analysis shows the conditions of wind shear at both sides of the jet axis, measured along a line normal to the jet axis at the location of the jet maximum.

Figure 5.33 contains a space-time section of wind speeds, constructed through a jet maximum which traveled around a long-wave trough between 26 February and 2 March, 1954. It is easy to see from this diagram that the wind speed in the jet center as well as the horizontal shear on the cyclonic side remained nearly constant during the whole period of time. The small decay of center speeds would hardly affect a 24-hour forecast. The changes of shear on the anticyclonic side, which become especially apparent on 28 February, are due to a merger of the polar-front jet with the subtropical jet, which frequently takes place in this area, and which, therefore, may be properly considered in a high-level wind forecast. If one assumed the jet-stream intensity to be constant over 24 hours, the average error in the estimate of wind speeds would hardly even exceed 10 per cent. (The somewhat stronger decay in wind speeds near the east coast of the United States is not very well documented by observations.)

Space-time sections for the height of the layer of maximum wind, as well as for its thickness, also reveal a remarkable tendency for conservation of these parameters near the jet center. Therefore, a forecast of the three-dimensional wind field which takes advantage of this conservation tendency has a great probability of verification. The prediction of these parameters, and also of the configuration of the jet axis, should be tested for consistency against the 300-mb contours.

In a procedure developed by the United States Air Weather Service (1956*d*) the 24-hour height changes of the *level* of maximum wind are extrapolated, as well as the pattern of isolines of vertical wind shear above and below jet-stream level. The forecast is checked against the 300-mb forecast. Harmantas and Simplicio (1958) recommend the calculation of the vertical wind shear from the forecasts of the relative topographies 300/500 mb and 200/300 mb. By means of these wind shears the wind speeds at flight level could be extrapolated from the conditions at the 300-mb level.

With the aid of LMW forecasts, and in consideration of the vertical structure of the LMW, wind forecasts may be obtained for stratospheric levels. This is of particular importance to jet air traffic. Generally it will have to be expected that the quality of the forecasts decreases with the distance of the respective level from the 300-mb surface (Sutcliffe and Sawyer, 1954), but since wind speeds usually are weaker at higher levels, there the per cent errors in forecasts are of less importance in flight planning.

6

JET STREAMS AND WEATHER

6.1. CYCLONE MODELS

"Weather" at a certain place and at a certain time is the result of the prevailing *state of the atmosphere* and the *motions of the atmosphere.* The atmospheric state is given by the air mass characteristics which are attached to a body of air covering a wide region and which are more or less homogeneously distributed therein. Especially in the meteorology of the thirties (Schinze and Siegel, 1943) there was an attempt to solve the problems of weather analysis and forecasting by considering the various air mass properties. The efforts of research were increasingly directed to the establishment of an atmospheric circulation model to demonstrate and to explain the atmospheric weather sequence satisfactorily. The Norwegian polar-front theory may be considered the climax of this direction of meteorological research. Its main emphasis was placed upon the more or less well-defined boundary surface between air masses of different nature. In this theory relatively much consideration has already been given to the second of the two aspects mentioned above—to atmospheric *motions.*

6.11. The Polar-Front Theory

It would go far beyond the scope of this book if we were to describe the details and the historic development of this theory. Some of the original literature (Bjerknes and Solberg, 1921) as well as treatises in various meteorological textbooks shall be pointed out, however (Defant and Defant, 1958; Godske, *et al.*, 1957; Haltiner and Martin, 1957; Hann and Süring, 1939; Malone, 1951; Petterssen, 1956).

The cyclone model of the Norwegian meteorological school essentially consists of two bodies of air with different temperatures, which meet each other in a strongly baroclinic zone—the "front."[1] The inclination of this boundary surface or boundary zone is given approximately by Margules' equation

$$\tan \varepsilon = \frac{f}{g} \cdot \frac{(\rho V_g - \rho' V_g')}{\rho - \rho'}. \qquad 6.11\ (1)$$

From this equation it follows that a boundary surface of a certain slope is stable only if there is a wind velocity gradient normal to this surface such that the warm air moves eastward relative to the cold air.

According to the polar-front theory, it is now assumed that perturbation components in the wind field acting normal to the frontal surface cause a deformation of the front, which shows an unstable character and which amplifies through the stage of a wave disturbance into a cyclone and finally—through an occlusion process—leads to a closed vortex.

[1] This expression was probably coined by Bjerknes and Solberg under the impression of the events of World War I.

This theory contributed substantially to a clear illustration of the weather sequence; it has, however, impeded meteorological research inasmuch as the main emphasis was placed upon processes in the atmospheric layers near the ground, and the exploration of the flow patterns of the upper atmosphere has been somewhat slighted. Furthermore, the usage of some of the terms, especially of the term "front," harbored the temptation to transfer subconsciously the characteristics of these terms from the field in which they had been applied originally to the field of meteorology. So it could be shown—as will be proved later—that the "front" in the jet-stream region is not a physical boundary surface between two different air masses (Flohn, 1958*b*).

The difficulties of the polar-front theory are easy to perceive. Let us assume that near the ground a perturbation component has developed in the flow of warm air, initiating the formation of a warm sector. This perturbation would cause the warm air masses to move against the cold air, forming an indentation toward the north in the frontal surface. This process, however, would cause a *convergence of flow*, which, in turn, would result in a *pressure rise*. Cyclogenesis, on the other hand, is characterized by *pressure falls*. The pressure rise which is to be expected from the convergence of flow, thus, would counteract the disturbance, it would have a damping influence and would start frontolysis. In reality, however, we observe the development of a cyclonic vortex together with surface pressure falls. The reasoning, that the warm air flowing northward replaces cold air and, because of its lesser density, causes pressure falls at the ground, cannot disprove the objection that the *start* of the wave disturbance would be characterized by convergence and pressure rises (see also Hollmann, 1953; Raethjen, 1949).

The density differences between warm and cold air would hardly suffice to explain the strong pressure falls preceding the development of a frontal cyclone, even before marked components of wind velocity normal to the frontal surface are observed in the atmospheric layers near the ground. One, therefore, is forced to the conclusion that the *cyclogenetic properties of surface pressure falls are caused by processes at higher levels*. Thus, cyclogenesis becomes a baroclinic problem in which the wind field is a function of height. Low-level convergence is superimposed by upper divergence, which, again, shows its maximum values in the jet-stream region. Baroclinicity as a prerequisite for cyclogenesis is also the reason why numerical forecasts based upon *barotropic* models describe the cyclogenetic processes only poorly (Bjerknes, 1954; Bjerknes and Holmboe, 1944; Hinkelmann, 1956; Hollmann, 1953; Reuter, 1955). Considerations of this kind (see also Bjerknes, 1951*a*) lead to a revision of the polar-front theory, which now in its amended form could be called the "vorticity-advection theory."

Besides all this, in practical synoptic experience departures from the normal weather sequence are frequently observed which cannot be explained by the Norwegian cyclone model, as for instance wide-spread precipitation in the warm sector, or far from any front. It turns out that the cause for these observations also will have to be sought in the upper-flow pattern and its divergence distribution (Dahler, 1954). The significance of air masses and fronts, thus, in modern meteorology recedes more and more into the background, being replaced by the consideration of the continuous fields of pressure and temperature, which contain wide, sometimes diffuse, baroclinic zones that are of decisive influence upon the weather sequence (Reed, 1957*a*).

6.12. The Vorticity-Advection Theory

6.121. Vorticity and Divergence—Their Influence on Weather Patterns

The vorticity-advection theory emanates from the vorticity equation, 1.233 (7). In most cases the assumption of *isobaric* motions will suffice as a first approximation in considering cyclogenesis and anticyclogenesis so that the vorticity equation may be used in its simple form 1.233 (6), neglecting the terms for vertical motion. This equation states that the relative decrease of absolute vorticity of an air particle along a streamline is equal to the horizontal divergence of the flow.

$$\frac{1}{Q}\frac{dQ}{dt} = -D. \qquad 6.121\ (1)$$

In many cases, however, the terms of the vorticity equation which are caused by vertical vorticity advection and by transformation of horizontal into vertical vorticity, and which have been neglected here, will be important for cyclogenesis (see Chapter 4.221; Estoque, 1955; Newton, 1954; Raethjen, 1953*b*; Reed, 1951; Sherman, 1953). In these cases, therefore, the complete vorticity equation 1.233 (7) will have to be used (Sawyer, 1958; Staley, 1960; Van Mieghem, 1956*a*).

According to the above equation, the cyclogenetic influence of vorticity advection would be more pronounced with an equal vorticity gradient along a streamline, the smaller the absolute value of vorticity. This may serve as an explanation for the observation that strongest and most frequent cyclogenesis along the polar-front jet occurs, on the average, where its position has shifted to relatively low latitudes (see Petterssen, 1950). On the anticyclonic side of a jet maximum one might expect a more intense divergence field, since the absolute vorticity in this area is close to zero. On the other hand, however, in this area $\mathbf{v} \cdot \nabla Q$ is small, or even zero, so that Eq. 6.121 (1) assumes an undetermined form in this region whose value could be determined by further differentiation. It also has to be assumed that the vertical terms of the vorticity equation neglected in 6.121 (1) may be of relatively great importance upon the development of the divergence pattern in this region.

Schematically, one may distinguish among four sectors around a jet maximum which are more or less pronounced, depending on the predominance of curvature or shearing vorticity. Let us first assume straight flow conditions (curvature vorticity equal to zero). In this case conditions are rather simple. Figure 4.122.3 shows the divergence resulting from vorticity advection [Eq. 6.121 (1)]. The polar-front theory on the formation of cyclone families stands in good agreement with this upper-flow model (see Bleeker, 1949, 1950; Flohn, 1959*a*).

The weather patterns at the earth's surface follow the same scheme that has been devised by the Norwegian school. The consideration of the vorticity advection in the upper current, however, solves the problem of the phase difference between incipient wave disturbance and pressure tendencies with which the polar-front theory had great difficulties. The primary event, now, is the *upper divergence* in the left forward and in the right rear quadrants of a jet maximum. This upper divergence brings about the pressure falls near the ground, which, in turn, are the prerequisites for an incipient wave disturbance at the surface front, and for low-level convergence and cyclogenesis.

Whether cyclogenesis actually occurs, i.e., whether a *frontal cyclone* with closed isobars appears, depends on several circumstances which may not be fulfilled every time. *Therefore, not every jet stream is accompanied by a cyclone; each cyclone, however, is attached to a jet stream which is continuously changed by the life cycle of the cyclone* (Teweles, 1954; Verderman, 1954).

If a cyclonic vortex is to develop near the ground from an initially undisturbed flow, the following will have to be considered: In a relatively small region (order of magnitude 10^6 km^2) near the ground a concentration of cyclonic vorticity is observed, which is constantly consumed by surface friction, and which, in the case of a deepening cyclone, constantly has to be replenished (Starr, 1953*b*). This might be accomplished by air masses with originally weak cyclonic vorticity being entrained near the ground into the influence region of the forming cyclone, thus strengthening the cyclonic rotation on the one hand by import of vorticity and on the other hand by convergence of flow according to 6.121 (1). Since these air masses would have to travel a relatively large distance in the friction layer near the ground in order to reach the influence region of the cyclone, thus giving off the larger part of their vorticity to the ground, one can hardly expect the cyclogenesis initiated by the upper divergence to be maintained or even intensified by the low-level convergence that begins to develop. Therefore the model set up for the polar-front theory cannot satisfy the actual conditions with this respect.

In order to explain the consumption of positive vorticity and, furthermore, its increase in a deepening cyclone, we will have to assume that a sufficient supply of cyclonic vorticity is transported from the convergence areas in the upper current toward the ground (Fisher, 1956; Spar, 1956; Spar *et al.*, 1955). This, in fact, agrees with the synoptic conditions: Strong cyclonic curvature of isobars is observed on the surface weather map within the sinking cold air, while in the warm sector the isobars are nearly straight. As Danielsen (1959) was able to show, the descending air masses, in following an isentropic surface, come from high (at times even stratospheric) levels. Part of their cyclonic vorticity, though, is lost by horizontal divergence due to conservation of potential vorticity [Eq. 1.235 (4)], when air masses spread out near the ground and simultaneously stabilize (Austin, 1954; Reed and Sanders, 1953). There are also, however, atmospheric layers in which a vertical gradient of sinking velocity is observed in such a manner that a vertical unit layer stretches and at the same time de-stabilizes, which, according to 1.235 (4) leads to an intensification of cyclonic vorticity (Raethjen, 1955). These processes seem to take place mainly in the middle troposphere to the rear of a cyclone. Air masses ascending (moist adiabatically) on the forward side of a cyclone, causing precipitation and de-stabilization during the rising process, also would assume cyclonic vorticity of an increasing magnitude (see Kruhl, 1952; Raethjen, 1953*a*).

The cyclogenetic influence of these non-adiabatic condensation processes has been interpreted by Kleinschmidt (1950, 1951) as the cause of the formation of cyclonic potential vorticity, which, in turn, is responsible for cyclogenetic processes. Since these rising motions do not become active as a vorticity source until cyclogenesis has started, they can be considered only as a mechanism of intensification. The initial impulse has to come from a potential vorticity advection along the jet stream from regions located upstream.

The vertical stretching and de-stabilization of the lower atmospheric layers, which, according to 1.235 (4) leads to vorticity production, and perhaps even to cyclogenesis, is especially favored in the lee of mountain ranges, when the rising motion underneath the jet stream is superimposed upon a descending motion forced by the sloping terrain to the lee of the range (Hage, 1957; Newton, 1955, 1956*a*). *This vertical gradient in the vertical motion* is responsible for preferred cyclogenesis on the eastern slopes of the Rocky Mountains, especially in the Colorado region, and for the formation of "Genoa Cyclones."

Another vorticity source is available to the incipient cyclone from the air mass which comes from the warm anticyclone and flows anticyclonically into the warm sector, because this air mass loses some of its anticyclonic vorticity by surface friction.

Under the assumption of adiabatic changes of state and of frictionless flow, the vorticity transports naturally must occur along isentropic surfaces. These transports are able to attain magnitudes necessary for surface cyclogenesis only if the isentropic surfaces are inclined against the isobaric surfaces, i.e., if the atmosphere is baroclinic in this region. *Baroclinicity, therefore, is a necessary but not sufficient condition for cyclogenesis* (Petterssen, 1955*a*, *b*, *c*; Spar, 1956). Newton (1958) was able to show that in many cases shallow baroclinic layers may exist for a long time in the lee of the Rocky Mountains without being cyclogenetically active. Cyclogenesis, however, occurs if a high-tropospheric "front" associated with a jet maximum and with well-pronounced vergences and causing strong vertical motions (see Chapter 4.221) is superimposed upon these low-tropospheric frontal zones. The vorticity advection at jet-stream level, which is the cause of these vergences, thus, becomes a powerful tool in surface weather forecasting (Breistein, 1954; Bugaev, 1955; Clarke, 1956; Gibbs, 1955; Hoyle, 1955*b*; Petterssen, 1955*a*, *b*; Petterssen and Bradbury, 1954; Petterssen, Dunn, and Means, 1955; Raethjen, 1956; University of Chicago, 1954). This baroclinicity, on the other hand, may have a damping influence upon cyclogenetic processes, because of its static stability, as will be shown in Chapter 6.13.

Thus, a criterion for frontal cyclogenesis is given by the superposition of a field of upper divergence, i.e., of an area with advection of positive vorticity according to 6.121 (1), *upon a baroclinic zone near the earth's surface.* If a baroclinic zone is *not* present near the ground, i.e., if the isentropic surfaces are oriented nearly horizontally, the surface pressure falls caused by the upper divergence will not result in an organized lifting motion along surfaces of constant potential temperature. These surfaces will rather be lifted slowly under the influence of a relatively weak upward motion which is spread over a wide area. This will lead to a gradual destabilization of the atmospheric layers near the ground and—after destruction of an impeding inversion—this may result in the development of strong convective motions, in which the upward component will exceed the downward component of flow, when integrated over a wide region. If the stratification, finally, becomes convectively unstable, and if the level of condensation is reached by the convective currents, cumulus formation will commence over a large area and thunderstorms will form if the freezing level is exceeded far enough by the vertical currents.

This kind of destabilization of the lower atmospheric layers under the influence of a divergent upper-flow pattern and in the absence of a frontal "sliding" surface is typical for subtropical and tropical regions (Colon, 1954). Here pronounced air-mass contrasts are missing, and the thermal structure of the lower atmospheric layers is nearly homogeneous over wide regions. In Chapter 4.413 the easterly jet stream of the tropics has been described in detail. It is characterized by wave disturbances with well-pronounced vergences, just like the polar-front jet. It, therefore, should be expected that a station lying under this tropical jet should experience temporary destabilization with precipitation and thunderstorm activity, and again fair weather periods with suppressed convective cloud formation, depending on the divergence and convergence distribution in this jet stream. This, again, is the typical pattern of the tropical rainy seasons which can be explained neither by upward sloping processes of a frontal character nor by convection due to insolation. The former are eliminated because of the insignificance of air-mass contrasts, and if the latter were to apply, the precipitation of the rainy season would primarily be affected by the direction of ground slope and by albedo, which would contradict all experiences.

Koteswaram (1956, 1958) showed that this easterly jet stream and its upper divergence is responsible for the precipitation during the Indian summer monsoon season. Thus, monsoonal precipitation, too, may be related to the influence of the upper-flow pattern, while in the climatology of past decades it was explained by over-heating of the continents due to insolation. A further discussion of this will be reserved, however, to Chapter 7.413.

Since the thunderstorms of the tropical rainy season are caused by a jet stream that flows across an almost barotropic layer near the earth's surface, one might offhand assume, that the wide-spread "heat thunderstorms" of summer, occurring in temperate latitudes mainly along the northern rim of the subtropical high-pressure belts might also be ascribed to the influence of the upper-flow pattern (Neuwirth, 1954). Under normal conditions insolation alone would hardly ever suffice to cause a large-scale destabilization as it is observed with wide-spread thunderstorm activity. Divergence in the field of flow aloft will have to exert its supporting influence. Thunderstorms which might form by convergence of a land- or sea-breeze circulation (e.g., over Florida during summer) will be disregarded here, although even here thunderstorm activity is drastically influenced by upper divergence and convergence.

A statistical investigation by Petterssen (1949) may be interpreted in this sense. Over the British Isles the convective activity during 150 days has been correlated with relative vorticity according to Eq. 1.231 (3). (Cases in which the curvature and shearing terms were of opposite sign have been classified as "undetermined cases.") The results of the investigation are presented in Table 6.121.

TABLE 6.121. CONVECTION AND VORTICITY

VORTICITY	TOP OF CONVECTIVE CLOUD		
	Below 800 mb	600 to 400 mb	Above 400 mb
Anticyclonic	41	1	0
Undetermined	30	14	6
Cyclonic	29	85	94

Thus, weak convection may occur also during anticyclonic weather situations with wide-spread sinking motions, and it is at least partially caused by heating of the surface due to insolation. Thunderstorm clouds, however, may be expected only in cyclonic weather situations with low-level convergence and corresponding high-level divergence with resulting rising motions. The destabilization observed in troughs corresponds well with the conservation of potential vorticity [Eq. 1.235 (4)].

Malkus and Ronne (1954b) obtained an interesting series of photographs of trade-wind cumuli taken from an aircraft. These cumuli developed into large cumulo-nimbi with the approach of a trough in the westerly upper current. A picture of a cumulonimbus about 100 km north of Anegada shows an anvil of cirrus which under the influence of strong upper winds and of large wind shears is shearing off like a tremendous smoke plume. Such observations can hardly ever be made from the ground because of impeding low-level cloud layers. Such cirrus "plumes" might however be a quite frequent phenomenon with thunderstorms in the jet-stream region.

Detailed investigations on the correlation between jet stream and thunderstorms are presently in progress in the United States. Details are not yet known: Schaeffer (1955*b*, *c*, *d*, *e*, 1957) reports, however, on preliminary results which have been gained during "Project Skyfire" in the Northwestern part of the country (in the states of Montana, Idaho, and Washington) during the years 1952 and 1953. It became apparent that two-thirds of the forest fires in this area are caused by lightning. For instance on a single afternoon of August of 1953 more than 400 fires were ignited in this way. A dense network of mountain observatories was supposed to render an insight into the mechanism of the thunderstorm activity over this area. Rapidly moving thunderstorms which gave little precipitation and which could be classified neither as "heat" nor as "frontal" thunderstorms showed an especially large lightning frequency. Judged from the large number of discharges between clouds and earth, the potential gradient in this direction seemed to be well developed during these thunderstorms. By means of observations of cloud form and cloud movement Schaefer associated these thunderstorms with the jet streams over these areas (see Schaefer and Hubert, 1955). Thus, one might be able to attribute the scarceness of precipitation of these thunderstorms as well as their rapid movement to the vertical wind shear, as has been done with tropical cumuli (Riehl, 1954*c*). On the other hand one will have to assume, however, that the forces which generate and separate the electrical charges are not impeded by the presence of the jet stream. Thus it will be necessary that the instability of the atmosphere extends over a deep layer. The destabilization will be accomplished on the one hand by large-scale rising motions and by an increase of the positive vertical component of flow with height, and on the other hand by differential advection with height of different air masses. Strong cold-air advection at high levels has already been mentioned earlier as a thunderstorm-generating mechanism (Hoinkes, 1951; Reidat, 1930; Rodewald, 1935). The effectiveness of this advection depends upon the differences in the vertical gradient of potential temperature in the different air masses, and on the magnitude of the vertical wind shear. It may be expected, therefore, that this thunderstorm-generating effect is especially potent in the jet-stream region.

Nakayama (1957) arrives at similar conclusions by theoretically considering the buoyancy force of an air particle—which is caused by horizontal differences in density, which are especially effective at low levels during the onset of convection—and a term which contains the wind speed and the vertical shear as most important factors. Since in the cases investigated by Nakayama the strongest thunderstorm activity also occurs near troughs in the upper current, one might arrive at usable results also by applying the theorem of potential vorticity.

Penn (1955) investigated a case of high-level thunderstorms, and he arrived at the conclusion that a weak jet stream (approximately 70 knots) at the 300-mb level and at the east side of an upper-level trough with its advection of cyclonic vorticity is responsible for the upper divergence. At the 500-mb level, however, convergence had to be expected from the flow patterns. Thus convective currents may penetrate from the earth's surface to great heights.

The formation of squall lines and instability lines, which is frequently observed over the United States and which is often accompanied by tornadoes, also seems to be connected with vertical wind shears and with cold-air advection aloft (Baird, 1956). These squall lines frequently precede the cold front by a large distance (at times by more than 400 km) thus occurring *in* or *ahead of* a more or less well-developed trough in the upper current, which seems to be associated with the cold front (Fulks, 1951). The mechanism of propagation of these squall lines seems to be given by a certain divergence and convergence distribution, which, in turn, may be explained by the vertical exchange of horizontal momentum of flow: air masses which are ascending on the leading edge of the thunderstorm cell import momentum from levels close to the earth's surface (influenced by friction). Thereby the speed of the upper current within the clouds is reduced, and on the leading edge of the thunderstorm cell a divergent area is generated aloft, while to the rear a convergent region appears. In the latter the air masses sink toward the ground thus importing larger values of horizontal momentum from aloft. Thereby a divergent area is created on the rear side of the convective cell near the ground, and a convergence region on the leading side (Fig. 6.121). By this constant dissipation and reformation process the squall line, consisting

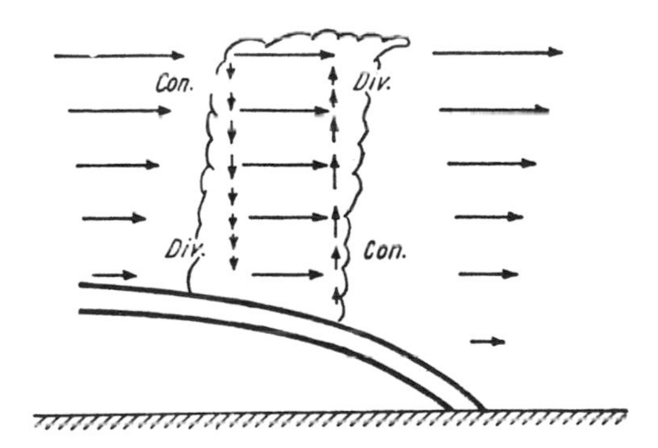

FIG. 6.121.—Displacement of a squall line in a shearing current. (Newton, 1950.)

of a row of thunderstorms, propagates in the direction of the upper flow, at a rate exceeding, in general, the speed of the cold front, which usually is well expressed only in the lower layers of the atmosphere close to the ground (Newton, 1950). A similar mechanism may be found for the "disturbance line" of Central Africa under the influence of an easterly upper current (Hamilton and Archbold, 1945). The formation of tornadoes depends on additional factors, since not every squall line is accompanied by such twisters. The cooling process aloft caused by precipitation falling ahead of the squall line might explain the spontaneously occurring instability (Showalter and Fulks, 1943). Other authors, however, hold that the lifting of the total air mass ahead of the squall line is responsible for the destabilization. A study by Lee and Galway (1956) correlates the cold tongue (an area which is enclosed by the $-60°$ isotherm) at the 200-mb level south of the jet stream with the occurrence of tornadoes. Large-scale lifting motion would show up at this pressure level by low temperatures and by warm-air advection.

In general one may say that such well-pronounced low-level convergence and upper-level divergence as may be found in the jet-stream region (see Georgii, 1957) will have to be present in order to account for such strong convection as may be observed in prefrontal squall lines and in occasional tornado formation. The influence which a low-level jet stream may have upon the superposition of divergence and convergence areas has already been pointed out in detail in Chapter 4.416.

Slow destabilization by upper divergence and by a vertical gradient in ascending air motions may also be found with weaker upper winds outside the jet-stream region. The upper wind field will have to show the necessary divergence and vorticity-advection characteristics, however (Ramaswamy, 1956). This is the case during increased thunderstorm activity on summer days, as has already been mentioned earlier.

6.122. Energy Conversions During Frontal Cyclogenesis

A further way of considering cyclogenetic processes which should not be neglected is given by the conversion of potential into kinetic energy and vice versa. In Figure 4.122.3 it has already been pointed out that the surface cyclone forms in the front left quadrant of a jet maximum, i.e., in an area which is characterized by *decreasing* upper-wind speeds. Thus, in this area kinetic energy is dissipated in the upper troposphere and potential energy is generated (see Piper, 1956). This is accomplished by the lifting of cold air masses which flow into the influence region of the cyclone, and by sinking warm air masses in the area of upper convergence in the high-pressure wedge south of the jet stream. By this lifting process the cold air masses will be cooled further, the warm air masses, however, are heated further during the sinking process. This means that, because of the *indirect* circulation in the delta area of a jet maximum, the baroclinicity in this area will be strengthened; the jet stream which may be identified with this baroclinic zone, therefore, propagates downstream by a self-sustaining mechanism which is based upon the vertical circulation.

From the given distribution of divergence at the jet-stream level this indirect circulation would have to be expected especially in the region of a deepening cyclone (Spar, 1950). Offhand this contradicts Margules' notion of the energy transformation in a cyclone. While Margules only considers the system "cold air" and "warm air," and while he obtains the kinetic energy from a lowering of the common center of gravity, more recent investigations indicate that the generation of kinetic energy does not occur in the cold dome associated with the cyclone itself but farther upstream in the entrance region of the jet maximum in whose delta region the cyclone is located. Cyclogenesis, therefore, is induced by a direct circulation farther upstream, which sustains the jet stream by sinking cold air and rising warm air (Uwai, 1952). Margules' line of reasoning, therefore, should not be confined to the region of the cyclone itself but it will have to comprise the total entrance area, too.

A cold dome may even be "pumped up" or raised temporarily by the import of kinetic energy which has been generated upstream and which is partly transformed into potential energy in the delta region of the jet maximum (Fig. 6.122.1; see also Nyberg and Riehl, 1953; Riehl and Teweles, 1953). By this process on the one hand the frontal zone will be steepened and the wind speeds will increase, and on the other hand the cold dome will collapse in the end because of the outflow of air near the ground and the release of potential energy.

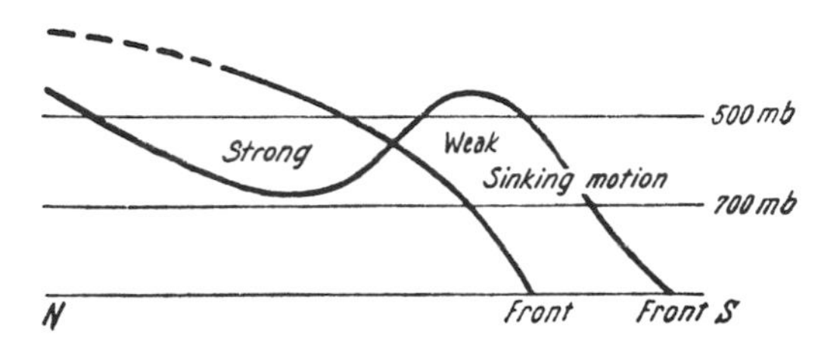

Fig. 6.122.1.—Schematic cross section along the axis of an upper trough showing the formation of a cut-off low due to differences in sinking motion. (Palmén, 1949.)

The frontolytic effect of the delta region of a frontal zone shown in Chapter 4.221 may now be understood in the following way: the air masses which flow through a jet maximum are subject to a frontolytic influence in the delta region because of the strong high-level divergence (Fig. 4.221.3); at the same time, however, the whole frontal zone moves downstream slower than the speed of the wind.

The rear side of a cyclone (entrance region of a frontal zone) has a frontogenetic influence upon the transient air masses according to what has been said in Chapter 4.221. Because of the adiabatic warming of the sinking cold air, and because of the resulting decrease in the horizontal temperature gradient, the frontal zone itself is slowly dissipated. The direct circulation in the entrance area of a frontal zone (Lee, 1955) and in the region of the sinking cold air of a cyclone uses up potential energy. The same is to be expected from the rising warm air above the warm front. If we neglect the heat produced by friction and the increase of internal energy of the total system, this potential energy has to be transformed into kinetic energy, which manifests itself in a "jet-stream genesis" downstream from the surface cyclone. Thus, kinetic energy is also exported out of the cyclogenetically active area. In fact, one may observe during such a strong cyclogenesis, especially in the lee of the Colorado portion of the Rocky Mountains, that a usually cyclonically curved stream which triggers off the cyclogenetic processes at the tip of the trough slowly decreases in intensity, while farther to the northeast (over the Great Lakes region) and downstream from the position of the surface low, an anticyclonically curved jet stream is newly formed or intensified.

The energy transformations during the transitions of hurricane Hazel (15 October, 1954) into a temperate latitude cyclone have been investigated in detail by Palmén (1958). Because of its incorporation of an intensive tropical circulation system the case considered here will serve to outline rather extreme conditions in many respects; nevertheless, it may be regarded as typical for cyclogenesis in extratropical latitudes. Figure 6.122.2 shows the surface weather situation and Figure 6.122.3 contains the 300-mb chart of 15 October, 1954, 1500 GCT. At this time the hurricane, coming from

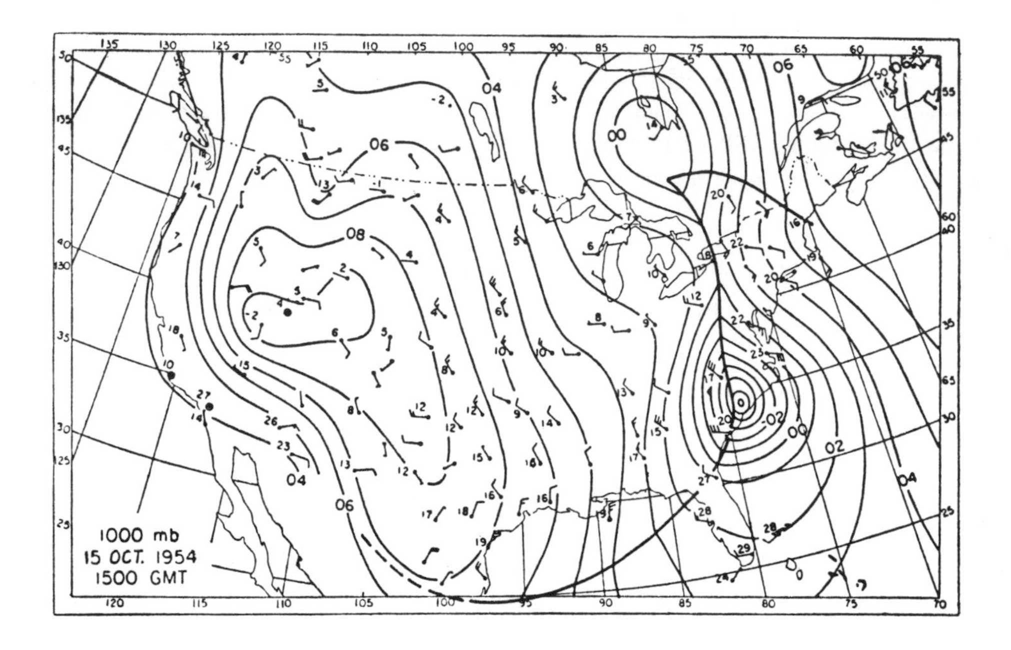

FIG. 6.122.2.—Absolute topography of the 1000-mb surface, 15 October, 1954, 1500 GCT. (Palmén, 1958.)

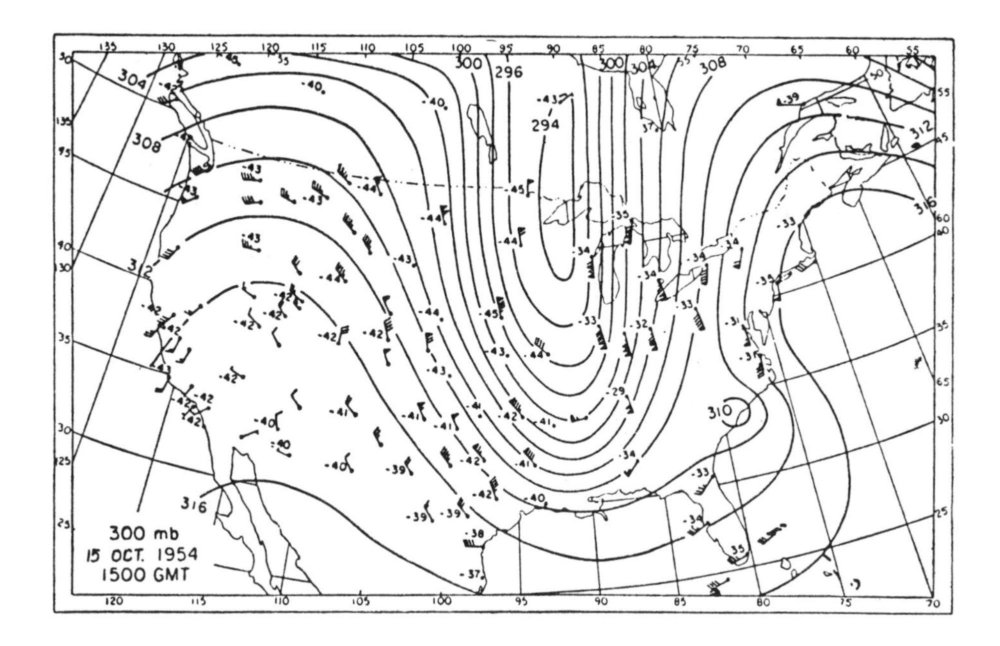

FIG. 6.122.3.—Absolute topography of the 300-mb surface, 15 October, 1954, 1500 GCT. (Palmén, 1958.)

the south, had just reached a frontal system which was connected with a deep trough in the upper current. Figure 6.122.4 shows the distribution of area elements over which Palmén calculated the mean vertical velocities (Table 6.122.1).

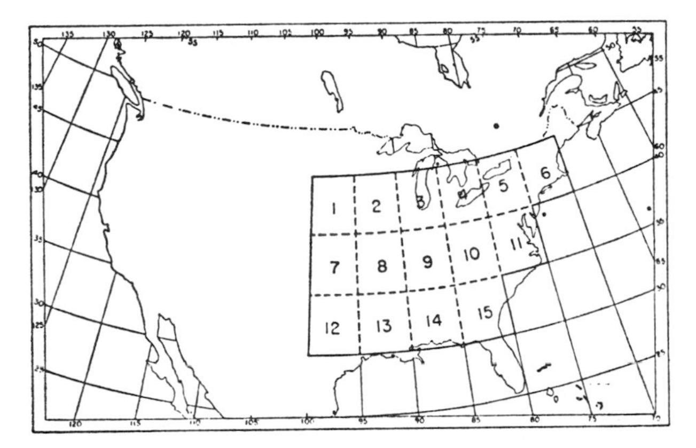

FIG. 6.122.4.—Boundaries of area elements (see text). (Palmén, 1958.)

TABLE 6.122.1. VERTICAL VELOCITIES (cm/sec) IN THE INDIVIDUAL AREAS OF FIGURE 6.122.4

AREA NUMBER	ISOBARIC SURFACE (mb)						
	900	800	700	600	500	400	300
1	−0.7	−2.4	−5.2	−9.8	−14.4	−19.0	−22.1
2	0.6	0.1	−1.2	−3.4	− 5.8	− 8.0	−10.6
3	−0.4	−0.8	−1.1	0.3	2.4	7.1	16.5
4	0.8	3.0	5.4	7.2	6.7	6.2	2.4
5	0.7	2.4	3.5	5.6	10.2	14.4	12.8
6	−1.3	−2.3	−2.0	−0.5	2.8	6.0	5.9
7	−0.2	0.1	−0.2	−1.2	− 1.3	− 2.0	− 3.5
8	−0.6	−1.4	−3.6	−6.6	−10.4	−15.1	−21.6
9	0.2	−0.6	−2.4	−5.0	− 6.6	− 6.6	− 3.0
10	1.5	3.6	7.2	11.6	16.8	23.0	27.6
11	5.9	10.3	13.1	14.7	13.7	9.4	2.6
12	−0.2	−0.1	−0.4	0.1	− 0.1	− 1.8	− 1.8
13	−0.8	−2.2	−3.4	−4.3	− 6.8	− 9.2	−10.6
14	−1.4	−3.6	−4.2	−3.2	− 4.0	− 6.4	− 9.8
15	−1.2	−0.1	1.2	2.7	2.6	2.1	− 0.1
Total Average	0.2	0.4	0.5	0.5	0.3	0.0	− 1.0
Average							
1, 2, 3, 7, 8, 9, 12, 13, 14	−0.5	−1.2	−2.4	−3.6	− 5.6	− 6.8	− 7.4
4, 5, 6, 10, 11, 15	1.1	2.8	4.7	6.9	8.8	10.2	8.5
2, 3, 8, 9, 13, 14	−0.4	−1.4	−2.7	−3.7	− 5.2	− 6.4	− 6.5
4, 5, 10, 11 Precipitation area	2.2	4.8	7.3	9.8	11.9	13.2	11.3

An inspection of these values shows that the rising motion is confined to the anticyclonic side of the jet stream. The jet axis roughly corresponds to the north-south oriented dividing line between the areas 3, 9 and 4, 10. Strongest ascending motion may be found in the lower layers of area 11 and in the upper layer of area 10. We are here dealing with moist tropical air masses which have been imported from the southeast by the circulation around the tropical cyclone on its northern edge and which now are incorporated into the jet-stream circulation of the incipient extratropical cyclone. Since warm air masses are rising here, we have to expect the release of large quantities of potential energy and its transformation into kinetic energy.

At the same time the cold air masses are sinking along the cyclonic side of the jet stream, where at the 250-mb level usually one finds a tongue of warm air parallel to the jet axis. Sinking also occurs in the entrance region of the jet maximum. The largest values of sinking motions Palmén finds in area 1, i.e., in the rear of the trough at the 300-mb level. Area 8 is second in its contribution to the sinking motion. According to what should be expected area 9 shows the maximum downward motion already in the *middle* troposphere, while number 14 shows highest values of negative vertical motion at the 900- and 800-mb levels, as compared with other areas. It is here that the cold air in the rear of the cyclone spreads out near the earth's surface. The highest values of vertical motion are, however, found near the jet-stream level (300 mb). Here, therefore, the main transformation of potential into kinetic energy is taking place. When averaging over several blocks (lower part of Table 6.122.1) these conditions are distorted in favor of the 400-mb surface.

The vertical overturning of the atmosphere (sinking of cold air, rising of warm air) seems to take place mainly in vertical planes oriented in a west-east direction (Palmén, 1959), as has also been found by other authors (Fleagle, 1947; White and Saltzman, 1956). This may be the reason why a mean meridional circulation between high and low latitudes which has been postulated for the maintenance of the kinetic energy of the general circulation may hardly ever be found (Starr, 1954). The reorientation of the vertical circulation cells which generate kinetic energy into west-east oriented vertical planes is due to the effects of the earth's rotation, which lies above a certain critical value. This has been corroborated by experiments with rotating dishpans. (Hadley cells collapse above a certain critical value of rotation [Kuo, 1953*b*; see also Chapter 4.43].) While the vertical overturning of the atmosphere within west-east oriented planes in the *troposphere* mainly generates kinetic energy at the expense of potential energy, the energy transformation on the average seem to have the opposite direction in the *lower stratosphere*. From this we might conclude that the processes of flow in the lower stratosphere owe their existence to the adjacent atmospheric layers (White and Nolan, 1960), with which they are connected by vertical transport processes (Starr, 1960).

Palmén (1958) also undertook a quantitative investigation of the energy budget in the synoptic example of intensive cyclogenesis mentioned above. He departed from the assumption that *kinetic energy* is generated by the *pressure field* by means of ageostrophic components of flow. Frictional forces may use up part of the kinetic energy. Any surplus will be transported out of the area under consideration.

The equation giving the change of kinetic energy within a volume element dV over a certain area of limited extent reads as follows,

$$\frac{\partial}{\partial t}\int_V K\,dV = -\int_V \left(\frac{\partial p}{\partial x}\,u + \frac{\partial p}{\partial y}\,v\right) dV - \int_S \tfrac{1}{2}\rho(u^2+v^2)v_n\,dS + \int_V \left(\frac{\partial \tau_{xz}}{\partial z}\,u + \frac{\partial \tau_{yz}}{\partial z}\,v\right) dV. \qquad 6.122\,(1)$$

v_n is the component of flow normal to the area element dS. τ_{xz} and τ_{yz} are the zonal and meridional shearing stresses at the level z. The first term on the right hand side of the equation gives the generation of energy by gradient forces, the second term indicates the export of energy out of the volume bounded by the area S, and the third term stands for the dissipation of kinetic energy by friction.

The ageostrophic component of flow, which causes the accelerations and decelerations, has been computed from independently prepared analyses of the pressure and wind fields, using Eq. 6.122 (2).

$$\int_V (\nabla p \cdot \mathbf{v})\, dV = A \int_{p_2}^{p_1} (\mathbf{v} \cdot \overline{\nabla z})\, dp. \qquad 6.122\ (2)$$

V is the volume, A is the area of integration, and $\bar{z}$ is the mean height of the isobaric surfaces between p_1 and p_2. Since the deviations from the mean values of the current and the slopes of the isobaric surfaces in the individual rectangular areas were difficult to determine, Table 6.122.2 contains only the values of

$$A_i \int_{p_2}^{p_1} \left[\bar{u} \frac{\overline{\partial z}}{\partial x} + \bar{v} \frac{\overline{\partial z}}{\partial y} \right] dp.$$

The term

$$A_i \int_{p_2}^{p_1} \left[\overline{u^* \left(\frac{\partial z}{\partial x} \right)^*} + \overline{v^* \left(\frac{\partial z}{\partial y} \right)^*} \right] dp$$

has been neglected.

TABLE 6.122.2. WORK ACCOMPLISHED BY PRESSURE GRADIENTS, IN 10^8 kilojoule·centibar^{-1} sec^{-1}

AREA	ISOBARIC SURFACE (mb)				
	850	700	500	400	300
1	0.32	1.75	0.85	3.00	−4.87
2	0.70	2.58	1.14	−0.58	−3.66
3	−0.83	0.04	2.43	1.00	37.61
4	−0.24	1.29	4.50	18.36	16.81
5	0.81	1.69	2.94	4.56	7.30
6	−0.21	0.19	2.29	0.71	−0.45
7	0.34	1.48	−0.44	−4.73	−9.90
8	0.56	1.88	−0.23	6.94	−3.78
9	0.92	−1.50	−0.11	8.35	20.39
10	2.97	−1.17	2.96	5.65	17.92
11	1.98	2.17	−1.90	−0.12	−1.87
12	−0.51	1.34	−1.68	−5.58	−3.09
13	−0.62	−1.54	−6.26	−8.09	−5.86
14	0.52	−0.15	−4.20	−3.56	3.95
15	0.79	4.51	4.58	4.78	7.61
Sum	7.50	11.60	6.87	30.69	78.11

From this table it becomes apparent that accelerations and decelerations are not evenly distributed throughout all levels of an air column. It illustrates the layered structure of the atmosphere which is characteristic for large-scale mixing processes as they occur in cyclones. The largest absolute values are found at the 400- and 300-mb levels. Figure 6.122.5 shows the amounts of work done by pressure gradients integrated separately over the eastern and western parts of the area shown in Figure 6.122.4. *When averaged over a large area, the jet-stream level contributes the major part of kinetic energy formation by ageostrophic components of flow.*

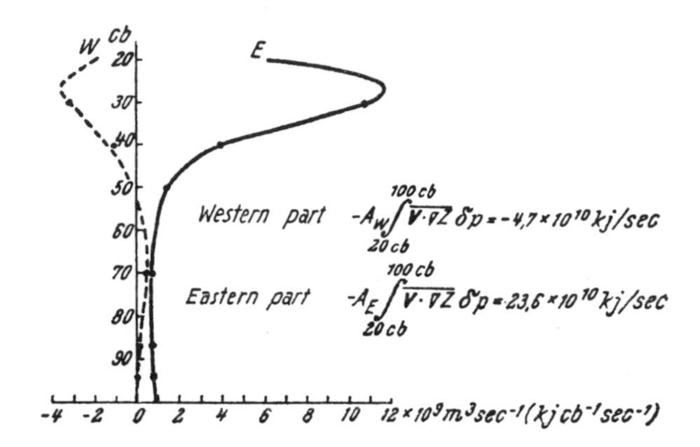

FIG. 6.122.5.—Work done by the horizontal pressure forces per 100-mb layer. Dashed line, western part; solid line, eastern part of the area elements shown in Figure 6.122.4. (Palmén, 1958.)

That the work done by the pressure field on the average shows large positive values may be due to the choice of the integration surface. Negative values are observed to a great extent only on the west side of the trough, which marks the leading edge of a newly appearing jet maximum. The largest accelerations occur in the jet

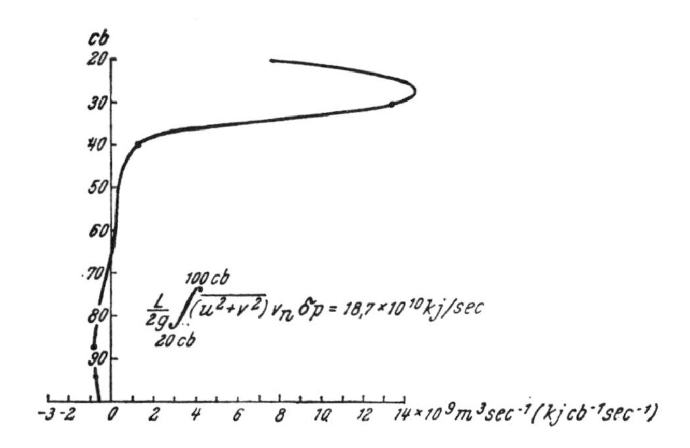

FIG. 6.122.6.—Export of kinetic energy from the total of all area elements shown in Figure 6.122.4. (Palmén, 1958.)

maximum which is connected with the extratropical cyclone that has formed out of the hurricane. The leading edge of this maximum, where we also would have to expect a dissipation of kinetic energy, is not covered by this analysis any more.

The export of kinetic energy out of the cyclogenetically active area is accomplished by the intensifying, or even newly forming, jet stream, as shown in Figure 6.122.6.

The energy released in the cyclone is transported far downstream and is gradually transformed into potential energy and dissipated by frictional forces (see also Starr, 1948*b*).

For the case investigated by Palmén the following energy budget results:

Production of kinetic energy from potential energy	$18.9 \cdot 10^{10}$ kilojoule/sec
Export out of the cyclogenetically active area	$18.7 \cdot 10^{10}$ kilojoule/sec
Dissipation of kinetic energy by friction	$2 \cdot 10^{10}$ kilojoule/sec.

One would have to conclude, therefore, that the kinetic energy of the total area decreases by about $2 \cdot 10^{10}$ kilojoule/sec. Since the total kinetic energy of the area amounts to $89 \cdot 10^{14}$ kilojoules. The energy decrease would be about 19 per cent if it kept up during 24 hours. At the same time, however, in the whole area $155 \cdot 10^{10}$ kilojoule/sec of latent heat were released, which is considerably more than the production of kinetic energy. Therefore, one cannot compute the time variation of kinetic energy over the area by estimating the consumption of potential energy only, although one may assume that the larger part of the energy of latent heat also will be exported—by falling precipitation, and by warm air masses flowing out of the area, thus contributing to regions farther downstream.

The following consideration indicates that cyclones and their kinetic-energy producing processes are a necessary factor in the maintenance of the general circulation.

The integration area of the case considered above ($366 \cdot 10^{10}$ m^2) constituted about one-thirty-fifth of the hemisphere north of 30° latitude ($127 \cdot 10^{12}$ m^2). The dissipation of kinetic energy due to friction amounts to $2 \cdot 10^{10}$ kilojoule/sec or $5.5 \cdot 10^{-3}$ kilojoule/sec m^2 in hurricane Hazel. Pisharoty (1955) computed an energy dissipation due to friction of $2 \cdot 10^{-3}$ kilojoule/sec m^2 for the belt of westerlies. This would mean a value of $37 \cdot 10^{10}$ kilojoule/sec when applied to the total hemisphere north of 30° latitude, while the dissipation values obtained from hurricane Hazel would render a total value of $70 \cdot 10^{10}$ kilojoule/sec for the hemispheric area. Thus, only 2 to 3.5 disturbances of the intensity of hurricane Hazel would have to be active, in order to supply the total hemisphere north of 30° with the kinetic energy necessary to maintain the general circulation. In reality, however, the number of disturbances necessary to maintain the circulation is still smaller, because Mintz (1955) and Pisharoty (1955) computed an import of kinetic energy across the 30th parallel from lower latitudes, of about 17 to $20 \cdot 10^{10}$ kilojoule/sec (see Palmén, 1959; Palmén, Riehl, and Vuorela, 1958).

Since in the westwind belt ordinarily there are more than two cyclones present, it is reasonable to assume that a large portion of the kinetic energy produced is consumed in building up potential energy within this zone. Thus, the jet-stream region with its migrating disturbances constitutes a sequence of sources and sinks of kinetic energy, which—in their net effect—maintain the general circulation against the ever present frictional forces. As the preceding discussion brought out, the jet-stream level itself is the main location in which these energy transformations take place.

By introducing the upper-flow conditions into the considerations of the polar-front theory, our view of the mechanism governing the general circulation has not been simplified. Now we are faced with a complex interplay of rising and descending motions, of direct and indirect circulations, and of vorticity and momentum transports, all of which have to be taken into account to describe completely the life cycle of a cyclone. In spite of the numerous literature dealing with the description and exploration of individual cases of strong cyclogenesis, detailed studies giving the trajectories of three-dimensional flow are still missing. They alone could give a picture of the complicated and multilayered interactions of flow patterns.

That the flow in the vicinity of a cyclone is not as simple as the polar-front theory sometimes assumed is evident from studies by Danielsen (1959), who believes that the layered structure of the atmosphere, which manifests itself in carefully evaluated radiosonde ascents, is due to the interaction of currents of different origins. Hislop (1951) for instance reports about thin unstable layers with cirro-stratus, which have been observed during British research flights and which were sandwiched between isothermal layers on either side. Reiter (1960*b*, *c*, *d*, *e*; 1961*a*, *b*, *d*, *e*), arrives at similar results (see Chapter 4.3). The large horizontal vortices in the influence region of the polar-front jet give rise to large-scale mixing processes, as has already been deduced by Defant (1921). In the course of these, the structure of the air bodies is changed only gradually.

6.123. "Cross-Stream" Circulation and Non-Gradient Winds

In Eq. 4.122 (11) it has been shown that horizontal divergence is possible only through ageostrophic components of flow, if we disregard the term in 4.122 (10) which is produced by the latitude dependency of the Coriolis parameter. *Thus, cyclogenesis and anticyclogenesis in the end are effects of vertical and horizontal distributions of these ageostrophic components of flow.* In Chapter 4.221 it has already been pointed out that in the delta region of a jet maximum the ageostrophic component of flow is directed toward higher pressure. This may be seen clearly from Figure 4.221.3. According to Murray and Daniels (1951), this flow component toward higher pressure also prevails in the center of the jet maximum. In the entrance area, on the other hand, one finds the opposite conditions: The accelerating current shows a component toward lower pressure. The ageostrophic (non-gradient) motion across the jet axis sometimes is referred to as "cross-stream circulation." It is "direct" or "indirect" depending on the solenoidal circulation accelerations which it gives rise to (Van Mieghem, 1950).

In order to estimate the conditions correctly, one has to consider the three-dimensional field of flow. The air masses which flow toward the anticyclonic side in the delta region of the frontal zone (Fig. 4.221.3) and converge and sink at some distance from the jet stream, have traveled the whole length of the frontal zone while covering this relatively short lateral distance. If one considered trajectories of these air particles one would arrive at the conclusion that the jet axis is crossed only at a very small angle, if at all (Staley, 1960).

Studies by Reed and Danielsen (1959) corroborate the conclusion that the air masses traverse the frontal zone, and with this also the jet axis, only in very insignificant amounts. This may be deduced from the sharp discontinuities which the potential vorticity shows on the warm and on the cold sides of a frontal zone (Fig. 6.123; see also Reiter, 1961*d*). Since the potential vorticity is a conservative quantity, one has to assume that the air masses in the upper part of a frontal zone are imported from the stratosphere by sinking along isentropic surfaces (Reed and Sanders, 1953). Thus, the sinking motion in the left-hand portion of the entrance region would carry with its ageostrophic flow accelerating air masses from the upper troposphere and stratosphere (Nyberg, 1950). Such sinking motions of originally stratospheric air could be observed over North America down into the 700- and 800-mb region (Boville, Creswick, and Reed, 1957; Reed, 1955; Staley, 1960). They may be the reason for the

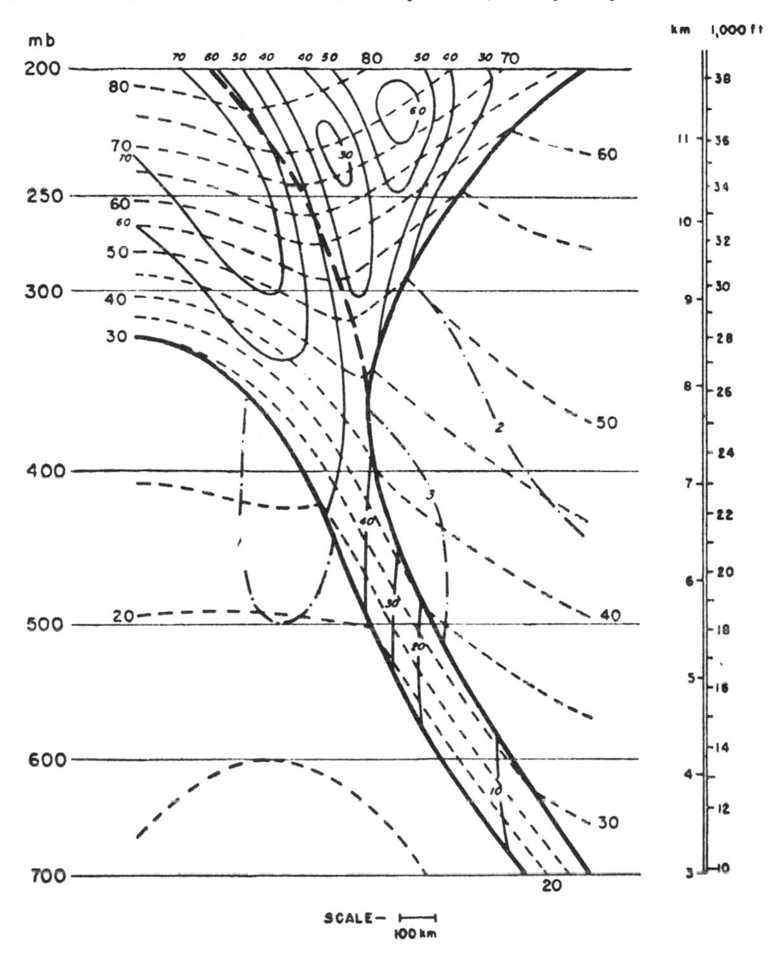

FIG. 6.123.—Mean pattern of isentropes (light, dashed lines) and isolines of potential vorticity $-Q_z \cdot (\partial\Theta/\partial p)$ (thin solid lines and dashed-dotted lines) in the vicinity of a jet stream. Frontal boundaries and tropopause are marked by heavy solid lines, the warm-air axis (isentrope trough) by a heavy dashed line. (Reed and Danielsen, 1959.)

dry warm air which is frequently found over the cold air masses behind a cold front (Miles, 1954). These vertical motions cause temperature changes in the layers of the lower stratosphere which could not be explained by advection. In the stable stratification of the stratosphere vertical motions have much more effect upon the temperature field than in the relatively unstable troposphere (Reinecke, 1952).

Sinking motions would also help to explain the great dryness of air masses, which has been found by Vuorela (1957*a*) by means of cross sections, and by Sawyer (1955) in evaluating research flight data. So, for instance, an extremely dry tongue of air within a warm front could be traced for the preceding 36 hours by means of trajectories on an isentropic surface. Its origin could be proved to be in the stratosphere above the entrance area of the frontal zone.

Such dry tongues are of great importance for the cloud distribution near fronts. In the upper troposphere the clouds lie along the warm side of the frontal zone (Pothecary, 1956), and usually terminate abruptly at the edge of the frontal zone itself.

These sinking motions out of the stratosphere in the region of a frontal zone have already earlier been hinted at by Bjerknes and Palmén (1937). They were corroborated in an impressive study by Van Mieghem (1939), who interpreted them as "foehn" phenomenon. The cross sections constructed by him show the characteristics, even into details, of later studies by Endlich (Chapter 4.232; see also Reed and Danielsen, 1959), without, however, pointing out the jet-stream character of the wind field.

Even if one assumed additional forces (Kleinschmidt, 1955)—as for instance frictional forces (Hsieh, 1949; Staley, 1960)—which might cause the change of potential vorticity of an air particle in the course of time, it is difficult to see how a trajectory

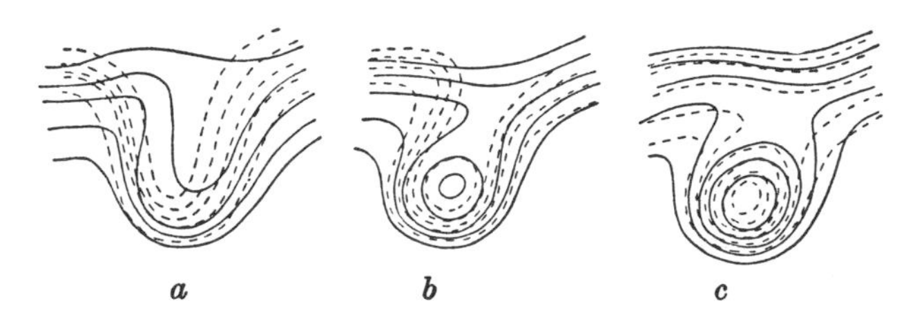

Fig. 6.124.1.—Schematic representation of the formation of a cut-off low. Solid lines, contours of the 500-mb surface; dashed lines, isotherms of the 500-mb surface. (Hsieh, 1949.)

may ever cross the jet axis in the fashion indicated in Figure 4.221.3, since it would have to traverse a strong gradient of potential vorticity. The terminology "cross-stream circulation," therefore, appears to be misleading. One will rather have to argue in the fashion outlined above, that air masses coming from the entrance region of the frontal zone diverge in the delta region and flow toward the high-pressure side. The sinking of stratospheric air shown in Figure 6.123 mainly occurs to the rear of cyclones and in the entrance region and the core of the frontal zone.

The tongue of cold air mentioned in Chapter 4.112 is clearly visible in Figure 6.123. The tendency of the jet stream to split into two branches at about 11 km height found by Dickson (1955) and described in Chapter 4.122 also seems substantiated by this cross section. The warm tongue which extends along the dashed line of Figure 6.123 far into the stratosphere is the result of strong sinking motions.

6.124. The Cut-off Low

The influence of vorticity advection and vertical circulations is clearly expressed in the formation of cut-off lows and shear lines.

Cressman (1950) pointed out that cutting-off processes usually are not confined to *one* area but that they occur in several places of the hemisphere in short sequence.

These processes occur in low-index situations with large amplitudes of the upper current. Breakdowns of these weather patterns, which are characterized by the formation of a new polar-front jet at higher latitudes, usually propagate rapidly around the hemisphere. Hsieh (1949) made a detailed study of the formation of a cut-off low over the United States. Figure 6.124.1 shows the schematic 500-mb contour and isotherm patterns.

In this, a strongly developed frontal zone has moved from the American west coast into the region of Colorado and New Mexico. By the following day a new jet maximum had already appeared from a southwesterly direction over Alaska (Fig. 6.124.1*b*), and, because of the strong warm-air advection, led to the formation of a powerful high-pressure ridge. On its leading edge the advection of anticyclonic vorticity imported from the ridge causes an increase of the wave amplitude, and thereby a deepening of the trough located downstream, as well as a tilting of the trough axis from southwest toward northeast (see Bjerknes, 1951*a*). If the upper current were to follow the strongly anticyclonic curvature, and if it were to flow into the deeply elongated low-pressure trough, this would apparently cause dynamic instability (see also Orihata, 1957), because the minimum anticyclonic radius of curvature that the upper current of the following jet maximum is still able to follow is given by

$$r = 4v_g/f \qquad 6.124\ (1)$$

according to the gradient wind equation [see 1.223 (4) and 1.223 (6)].

One arrives at the same result by considering the vorticity theorem: For nearly non-divergent flow one is able to construct CAV trajectories which would indicate too much anticyclonic curvature in the high-pressure ridge, as compared with the anticipated trajectories out of the jet maximum following on its west side. First, by advection of *anticyclonic* vorticity out of the ridge, the trough amplitude has increased. Now, by advection of *cyclonic* vorticity from the subsequent short-wave trough and its associated jet maximum the amplitude of the wave is suddenly reduced. A new frontal zone will now form over northern Canada (Fig. 6.124.1*c*) underneath the advancing jet stream, while the cold air masses which have traveled southward along the elongated trough now are cut off from the cold reservoir over Northern Canada. A confluence region appears over the American east coast, leading to an intensification of the jet stream over this area. In this way, the tendency for the establishment of a high-index situation is carried further downstream to the next low-pressure trough which shows an excessively large amplitude. It seems logical now why the "cutting-off" process appears in several places of the hemisphere, and why a disturbance in the equilibrium between planetary wave lengths and mean zonal wind speed [3.251 (6)] is carried downstream around the whole hemisphere (Rex, 1950*a*).

Studies by Palmén (1951*a*; Palmén and Nagler, 1949) corroborate this scheme. An analysis of the intersection line of the frontal zone with different isobaric surfaces during the developing stages of a cut-off low reveals the following interesting facts:

1. The frontal zone is steepest on the leading edge of the upper low. Margules' equation 6.11 (1) for the inclination of a boundary surface indicates that in this sector the jet stream has to be developed strongest.

2. In the lower layers the frontal zone, as far as it can still be identified, follows the amplitude of the trough, while in the higher layers the cutting-off process appears first (19 November, 1948, 1500 GCT). It has been shown in Chapter 4.221 that the baroclinicity in a frontal zone is better developed in the lower and upper levels of the troposphere, depending on entrance or delta region. If the delta region of a new jet

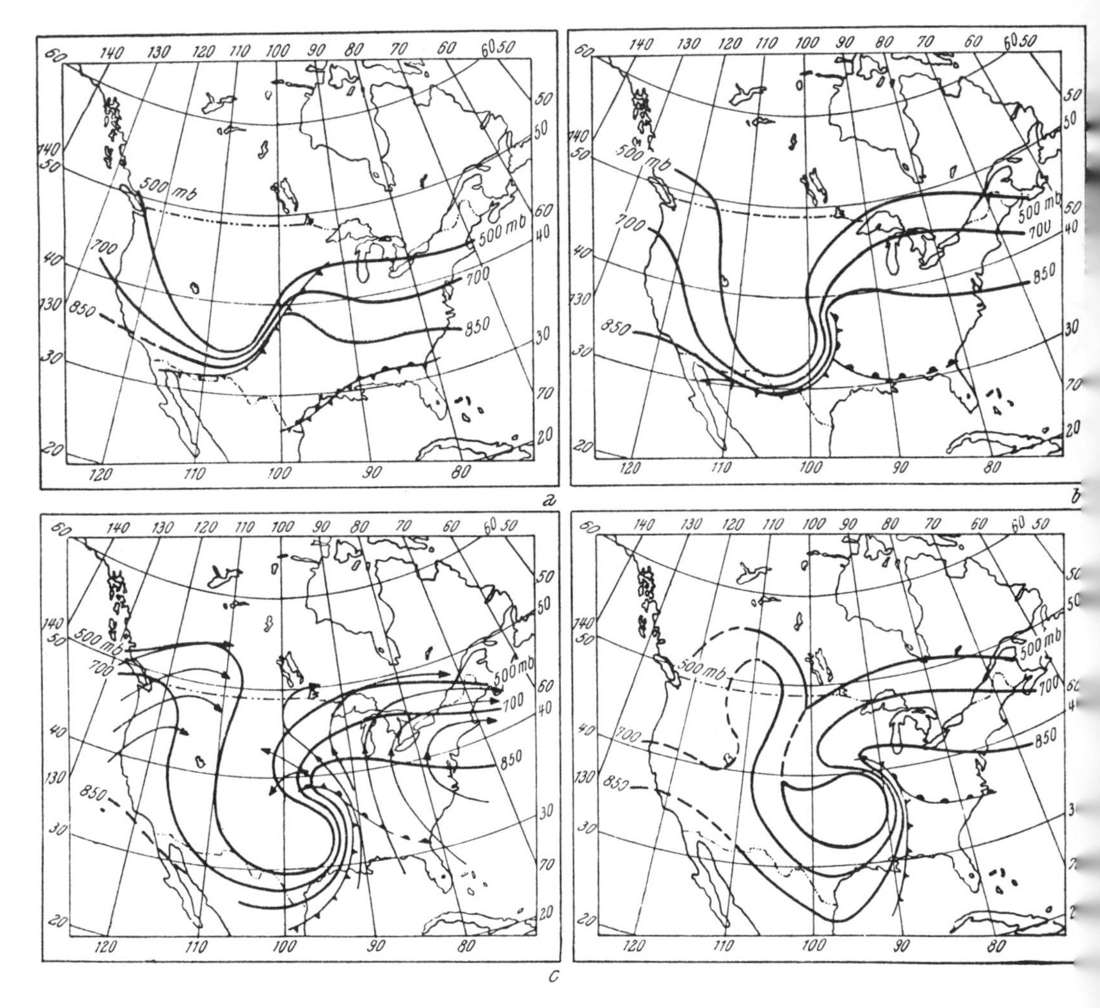

FIG. 6.124.2.—Idealized pattern of fronts, 18 and 19 November, 1948, 0300 and 1500 GCT. Arrow lines in c indicate streamlines. Diffuse intersections of fronts are shown by dashed lines. (Palmén, 1951*a*.)

maximum advances around the ridge upstream, the cutting-off process will be initiated by the upper baroclinic zone immediately connected with the jet maximum. Pressure rises in the ridge cause a splitting (diffluence) of the jet stream and the subsequent break-through of the new wind maximum in the north (Newton *et al.*, 1951; Fig. 6.124.3). In this manner the jet stream itself is directly responsible for the separation process leading to the formation of a cut-off low.

In most cases the cut-off low itself undergoes at first a marked low-level divergence.

This leads to an increase in area enclosed by the intersection line of the frontal zone with a pressure level close to the earth's surface, say, the 850-mb level (see Fig. 6.124.2, 19 November, 0300 and 1500 GCT). For reasons of continuity the area taken up by the cut-off low at higher levels (500 mb) shrinks at the same time. The potential energy released during the sinking process is made available to the frontal zone downstream of the cut-off low in the form of kinetic energy (Palmén and Newton, 1951). The

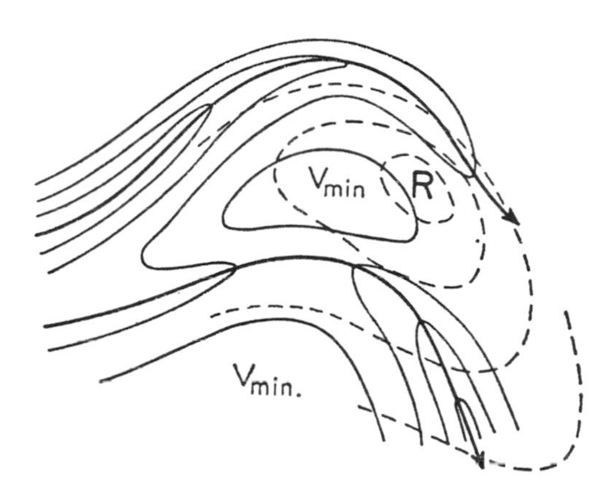

FIG. 6.124.3.—Schematic representation of the splitting of a jet-stream system caused by pressure rises (R, dashed) in the northern parts of a high-pressure ridge. V_{min} = area of weak winds. Lines with arrows, jet axes; light lines, isotachs. (Newton *et al.*, 1951.)

strongest sinking motion occurs to the rear of the cold-air outbreak—within the anticyclogenetically active sector of a jet maximum newly advancing around the bend of the high-pressure ridge upstream (see Chapter 6.122). This strong sinking motion in the northern part of the deeply elongated trough makes the cutting-off process of the cold-air mass at the 500-mb level final (Palmén, 1949). A schematic representation of the vertical motion may be seen from Figure 6.122.1. The sinking motion of the cold air is stronger in the north than in the tip of the trough. A comparison with Figure 6.124.2 actually shows the largest distance between the intersection lines of the frontal surface with the isobaric surfaces in the rear sector of the upper low. Therefore the low-level divergence of the cold-air mass attains greatest magnitudes here. Warm air ascending along the frontal surface on the leading side of the upper low causes wide-spread precipitation.

In the above-mentioned case of the cut-off low over North America Hsieh (1949) was able to show that the influence region under the upper low may become cyclogenetically active. Thus, the low-level divergence is replaced by convergence. Accordingly, an upward motion has to take place within the cold air, and sinking motion within the surrounding warm air (see also Kuei, 1959). This corresponds to an indirect circulation (Bjerknes, 1921). By adiabatic cooling of the rising cold air and by warming of the sinking warm air, the horizontal temperature gradient in the upper troposphere will be strengthened. As a mechanism which might cause this indirect vertical circulation, Hsieh proposes the turbulence of the upper current (Rossby *et al.*, 1937). The jet stream which is entirely located in the warm air accelerates the air masses within the cold dome. Because of the increased centrifugal force a mass divergence arises at jet-stream level. The cold dome is lifted, and the tropopause sinks. This becomes evident from the west-east sections shown in Figure 6.124.4. The isentropic surface 330° K roughly corresponds to the tropopause and clearly indicates a sinking tendency between 4 and 7 March. The isentropic surface 290° K, which approximately corresponds to the frontal zone shows a marked rise during the same period of time.

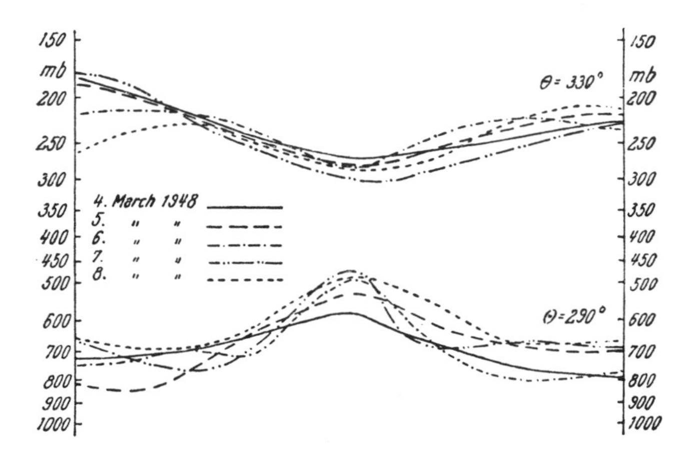

FIG. 6.124.4.—Atmospheric pressure at isentropic surfaces 330° K (upper part) and 290° K (lower part of diagram) in west-east cross sections through a cut-off low over North America on 4 to 8 March, 1948. (Hsieh, 1949.)

Due to the adaptation of the pressure field to the velocity field (Rossby, 1938) the frontal surface steepens especially along the leading edge of the cut-off low where the warm air advection is most intense.

The surface cyclogenesis may be obtained from the pressure tendency equation

$$(1/g)(\partial p/\partial t)_0 = -\int_0^\infty \mathbf{v}\cdot\nabla\rho\, dz - \int_0^\infty \rho\nabla\cdot\mathbf{v}\, dz. \qquad 6.124\ (2)$$

For horizontal terrain the term which contains the vertical component of motion vanishes. $\mathbf{v}$ and ∇ refer to a horizontal plane. Substituting from the vorticity equation, 1.233 (6) and considering that friction in the atmosphere destroys vorticity, i.e.,

$$dQ/dt = -QD + (\nabla\times\mathbf{F})_z \qquad 6.124\ (3)$$

(see Petterssen, 1950), we obtain the following equation:

$$(1/g)(\partial p/\partial t)_0 = -\int_0^\infty \mathbf{v}\cdot\nabla\rho\, dz + \int_0^\infty (\rho/Q)(dQ/dt)\, dz - \int_0^\infty (\rho/Q)(\nabla\times\mathbf{F})_z\, dz. \qquad 6.124\ (4)$$

$(\nabla\times\mathbf{F})_z$ is the vertical component of the rotor of the frictional forces.

Let $\mathbf{C}$ be the velocity of the cutoff low. With respect to the co-ordinate system which moves with this low we obtain

$$(\delta p/\delta t)_0 = (\partial p/\partial t)_0 + \mathbf{C}\cdot\nabla(p)_0. \qquad 6.124\ (5)$$

Hsieh was able to show that in the case of the cut-off low he investigated, $\mathbf{C}\cdot\nabla(p)_0>0$, because the motion of the system was directed toward an area with higher surface pressure. At the same time $dq/dt>0$ and $df/dt>0$, because the motion of the system had a component directed north. Therefore the decreasing surface pressure $(\delta p/\delta t)_0$ may be entirely related to the frictional term, if one neglects the small effects of density advection in the closed area of the cut-off low. As long as anticyclonic influence prevails near the ground, the frictional influence there will generate cyclonic angular momentum, which is equivalent to the dissipation of anticyclonic momentum. At the same time cyclonic angular momentum is produced at high levels, where the cyclonically rotating warm air affects the cold air. As soon as a low-pressure influence is established near the ground, cyclonic angular momentum will be destroyed here by friction. The upper current, therefore, has to overcome this influence by its own friction so that still $\int(\rho/Q)(\nabla\times\mathbf{F})_z>0$.

The turbulent exchange processes, and the momentum transport associated with them, thus plays an important role in the free atmosphere. A "frictionless" atmosphere may only be accepted as a first approximation to the actually prevailing conditions.

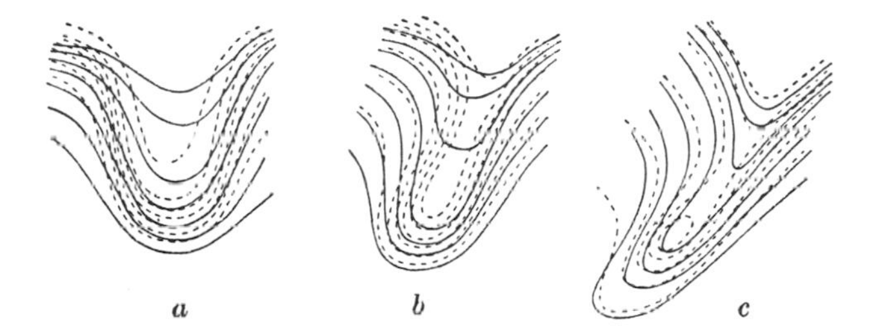

FIG. 6.124.5.—Schematic representation of the formation of a shear line in the upper wind field. Solid lines, 500-mb topography; dashed, isotherms. (Hsieh, 1950*a*.)

The displacement of cut-off lows sometimes offers difficult problems for the forecaster, especially in the European region. Surface-pressure distribution and temperature gradients usually are very diffuse in the influence region of these upper cyclones, so that the precipitation areas at the ground cannot be identified with discontinuities of a frontal character. A detailed consideration of the upper current in the vicinity of a cut-off low might be especially fruitful. The flow within the cut-off low has a small effect upon its displacement because of the latitude dependency of the Coriolis parameter (Rossby, 1948). In forecasting the displacement, experiments involving the computation of the geostrophic steering current by means of a grid with an empirically determined optimum grid distance should be recommended. More about this "grid" or "box" method has been said in Chapter 5.32. Klug (1956) computed a steering current from the resulting mean wind vector which is found within a circular area of about 300 to 500 km radius and which is centered in the low-pressure vortex. It is this vector which constitutes a pure translatory motion and which, when added to a pure rotational motion, renders the individual wind vectors that are observed in the area of a vortex (see Scherhag, 1948*b*).

If one compares the formation of a cut-off low with the formation of a *shearline*, at first several parallels become apparent (Hsieh, 1950*a*; Lee, 1956; Newton, *et al.*, 1951; Newton and Carson, 1953). Figure 6.124.5 contains a schematic representation of a shear-line formation. The basic weather situation is very similar to the one shown in Figure 6.124.1, with the exception that the warm-air advection aloft takes place uniformly along the whole rear side of the trough and not only—as in the case of a cut-off low—in the north. Thus a direct circulation is established which consumes potential energy by sinking of cold air and by rising of warm air along the frontal slopes of the cold dome. A schematic representation of this vertical circulation is shown in Figure 6.124.6. Because of the outflow of cold air near the ground and the decrease of the cold-air area aloft produced by reasons of continuity, two jet streams of opposite direction approach each other in the upper troposphere. By this, the cyclonic shearing vorticity of the middle troposphere (500-mb) where the shear line is most pronouncedly developed, will increase (see Fig. 3.242.1). At the same time it may be observed that the level of non-divergence lies relatively high—on the average of the case investigated by Hsieh (1950*a*) near 400 mb. Below this level we find a well-pronounced divergence which—according to the vorticity theorem—should bring about a decrease of cyclonic vorticity. Since this is not observed, however, and since, on the contrary, the cyclonic shear is intensified, one will have to conclude that *more* cyclonic vorticity is supplied from higher levels than is consumed by divergence at lower levels.

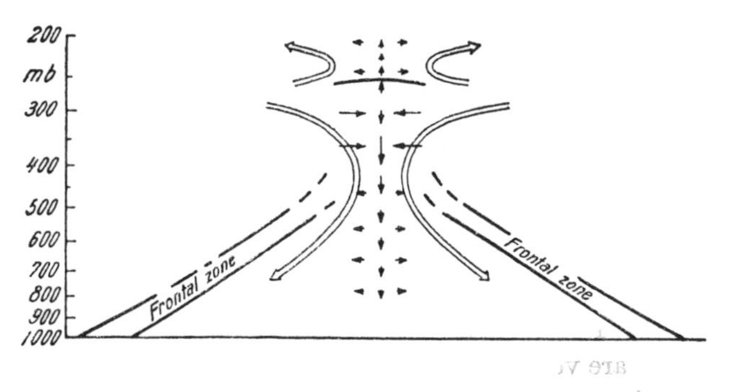

Fig. 6.124.6.—Schematic representation of vertical motion and divergence during the formation of a shear line. Vertical and horizontal velocities are proportional to the length of the black arrows. (Hsieh, 1950*a*.)

Whether in a particular case a shear line or a cut-off low will develop out of an elongated trough thus depends on the distribution of direct circulation: A uniform distribution along the total length of the trough and especially a direct circulation at the tip of the trough leads to the formation of a shear line. Strong direct circulation to the north and weak direct circulation, or even indirect circulation, to the south results in the formation of a cut-off low. Because of the strong divergence near the ground fair, high-pressure type weather dominates underneath a shear line, while in the case of the cut-off low, as described above, the high-pressure situation may be relieved by low-pressure activity with precipitation.

6.125. Blocking Anticyclones

Under a "blocking high"—or sometimes also shortly referred to as "blocking"—we understand the formation of a quasi-stationary high-pressure ridge which is embedded in the westerlies. It can even be recognized from the surface-pressure distribution (Mook, 1954), and it causes a large-scale meridional exchange of air masses. Together with the formation of a "block," the zonal index decreases. (Saito, 1955).

As the cause of the development of a cut-off low we have found the diffluence of two jet streams. The formation of a blocking high, on the other hand, starts with the confluence of the subtropical and the polar jet streams upstream from the ridge (see Fig. 4.141; Defant and Taba, 1957). The confluent zone, again, forms to the east of a trough which has developed under strong vorticity advection (Elliot, 1955; Gazzola, 1954, 1955). By the resulting strong warm-air advection from the southwest the blocking ridge is constantly fortified on its western slopes. By cold advection from the north, occurring on the east side of the ridge, it is constantly dissipated there. Figure 6.125 shows schematically the flow pattern during the formation of a blocking

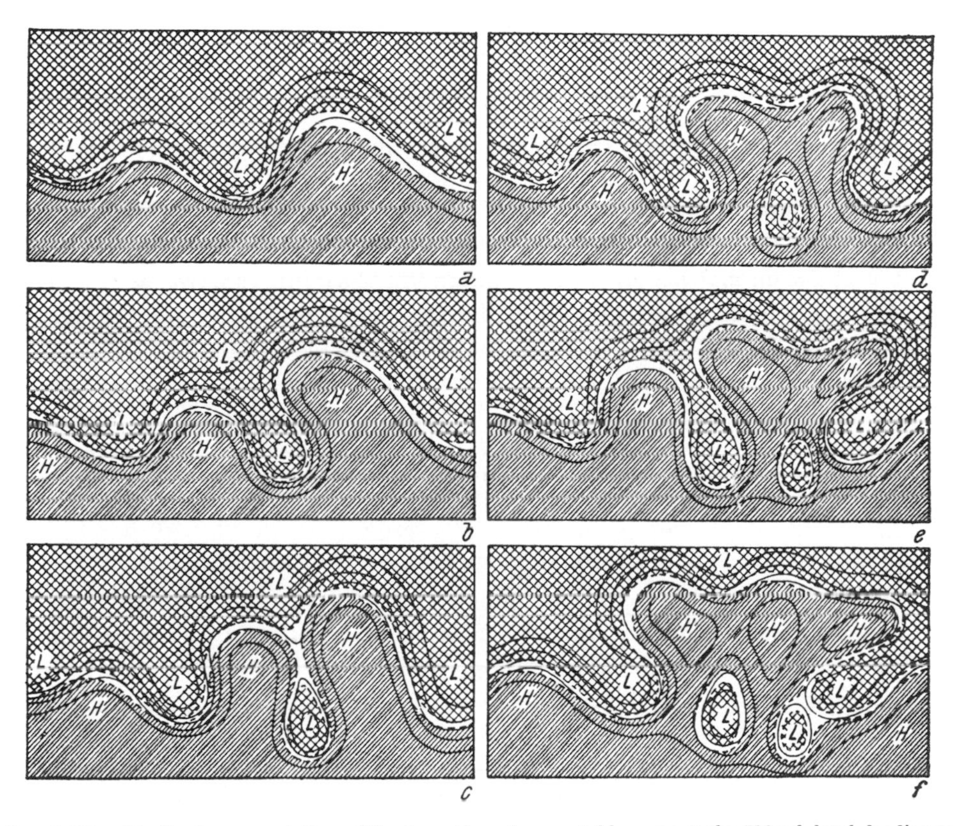

Fig. 6.125.—Idealized representation of the formation of an unstable wave at the 500-mb level, leading to the development of a blocking anticyclone in the north. Solid lines, stream lines; dashed, isotherms. Cold and warm regions are indicated by different shading. (Berggren, Bolin, and Rossby, 1949.)

wave. When the high-pressure ridge finally is cut off due to the cold advection in the trough to its east, the block usually becomes somewhat retrograde and the jet-stream system splits: The PFJ flows around the anticyclone's northern slopes while the STJ crosses the high-pressure bridge in the south and flows into the trough on the east side of the ridge, and around the cut-off low which is frequently found there.

Another confluent zone with the polar-front jet coming from the north will develop here. The wave disturbances which migrate along the two jet streams—one over the Norwegian Sea, the other over the Mediterranean—may have different velocities (Berg, 1953). Each of the two tracks of disturbances is characterized by a precipitation zone (Rex, 1950*b*).

Detailed studies by Rex (1950*a*) and by other authors (Hawkins, 1955; Stark, 1957) confirm the development scheme of "blocking" outlined above. The confluence region upstream of the developing blocking anticyclone is characterized by increased zonal circulation (Miller and Vederman, 1951; Rex, 1950*a*). When the blocking high is established, the zonal wind profile shows two maxima, which correspond to the latitudes of the polar and of the subtropical jet streams. Between these two maxima easterly winds aloft prevail. Precipitation areas, associated with ascending motions, are mainly concentrated along the west side of the "block," while the east side is characterized by sinking cold air (Eliassen and Hubert, 1953).

Blocking anticyclones, at times, are extremely stable and may continue during several weeks (Reiter and Szekeres, 1960). They play an important role in the heat exchange between tropical and polar latitudes. They are also important in their influence upon the planetary wave pattern. Usually a wave caused by "blocking" is somewhat longer than would correspond to normal conditions of a zonal current (Elliot and Smith, 1949; Garriot, 1954; Namias and Clapp, 1944; Sanders, 1953; Sumner, 1954). The influence of these stationary blocking anticyclones on jet streams is felt downstream as well as upstream, sometimes in the form of a retrograde diminishing of the zonal index (Allan *et al.*, 1940; Berggren, Bolin, and Rossby, 1949; Namias, 1952*a*; Rossby, 1949*a*, 1950; Yeh, 1949). Hawkins (1955) found that during the period of May to June, 1955, blocking anticyclones were constantly re-forming in a discontinuous retrogression. This blocking wave circled the whole hemisphere twice within the given period, traveling from east to west.

The preferred regions for the formation of blocking anticyclones will be discussed in detail in Chapter 7.33.

6.13. Cyclones as Wave Disturbances of a Basic Current

In an effort to compute cyclogenetic processes numerically, theoreticians have, in a certain sense, gone back to the concepts of the polar-front theory. In a mathematical and analytical treatment of cyclogenesis, we are not so much concerned with a physically well-founded explanation of the time sequence of flow patterns causing the observed weather sequence, but rather with the formulation of differential equations whose solutions indicate, whether a disturbance of a certain wave length will amplify in time (unstable state) or whether it will remain constant or decay (stable state). Thus, the state of the basic current's stability with respect to a spectrum of wave disturbances will be investigated. For this, one makes use of the perturbation theory (see Chapter 4.321). It would lead beyond the scope of this book to cover more details see Fjørtoft, 1951).

In considering the energy of the current, two viewpoints are opposed to each other: According to Charney (1947), Eady (1949), and Fjørtoft (1951), a baroclinic or *potentioclinic* flow (in the latter the surfaces of constant potential energy are sloping, and the number of isosteric-isopotential solenoids per unit area gives a measure of the potentioclinicity of the flow) is unstable with respect to waves of sufficiently large wave length. The instability is produced by a transformation of potential energy into kinetic energy of the *perturbation motion.*

It is Solberg's (1930) opinion, however, that no potentioclinic energy is consumed during a cyclogenetic process. The energy of the wave disturbance is taken from the kinetic energy of the basic current, instead.

Höiland and Pedersen (1954) tried to weigh the merits and drawbacks of both opinions against each other, by using synoptic data. The computation of kinetic energy proved to be too inaccurate, however, to settle the dispute. The changes of potential energy were large enough so that the difficult to calculate transport of potential energy could not be neglected any longer.

In the case considered by Höiland and Pedersen, the mean meridional pressure gradient of the troposphere decreased within the area under observation. The assumption that the basis current lost some of its kinetic energy might therefore appear justified. Just as well, however, the kinetic energy of the basic current could have increased because of a *concentration* of the mean meridional wind profile, while at the same time the mean meridional pressure gradient had decreased. Unfortunately, Höiland's results give no indication in this direction.

In order to study the problem of cyclogenesis one will have to consider gravitational stability, dynamic stability (lateral shear and constancy of angular momentum), baroclinic stability (thermal wind), and stabilities of velocity discontinuities (Arakawa, 1951*a*; Eady, 1951; Fleagle, 1957; Fleagle and Izumi, 1955; Godson, 1950*b*, *c*; Petterssen, 1955*c*; Queney, 1952). As is evident from Chapter 1.236, the earth's rotation has a stabilizing influence which increases poleward with increasing Coriolis parameter f, and which vanishes at the equator (see Starr, 1959). In temperate latitudes the earth's rotation is sufficiently stabilizing upon the turning-over of adjacent air masses so that dynamic instability has hardly any great significance in cyclogenesis. In strongly developed jet streams, however, we still may find a zone on the anticyclonic side of the axis, where the absolute vorticity $Q \leqq 0$. Thus, small areas with negative absolute vorticity may contribute to an amplification of disturbances, even in temperate latitudes.

The significance of jet streams—even in these theoretical considerations of cyclogenesis—is stressed by the fact that static stability, baroclinicity, and wind shear attain maximum values within frontal zones associated with jet maxima.

6.2. PRECIPITATION AND MOISTURE DISTRIBUTIONS AS INDICATORS OF VERTICAL CIRCULATIONS

The location of the main precipitation area in the influence region of a jet stream depends upon the position of the area of upper divergence, and is *not* immediately connected with the surface fronts (Curtis and Panofsky, 1958; Schulte-Vennbur, 1953). This observed fact also contradicts the original Norwegian cyclone model.

In the paper by Palmén already quoted earlier the values of divergence have been computed for the areas shown in Figure 6.122.4. The mean divergences, averaged over areas 1, 2, 3, 7, 8, 9, 12, 13, 14 on the one hand, and over areas 4, 5, 6, 10, 11, 15 on the other hand are shown in Figure 6.2.1. The level of non-divergence near the 500-mb surface may clearly be distinguished.

TABLE 6.2. MEAN SPECIFIC HUMIDITY $\bar{s}$, MEAN DIVERGENCE, AND THEIR PRODUCTS, COMPUTED FOR AREA 11 OF FIG. 6.122.4 (15 October, 1954, 1500 GCT)

ISOBARIC LAYER (centibar)	$\bar{s}$	$\overline{\nabla_H \cdot \mathbf{V}}$	$\bar{s}\ \overline{\nabla_H \cdot \mathbf{V}}$
100–90	$16.0 \cdot 10^{-3}$	$-6.2 \cdot 10^{-5}$	$-99.2 \cdot 10^{-8}$
90–80	13.8	−3.8	−52.4
80–70	11.5	−1.9	−21.9
70–60	9.0	0.1	0.9
60–50	6.2	2.4	14.9
50–40	3.8	3.7	14.1
40–30	1.7	4.0	6.8
30–20	0.4	3.2	1.3

The precipitation area (Fig. 6.2.2) is characterized by strong low-level convergence, and it is mainly concentrated in area 11. In Table 6.2 the moisture and divergence values and their products are summarized for this area.

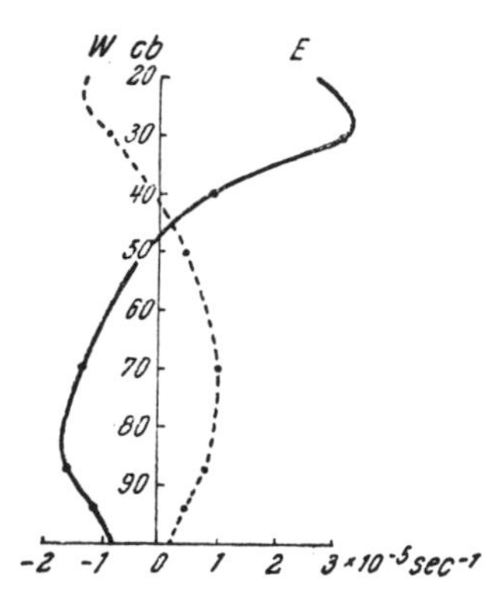

FIG. 6.2.1.—Mean divergence in the eastern (solid line) and in the western part (dashed) of the area outlined in Figure 6.122.4. (Palmén, 1958.)

The water transport in a column of air may be expressed by

$$-\int_0^\infty \int_0^{L_l} s\rho v_n \, dL \, dz, \qquad 6.2\ (1)$$

where L_l is the lateral boundary of the area element, and v_n is the component of flow normal to these boundaries. By simple transformation one obtains

$$-\frac{L_l}{g}\int_0^{p_0} (\bar{s}\ \bar{v}_n + \overline{s^* v_n^*})\, dp. \qquad 6.2\ (2)$$

The bars indicate average values taken along the boundaries of the area element which is located on a certain isobaric surface, and the asterisks denote quantities which stand for the deviations from these mean values, i.e., for the perturbation components which, depending on the correlation between normal component of flow v_n and humidity, may cause a moisture transport into a direction opposite to the basic current. The precipitation per unit time over the area under consideration is given by

$$P = E - \frac{L_i}{g} \int_0^{p_0} (\bar{s}\,\bar{v}_n + \overline{s^* v_n^*})\,dp. \qquad 6.2\ (3)$$

E is the evaporation per unit of time within the area under study. In the case treated by Palmén the evaporation had been neglected because it was small when compared with the precipitation amounts. Furthermore, the perturbation terms in the above equation have not been considered, because they were difficult to evaluate. Thus, one arrives at

$$P \cong -\frac{A_i}{g} \int_0^{p_0} \bar{s}\,\overline{\nabla_H \cdot \mathbf{v}}\,dp. \qquad 6.2\ (4)$$

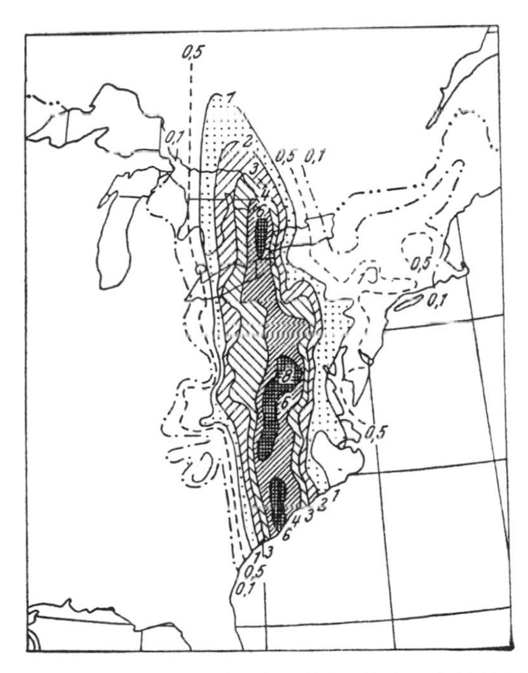

FIG. 6.2.2.—Precipitation in inches between 15 October, 1954, 0600, and 16 October, 0600 GCT. (Palmén, 1958.)

$\overline{\nabla_H \cdot \mathbf{v}}$ is the mean divergence, taken over the area A_i of the element under consideration.

The evaluation of the integral in 6.2 (4) rendered a precipitation value of 30.6 mm within 6 hours for area 11, while the actually observed value was 33 mm. These two values stand in excellent agreement.

If one compares the position of the precipitation area in Figure 6.2.2 with the location of the jet stream at the 300-mb level (Fig. 6.122.3), it is evident that the enormous amounts of rainfall are associated with the upper divergence in the right rear quadrant of a slightly anticyclonically curved jet maximum. This agrees well with the jet-stream model shown in Figure 4.122.3. Since the upper divergence in turn depends upon the vorticity advection according to Eq. 6.121 (1), it is possible to forecast precipitation from the vorticity distribution (Bailey, 1958; Jenrette, 1960; Riehl, Norquest, and Sugg, 1952; see also Riehl and Teweles, 1953; Starrett, 1949).

In cases of an upper wind field which is less pronounced than in the cyclogenesis described by Palmén the inaccuracies in the computation of vorticity and divergence become more apparent (Riehl and Teweles, 1954; Teweles, 1953). It may also be expected that the application of the geostrophic instead of the actually observed vorticity may lead to wrong estimates (see Chapter 1.239). Furthermore, orographically induced vertical motions (foehn and barrage) may modify the precipitation pattern. If for the computation of vertical motions adiabatic conditions have been assumed, the release of latent heat due to condensation processes will have to be considered. Due to the destabilization during moist adiabatic vertical motions the rising component of velocity may be considerably increased (Smebye, 1958).

In spite of all these factors which may make a quantitative forecast of precipitation from the motions in the atmosphere rather difficult, an objective prognosis does not seem impossible. Komabayasi and others (1955) have tried successfully the computation of expected precipitation amounts from the changes of temperature (change of the relative topography 500/700 mb) and from the water vapor distribution by means of a graphical integration method according to Fjørtoft. The results seem to be promising.

The qualitative agreement of precipitation patterns with the model of upper divergence and convergence distribution shown in Figure 4.122.3 also appears in a statistical average. Anticyclonically curved jet maxima show an increased tendency for the formation of precipitation in the right rear quadrant, whereas cyclonically curved maxima show this tendency in the front left quadrant. The quadrant diagonally across the precipitation sector apparently is less well pronounced in its upper divergence and in its precipitation pattern (Jenista, 1953; Kikuchi, 1957; Wolff and Dickson, 1953).

Jet streams with approximately straight axes show a distinct shift of maximum precipitation toward the right side in the entrance region. In the delta region, however, the jet maximum shows a significant excess of precipitation amount in the left sector, where the main amounts on the average fall about 600 km to the north of the jet axis (Johnson and Daniels, 1953).

The precipitation controlling influence of the PFJ may be followed far into the subtropical belt. A study by Yeh, Carson, and Marciano (1951) shows for instance that the rainfall in Hawaii increases with the distance of the jet stream from the islands, and with the anticyclonic shear along the south side of the jet; it decreases, however, with increasing wind speeds in the jet core. Apparently one finds a zone with prevailing sinking motion to the south of the polar-front jet which impedes the precipitation activity over the Hawaiian Islands as soon as the position of the jet stream shifts south of about 41° N.

In general, the precipitation pattern may be taken as a valuable indicator for the sign of vertical motions in the middle troposphere.

Studies by Palmén (1958) and other authors (Chapter 6.122) rendered a schematic pattern of vertical motions in an east-west cross section through the atmosphere. According to this, sinking motion has to be expected to the rear of a trough, rising motion on its leading side. As Reed and Danielsen (1959) were able to show, the vertical motions are not confined to the troposphere. Maximum sinking motions are observed right underneath the jet-stream level, and the vertical transport, coming from the stratosphere, moves through the level of maximum wind. In this manner stratospheric air is transported within the frontal zone into the levels of the middle troposphere. The transport of stratospheric air into the troposphere which Raethjen (1954) postulated in connection with a remanent meridional circulation over polar latitudes and which would help to explain the extreme visibility in polar air, thus would mainly be concentrated in the jet-stream region. The assumption that "zero layer" and layer of maximum wind are identical, therefore, may hold only on the average in the jet-stream zone, and not in individual weather situations (see Chapter 4.122).

Remarkably large values of vertical wind speeds have been computed by Endlich (1953) from analyses of upper-level charts, assuming adiabatic conditions of flow (up to 16 cm/sec as three-hour mean values). Even though there may be some objections to his methods of computation—especially against the fact that he combined three hour trajectories with one-quarter of the 12 hour temperature changes (Fleagle and Endlich, 1954)—the order of magnitude of Endlich's results still should be correct, as investigations by Brundidge (1956) and Reiter (1961*a*) showed. In Endlich's study the order of magnitude of vertical motions was about the same at the 500- and the 300-mb levels. The centers of maximum vertical velocity lay either in, or in the close vicinity, of the jet axis. (Mean vertical velocities > 5 cm/sec are found only rarely at a distance of more than 450 km from the jet axis. Sugimoto [1958] finds upward motions of 50 cm/sec close to the axis of the PFJ over Japan.) The author (Reiter, 1961*e*) computed vertical motions in the jet-stream region over the United States of up to 2.5 m/sec from aircraft data.

The further conclusions Endlich drew from his computations deserve some correction, however. Endlich considered the distribution of centers of upward and downward motion relative to the position of the jet axis, without reference to entrance or delta regions. This led him to the conclusion that the distribution of vertical motions is more or less random. A closer scrutiny of Endlich's analyses reveals, however, that the centers of maximum vertical velocities, at the 300- as well as at the 500-mb levels, are in good agreement with the schematic east-west cross section devised by Fleagle (1947). Areas of maximum rising motion are concentrated near the leading edge of cyclonically curved jet maxima, i.e., on the forward side of troughs, while maximum sinking motions mainly occur to the rear of jet maxima. Endlich has not considered any anticyclonically curved jet maxima; following Palmén's computations, one would expect maximum rising motions to the *rear* of such maxima.

Investigations by Montalto (1959), who based his velocity computations upon the equation of continuity, corroborate the occurrence of maximum vertical motions near the jet axis.

In considering the turning of wind with height, which may be computed from the component of flow normal to the vector between radar set and balloon, Barbé (1956) arrives at a jet-stream model which also allows one to expect strong vertical motions at jet-stream level.

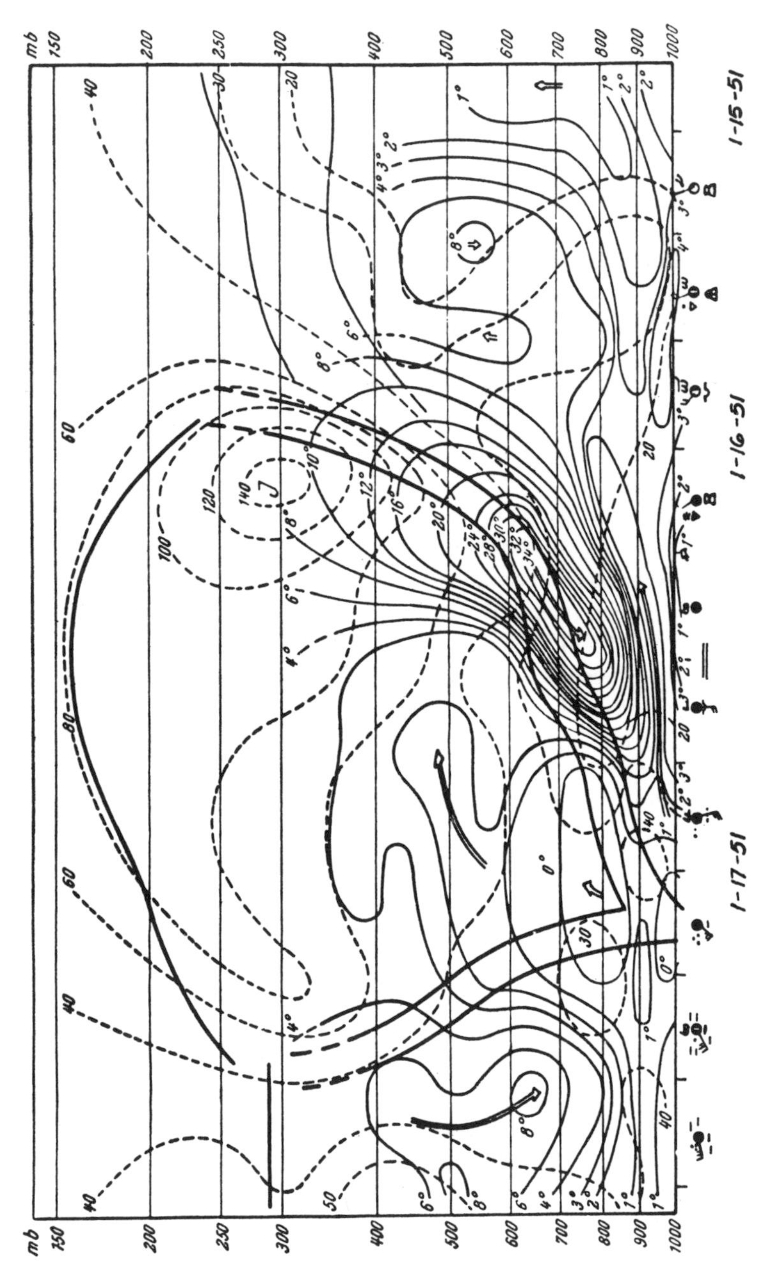

FIG. 6.2.3.—Time section of the radiosonde at Lerwick, 15 to 17 January, 1951. Tropopause and frontal zones are marked by heavy solid or dashed lines. Light dashed, isotachs (knots); light solid lines, dewpoint-temperature spread (°C). The arrows indicate the vertical motions deduced from the moisture distribution. (Vuorela, 1957*a*.)

A qualitative estimate of the vertical circulation in the jet-stream region has been made by Vuorela (1953, 1957*a*), who considered the differences between dew point and free-air temperatures. The above conclusions were fully corroborated by his studies. Figure 6.2.3 shows the dew-point differences in a time section through a well-pronounced jet stream which crossed the British Islands from a northwesterly direction on 16 January, 1951. The extreme dryness of the air within the frontal zone will have to be explained by sinking of air masses maybe even out of the stratosphere, in accordance with the findings by Reed and Danielsen (1959). Vuorela computed the vertical velocities in this time section by different methods, which rendered slightly discrepant results. All estimates, however, showed maximum sinking in the close vicinity of the jet stream (order of magnitude 10 cm/sec as a mean value taken over 12 hours). The values for ascending motion (maximum 80 cm/sec) have been computed by taking into account moist adiabatic changes of state. These analyses, again, reveal that "zero layer" and maximum wind layer are *not* identical in the jet-stream region. All other cross sections analyzed by Vuorela in this context also show a maximum of sinking motion in the jet stream.

Vuorela's analyses were corroborated by Sawyer's (1953, 1955) and Murray's (1953, 1956) findings from British research flights. From these it became apparent that underneath the jet core dry air of extremely low frost point (which gives a measure of the relative humidity with respect to ice) is embedded in the frontal zone. The transition from the cloud and precipitation zone into this dry "tongue," which seemed to continue vertically all the way into the jet-stream region, is very well pronounced and abrupt. Sawyer (1958) also arrived at the conclusion that this dry region is constituted by air masses which have undergone strong sinking motions and is not produced by mixing processes between the two air bodies on either side of the frontal zone. The horizontal gradient of vertical velocities (strong downward motion underneath the jet, only slight sinking motion within the cold air), which becomes apparent from the moisture distribution and which is in agreement with the marked gradient normal to the jet axis of the divergence field at jet stream level, still manifests itself in the strong horizontal temperature gradients at the 500-mb level. At the 600-mb level the "dry tongue" of Sawyer's measurements appears less pronounced, and also the horizontal temperature gradient normal to the front lies appreciably below the values observed at the 500-mb surface. The warm side of the frontal zone in this lower level is relatively moist and cloudy. Thus, this part of the front corresponds closest to the model developed from the Norwegian polar-front theory with respect to the "up-gliding" of warm air masses.

In the higher regions of the frontal zone the concept of a front being a Margules boundary surface which, according to the polar-front theory, separates two air masses is rendered invalid. The frontal "zone," which so far has been thought of as the mixing zone between two air bodies of different potential temperature, in reality forms by the intrusion of high-tropospheric or stratospheric air masses. By this the polar-front theory which has already been criticized in the first part of Chapter 6 becomes questionable even from another point of view. But also the exclusive consideration of air mass properties in explaining the weather sequence loses much of its potential (see Reed, 1957*a*).

According to the new concept, "frontal zones" are not only boundaries between air masses whose existence and changes could be treated *kinematically*, but they have to be considered as long and narrow regions in which most of the transformations between potential and kinetic energy of the atmosphere take place. This becomes apparent from the baroclinicity and from the jet-stream-like concentration of momentum, as well as from the strong horizontal gradients of vertical velocity which appear here. The "frontal zone," thus, has become a *dynamical* problem.

The moisture distribution described above is corroborated by observations of condensation trail formation (Murray, 1956). The appearance of such contrails depends on air pressure, temperature, and relative humidity of the surrounding air, as well as on the mixing ratio between exhaust fumes and air within the condensation trail zone. The latter factor is of importance insofar as the combustion gases contain a certain amount of water vapor and heat (Appleman, 1952, 1953; U.S. Air Weather Service, 1956*b*). A *critical temperature* may be stated for a given pressure and a given

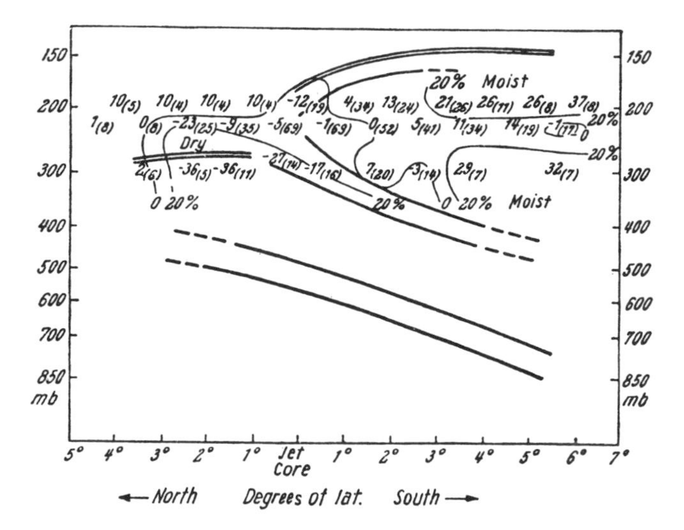

FIG. 6.2.4.—"Excess frequency" of condensation-trail formation in the jet-stream region, in per cent. In parentheses, total number of observations (see text). (Endlich and McLean, 1957.)

relative humidity above which no contrails can form. Brundidge (1958) quotes −47° C as absolute upper limit of condensation trail formation during the research flights of Project Jet Stream. If pressure and temperature are given, there exists accordingly a minimum relative humidity below which no condensation trails can form.

In the course of the investigation Endlich and McLean (1957) conducted with material from jet-stream research flights, the probabilities of condensation trail formation have been computed as functions of pressure and temperature. These probabilities were compared with actual observations. Figure 6.2.4 shows the "excess frequency" of contrail formation (defined as observed frequencies minus theoretical frequencies divided by the total number of observations), plotted relative to the idealized jet-stream cross section devised by Endlich and McLean. The dry region (negative "excess frequencies") extends along the baroclinic zone of the upper troposphere, just underneath the jet maximum, and in the stratosphere along the cyclonic side of the jet axis (see Dunning and La Seur, 1955). The existence of the tongues of dry air is thus confirmed. The air on the anticyclonic side of the frontal zone, on the other hand, is rather moist.

Ozone may serve as another indicator of large-scale vertical motions in the atmosphere, especially since refined techniques of measurement have recently made it possible to measure its detailed distribution.

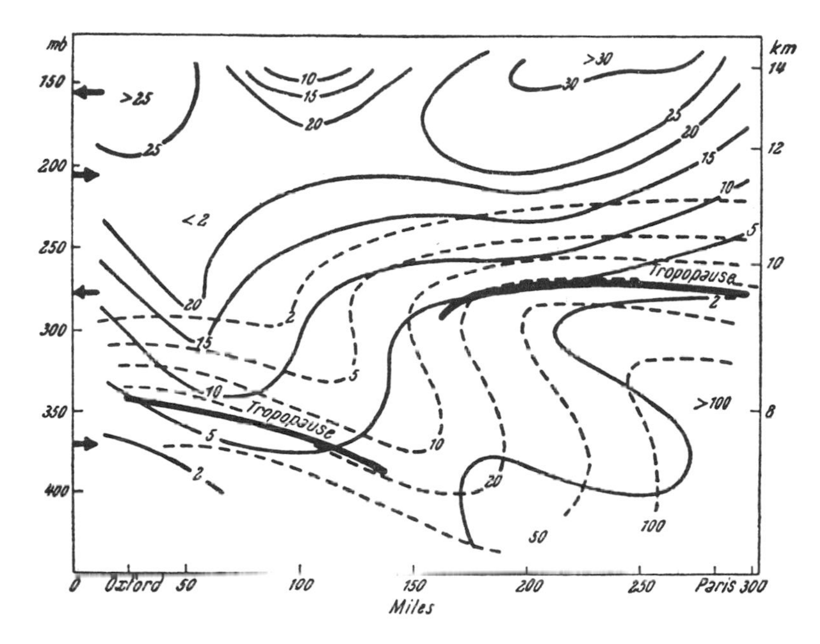

FIG. 6.2.5.—Cross section through a jet stream over the English Channel at the inflection point between trough and ridge, 6 March, 1959, 1150 to 1400 GCT. Solid lines, ozone contents (10^{-8} mol/mol); dashed, mixing ratio of humidity (milligrams/gram). The flight levels are indicated by arrows along the left margin of the diagram. (Murgatroyd, 1959.)

In Chapter 4.415 the correlation between mean ozone content of the atmosphere and mean state of the circulation has been pointed out. It has been known quite some time that polar air masses, because of the large-scale sinking motions which they undergo, have a higher ozone content than tropical air masses. The downward transport of ozone out of the stratosphere is accomplished by the slow acting meridional circulation and by turbulent exchange processes. The atmospheric large-scale "exchange" through large-scale vertical motions within migrating pressure systems has to be regarded, however, as the most effective means of transport (Ramanathan, 1954; Reed, 1953). This opinion is strengthened by the increase of the ozone content of the atmosphere during winter, when the cyclonic activity reaches its maximum and therefore also vertical transport is best developed. There are indications of an ozone maximum at 50° to 60° N. In these latitudes the interdiurnal pressure changes, i.e., the cyclonic activity, attain their highest values. This permits some conclusions on the effectiveness of vertical motions, since the measured ozone fluctuations are mainly due to changes of concentration below 20 km. Measurements of the ozone distribution in cyclones corroborate the prevailing sinking motions in the northerly current to the rear of the vortex by the ozone maximum appearing there. (An extensive bibliography on this subject may be found in Craig [1950].)

More recently it has been possible to conduct successful ozone measurements in short intervals from aircraft (Murgatroyd, 1959, 1960). The results obtained from the research flight of 6 March, 1959, are shown in Figure 6.2.5. The flight has been conducted on the east side of an upper trough. The ozone content of the air shows a well-marked maximum in the region of the tropopause break, below and to the left of the jet core, indicating the import of air masses rich in ozone from greater heights and from the entrance region of the jet maximum (see Brewer, 1959; Wexler, Moreland, and Weyant, 1960). The moisture distribution, which at the same time has been measured with a Dobson frost-point hygrometer (dashed lines in Fig. 6.2.5), shows a minimum in the same location, which corroborates the conclusions on the sign of the vertical motions. In the stratosphere the ozone concentrations have a distribution opposite to the one in the troposphere. From this one might conclude that also the large-scale vertical motions have the opposite sign here.

From investigations conducted by the author (Reiter, 1961*a*, *d*) it becomes evident that in the region of the baroclinic layers above and below the jet maximum strong horizontal convergences are concentrated. Since along the "zero layer" the vertical motions reverse their sign, one may assume that these strong convergences cause a reversal of vertical motions in the stratosphere as compared with the troposphere.

6.3. CLOUDS IN THE JET-STREAM REGION

Cloud observations in the jet-stream region allow conclusions on sign of the vertical motions and on the moisture distribution in the atmosphere, and they give an indication of the position of the jet stream. Furthermore, they reveal some of the fine structure of the atmosphere (see Bannon, Frost, and Kirk, 1956; Frost, 1954).

During the Project Jet Stream flights valuable data on cloud distribution in the vicinity of jet streams have been obtained, which were treated statistically by McLean (1957). Figure 6.3.1 gives the per cent frequency distibution for *all* cloud types observed during Project Jet Stream flights. The greatest probability for cloudiness occurs on the anticyclonic side of the baroclinic zone (see Murray, 1953) and also within the cold air at some distance from the jet axis (*ca.* 5° of latitude north of it) (James, 1955; Sawyer and Ilett, 1951). The former of the two maxima obviously is associated with the "direct circulation" of the warm air along surfaces of constant pseudo-potential temperature. The second maximum within the cold air probably is a result of the "indirect" circulation, which, by virtue of divergence at jet-stream level, brings about a lifting of the air masses. Even in the statistical average, the baroclinic zone itself shows only little cloudiness (Fig. 6.3.1), which indicates prevailing sinking motion in this region.

The maxima of cloudiness in the upper troposphere shown in Figure 6.3.1, and extending along the "jet-stream front" and below the tropopause in the cold air-mass, consist entirely of clouds of the cirrus variety. Studies by Bundgaard (1956*a*) revealed a good agreement between cirro-stratus cover and areas with positive vorticity advection (see French and Johannessen, 1954). Underneath the polar tropopause,

75 per cent of the observations indicated cirrus, and 25 per cent cirro-stratus. About 5° to 6° of latitude south of the jet core cirro-stratus was observed in 80 per cent of the cases, and cirrus in only 20 per cent. Cirro-cumulus was observed only rarely, and seemed to be confined to the warm edge of the "jet-stream front." The formation of this type of clouds might be attributed to the wind shear and the resulting mixing of dry and moist air, i.e., to a certain instability. Along this stable interface one frequently observes the formation of waves, which at times show a very regular pattern of cirro-cumulus and alto-cumulus (Barbé, 1956; Schaefer, 1953*a*).

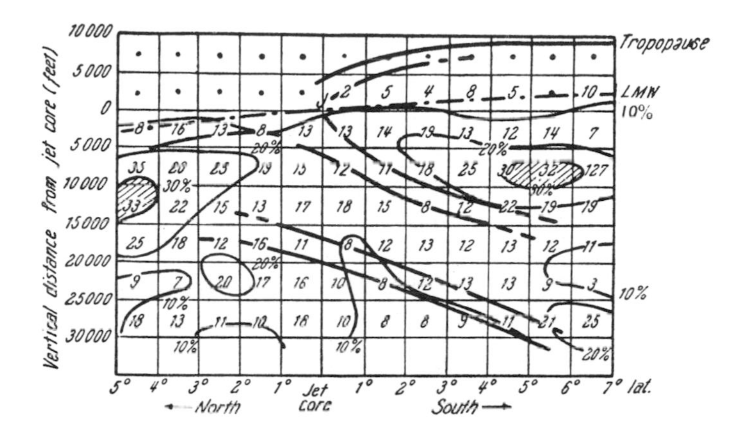

FIG. 6.3.1.—Per cent frequency of cloudiness in the jet-stream region. (McLean, 1957.)

During several of the aforementioned research flights it was observed that the cirrus clouds ended in a sharp discontinuity in the jet core (Conover, 1960*a*; Kuettner, 1959*a*; see Reiter, 1961*d*). North of the core, cloudless conditions prevail. According to observations by Schaefer (1953*a*), the precipitation area most frequently starts right underneath the jet axis and extends south of it. If cirrus clouds are not obscured by low cloudiness, one may draw conclusions from the position of the sharp edge of cloud banks about where the jet axis is located. Such favorable conditions for observation usually are present in the entrance region of a jet maximum, where the sinking motion in the lower levels impedes the formation of clouds (Sawyer and Ilett, 1951).

Cirrus clouds on the south side of the jet stream frequently are oriented in long bands approximately parallel to the wind direction (Conover, 1959, 1960*a*; Barbé, 1956). In some cases these bands were several hundred kilometers long (in one case even more than 2000 km) (Kuettner, 1959*b*). 50 per cent of the weather situations investigated by Conover showed cirrus bands in the entrance region of a jet maximum on the anticyclonic side of the axis and in less than 370 km distance from the axis. Cirrus may also be observed on the cyclonic side of weak jet streams, especially when a second jet stream is located farther to the north. An orientation of the bands parallel to the wind direction may only be found, though, with stronger wind speeds and stronger wind shears (Sekera, 1948). This indicates the existence of "helical" vortices with horizontal axes.

The banded structure of clouds becomes especially apparent from photographs taken at great height (Conover, 1960*b*; Fritz, 1959; Kuettner, 1959*b*). Weather satellites of a kind similar to Tiros may furnish us with the possibility of correlating such cloud photographs with atmospheric flow patterns over areas lacking aerological observations (see Anonymous, 1960; Fritz and Wexler, 1960; Hubert, Fritz, and Wexler, 1960; Wexler and Fritz, 1960). Figure 6.3.2 shows frame 10 obtained from weather satellite Tiros I during orbit 543 of 8 May, 1960, 2048 GCT.[2] At that time

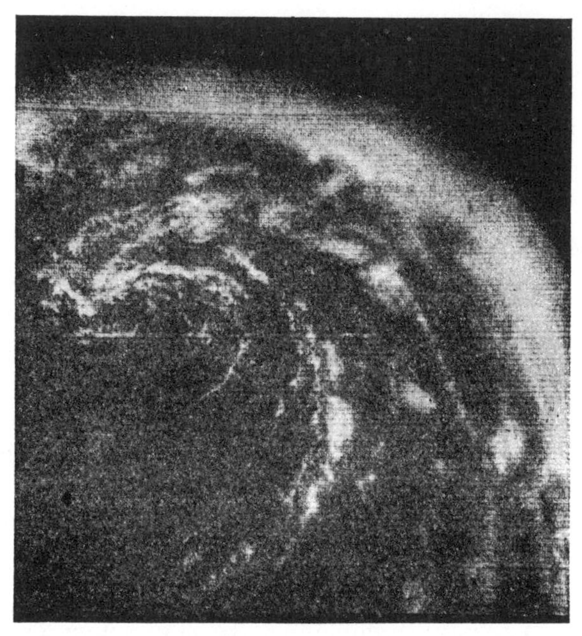

FIG. 6.3.2.—Meteorological satellite "Tiros I," frame 10, orbit 543, 8 May, 1960, 2048 GCT. (Photo: U.S. Weather Bureau and National Aeronautics and Space Administration.)

the satellite was positioned at 27° N and 70° W, the direction of view (given by the vector which points from the center of the frame [29° N, 66° W] toward the center of the visible arc of the horizon) was toward 63°. The weather situation of 9 May, 1960, 0000 GCT is shown by the surface weather chart (Fig. 6.3.3) and by the 500-mb chart (Fig. 6.3.4). Both maps have been taken from the Taeglicher Wetterbericht des Deutschen Wetterdienstes (Daily Weather Report of the German Weather Service). In Figure 6.3.2 a low-pressure vortex in the region of the Bermuda Islands is clearly indicated, which has eluded the analyses of Figures 6.3.3 and .4. The cloud pattern is similar to what is found in a tropical hurricane; the vortex outlined here, however, is an extratropical cyclone. The narrow, elongated, and sharply bounded cloud bands, which probably are made up by larger cumuli, indicate a banded structure of the convergence zones (see also Chapter 4.311), which spiral into the low-pressure vortex. The more diffuse white areas indicate the presence of cirrus sheets, whose orientation fits well into the upper flow pattern (Fig. 6.3.4). Most likely the upper

[2] The photograph has kindly been made available by Mr. Lester F. Hubert, U.S. Weather Bureau.

field of flow shows much more detail than is indicated in Figure 6.3.4. Already the existence of an individual low-pressure vortex indicates the presence of a separate jet finger, whose maximum probably lies to the south of point B (Fig. 6.3.3), being associated, according to the foregoing discussion, with the cloud bands (probably cirrus) which appear in the center of Figure 6.3.2 and run toward the bottom of the photograph. The opportunities offered by high-altitude cloud photography make a continuation of studies initiated by Schaefer and Conover most desirable.

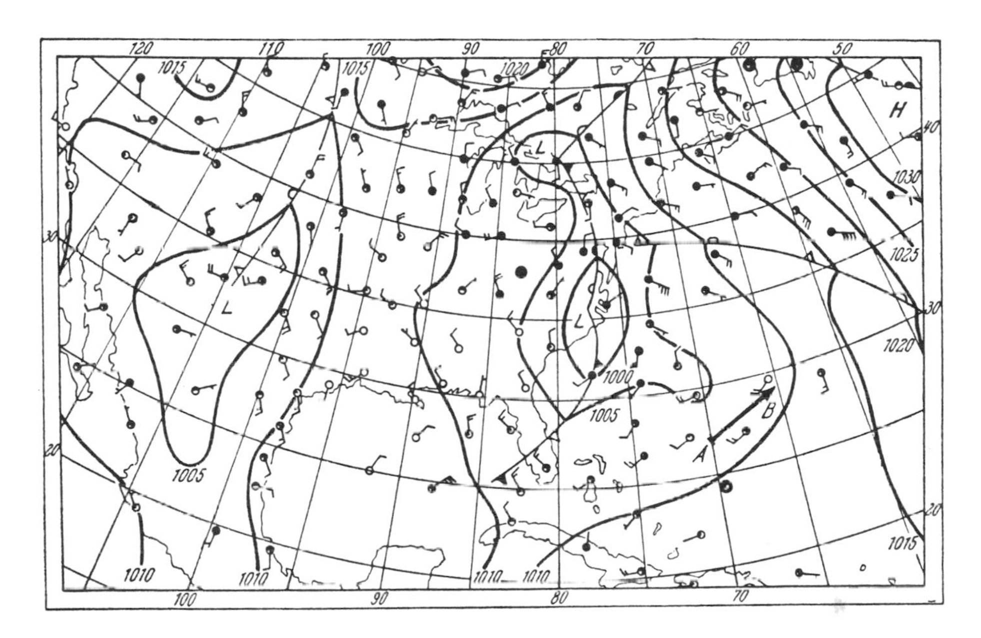

Fig. 6.3.3.—Surface weather map (mb) of 9 May, 1960, 0000 GCT. The arrow indicates the direction of view of satellite "Tiros I." A = position of subpoint, B = center point of Figure 6.3.2. (Weather map from Täglicher Wetterbericht des Deutschen Wetterdienstes.)

The cloud drift at high levels approximately corresponds to the wind speed and direction at these levels (Saito and Narikawa, 1954). Long virga sometimes fall from cloud bands with considerable lateral drift indicating strong shears in direction and speed within the stable layer below the jet maximum mentioned earlier.

The vertical wind shear causes small values of Richardson's number. Schaefer and Hubert (1955) found that the region of unstable jet-stream clouds with virga observed by them was associated with Richardson's numbers < 1 and with dynamic instability, i.e., with strong horizontal shears. It may well be possible that the applicability of both these instability criteria contributes to the turbulence observed in these clouds.

The layered structure of the atmosphere may be observed especially well where cloud formations are triggered by orographically induced lifting processes. This is the case when a jet stream impinges upon a mountain range causing the formation of standing lee waves. In observing the structure of the lenticular clouds thus formed, which may frequently reach all the way to the tropopause level, one may clearly distinguish moist and dry layers, which sometimes are less than 100 m thick and which may give a strange pagoda-shaped appearance to these clouds. That the layered structure of the atmosphere reaches high into the stratosphere may be deduced from observations by Hyde (1954*b*), who reported relatively dense haze layers which have been encountered by aircraft even at 46,000 ft (14 km).

According to McLean (1957) clouds of the altus type and low-level clouds are mainly associated with the baroclinic zone of the "polar front" near the ground. These clouds, too, are sometimes oriented in billows which, because of the lesser vertical wind shear usually extend normal to the wind direction (Schaefer, 1953*a*).

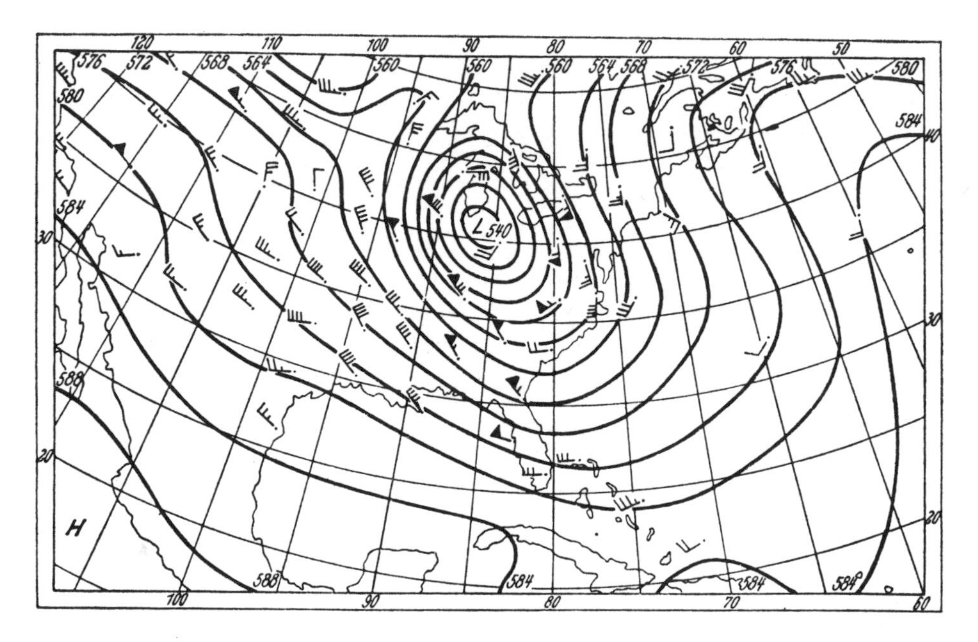

Fig. 6.3.4.—Absolute topography of the 500-mb surface (decameters), 9 May, 1960, 0000 GCT. (From Täglicher Wetterbericht des Deutschen Wetterdienstes.)

McLean's statistics on low-level clouds, unfortunately, are incomplete, since the observations have been made from aircraft flying at great heights, and the view may have been impeded by higher cloud layers.

Most of the cloud types observed in the jet-stream region show rather greater travel speeds. An exception to this are the lenticular clouds.

Careful observations especially of the cirrus and altus clouds may give valuable hints on the position of the jet stream. Especially the following four types of clouds permit a positioning of the jet stream (Schaefer, 1953*b*; see also Dwyer, 1955; Anonymous, 1953):

1. Cirrus in bands or long filaments;
2. Banks of cirro-cumulus and several forms of alto-cumulus;
3. Lenticular cloud forms in standing or migrating waves;
4. Individual billow clouds which obscure only part of the sky.

The jet-stream axis is close to the station if

1. At least three of the aforementioned cloud forms are observed over the station within several hours;
2. The clouds are part of a coherent system which extends over the whole sky;
3. The clouds show signs of rapid migration or rapid structural changes.

6.4. ELECTRIC PHENOMENA OF THE ATMOSPHERE NEAR JET STREAMS

In Chapter 6.121 it has already been pointed out that thunderstorms in the northwestern United States, which are associated with jet streams, are characterized by great lightning frequency. Investigations conducted in Schenectady, New York, with a radioactive gold probe mounted on a 12 m aluminum mast, led to the conclusion that jet-stream weather situations show a special electric activity. This technique of measurement, however, has to cope with several difficulties inherent in the ion production of the radioactive probe, which makes the results of measurement dependent upon wind speed, and in the definition and exact positioning of the jet stream (Falconer, 1953; Falconer and Schaefer, 1954; Schaefer, 1955*a*), so that Israël voiced some justified doubts about the reliability of the results. A positive current of the order of magnitude of 0.0005 to 0.01 μA, depending on the exposition and the height of the mast, is found to flow from the tip of the mast toward the earth during calm weather, or with only slight winds, with cloudless skies, with fair weather cumuli, with stratus or slowly drifting alto-cumuli, or with cirrus. Weather situations with precipitation are characterized by frequent changes of the sign of the current, at intervals of about 10 to 30 minutes (see Israël, 1957). These variations in the current show a marked correlation with snow and rain falls, with lightning discharges, and with the transition of large convective cloud cells, or with the movement of cold- and warm-front systems. Usually the vertical potential gradient attains an absolute maximum in the lower cloud layer, then decreases toward the tropopause and remains approximately constant in the stratosphere (Koenigsfeld, 1955). The instrument used in Schenectady measured a current of >0.1 μA during such weather situations, and at times exceeded 5.0 μA with positive as well as negative sign.

Besides the positive fair-weather current and the current with alternating signs during precipitation weather situations, Schaefer (1955*a*) finds the so-called jet-stream effect, which consists of a positive current which exceeds the fair-weather effect by at least one order of magnitude (0.015 to 0.10 μA). Such high and steady positive values usually were observed, when the jet axis was close to the observation site. Koenigsfeld (1955) also reports on a strong potential gradient reaching to about 300 mb after the passage of a cold front, i.e., in the region of a jet stream. Usually the recordings of the potential gradient are rather complex. The formation of water clouds above the station is most every time accompanied by a decrease in the potential gradient. For this effect a thin strato-cumulus layer suffices, which may be forming over the area. Precipitation and thunderstorm disturbances in the potential gradient may be superimposed upon the high positive electric level of the "jet-stream effect." (Convective clouds and thunderstorm activity should be expected in the jet-stream region, as has been described in detail in the preceding chapter.) By these, the positive current which flows from the radioactive probe toward the earth appears to be interrupted for several hours and replaced by a varying, or even negative, current. So, for instance, a case studied by Falconer and Schaefer (1954) revealed that the "jet-stream effect" was suppressed for some time by incipient thunderstorm activity, with very strong negative peaks appearing in the potential gradient at times, reaching exceptionally high values during the occurrence of tornadoes in the wider vicinity of the station. After the passage of the disturbance the positive electric "jet-stream level" was re-established, however, in the current measurements. Graystone (1954) on the other hand was not able to find a well-marked jet-stream effect over Lerwick. It will have to be left to further investigations to prove conclusively the existence of a "jet-stream effect."

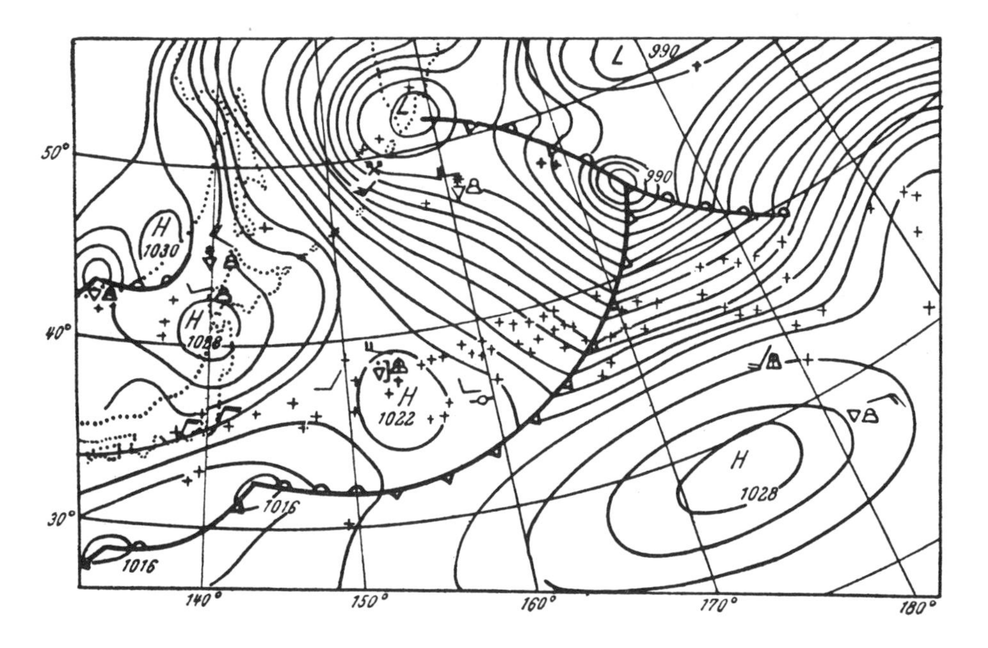

Fig. 6.4.—"Sferics" in the jet-stream region (indicated by crosses), 1 February, 1952, 0250 JMT. (Kimpara, 1953.)

A spread of radioactive dust drastically reduces the atmospheric potential gradient, also during jet-stream weather situations. Depending on the half-life and the concentration of the radioactive particles on the ground which are responsible for the increased ion production, it may at times take several days before the normal level of the electric potential is re-established.

The opinions on the causes of the stronger electric field underneath and in the vicinity of the jet axis are widely divergent. Measurements still are too scarce to permit any definite conclusions. Falconer assumes that the positive charges which are found in the iced-up parts of cumulus clouds are transported over wide areas, where they cause the increased potential gradient. Under these circumstances the approach of a thunderstorm should become apparent in the potential gradient over the respective station; this, however, is not observed in reality (see Israël, 1959). It might also be that the electric effects of the freezing process (Reynolds, 1955) may have some influence, since, especially in the jet-stream region, vertical motions, wind, shear, and instability are present with sufficient magnitude. This might lead to a separation of charges in the horizontal similar to what the various thunderstorm theories postulate for the vertical.

If, according to the American measurements, the fair-weather potential is considerably increased in the jet-stream region, it could be understood, at least qualitatively, following the induction theory of thunderstorm formation, which operates with an external electrical field, why the processes separating electric charges are especially active in the jet-stream region. The great frequency of lightning in North American jet-stream thunderstorms mentioned above would follow this reasoning.

Observations of disturbances in radio transmission, the "atmospherics," or shortly "sferics" stand in agreement with the described increase in electrical activity in the jet-stream region. These disturbances usually have their origin in areas of strong instability and thunderstorm activity. Their location may easily be found by radio direction finding. Sferics reports today constitute a valuable aid in bridging observational gaps, especially over the oceans (Kimpara, 1953). The close correlation between frontal zone and jet stream, and sferics is shown in Figure 6.4. According to this figure, the disturbances in radio transmission seem to be clearly concentrated in the jet-stream region. Some of these disturbances, the "whistlers," are observed as whistling noise; they are associated with electric activity in the magnetically conjugated areas of the other hemisphere (Helliwell, 1958). Part of the electromagnetic energy of a lightning discharge enters the exosphere and is conducted into the other hemisphere by the earth's magnetic field. So, for instance, Mook (1959) was able to correlate "whistlers" observed at Cape Horn with cyclones at the United States West Coast, which, again, lay in the region of well-pronounced polar-front jets.

In dealing with phenomena of atmospheric electricity the techniques of measurements as well as their accuracy still leave much to be desired. Research along these lines, therefore, still has many opportunities. Above all, the results reported by Schaefer would have to be checked with more refined methods, and the cause of the increased supply, if there is any, of positive charges in the jet stream would have to be explored.

6.5. THE SURFACE WEATHER AND ITS FORECASTING

From the relationships between vorticity advection, divergence, and vertical motion a good correlation between jet-stream position and precipitation activity has been pointed out already in Chapter 6.2. With the aid of such correlations the atmospheric flow patterns in the jet-stream region may be utilized for a surface-weather forecast.

While any approach starting from air mass or frontal characteristics mainly utilizes kinematic prediction techniques for forecasting the advection of air bodies with their various properties, the considerations derived from jet-stream research introduce "dynamic" prediction methods. One strives not only to recognize correctly the motion of fronts and pressure centers, but to understand and interpret these motions from their steering causes. By this approach, which is also taken by numerical weather prediction, the dynamics of the upper currents, especially of jet streams, become increasingly important in modern weather forecasting.

It has been pointed out several times that the concept of an impermeable "front" in the jet-stream region of the upper troposphere cannot be maintained any longer. At these levels vertical motions decisively influence the horizontal temperature gradients. Other concepts of the "polar-front theory," too, may be interpreted differently now. So, for instance, the formation of "daughter cyclones" within a "cyclone family" may be readily understood from the scheme devised in Figure 4.122.3 with its characteristic divergence distribution (Leese, 1957; Orihata, 1956). Since the prevalence of divergence or convergence on the cyclonic or anticyclonic side of the jet stream is influenced to a large extent by the curvature vorticity (assumed to be zero in Fig. 4.122.3), one may expect the formation of secondary cyclones only, as long as the right rear quadrant of the jet maximum shows well-pronounced divergence in the upper wind field. This, again, is only the case as long as the anticyclonic shear increases much more strongly along a streamline in this area than does the cyclonic curvature. Such conditions, however, are given only in straight or slightly curved jet-stream bands. In troughs with strong cyclonic streamline curvature, this rear quadrant loses its cyclogenetic effectiveness, and an intensive but shallow outbreak of cold air is initiated.

Such cold outbreaks, therefore, occur most frequently in regions which are favored by orographically induced upper troughs. Namias (1953, 1954) reports on periodic cyclogenesis in the lee of the Rocky Mountains in connection with intrusions of cold air advancing far to the south. In the southern hemisphere such intensive cold outbreaks are reported from the area of the Bellinghausen Sea and of Ellsworth Highland (Schmitt, 1952). They, too, occur in the lee of the highland and of the Andes, and they are rather long-lived and of great intensity. Some of these outbreaks may be followed to the Kerguelen Islands in the Indian Ocean. They are accompanied by very intense jet streams (>250 knots).

With the aid of the jet-stream model shown in Figure 4.122.3 one may, with some precautions, draw inferences from the position of the surface fronts to the location of the jet stream (Mildner, 1954; Pogosian, 1957*a*; see also Shimizu, 1958). This is of special importance for upper-wind diagnoses and prognoses over the oceans where no upper-wind measurements are available, and where a surface map analysis is possible, however, thanks to ship observations.

Usually one carries the conclusions in the opposite direction, however: From the displacement of jet maxima and from the orientation of frontal zones one may predict the tracks of cyclones. Thus the classical study by Van Bebber may be interpreted in a new way. Supplemented by the studies of Petterssen (1950) and others (see Astapenko, 1960*a*; Reed, 1960*b*; Van Loon, 1960; Weickmann, 1960) on the frequency of cyclogenesis and anticyclogenesis, one obtains a picture of the mean position of the frontal zones. Especially during winter two cyclogenetically active belts are clearly indicated, one of them originating on the east coast of Asia and, with cyclonic curvature, merging into the Aleutian low; the other extending from the lee of the Rocky

Mountains into the Norwegian Sea. Thus, both bands follow the mean jet-stream position. The region of the Genoa cyclones, which form under the influence of a northwesterly jet stream, is especially well marked in these statistical distributions (see Berkes and Borsos, 1955). During summer the belts with cyclogenetic activity shift northward with the position of the jet stream.

Anticyclogenesis is most frequent along two belts south of the jet-stream position. The maximum over North America, which is split into several secondary maxima, is caused by cold outbreaks in the lee of the Rocky Mountains, and thus is also associated with the upper current. Similar conditions prevail over the region of southeast Asia, where cyclogenetic and anticyclogenetic areas overlap.

Klein (1958) considers the annual variation of frequency of cyclogenesis and anticyclogenesis as well as of cyclones and anticyclones. He, too, finds a good correlation with the position of the jet stream. Cyclones show their greatest frequency on the left side of the mean jet-stream position, anticyclones on the right side, looking downstream. Lowest latitudes of these genetic processes are reached during February, highest latitudes during August.

Of special interest to the European region are the tracks of Vb-cyclones, which travel along the leading side of a trough located over the Alps and which may cause heavy precipitation and inundations in the Danube plains. This precipitation is considered the effect of small wave disturbances which travel along a frontal zone oriented from south to north on the east side of the trough. One may also reason that a jet maximum on the east side of the trough is maintained by a direct circulation which consists mainly in the rising of warm air masses, similar to the picture which Palmén devised for hurricane Hazel's transformation into an extratropical cyclone (see Chapters 6.122 and 6.2). Such an interpretation agrees better with the narrowly concentrated band of heavy rain, oriented from south to north, in which the precipitation pattern may be accentuated by orographic effects (Carpathian Mountains). Vb-weather situations may last for considerable time if along the west side of the trough new cold air is constantly supplied by a northwesterly jet stream. Over the United States such well-pronounced trough patterns usually lack a lasting supply of cold air from the northwest, so that the disturbances usually travel rather rapidly toward the northeast. A detailed investigation of European weather patterns of the Vb-variety with respect to jet-stream position and its changes and with respect to energy transformations would be most desirable.

According to what has been said above, from the displacement of jet maxima one may draw valuable conclusions about the tracks of disturbances on the surface-weather chart. It is mainly the jet-stream level which steers the weather patterns. This view corresponds to a certain extent to the opinions expressed by the German and Austrian meteorological schools (see Scherhag, 1948*a*). That the rate of displacement of the disturbances does not correspond to the upper-wind speed but only to a fraction thereof becomes apparent from the mechanism of propagation of jet maxima and of frontal zones: On the leading side (delta region) the frontal zone is formed by an indirect circulation, while on the rear side it is dissipated by a direct circulation.

It has been pointed out in Chapter 3.251 that a displacement tendency of the hemispheric jet-stream belt may, at times, be recognized in advance from an index cycle in a trend diagram (Kopcewicz, 1954). Although such forecasts are not very dependable, they may contain some possibilities for intermediate and long-range forecasting (Snellman, 1953).

One may also draw conclusions from jet-stream analyses and forecasts on the intensification or weakening of surface-pressure patterns. The consideration of vorticity advection plays an important part in this (Reuter, 1955). In general a surface cyclone will intensify if the field of positive vorticity, located upstream in the jet stream, intensifies too. This may be caused on the one hand by increased cyclonic curvature, or, on the other hand, by increased horizontal wind shear. Weakening and filling of surface cyclones, however, occurs with the decay of this vorticity field. In American cyclones it may be observed that, concurrent with their filling, the jet maximum (up to this time located in the tip of the trough) "overshoots" the trough, which leads to a decrease of the vorticity gradient along the streamlines. At the same time the amplitude and the cyclonic curvature of the upper trough associated with deep cyclones migrating northeastward decreases, thus indicating a decrease of positive vorticity, too. Last but not least, after the consumption of potential energy in the entrance region of the jet maximum (i.e., after the sinking and spreading of the cold air) the wind speeds in the jet stream, and thereby the horizontal shear, decreases.

Orographic effects upon the surface weather.—The vertical motions caused by divergence and convergence in the upper current may be accentuated or diminished by orographic effects. Estoque (1957*a*) considers this slope influence in the graphical integration of the prognostic equations. The effect of a mountain range of sufficient extent, as for example, the Alps, Pyrenees, or Apennines, or sometimes even the British Isles, on the one hand shows as foehn, and on the other hand as barrage.

One may distinguish between anticyclonic and cyclonic foehn, depending on the superposition of convergence or divergence upon the upper current. Anticyclonic foehn is characterized by great dryness, unusual visibility and clear skies, or scattered clouds at the most. On the windward side of the mountains hardly any barrage clouds form. Under cyclonic foehn conditions the barrage clouds along the windward slopes sometimes attain spectacular dimensions (foehn wall). Depending on the instability of the air masses rising along the mountain slopes, torrential rains, often associated with thunderstorms, may cause devastating inundations. Although on the lee side of the mountains the weather, in general, is free of precipitation and good visibility prevails; under this weather pattern stationary lenticular clouds may be observed all the way up into the cirrus level. With their everchanging structure and intensity they render an impressive picture of the structure of the atmosphere and of the passage of divergent and convergent waves of several hundreds of kilometers length.

European south-foehn weather situations, especially those of long continuation and with only little precipitation (i.e., with prevailing anticyclonic conditions), sometimes are associated with an unusual turbidity of the air and with striking optical phenomena. These indicate the presence of tiny dust particles in the air, which have been carried into Europe from North Africa ("Dimmerfoehn"; Streiff-Becker, 1942). Such dust deposits usually are confined to the leading side of deep upper troughs, when rapidly advancing cold fronts to the rear of a cyclone cause dust storms over North Africa, thus supplying the air mass with its aerosol contents (Brandtner, 1948).

In the Swiss-Austrian Alpine regions the passage of the jet axis and of a jet maximum in a southerly upper current becomes impressively evident from the sequence of foehn stages. The right front quadrant of a maximum causes the typical anticyclonic foehn weather pattern. In this, the import of warm air masses is accentuated in its effect by the adiabatic warming of the sinking air.

With the approach of the jet axis and its subsequent passage the weather characteristics become increasingly cyclonic. If with a stationary long-wave position the southerly upper current is maintained over the Alpine area, the transient jet maxima may be identified day after day from weather and cloud patterns. Such stationary trough positions are especially frequent over western Europe during the months of March to May and September to November, and they are responsible for the large frequency of foehn days in these months (Reiter, 1958*b*).

The barrage effect also becomes apparent in a very characteristic manner in the Alpine region. It sometimes starts with short periods of northerly chinook winds in the lee of the northern ranges, and to the south of the main range it is accompanied by cold dry and gusty north winds with generally clear weather. Persistent weather patterns in the Alpine region with barrage from the north are associated with a northerly to northwesterly upper current. The approach of the jet stream is heralded by the characteristic cirrus cloudiness described earlier, which over the mountains usually shows a well-marked lee-wave structure. To the rear of the surface cyclone strong convective cloud formation prevails in the Alpine region, which, when viewed from below creates the impression of a solid overcast which releases a lot of precipitation. If this weather situation prevails for a longer time (June, 1954), it causes devastating inundations in the plains to the north of the Alps. During winter such weather patterns usually carry an increased danger of avalanches.

If a jet maximum coming from the northwest impinges upon the Alps in their western ranges so that large amounts of cold air flow into the Mediterranean region, lee cyclogenesis will result usually in the area of Genoa. Frequently such cyclones set off a Vb-weather pattern. If the jet axis crosses the main range of the Alps farther to the east, strong pressure falls may be observed in the Upper Italian plains, but there will rarely be cyclogenesis. The cyclogenetically active region below the upper divergence near the jet stream, then, is too far to the east already. The Alps shield the Mediterranean from the cold-air import, at least in the lower levels. Aloft the cold air may still overflow the main range of the Alps and cause strong destabilization to its south, associated at times with thunderstorm formation.

As the frontal zone slowly proceeds to the east, the anticyclonic sector of the jet stream now becomes effective, and in general the weather will improve rapidly to the south of the main range of the Alps. Also over the plains to the north of the mountains the weather will improve gradually—the faster, the greater the distance from the mountains. The region immediately to the north of the Alps may, however, still remain under the influence of convective cloudiness for several days. In maritime air masses hazy weather with poor visibility prevails but improves with the increasing influence of sinking motion in the atmosphere.

If, however, a Genoa cyclone has formed, high-level stratus cloud decks may prevail for days to the north of the Alps. They form under the influence of warm air rising in the jet stream farther to the east. Precipitation from such weather patterns usually is rather sporadic in the Western Alps, abundant however in the Eastern Alps.

6.6. TRANSPORT OF AEROSOLS

In most recent times the general circulation of the atmosphere as well as of the oceans has become the subject of heated discussions in view of its transporting radioactive particles. From test explosions of nuclear weapons large quantities of radioactive substances have been dispersed in the atmosphere, and via drinking water, milk, vegetables, and the like, they enter into the human metabolism. Especially the radioactive isotope strontium 90 has caused justified concern about health and genetic hazards, because it is retained by the human skeleton. It is not the purpose of this book to point out the devastating effects of radioactive contamination. We shall only discuss here the importance of jet streams as mechanisms transporting radioactive and other aerosols. These may be dust, volcanic ashes, smoke, etc.

Radioactive debris may enter the atmosphere from accidents in nuclear reactor plants, or from nuclear explosions (Sheppard, 1959). The largest part of radioactive debris is attached to the dust and sand particles which are blown up within the characteristic mushroom cloud. The heavier particles descend at some distance from the site of the explosion, partly due to their large sinking velocity, partly due to condensation products to which they either serve as condensation nuclei, or by which they are captured in a collision and washed out in precipitation (Flohn, 1959*c*). This radioactive material descending more or less strongly concentrated in the vicinity of the explosion site constitutes part of the strategic effect of nuclear weapons. Today the characteristic fallout distribution as a function of upper winds is computed by the weather service on a routine basis for the larger American cities. The weaker the upper winds, the more concentrated the fallout will be. Strong upper winds separate the particles—almost like a mass spectrograph—according to their fall velocities (Laird, 1958; List, 1954; McCabe and Potter, 1959; Ratner, 1955*b*; U.S. Air Weather Service, 1954*d*; U.S. Federal Civil Defense Administration, 1955; U.S. Weather Bureau, 1955, 1956). In jet-stream weather situations elongated fallout patterns will result, which make the strategic value of the weapon questionable, and which may gravely endanger non-military targets. Thus the jet stream has a direct effect upon the drift of the heavier components of the particle "spectrum."

While *atomic bombs* mainly contaminate the troposphere, in the radioactive mushroom clouds of *fusion bombs* (hydrogen bombs) tiny dust particles of submicroscopic sizes are carried up to 40 km height, where they spread by turbulence and diffusion processes, and where they may float for a long time because of the stable stratification of the atmosphere (Machta, 1959; Sittkus, 1958). That contaminated debris actually enters the stratosphere may be seen clearly from photographs. At great heights, as soon as the stable stratification above the tropopause is reached, the cloud which has been extending vertically, now spreads out horizontally like a mushroom.

It was generally assumed that the particles suspended in the atmosphere would take in the order of about 10 years to fall out. This assumption probably was made by considering a stable atmosphere with not much vertical motion, in which the particles would follow approximately the sinking velocities according to Stokes' law. Actual experience shows, however, that the radioactive particles scarcely need half of this time to reach the earth's surface (Storebø, 1960). One will have to expect that 10 to 20 per cent of the radioactive aerosol distributed in the stratosphere reaches the troposphere each year (Machta, 1959). This rapid sinking causes an unexpected rise of the radioactivity level over wide—and sometimes densly populated—areas. Apparently there are vertical motions present in the stratosphere which have not been accounted for so far. Vertical velocities of about 1cm/sec have been computed for the region of the Arctic stratospheric jet stream at about 30 km height (cf. Chapter 4.414). This value exceeds the sinking motions of suspensions of fine particles by at least two orders of magnitude.

It has been pointed out that in the region of strong jet streams the air within the frontal zone is sinking out of the stratosphere, at times down to the 700-mb level. If we assume that the stratosphere has been contaminated by nuclear test series to a degree that the radioactive aerosol may be taken as an indicator for vertical motions, one would have to expect an increase of the number of radioactive nuclei in regions with strong sinking motions—similar to what has been experienced with ozone. The radioactive aerosol would move approximately along isentropic surfaces in areas of strong sinking motion, where Stokes' fall velocities and diabatic mixing processes may be neglected (Gabites, 1954). This may help to explain the fact that *not all* high-pressure regions show an increase in the level of radioactivity, but only those which contain air masses that have come from the stratosphere following approximately isentropic trajectories. The maximum of radioactive strontium-90 fallout between 30° and 50° N is without any doubt caused by intrusions of stratospheric air masses into the troposphere (Machta, 1959; Stewart, 1960). This latitude belt corresponds approximately to the width of migration of the PFJ (see Fig. 4.211.4), whose special role in the development of sinking motions has already been stressed several times. Since the sinking motions may last for several days, during which time the air masses may travel large distances, non-adiabatic processes have some influence upon the course of the trajectories. *Isobaric* trajectories permit only an order-of-magnitude estimate of the track of radioactive debris, because vertical motions are not taken into account to a sufficient degree (Haarländer, 1957, 1959).

Because of their *vertical circulations* the jet streams become a very important factor of mass exchange, which may bring particles originally suspended in the stratosphere and in the upper troposphere down to the earth's surface within a short time. That vertical exchange processes are active even in the highest layers of the atmosphere is demonstrated by the fact that heavier and lighter gas components of the atmosphere do not separate.

Since, for the removal of radioactive aerosol from the atmosphere, not only sinking motions are of importance but also the "washing-out" effect of precipitation—due to the consumption of condensation nuclei as well as to collision processes—the interpretation of the measured variations in the long-lived nuclear components near the ground may become very difficult at times (Machta *et al.*, 1956; see also Lockhart and Patterson, 1960).

In considering the trajectories of radioactively contaminated air masses, the meteorologist is provided with a tool for detailed studies of the general circulation of the atmosphere (Bleichrodt, Bleeker, and Schmidt, 1960; Herbst and Philipp, 1953; Herbst, Neuwirth, and Philipp, 1954; Neuwirth, 1955). Measurements of radioactivity from an aircraft permit, among other things, a direct estimate of diffusion processes active in the free atmosphere (Machta *et al.*, 1957). The American test series of 1953 over Nevada made it possible to use radioactive aerosol as an air mass indicator. On the Schauinsland (1280 m) near Freiburg, Germany, the radioactive debris could be detected on the average 10 to 20 days after the nuclear explosions. A favorable jet-stream situation caused the arrival of the aerosol after only 5 days in one instance. The air masses containing the radioactive aerosol seem to be mixing only slowly. So for instance on the German measurement site mentioned above fission products of the atomic explosion of 31 March, 1953, could be detected clearly in samples of rainwater between 13 and 14 April, between 27 and 28 April, and between 22 and 26 June, i.e., 84 days after the explosion, by considering the activity decay curves. In these measurements the air mass did not show any appreciable mixing with other air bodies containing debris from previous or more recent explosions. Thus, the identity of air bodies seems to be conserved for a long time (see Dyer and Yeo, 1960), although the air-mass characteristics in the meantime may change through the whole scale from polar air to tropical air.

With the development of isotope research we are presented with the possibility of utilizing natural radioactive decay products, which originate at great heights under the influence of cosmic radiation, as tracer elements in the study of the general circulation of the atmosphere (Lal, 1959; Peters, 1959).

Previous to the atomic age aerosols were used for research on large-scale circulations, which originated from catastrophe areas. So for instance the dispersion of the ashes from the eruptions and the explosion of Krakatoa in 1883 led to the discovery of the belt of easterlies over the equator, the "Krakatoa winds" (see Chapter 4.415). One could also gain some insight into the lateral exchange processes present in the stratosphere, which seem to be rather sluggish (Brooks, 1932).

The great Canadian forest fires in the latter part of September, 1950, gave rise to studies of upper winds over the North Atlantic (Elsley, 1951; Haarländer, 1959; Smith, 1950; Wexler, 1950). The turbidity of the atmosphere could be observed even in Central Europe (26 to 27 September) and gave rise to abnormal optical phenomena ("blue sun") (Bull, 1951; Rodewald, 1952; Runge, 1951).

The dust from the Sahara Desert, which during some south foehn weather situations may be carried into the Euopean region, has already been mentioned briefly in Chapter 6.5. Since the transport of these particles also occurs approximately along isentropic surfaces, it may be readily understood that the flow patterns of the lower troposphere (e.g., 500 mb) mainly influence the trajectories of the dust particles (see Haarländer, 1959). Average transport rates of 81 and 95 km/h in several cases of dust fallout indicate, however, that a southwesterly jet stream contributes prominently to the formation of these weather situations.

7

JET STREAMS AND CLIMATE

7.1. GENERAL REMARKS

According to a definition by Köppen (1931), "climate is the average condition and the normal course of weather in a given location." It has been the task of *classical climatology* to find this average condition from as many as possible uninterrupted observation sequences, reaching far back in time. From the abundance of data which by and by became available, two main problems arose with which a "climatology of mean values" is still faced.

1. With the increasing density of the observational network *climatological classifications* had to be more and more refined, and they had to be adapted to special needs. A coarse division into oceanic and continental climates, or into polar, subpolar, temperate, subtropical, and tropical climates did not suffice any longer. In many cases the classifications were made from plant-ecological considerations, as for instance the one devised by Köppen and Geiger (1953), which is based upon temperature and precipitation conditions (see Hendl, 1960). Other climatological classifications reflect the experience of seafaring, the main concern of which rested with the wind conditions over the oceans (westerlies, horse latitudes, trade winds, doldrums). Many needs which arise from the rather coarse general classifications are met by the field of *synoptic climatology*, which is not so much concerned with "the normal course of weather over a given location," but rather with its *characteristic course in different weather patterns*. In such a treatment the variability of weather over a given location as produced by the respective state of the atmospheric circulation is duly taken into account.

2. With the increasing length of observation sequences, *climatic fluctuations* became clearly evident. These make the statement of "normal conditions" of the atmosphere difficult, because we do not know whether the climatic changes over a longer period of time correspond to a normal or an abnormal behavior of the atmosphere.

Especially the correlations between upper flow patterns and surface weather described in the preceding chapters gave rise to a new impact upon climatological research, emanating from the field of jet-stream meteorology. The flow processes in the higher layers of the atmosphere increasingly are considered of primary importance. The surface-weather phenomena, on the other hand, are more and more viewed as secondary processes. This line of reasoning brought about the existence of the field of *synoptic climatology*. Climatic fluctuations may now be interpreted as small changes in the general circulation of the atmosphere, which have the observed long-range effects in a given locality. If a certain weather pattern which is brought about by a certain state of the general circulation, appears more or less frequent, monthly and yearly average values of meteorological parameters will be changed significantly.

Thus, as an important branch of climatology, a frequency statistics of weather patterns is introduced into this field.

In the course of the development indicated here climatology is searching more and more for the *cause* of climatological similarities and differences. Again it is the exploration of the flow conditions in the upper atmosphere, and of the *forces* which maintain this flow, which may provide an answer to this problem. The part of climatology which is concerned with atmospheric circulations, their normal state and their perturbations is called *dynamic climatology* (Flohn, 1950*e*, 1951*a*; Gião, 1956).

In the following we will confine ourselves to several viewpoints of dynamic climatology, as far as they are directly concerned with the meteorology of jet streams.

The climate of a given location is influenced not only by the radiation budget but also rather decisively by advective phenomena. Heat and moisture budget of a given location, therefore, are in close correlation with the mean state of the general circulation of the atmosphere which prevails over this location.

It will be our task, therefore, to point out the connection between jet streams and climate. Orographic influences and monsoonal (seasonal) effects upon the jet streams are reflected in the large-scale climatological zones of the earth.

7.2. JET STREAMS AS CLIMATE-CONTROLLING FACTORS OF THE GENERAL CIRCULATION

We have pointed out in Chapter 6 that the velocity maxima are characterized by a marked vorticity distribution, which, in turn, causes a characteristic distribution of divergence and convergence patterns. These, again, cause large-scale vertical motions of the air, which may be associated with condensation processes and with precipitation.

In the influence region of the PFJ (or, for that matter, of any jet stream which is characterized by a baroclinic zone in the *lower* troposphere, be it the polar front or the arctic front) these vertical motions occur along isentropic surfaces. Since these are strongly inclined in the low-tropospheric baroclinic zone, the lifting of air masses may be accomplished without great energy expense. Air masses in the region of the frontal zone associated with the PFJ, therefore, readily subject themselves to lifting processes and to the formation of precipitation. Thus, we may expect a zone of increased precipitation activity along the average position of the PFJ. This may be readily seen from a diagram containing the average meridional distribution of precipitation: one maximum each appears at 50° N, 0°, and 45° S (Brooks and Hunt, 1930). The precipitation maximum of temperate latitudes is more sharply pronounced in the southern hemisphere than in the northern hemisphere (see Trewartha, 1954). This may be ascribed to the fact that the circulation of the southern hemisphere shows a higher zonal index and the jet stream deviates less from its average position than is the case in the northern hemisphere. The equatorial precipitation maximum shall be considered farther below. Besides these irregularities in the meridional distribution of precipitation, caused by features of the general circulation, apparently the temperature dependency of the saturation mixing ratio plays an important role. Thus, in temperate latitudes less precipitation falls on the average, than in the tropics, because of the lesser saturation mixing ratio in the cooler air masses.

Furthermore, the "continentality" of the area under consideration plays an important role. If part of the moisture content of the air is trapped by a mountain barrier, there will be less precipitation to the lee. Under otherwise similar conditions in the influence region of a jet stream the air masses now will have to be lifted higher until the condensation level is reached. Thus the interiors of continents show less precipitation than west coasts, even in the PFJ region (Koeppe *et al.*, 1958).

That the *east coasts* of Asia and North and South America again have abundant precipitation in temperate latitudes is not so much due to the small distance from the sea, but to the fact that here in the lee of the Himalayas and of the Andes there is a *confluence zone* between two jet streams, in which air masses of different origin are brought together. This is also indicated by a relatively strong baroclinic zone which appears in several mean meridional sections of this region, indicating a preferred area of ascending motion.

It has been stated in Chapter 6, that the delta region of a frontal zone is cyclogenetically active, because of the pronounced mass divergence at jet-stream level. According to Figure 4.122.3, one has to expect upper convergence in the left rear quadrant of a jet maximum, i.e., in the entrance region. Here the cold migrating high-pressure cells form in which the polar air masses flow into subtropical latitudes. Cyclone and subsequent cold anticyclone both are influenced by one jet maximum. Thus, along the course of the PFJ we have to expect a frequent and rapid change of low- and high-pressure weather patterns (Klein, 1951). This is clearly evident from an investigation by Petterssen (1950). The belts of greatest frequency of change between cyclones and anticyclones, which extend across the Atlantic into Europe, and across the Pacific, too, may be interpreted as the most common position of the PFJ.

An agreement of the position of these belts with mean precipitation patterns may easily be understood. The seasonal shift of the PFJ position, too, reflects itself in the mean precipitation amounts. The seasonal pattern is especially well established over the west coast of North America and over Europe. Van Bebber's cyclone tracks, of which only the Vb-tracks still retain importance, as well as Petterssen's frequency distributions, indicate most frequent jet-stream positions. (More recent statistics have been worked out by Klein [1956] for the northern hemisphere, and by Britton and Lamb [1956] for the southern hemisphere.) The band of maximum precipitation amount stretching across the Near East, North India, and Assam during winter may be attributed to wave disturbances in the STJ. The summer conditions over these areas, on the other hand, are controlled by the Indian monsoon, which shall be discussed in more detail below.

It was pointed out in Chapter 4.412 that the subtropical jet stream is located above the subtropical high-pressure belt, showing upper convergence and sinking motion on the average. In individual cases, however, the same correlations between vorticity advection, divergence, and vertical motions hold, as they have been applied to the PFJ. Figure 4.412.2 indicates that also along the axis of the STJ vorticity maxima and minima may be expected. Therefore, this jet stream, too, is accompanied by characteristic weather sequences.

Since in the STJ the baroclinic zone may only be found in the upper part of the troposphere, there will be no large-scale upward-sliding motions even in the influence region of strong upper divergence. Such upward-sliding motions without much input of work may only occur near the cirrus level along the strongly sloping isentropic surfaces; this may be gathered from the cloud patterns observed in the STJ. Within the quasi-barotropic lower troposphere the upper divergence and the incipient pressure falls near the ground cause convergence which leads to a slow destabilization of the air masses. If the latter has proceeded far enough to produce unstable lapse rates within convective clouds, large cumulo-nimbi may form whose cirrus anvils may at times drift for 60 and more kilometers in the upper current of the STJ (Malkus and Ronne, 1954*a*).

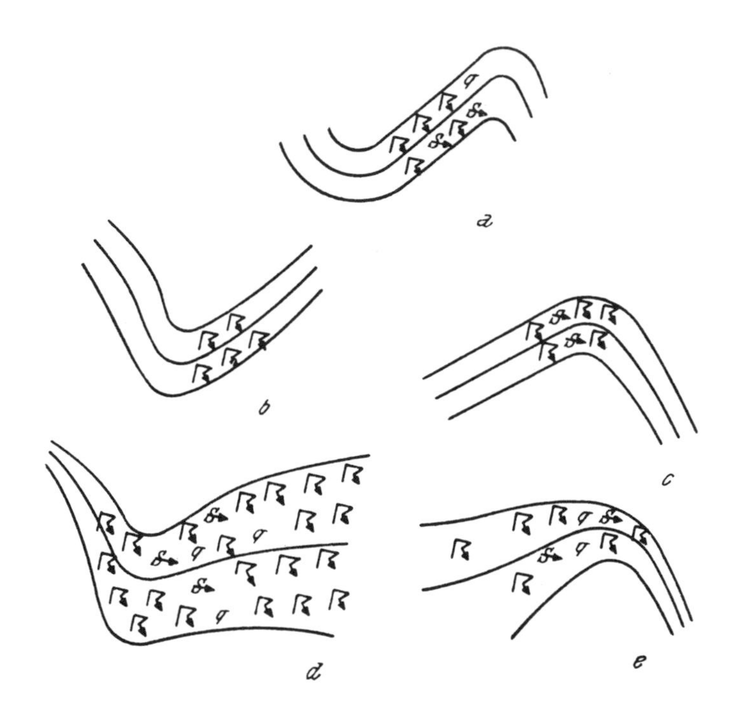

FIG. 7.2.—Schematic distribution of the occurrence of thunderstorms (), sand storms () and squalls () over North India and Pakistan, in connection with westerly flow in the upper troposphere. (Ramaswamy, 1956.)

Studies by Ramaswamy (1956) indicate that thunderstorms over Northern India (the so-called Andhis or Nor'western) are closely tied to the characteristics of the westerly upper current (see Desai, 1957; Koteswaram and Srinivasan, 1958). Figure 7.2 schematically gives the upper flow patterns during which one may expect strong thunderstorm activity in spite of the generally dry winter monsoon regime. All these types of flow patterns are characterized by a decrease of vorticity along the streamlines over the thunderstorm region. Synoptic examples fit well into this scheme.

These disturbances and the associated formation of convective clouds are the reason why over Northern India and along the slopes of the Himalayas—here accentuated by barrage effects—precipitation falls even during the dry season of the winter monsoon. This precipitation does not reach the plateau of Deccan, however.

The great steadiness of the STJ in the Indo-Pakistan region is expressed by a correlation between the number of days with thunder and the *mean* topography of the 300-mb surface of May (Ramaswamy, 1956). The thunderstorm activity concentrates very pronouncedly on the east side of the mean trough in the area of Calcutta. From this one may conclude upon the great persistence of the trough line in this region. This shall be discussed further in Chapter 7.413.

In Chapter 4.413 it has been pointed out that the equatorial maximum of precipitation is unduly attributed to a destabilization of the atmosphere caused by the zenithal position of the sun. We rather have to assume that the easterly jet stream of the tropics and the position of the intertropical convergence zone are responsible for the existence of this precipitation maximum. The baroclinicity of the lower troposphere is small in the equatorial zone. Contrasts between dry continental and moist maritime air masses do not reach great heights. It seems appropriate, therefore, to talk about a "convergence zone" rather than an "intertropical front." This should help to avoid any misinterpretations which might lead one to expect upward-sliding motions where we have only increased convective activity, similar to what is observed in the STJ region. Over the oceans the contrasts between air masses on either side of the intertropical convergence zone vanish almost completely, so that even from the surface temperature distribution one can hardly detect any frontal character. The cloud and precipitation zones are correlated with the upper vorticity pattern instead, which has been discussed in detail in Chapter 4.413.

This short resume may suffice to show that the mean global distribution of precipitation fits well into the pattern of upper-tropospheric jet streams. Similar conditions hold for the temperature distribution as will be shown in the following chapter.

Instead of comparing the *mean* state of the atmosphere with *mean* jet-stream positions, one now could begin to consider specific jet-stream positions and to average their characteristic atmospheric states according to various weather patterns. This would be the task of a regional synoptic climatology.

7.3. THE INFLUENCE OF HIGH MOUNTAIN RANGES UPON THE FORMATION OF PLANETARY WAVES

7.31. Theoretical Background

In a classical paper Bolin (1950) investigated the influence of a conic mountain upon the jet streams of temperate latitudes. Following theoretical considerations by Charney and Eliassen (1949), the top of the atmosphere is assumed to be at a constant height H_0. Thereby the model attains a certain degree of gravitational stability. The results obtained are similar to the ones by Queney (1948), who takes the vertical stability of the atmosphere into account (Colson, 1949).

An obstacle of the height $h=h(x,y)$ impedes the flow of a homogeneous zonal basic current without lateral shear and with the speed u in an incompressible atmosphere. The flow is characterized by constant potential vorticity [Eq. 1.235 (2)]:

$$d/dt[(q_z+f)/H]=0. \qquad 7.31\ (1)$$

H is the thickness of the atmosphere, which is given by

$$H+h=H_0=\text{const.} \qquad 7.31\ (2)$$

Considering 1.235 (1), the continuity equation reads

$$-(1/H)\, dH/dt = \partial u/\partial x + \partial v/\partial y. \qquad 7.31\ (3)$$

Equations 7.31 (1) and 7.31 (3) constitute a set of differential equations which may be solved if they are linearized, i.e., if the products of derivatives are neglected because of their relative smallness. Introducing the perturbation components u^* and v^* into the horizontal velocity components, and considering, furthermore, that u^* and $v^* \ll u$, $h \ll H$ and $q_z \ll f_0$ one obtains

$$-(1/H)\, dH/dt = \partial u^*/\partial x + \partial v^*/\partial y = (u/H_0)(\partial h/\partial x). \qquad 7.31\ (4)$$

For stationary conditions of flow ($\partial/\partial t = 0$) one obtains from 7.31 (1) and 7.31 (4) after linearization

$$u(\partial q_z/\partial x) + \beta v^* = -(f_0 u/H_0)(\partial h/\partial x). \qquad 7.31\ (5)$$

Introducing a new variable Ψ of the following definition

$$\begin{aligned} u^* &= -\partial\Psi/\partial y + uh/H_0 \\ v^* &= +\partial\Psi/\partial x, \end{aligned} \qquad 7.31\ (6)$$

the equation of continuity will be satisfied identically, and 7.31 (5) attains the form

$$\partial/\partial x(\partial^2\Psi/\partial x^2 + \partial^2\Psi/\partial y^2) + (\beta/u)(\partial\Psi/\partial x) = (u/H_0)(\partial^2 h/\partial x\, \partial y) - (f_0/H_0)(\partial h/\partial x).$$

Integration after x renders

$$\partial^2\Psi/\partial x^2 + \partial^2\Psi/\partial y^2 + \beta\Psi/u = (u/H_0)(\partial h/\partial y) - (f_0/H_0)h, \qquad 7.31\ (7)$$

where the constant of integration is given by the boundary conditions $q=0$, $\Psi=0$, and $h=0$ for $x=\infty$.

The homogeneous equation 7.31 (7) (for $h=0$) describes the free perturbations which may exist in the current without any orographic influences, while a partial solution of 7.31 (7) indicates the stationary waves which will be excited by the mountain range.

For a mountain with circular and concentric contour lines Bolin gives the following solution in polar co-ordinates which is symmetric with respect to the y-axis (r being measured from the center of the mountain peak):

$$\Psi = P(\rho) + Q(\rho)\cdot \sin\vartheta, \qquad 7.31\ (8)$$

In this equation $\rho = r\cdot\sqrt{(\beta/u)}$, $r^2 = x^2 + y^2$, and $\vartheta = \arctan(y/x)$. $P(\rho)$ and $Q(\rho)$ are partial solutions of two differential equations emanating from 7.31 (7) and 7.31 (8). They have the form

$$\begin{aligned} P(\rho) &= -(\pi u f_0/2\beta H_0)\left[Y_0(\rho)\int_0^\rho h(\rho)\rho^3 J_0(\rho)\, d\rho - J_0(\rho)\int_\infty^\rho h(\rho)\rho^3 Y_0(\rho)\, d\rho\right], \\ Q(\rho) &= +(\pi u/2H_0)\cdot\sqrt{(u/\beta)}\left[Y_1(\rho)\int_0^\rho (dh/d\rho)\rho^3 J_1(\rho)\, d\rho - J_1(\rho)\int_\infty^\rho (dh/d\rho)\rho^3 Y_1(\rho)\, d\rho\right]. \end{aligned} \qquad 7.31\ (9)$$

$J_0(\rho)$, $J_1(\rho)$, $Y_0(\rho)$, and $Y_1(\rho)$ are simple Bessel functions.

From 7.31 (6) and 7.31 (8) we may compute the wind field. In order to calculate the field of streamlines we have to make use of a stream function Φ, because $\nabla\cdot\mathbf{v} \neq 0$. This stream function is defined as volume transport within the total layer H in the following manner:

$$\begin{aligned} H(u+u^*) &= -\partial\Phi/\partial y \\ Hv^* &= \partial\Phi/\partial x \end{aligned} \qquad 7.31\ (10)$$

and

$$\Phi = H_0(\Psi - uy). \qquad 7.31\ (11)$$

According to 7.31 (10), the wind vector everywhere is tangential to Φ, which corresponds to the requirements of a streamline.

Figure 7.31.1 shows the flow pattern computed from the above derivations, for a mountain whose height is given by

$$h = h_0 \cdot e^{-r^2/l^2} \qquad 7.31\ (12)$$

l has been chosen so that $h = h_0/e$ at a distance of 1000 km from the mountain peak (h_0). This dimension approximately corresponds to the North American Rocky Mountains, which are shown in the right-hand portion of Figure 7.31.1. A mean

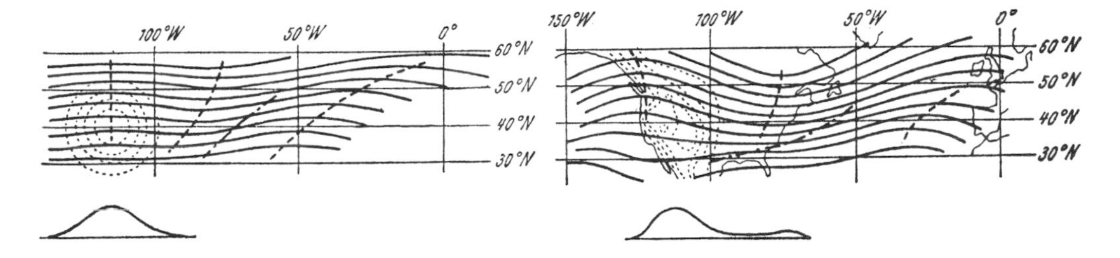

FIG. 7.31.1.—Left, theoretical flow pattern around a circular mountain deflecting a uniform basic current; right, actually observed flow pattern at the 20,000-ft level during winter over the western United States. Dashed, troughs and ridges; dashed-dotted, regions of maximum zonal wind speed. (Bolin, 1950.)

value of 20 m/sec, corresponding to winter conditions at the 500-mb surface, has been assumed for u. Although β has been assumed constant in the integration, its latitude dependency has been considered in the construction of the various streamlines. In order to be able to compare the actually observed streamline pattern (Fig. 7.31.1 right) with the theoretically computed pattern (Fig. 7.31.1 left), the former has been analyzed in units of $\Delta z \cdot \sin \varphi$ meters. The dashed lines indicate troughs and ridges, the dashed-dotted lines represent areas with maximum zonal wind speed u (see also Kawata, 1958; Magata, 1957).

From this diagram it is clearly evident that east of the *orographically* induced trough there appears an area with maximum jet-stream intensity (see also Defant, 1959*a*). This is at the same time an area of *increased confluence*, as is indicated by the streamline pattern. The influence of the high mountains extends far downstream and may even be recognized in the presence of a high-pressure ridge in the eastern Atlantic—a region which is frequently characterized by blocking anticyclones, as will be shown below.

Equation 7.31 (9) indicates that the streamline pattern of the disturbed flow strongly depends upon the horizontal dimensions of the mountain range (ρ^3 in the integrand). If one assumes, for instance, l^2 in 7.31 (12) to be only half as large, the values of $P(\rho)$ and $Q(\rho)$ reduce to one-tenth of the original values. Thus, only mountains of the dimensions of the Rocky Mountains and of the Himalayas will influence the planetary wave pattern. The north-south extent of the Alps has only a slight effect (Holzapfel, 1954, 1956*b*), which, however, may show itself in certain synoptic situations and which may lead to the formation of "Genoa cyclones" (Čadež, 1956).

The streamline pattern also depends upon the assumptions made for u. Above all, the wave length of the induced waves is proportional to the square root of u [7.31 (8 and 9)]. The general features of the flow pattern are, however, conserved within wide ranges of u.

In the above derivation the zonal current u has been assumed without any lateral boundaries, i.e., it was considered to be very broad as compared to the dimensions of the mountain. The conditions are rather different when individual, narrow jet maxima impinge upon a mountain range.

Let us assume that the speed V of the atmospheric layers remains constant while the air flows around the mountain. Vertical shrinking of an air column will be compensated by lateral stretching, under conservation of potential vorticity (see Gambo, 1956). The subscript "zero" is to characterize the conditions in the undisturbed current before it impinges upon the mountain range. According to 7.31 (1 and 2) we have for a zonal jet stream

$$(q_0+f_0)/H_0=(q+f_0)/(H_0-h)$$

or

$$q=-f_0h/H_0+q_0H/H_0. \qquad 7.31\ (13)$$

Replacing q by VK [see Eq. 1.231 (3)], we obtain the following expression for the curvature:

$$K=(d^2y/dx^2)/(1+(dy/dx)^2)^{3/2}$$
$$=-f_0h/VH_0+q_0H/VH_0.$$

A simple transformation renders

$$d\left(\frac{dy/dx}{(1+(dy/dx)^2)^{1/2}}\right)=-(f_0h/VH_0)\,dx+(q_0H/VH_0)\,dx.$$

Since $dy/dx=\tan\psi$, where ψ is the angle between jet axis and x-direction, we arrive at

$$d(\sin\psi)=-[(f_0h)/(VH_0)+(q_0H/VH_0)]\,dx$$

and by integration

$$\sin\psi=-(f_0/VH_0)\int_{x_1}^{x_2}h\cdot dx+(q_0/VH_0)\int_{x_1}^{x_2}H\cdot dx. \qquad 7.31\ (14)$$

Let x_1 be the co-ordinate at which the jet stream hits the mountain. The jet stream will cross the mountains, as long as $0\geqq\psi\geqq-90°$ and $0\geqq\sin\psi>-1$. According to 7.31 (14), ψ is a function of V (Berkofsky, 1952), and one may define a critical speed below which a jet stream is deflected so much that it will flow parallel to the mountain ridge:

$$V_{kr}=(f_0/H_0)\int_{x_1}^{x_1+\Delta x}h\cdot dx-(q_0/H_0)\int_{x_1}^{x_1+\Delta x}H\cdot dx. \qquad 7.31\ (15)$$

If $V<V_{kr}$ the jet stream will not cross the mountains, but it will turn back anticyclonically toward its original position.

If one assumes the vorticity of the undisturbed current, q_0, to be zero, and if one neglects the horizontal shear of the current, the last term on the right-hand side of 7.31 (15) vanishes, and only the expression derived by Bolin (1950) remains:

$$V_{kr}=(f_0/H_0)\int_{x_1}^{x_1+\Delta x}h\cdot dx. \qquad 7.31\ (16)$$

For $f_0=10^{-4}$ sec^{-1}, $H_0=10$ km, $\Delta x=1000$ km and $\bar{h}$, the mean height of the mountain range, equal to 2000 m, the critical speed is $V_{kr}=20$ m/sec. Again, only mountain ranges of the dimensions of the Rocky Mountains will have a detectable influence upon upper flow patterns.

Let us now consider the additional term on the right-hand side of 7.31 (14 and 15):

$$-(q_0/H_0)\int_{x_1}^{x_1+\Delta x} H\cdot dx$$

indicates the influence of the vorticity of the undisturbed current upon the magnitude of the critical speed. According to the sign of this expression, V_{kr} will be *less* with *cyclonic* vorticity q_0, it will be *larger* with *anticyclonic* vorticity, than would correspond to the conditions for $q_0=0$, i.e., the air mass will find a smaller obstacle in the mountain range with cyclonic flow than with anticyclonic flow (Colson, 1950). If $\bar{H}=H_0-\bar{h}$ is the average

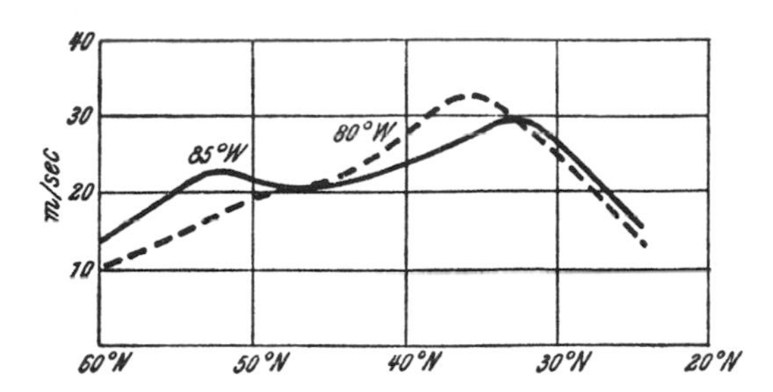

FIG. 7.31.2.—Meridional profiles of zonal winds at the 20,000-ft level. Solid lines, January mean values, 85° W; dashed, winter mean values, 80° W (according to Hess, 1948). (Bolin, 1950.)

height of the (finite) incompressible atmosphere over the mountain, it may easily be seen that the influence of the original vorticity upon the change of curvature, as compared with originally straight-flow conditions follows the ratio $(q_0\bar{H}):(f_0\bar{h})$. Let us consider the conditions in the jet axis, where the wind shear is zero, and where the vorticity, therefore, is given by q_0-V/R_0. Here the vorticity is about one order of magnitude smaller than the Coriolis parameter, if one assumes a radius of curvature of the jet axis of about 2000 km. The above ratio thus assumes the value of about 0.4.

For streamlines outside the jet axis the conditions become more complicated. According to what has been said in Chapter 4.121, let us assume a wind profile with $Q=$const on the cyclonic side of the jet axis, and a profile with $Q=0$, or $-q\cong f_0$ on the anticyclonic side. Under the assumption that the individual air particles will cross the mountains under conservation of their potential vorticity, one will obtain different values of $\sin\psi$ for the cyclonic and the anticyclonic side of the jet stream, according to 7.31 (14). If q_0/V has rather high positive values on the north side of the jet stream, ψ will be positive, too, i.e., the current will cross the mountains in a northeasterly direction. On the anticyclonic side, however, $q=-f$ will act in the sense of a deflection of the current toward the south. Because of the different vorticity regimes on either side of the jet stream a splitting of the upper current, when impinging upon a mountain range, is indicated.

Figure 7.31.2 shows a mean meridional wind profile of the zonal component of flow at the 20,000-ft level for January along 85° W (full line), and for the whole winter along 80° W (dashed line). In the lee of the Rocky Mountains, which have their largest extent at about 40° N, such a split in the upper current actually seems to occur. Farther to the east (80° W) both jet streams reunite into a single jet in a broad confluence zone.

Similar conditions prevail over Eastern Asia under the influence of the Himalayas (see Chapter 7.413).

7.32. The System of Planetary Waves

Figure 7.32.1 contains the mean height of the absolute topography of 500 mb, averaged over the belt between 45° and 50° N for summer, and between 35° and 40° N for winter. The conditions in the southern hemisphere are shown in Figure 7.32.2 as a comparison. The effect of the North American Rocky Mountains with their center at about 40° N and 110° W is clearly established in summer as well as in winter by the existence of a well-pronounced high-pressure ridge (Wilkins, 1949). The same holds for the South American Andes at about 70° W. A well-marked low-pressure trough is evident in the lee of these mountain ranges (Boffi, 1949*a*, *b*). In both hemispheres a train of well-established waves follows to the east.

The flow conditions over the northern hemisphere are controlled by *two* mountain ranges (Rocky Mountains and Himalayas), which produce a certain resonance effect in the wave pattern. In spite of the orographic differences between the two hemispheres the same mean wave number establishes itself in the southern hemisphere as in the northern hemisphere.

Especially the monsoonal effect of Asia is clearly evident from Figure 7.32.1.

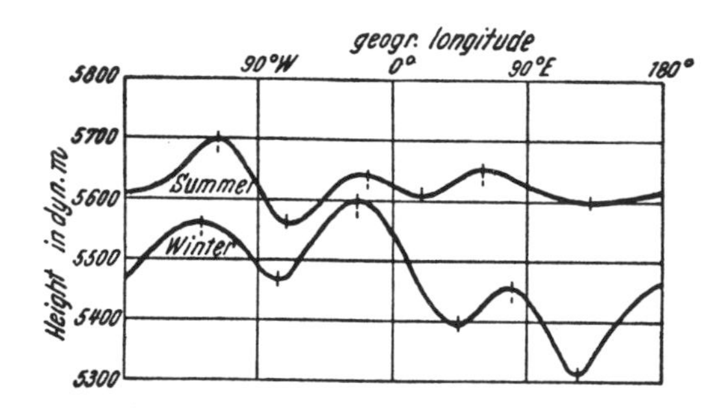

Fig. 7.32.1.—Mean height of the 500-mb surface as a function of geographic longitude, for the latitude belt 45° to 50° N (summer) and 35° to 40° N (winter). (Bolin, 1950.)

During winter the jet stream splits. Its subtropical branch flows around the plateau of Tibet on its southern slopes, which explains the drop of the 500-mb topography to such low values. In the lee of the mountains well-marked long waves with large amplitudes form. The confluence of warm- and cold-air masses in the lee is especially supported by the splitting of the jet stream upstream over the mountains, because the Himalayas act as a barrier between different air masses during winter. Over south China and the adjacent sea an especially intensive jet stream may be found, therefore, during winter.

During summer the jet stream runs farther to the north, where it does not split any more under the influence of the relatively low mountain ranges. It also causes much smaller wave amplitudes downstream. The slight shift in the long-wave position over Asia between summer and winter, which is caused by the configuration of the Himalayas, will be discussed further in Chapter 7.413.

The southern hemisphere (Fig. 7.32.2) has no mountain ranges which would compare with the Central-Asiatic plateau. The seasonal changes of the 500-mb surface, therefore, are less spectacular. They are largest again—as in the northern hemisphere—near 120° E. Thus it appears as though the monsoonal effect of the Himalayas also extends into the *upper* flow pattern of the southern hemisphere. That the southeast trades of the southern hemisphere over the Indian Ocean merge into the southwest monsoon of summer and of the northern hemisphere is already a well-known fact. A coupling of the circulations of both hemispheres, thus, seems to be indicated.

Rubin (1955) arrives at similar conclusions by comparing northern and southern hemisphere circulation indices. The existence of the trough near 120° E during winter in the southern hemisphere cannot be explained dynamically by the presence of the Australian land masses because, according to the considerations made in Chapter

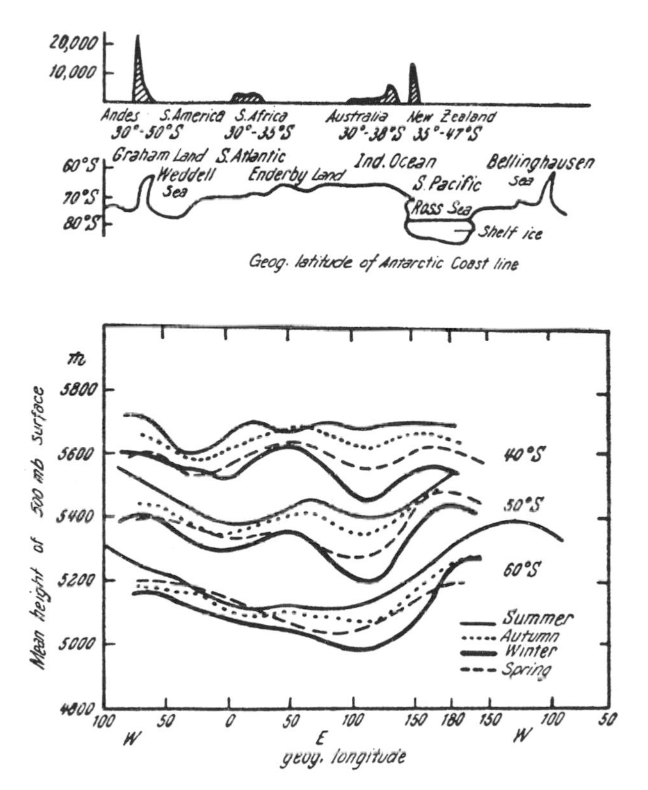

FIG. 7.32.2.—Orographic conditions in the southern hemisphere and mean seasonal profiles (1952–54) of the 500-mb surface along 40°, 50°, and 60° S. (Lamb, 1959.)

7.31, we should rather find a high-pressure ridge here. Lamb (1959) makes the eccentricity of the Antarctic circumpolar vortex responsible for this trough. This eccentricity, again, may have its cause in the asymmetry of the radiating surface of the Antarctic continent.

Planetary long waves naturally have a strong influence upon the temperature conditions near the ground. The low-pressure troughs in the lee of mountain ranges are characterized by frequent cold-air outbreaks (Suda, 1956, 1957; Triegaardt and Kraus, 1956; Wollschläger, 1959), while the high-pressure ridges located downstream often become the starting place of intensive warm-air advances toward the north.

The cyclone tracks also follow the orographically induced planetary long waves (Petterssen, 1950).

In Chapter 4.433 it was pointed out that the momentum transport necessary for the maintenance of the zonal circulation and of the jet streams against the influence of friction, is partly accomplished by the planetary waves. Westerly momentum is transported from south to north if the trough axes tilt from southwest to northeast, which is the case in most instances. With this flow pattern northerly or northwesterly winds prevail to the rear of the troughs, carrying no, or only little, westerly momentum toward the south. On the forward side of the troughs, however, appreciably more momentum is carried northward in a powerful southwesterly current. This westerly momentum is produced by surface friction in the trade wind region, and it is dissipated in the belt of westerlies (Starr, 1948*a*). The zonal circulation is constantly supplied with perturbation energy by the high mountain ranges, thus exciting it into meanders. Thus, the large mountain ranges of the earth play an important role in the transport of momentum. An investigation by White (1949) shows that the mountains may also have a direct influence upon the momentum budget of the circulation, which in its order of magnitude is comparable to the effect of surface friction. The pressure gradients which exist across the mountains in a west-east direction, impart a certain angular momentum to the atmosphere. Since within the west wind belt there usually prevails lower pressure to the east of the mountains than to their west, in co-existence with the orographically induced trough, the mountains exercise a certain force upon the atmosphere which is directed toward the west and which maintains this gradient, thus acting as a brake upon the circulation. In lower latitudes, however, the mountains act as a momentum source. Only during May and June the braking influence of the mountains seems to reach south of 25° N, according to the computations by White.

7.33. Preferred Areas of Confluence, Diffluence, and Blocking

In Chapter 4.14 the importance of confluence for the intensification of jet streams and for the formation of blocking anticyclones has been mentioned (see also Chapter 6.125). From Figure 7.31.1 it may be seen that confluent regions establish themselves in the lee of large mountain ranges, especially if the mountains cause a splitting of the jet stream. Because of the increased baroclinicity one has to expect an intensification of the upper current in these confluent zones. This is corroborated by the isotach pattern of the mean wind speeds of January shown in Figure 4.121.1. According to this figure, the maximum wind speeds on the average are located near the mean trough positions of Figure 7.32.1 (see also Murakami, 1956). This may be due to the asymmetric conditions of horizontal shear within the individual jet maxima (see Chapter 4.211) and does not necessarily hold for the individual maxima. Figure 7.33.1 shows the intensive jet stream which occurs with great persistence over south China and Japan during winter and which owes its existence to the confluence in the lee of the plateau of Tibet (Yeh, 1950). The precipitation which occurs in association with wave disturbances traveling along the jet stream is concentrated in a narrow zone underneath the jet axis, as may be seen from this figure. The confluent entrance region of this jet stream extends back into Burma and Northern India, as may be gathered from streamline analyses of winter weather patterns over these parts of Asia (Ramage, 1952; Venkiteshwaran, 1950*a*, *b*).

Analogous, but less stationary conditions may be found in the lee of the Rocky Mountains (Palmén, 1954*a*). The stabilizing influence of a high mountain range upon the circulation of the atmosphere may be seen from a study of James (1951*b*, 1952), according to which the seasonal variation of wind speeds in a meridional wind profile between Charleston, South Carolina, and Caribou, Maine, amounts to less than half of the variation found in the profile Larkhill-Lerwick (Greenwich meridian).

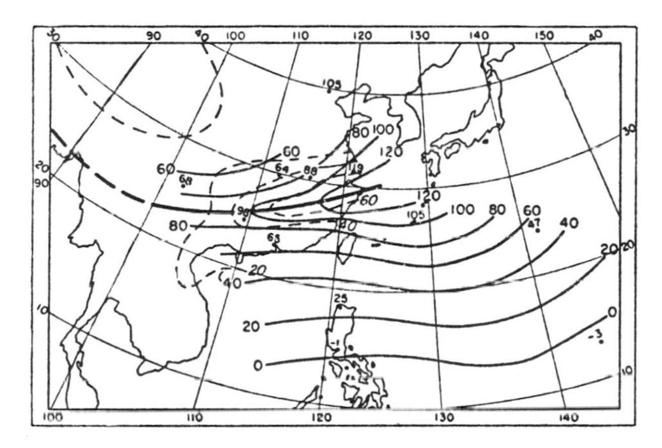

FIG. 7.33.1.—Mean zonal wind speed (mph) during December, 1945, and January, 1946, at the 40,000-ft level (solid lines) and precipitation distribution during winter (cm, dashed). The heavy line indicates the axis. jet (Yeh, 1950.)

The Asiatic as well as the North American confluence regions are characterized by cases of intensive cyclogenesis. In the United States there are mainly the "Colorado Lows," which form especially during the spring season in the lee of the Rocky Mountains over the state of Colorado, and, when traveling northeastward, may cause heavy blizzards. That tornadoes and squall lines form most often over the American Midwest may probably be ascribed to the sharp air mass contrast which exists in this confluence zone (Godske *et al.*, 1957). The storms of the China Sea are dreaded by coastal traffic. The frequent occurrence of cyclongensis in this region apparently is correlated with the advection of positive vorticity out of the quasi-stationary long-wave trough.

The southern hemisphere seems to have a cyclogenetically active area in the lee of the Andes (Viaut, 1956).

A confluence zone in the long-wave trough over Australia has already been mentioned in Chapter 4.212. South of Africa there seems to be another confluent region (Triegaardt and Kraus, 1957).

The ridge over the East Atlantic located downstream from the confluence zone has a tendency to assume a "blocking" character (Essenwanger, 1953). The same holds for the North Pacific region and for the South Pacific east of Australia, where polar and subtropical jets seem to be split even in mean wind profiles. Thus, in these regions diffluence is indicated even in mean cross sections.

Let us first consider the European blocking. The blocking high assumes its most frequent position between about 0° and 20° W, while the confluence zone farther downstream lies near 40° to 60° E (Berg, 1953). Figure 7.33.2 contains a frequency distribution for the years 1933 to 1940 and 1945 to 1949 (Rex, 1950*b*; see also Teich, 1955). In this diagram the Pacific block is shown, too, which establishes itself downstream from the confluence zone over Eastern Asia. The small seasonal variation which the mean position of the blocking anticyclones shows occurs parallel to the displacements of the Icelandic Low. During July the block is located near 0°; during November

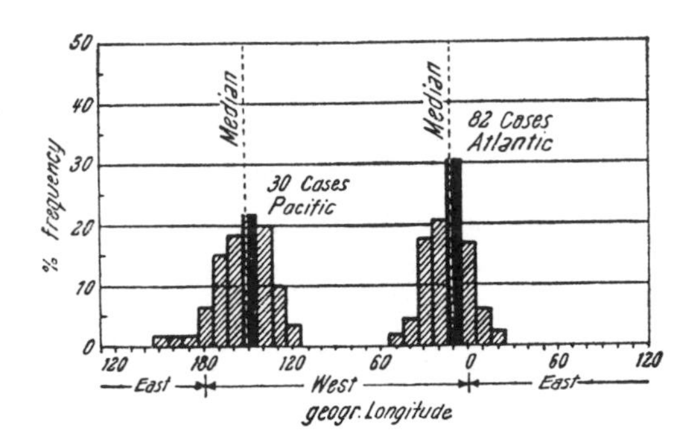

FIG. 7.33.2.—Per cent frequency distribution of the appearance of blocking anticyclones at the 500-mb level over Atlantic and Pacific at various geographic longitudes (112 cases between 1933 and 1940, 1945 and 1949). (Rex, 1950*b*.)

it assumes its westernmost position near 25° W. Analogous conditions hold for the Pacific block and the Aleutian Low. The frequency of blocking anticyclones in the Atlantic as well as in the Pacific shows a well-defined maximum during the transition season April-May, and a minimum during September (Fig. 7.33.3) (see Brezowsky, Flohn, and Hess, 1951). This may seem unlikely at first, since the upper-tropospheric westerlies of temperate latitudes show their greatest intensity during winter; one would expect offhand, therefore, a maximum frequency of blocking anticyclones during December and January. Rex (1950*b*) explained the continuing increase of blocking activity into spring by a rapid narrowing of the jet stream which is observed during this season. In order to give a satisfactory explanation of this phenomenon one probably would have to go back to the principles of atmospheric circulation. Obviously the heat budget of the hemisphere—especially over the polar cap—is strongly disturbed during the transition seasons. This will result in a rearrangement of meridional heat and momentum transports. Since especially the blocking anticyclones constitute a very effective part of the spectrum of meridional exchange processes, together with the incipient insolation over the polar regions, they are responsible for a decrease of the mean meridional temperature gradient thus characterizing the breakdown of zonal circulation of winter, which cannot be maintained any longer under this reduced temperature gradient. That the transition season of autumn is not characterized by a similar maximum in blocking frequency may seem strange at the beginning. The cooling of the polar atmosphere during autumn, from outgoing radiation, does not proceed as rapidly as the warming by incoming radiation in spring, however. During fall, therefore, the atmospheric circulation has more time to adjust to the changed conditions of the heat budget.

Lamb (1959) published a preliminary investigation on the southern hemisphere in which he counted the blocking anticyclones of summer (December, January, February)

1952/53 and of winter (June, July, August) 1952. During winter the frequency of blocking high-pressure ridges seems to be larger than during summer, as is the case in the northern hemisphere (Van Loon, 1956*a*; see Fig. 7.33.3). Above all the area east of Australia and New Zealand, as mentioned earlier, is characterized by relatively high frequencies of stationary high-pressure ridges. During winter "blocking" has also been

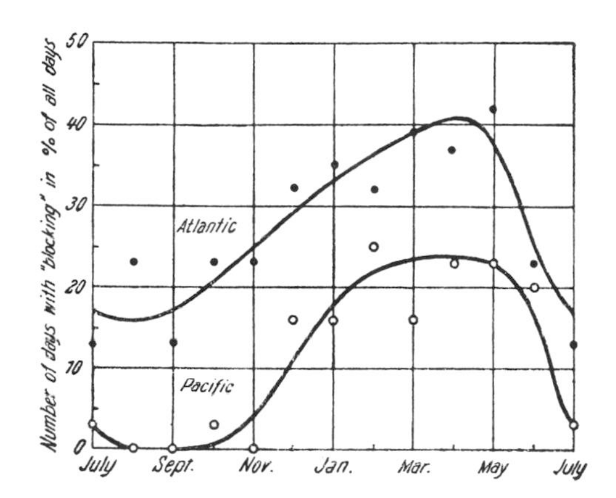

FIG. 7.33.3.—Mean monthly number of days (in per cent) on which blocking anticyclones are observed. (Rex, 1950*b*.)

observed in the ridge which is correlated with the Andes, and during summer also east of the southern tip of Africa (see Fig. 7.32.2). In some of these blocks the mean 10-day surface pressure anomaly may amount to as much as 30 mb (Grandoso and Núñez, 1955). Rare cases of blocking have also been observed in the central South Atlantic (Van Loon, 1956*b*). In general, however, the southern hemisphere is characterized by a stronger zonal index as compared with the northern hemisphere (Du Jonchay and Mironovich, 1953), although index cycles may be observed there as well as in the north. "Blocking," thus, would be indicative of low-index stages (Rubin and Van Loon, 1954).

Since the surface weather is controlled by the frontal zones and the jet streams associated with them, blocking high-pressure areas strongly influence the climate of the hemispheric sector in which they establish themselves. Since the tracks of the disturbances follow the polar-front jet which flows around the blocking high in the north, and since they travel with the subtropical jet, which crosses the high-pressure ridge (Robinson and Joseph, 1955), two belts with above-normal precipitation will have to be expected. Below the high-pressure ridge itself one may count on negative anomalies of precipitation amounts. The west side of the ridge is characterized by positive, the east side by negative temperature anomalies (Rex, 1950*b*, 1951). The anomalies will be the larger, the longer the weather pattern persists. So, for instance, the drought under which the northern parts of central Europe had to suffer during the summer of 1959, was caused by a blocking weather pattern, which formed during the last days of January of that year and continued into late fall with great persistence and with only a few short interruptions (Reiter and Szekeres, 1960). In the case of

Atlantic blocking a total of 82 cases showed the most frequent value of persistence around 14 days; the mean value of the distribution was found to be 16.6 days. In this sample a blocking ridge is contained which lasted for 34 days.

Detailed studies of the position of the Atlantic blocking revealed that on the average during the first week after the formation of the high-pressure ridge a slight retrogression may be observed. This continues as long as the block is strengthened on its rear side by excessive warm-air advection and reduced on its east side by cold-air advection from the north. As soon as the final separation of the high-pressure vortex and the split in the jet-stream system is accomplished, one usually observes a slight progression.

Brezowsky, Flohn, and Hess (1951) carried out a statistical investigation of the Atlantic "blocking" by means of a 70-year sequence of weather-pattern classifications (Baur, 1947; Hess and Brezowsky, 1952). In forming 10-year overlapping averages, they found a periodicity in blocking frequencies of 22 to 23 years. To what extent this periodicity is connected with solar processes has to be left to further speculations.

7.34. High Mountain Ranges as Climate-Controlling Factors

In the preceding chapters it has been stated that high mountain ranges of the dimensions of the Himalayas or of the Rocky Mountains control the planetary wave pattern and may thereby influence the distribution of climatic zones. We shall disregard here the foehn and barrage effects which become evident even near smaller mountain ranges in the isohyet pattern (lines of equal precipitation amounts). We shall rather consider only large-scale circulation patterns which incorporate the jet streams and discuss their effect upon local climates.

The two large mountain ranges (Himalayas and Rocky Mountains) induce one quasi-stationary long-wave trough each, one at 130° E (geographical longitude of Korea) and one at 80° W (eastern United States), as may be seen from Figure 7.32.1. These two troughs are not symmetric with respect to the earth's rotation pole; they cause a certain asymmetry of the circumpolar vortex instead. If both troughs were equally well developed, the pole of the atmospheric circulation would lie near 155° W. From studies by La Seur (1954) it appears that the circulation pole at the 700-mb surface on the average actually favors this geographic longitude during winter (Fig. 7.34.1). At the 500-mb level, however, the position of the mean circulation pole is shifted somewhat farther to the West (*ca.* 165° W). Apparently here the very stationary upper-flow conditions over Eastern Asia (see Chapter 4.412) have a greater effect upon the global zonal current than the flow conditions in the lee of the Rocky Mountains which, after all, are subject to larger fluctuations.

The quasi-stationary troughs in the lee of the two large mountain ranges have a very obvious effect upon the arrangement of climatic zones. So, for instance, the position of the two "cold poles" of the northern hemisphere—one located over Eastern Siberia, the other over Northeastern Canada—may be directly correlated with orographic influences (Flohn, 1950*c*; 1951*b*; Kühn, 1956; Maede, 1956; Scherhag, 1957). That the lowest temperatures at the earth's surface of the northern hemispheric winter have been observed in Siberia may be due to the continentality of this region. In the average upper-flow conditions, however, the North American vortex shows the lowest contour values (Teich, 1955; U.S. Weather Bureau, 1952). The core of this Canadian upper low is located not far from the magnetic north pole, a fact which has given rise to interesting speculations (Flohn, 1952*b*; Mironovitch, 1956; Reiter, 1961*c*).

Figure 7.34.2 contains the mean contours of the 300-mb surface for winter together with the magnetic meridians (directions of magnetic north), which have been obtained from most recent Russian measurements (for literature, see Mironovitch, 1956). The position of the newly discovered magnetic "pole" on Cape Chelyuskin (Siberia) agrees surprisingly well with the location of the mean atmospheric circulation center, as does the Northeast Canadian magnetic pole. Isolines of the horizontal intensity and of the vertical component of the magnetic field are almost parallel to the 300-mb contour lines over the Arctic. The circled line in Figure 7.34.2 shows the position of the Lomonossow ridge, which, according to the opinion of several Russian geophysicists, is responsible for the geomagnetic anomalies in this region (Flohn, 1959*b*). Although it may have a certain effect upon the magnetic field, it should be realized that its axis intersects the connecting line between the two magnetic poles and also the connecting line between the two atmospheric circulation poles, though by only a relatively small angle.

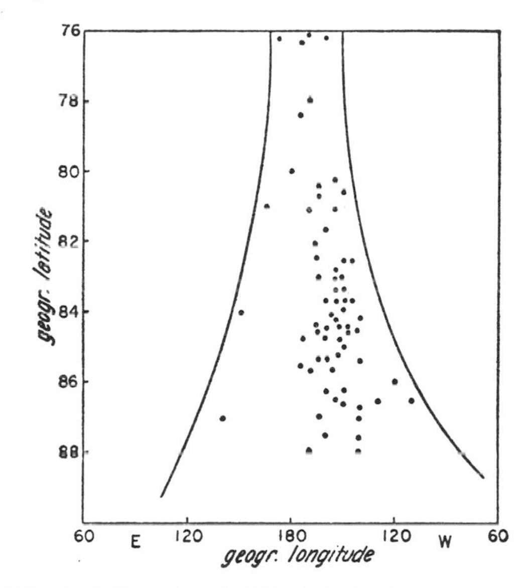

FIG. 7.34.1.—Position of the circulation pole at the 700-mb level; selected winter periods during 1945 to 1948. (La Seur, 1954.)

In the southern hemisphere, too, a certain parallelism between the magnetic field and the atmospheric circulation seems to be present. The magnetic south pole is located at 68.2° S and 145.4° E, i.e., about 1600 km from the antipodes of the magnetic North Pole (Landolt-Börnstein, 1952). In Figure 7.32.2 we have seen that the southern hemisphere circumpolar vortex has a certain asymmetry, probably due to the configuration of the Antarctic continent and its action as a cooling surface. The core of the low-pressure vortex is shifted toward 120° to 130° E, showing a displacement against the earth's rotation pole in a direction which approximately indicates the position of the magnetic pole.

A further remarkable agreement between atmospheric circulation and magnetic field is evident from the fact that the equator of the earth's magnetic field (inclination = 0), and the average meteorological equator (characterized by maximum temperatures, minimum pressure and convergence of the wind field) show indentations toward the north or south at almost the same geographic longitudes. The equatorial minimum of cosmic radiation, too, shows the same pattern (Flohn, 1959*b*).

How can this striking correlation between terrestrial magnetic field and atmospheric activity be explained? It can hardly be assumed that the atmospheric pressure field is steered by the magnetic field, since the latter has no influence upon the tropospheric equations of motion. Furthermore, the kinetic energy of the atmosphere is about 5000 times larger than the external part of the magnetic field.

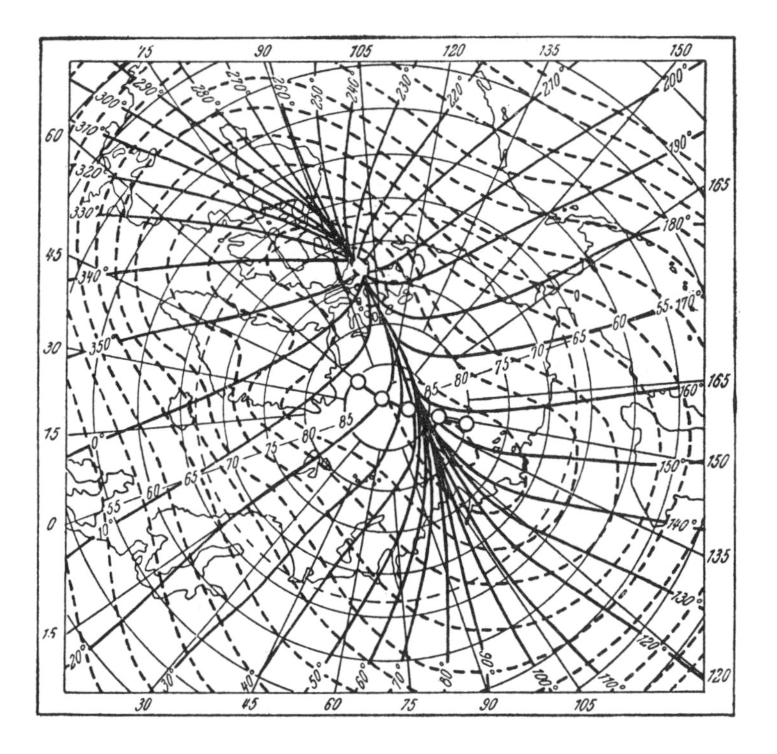

FIG. 7.34.2.—Solid lines, magnetic meridians; dashed, mean contours of the 300-mb level for winter Circles indicate the position of the Lomonossow ridge. (Mironovitch, 1956.)

It might be possible, however, that the atmospheric circulation influences the originally rotational symmetric magnetic field, by means of the ionospheric circulation. We have seen in Chapter 4.414 that the orographic influence may still be felt in the flow patterns of the lower ozonospheric layers. We may easily assume, therefore, that this influence extends even higher and that it affects the wind systems of the ionosphere, which show a daily periodicity. Chapman (1951) actually was able to prove that these wind systems, which are also connected with magnetic storms, show distortions similar to the ones of the upper tropospheric pressure field. One might assume that these distortions of the 24-hour periodic ionospheric wind systems which may be induced by the troposphere impress themselves upon the originally rotational symmetric magnetic field of the earth in the course of long periods of time.

This opens up new aspects of research on atmospheric circulations and their fluctuations in time. Not only does there seem to be a connection between the mean circulation patterns and the magnetic field, but also the seasonal—and even the interdiurnal—changes in the large-scale flow patterns seem to reflect themselves in magnetic records (Wulf and Hodge, 1950). By this a coupling between tropospheric flow processes and those in the high atmosphere is indicated. The interesting question arises whether the circulation of the lower atmospheric layers may also be influenced "from above." If one assumes the energy of solar radiation not to be constant, but variable, especially in its ultraviolet and corpuscular components, it might very well be possible that a change in the radiation budget triggers off local disturbances in the ionospheric and ozonospheric flow patterns which amplify under favorable circumstances and pass on their perturbation energy to lower layers. Since the kinetic energy of these high atmospheric layers is relatively small even with high wind speeds, the influence of ionospheric and ozonospheric disturbances upon the troposphere will be rather indistinct, and correlations between solar and geomagnetic quantities on the one hand, and terrestrial weather sequences on the other hand may show rather widely scattered results (Clayton, 1941; Macdonald and Roberts, 1958; Mironovitch and Viart, 1958; Palmer, 1956; Prudhomme, 1950; Riehl, 1956; Shapiro, 1956, 1959; Trenkle, 1957).

7.4. PERIODIC AND NON-PERIODIC FLUCTUATIONS OF THE GENERAL CIRCULATION, ESPECIALLY OF THE JET STREAMS

7.41. Seasonal Fluctuations

7.411. Fluctuations of Global Dimensions

If we consider the earth and its atmosphere as a closed system, without external forces, the angular momentum of this system will have to remain constant with time. (The secular effects of tidal friction will be neglected here.) Any changes of the angular momentum of the atmosphere will be compensated by a change in the rate of rotation of the earth. The momentum exchange between solid earth and atmosphere takes place within the friction layer of the latter.

It was pointed out in Chapter 4.414 that enormous amounts of momentum have to be exchanged between the two hemispheres in the course of a year. If this exchange occurred uniformly, the total amount of angular momentum of the atmosphere would not necessarily have to change. This is, however, not the case. Above all, the frictional conditions in the mainly oceanic southern hemisphere are different from the ones in the northern hemisphere. The magnitudes of the terms entering the momentum budget of the atmosphere, which are given in Table 7.411, have been computed by Van den Dungen, Cox, and Van Mieghem (1952). (A positive sign stands for momentum surplus as compared with average conditions, or for a transport from the earth's surface into the atmosphere.)

The relative fluctuations of the rate of rotation of the earth, $\Delta\Omega/\Omega$, and thereby of the length of day, which may be obtained from accurate time measurements, are largely due to these global atmospheric momentum fluctuations. $\Delta I_a \omega_a / I \Omega_e$ has the order of magnitude of $1.6 \cdot 10^{-8}$ (Munk and Miller, 1950). $I = I_e + I_a + I_o$ is the momentum. The subscripts stand for earth (e), atmosphere (a), and ocean (o). ω is the *relative* angular velocity component parallel to the earth's axis. The oceans contribute only an amount of about $\Delta I_o \omega_o / I \Omega_e \cong 0.15 \cdot 10^{-8}$ to the fluctuations of the length of day.

TABLE 7.411. MOMENTUM BUDGET OF THE ATMOSPHERE (Units 10^{32} g cm^2 sec^{-1})

	ATMOSPHERE (departures from yearly average)			MOMENTUM TRANSPORT FROM EARTH'S SURFACE INTO ATMOSPHERE		
	Northern Hemisphere	Southern Hemisphere	Global	Northern Hemisphere	Southern Hemisphere	Global
February	−0.6	+2.0	+1.4	+13.7	−12.3	+1.4
May	−1.4	−3.2	−4.6	+ 4.2	− 8.8	−4.6
August	+0.4	−0.8	−0.4	+ 0.8	− 1.2	−0.4
November	+1.4	+2.2	+3.6	+13.3	− 9.7	+3.6

The agreement between fluctuations of the rate of rotation of the earth due to angular momentum changes of the atmosphere with astronomical measurements of the length of day is surprisingly good (Rudloff, 1950; see also Sutcliffe, 1950; Van den Dungen, Cox, and Van Mieghem, 1950, 1956, 1959; Van Mieghem, 1952*a*). Since the main portion of angular momentum is concentrated in the jet streams, their seasonal shifts and intensity changes influence greatly the fluctuations described above.

Zonal currents are not alone in a certain influence upon the earth's rotation. Shifts of the axis of the circumpolar vortex relative to the earth's axis of rotation may cause small changes in the orientation of the latter (Bossolasco, 1949).

7.412. Regional Fluctuations

It has been shown in Chapter 7.33 that the mean positions of the atmospheric centers of action undergo a certain seasonal change. This apparently depends upon the seasonal changes of the intensity of the mean zonal current and the resulting change of mean wave number (4 during summer, 3 during winter; U.S. Weather Bureau, 1952). The long-wave troughs in the lee of the mountains are rather stably anchored, since they are orographically induced (Fig. 7.32.1). The ridges and troughs located downstream from these anchor positions, however, adjust themselves to the mean zonal flow conditions (see also Chapter 3.251.)

The European low-pressure trough is especially sensitive to changes in the intensity of the zonal current. This becomes apparent from statistics of foehn frequencies in Innsbruck (Reiter, 1958*b*). Although foehn may be observed with almost any weather patterns, it is most frequent with a southwesterly upper flow. According to the statistics, especially during March, April, and May, and again during September, October, and November, i.e., during the transition seasons, an upper trough is frequently located to the west of the Alpine region. This frequency distribution of foehn days is remarkable insofar as the *mean charts* of the 700-mb surface reveal a high-pressure ridge over England during the winter (average of October to April), which should bring a northwesterly component of flow aloft over the Alps, on the average. During summer, however, when a minimum of foehn frequency is observed in Innsbruck, the mean charts indicate a slight southerly component in the upper flow. This seasonal change in the mean 700-mb flow reflects itself also in the blocking frequencies, which have been shown in Figure 7.33.3.

The two foehn maxima observed in Innsbruck in spring and autumn thus cannot be explained from the *mean* position of the planetary long waves, while the latter stand in good agreement with the Atlantic blocking action. That the foehn periods are most frequent during the transition season again supports the conclusion that the atmospheric circulation during these months is rather *unstable.* This opinion has already been voiced in Chapter 4.414, where the large momentum shifts between summer and winter hemisphere which take place during these transition seasons have been pointed out. That the momentum transport is accomplished to a large extent by *meridional components of flow* within horizontal vortices of the dimensions of planetary long waves (see also Chapter 4.433) seems to be confirmed by the foehn observations made in Innsbruck.

Certain changes in the weather pattern which, especially during the transition seasons, may assume the character of singularities also indicate the unstable quality of the atmospheric circulation. Especially in the European region, where the planetary wave pattern is not anchored by orographic influences, shifts in the wave position bring about a pronounced change in weather character (Clauss, 1957; Grünewald, 1955; Namias, 1957; Wahl, 1953, 1955).

One of the most conspicuous effects of a climatic change during the last 50 years which may be attributed directly to a change in the general circulation of the atmosphere may also be taken from the above-mentioned foehn statistics of Innsbruck. A steady decrease of foehn frequency, interrupted by several cycles, could be observed between 1916 with 104 chinook days, and 1955 with 21 chinook days. In agreement with this, the westerly and northerly wind components show a secular increase in the Alpine region (e.g., on Sonnblick; Brezowsky, 1952; Tollner, 1954). This might be correlated with the intensification of the Azores High found by Bjerknes (1960) and with a pressure decrease in a zone between Iceland and Labrador. This trend apparently would intensify the Atlantic trade wind circulation as well as the west wind circulation, which again manifests itself in a marked increase of water temperatures in the Gulf Stream region south of Newfoundland (see also Lamb and Johnson, 1959). In other parts of the world climatic fluctuations may be found, too, which are caused by a shift of the general circulation and of the jet streams (Yamamoto, 1957, 1958).

Besides being influenced by the seasonally variable radiation conditions of the atmosphere, which cause a meridional shift of the jet-stream systems and which bring about the reversal of the circulation in the high atmosphere between winter and summer, the atmospheric circulation is also influenced by the different temperature properties of the earth's surface which act as a heat source.

The Asiatic monsoon may be considered one of the most spectacular effects of differential heating of air masses near the ground. This will be discussed further in the following chapter. The cold outbreaks which are observed in Europe during the early part of May ("Ice Saints") are sometimes considered a European "monsoon effect," following a model according to which the air masses heated over the continent by a positive radiation budget have a rising tendency and are subsequently replaced by cooler oceanic air. In reality, however, the singularities in the European weather patterns cannot be compared with the conditions over India and Southeast Asia. While a drastic change in upper-flow patterns occurs there, over Europe only the position of the planetary long waves shifts, so that to the rear of a trough polar cold air is transported into this area (Seilkopf, 1952). The occurrence of the various singularities seems to be strongly dependent upon the prevailing index of the zonal circulation (Wahl, 1953).

To what extent the generally unstable character of the jet stream during the transition season or the temperature differences between the Atlantic Ocean and the European continent are responsible for this rearrangement in the general circulation is difficult to decide. Probably the latter of the two factors has a certain influence; sometimes, however, the effect of the distribution of oceans and continents upon the upper flow patterns is overestimated. While the planetary surface-pressure distribution shows a distinct reversal of mean pressure gradients between oceans and continents (low pressure during summer over the continents, during winter over the oceans) (Mintz and Dean, 1952), the 700-mb contour pattern shows the same characteristics during all seasons—except for the already mentioned decrease of the meridional gradients and of the zonal wind speeds during summer, and the associated change in the number of long waves. A split of the polar cold vortex, whose two centers now appear in the Greenland and Labrador region and over the East coast of Asia, thus reveals a steering effect of the two large mountain ranges of the northern hemisphere. The influence of the land-sea distribution, therefore, can only be detected in the lowest layers of the troposphere.

On the other hand, of course, the temperature differences between continents and oceans create a certain baroclinicity of the *lower troposphere*, which is superimposed upon the upper-tropospheric wind field. In Chapter 4.412 a possible steering influence of the North African coastline upon the STJ has already been mentioned (see also Fig. 4.411). The shape of the North American east coast, by the same token, would have an intensifying influence on the winter jet stream coming predominantly from a southwesterly direction. With this respect Sutcliffe's (1951) comments in favor of baroclinic effects upon the planetary circulation, caused by differential heating of the earth's surface, may be well justified (see also Girs, 1955; Hwang, 1955). The influence of large mountain ranges upon the position of planetary waves will, however, have to be considered as *primary* factor—especially in view of the results obtained from geophysical model experiments (Chapter 4.431). The thermal influence of continents and oceans may be taken into account by computing the "effective elevation of the ground," as has been shown by Wippermann (1951). This contains the surface temperature distribution which is transformed into height values by means of the vertical lapse rate of potential temperature which is assumed to be constant (0.6° C/100 m during winter, 0.4° C/100 m during summer). Although with this consideration of the thermal conditions there is a very good agreement between observed and computed mean trough positions, the orographic influence cannot be regarded as insignificant or of secondary importance. As Charney and Eliassen (1949) have pointed out, the mean surface temperature is closely correlated with the flow conditions of the upper troposphere. This is shown by the mean January and July isotherm pattern (see Hann and Süring, 1939, pp. 175–76). Frequent cold outbreaks occurring during winter in the lee of the Rocky Mountains determine the relatively low temperatures of this area, while the West and North Atlantic show relatively high temperatures, which are due to the frequent warm air intrusions in the region of the Atlantic high-pressure ridge. Although during the summer there is a pronounced heat surplus over the continents, the presence of dynamic effects cannot be denied. So, for instance, the temperatures near the ground are lower over the central and eastern United States than in the Rocky Mountain region, which is in good agreement with the orographically induced trough in the upper current. Over the Atlantic there is still a tendency for the formation of a ridge of warm air whose axis is, however, shifted to the east because of the heat surplus over the European and Asiatic continent.

A true separation of the influences of orography and of temperature conditions is hardly possible, since, because of the above-mentioned correlation, both are tied up with each other and since the land-sea distribution as well as the position of the high mountain ranges may give rise to a resonance in the planetary wave pattern (Wippermann, 1952). An attempt at a separate estimate of the two effects on a theoretical basis is given by the staff members of the Academia Sinica (1958*b*). From this the in-phase superposition of thermal and orographic effects, especially over Eastern Asia, is clearly evident. The already mentioned geophysical model experiments also yield objective clues when considering the two effects separately. Even in the predominantly oceanic southern hemisphere, conditions are rather complex. So, for instance, Australia shows more than twice as large a mean temperature variation between January and July (from 32° to about 16° C) than South Africa or South America. The size of the continents can hardly explain this strange fact. In discussing Figure 7.32.2, we have seen, however, that the upper-wind conditions west of Australia are characterized by an exceptionally large seasonal shift, although no significant displacement in the average long-wave position takes place. This fact also is opposed to any predominance of the thermal effects of continental or oceanic areas. We have pointed out earlier that the monsoons of India and Southeast Asia, and therefore the jet-stream conditions of the northern hemisphere, may be held responsible for these changes in the southern hemisphere circulation.

In accordance with the mean advection pattern the oceans of temperate and higher latitudes on the average act as a pronounced heat source during winter and as a (somewhat weaker) cold source during summer. In this the different effects of continents and oceans become most strikingly evident, but even here the superimposed influence of planetary waves is apparent: During winter the main heat flux from the surface into the atmosphere occurs in the western parts of the oceans; these areas with an upward transport of heat, however, extend far into the eastern parts of the continents. Apparently the cold air intrusions which occur to the rear of long-wave troughs are heated here from below. The Eastern Pacific and the Eastern Atlantic, on the other hand, are *heat sinks* even during winter. Here warm air masses are imported from the south in the region of quasi-stationary high-pressure ridges and are cooled from below. The heating of the air between the surface and the 10,000 ft (3000 m) level due to horizontal advection over a surface of different temperature, which according to an investigation made by Aubert and Winston (1951) constitutes the main part of the non-adiabatic temperature changes in the lower troposphere, reveals a significant correlation with the mean flow conditions at jet-stream level.

That the warmest regions of the oceans (East Atlantic and East Pacific) on the average act as heat sinks, while the cold regions off North America and East Asia constitute heat sources for the atmosphere again speaks in favor of the primarily orographic origin of the planetary waves.

The same study by Aubert and Winston (1951) indicates that the distribution of heat sources and sinks during the various months depends in a significant manner upon the jet-stream position. The heating of the lower troposphere from the earth's surface mainly occurs in the left rear quadrant of a jet maximum where the fresh cold air masses intrude into warmer regions. The right front quadrant on the other hand is characterized by a somewhat weaker heat flux from the atmosphere into the ground.

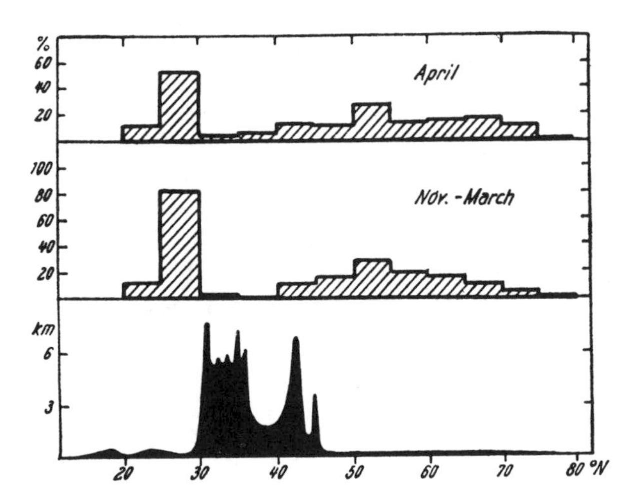

FIG. 7.413.1.—Frequency of jet streams at the 500-mb level (1949 and 1950) and topographic cross section along 80° E. (Ramage, 1952.)

7.413. The Indian Monsoon

The most drastic seasonal changes in the upper- and surface-wind regimes are experienced by the Indian subcontinent. This is characterized by the Arabic word *mausim*, "season," which became a synonym for these flow patterns. While in the older theories the heating of the Asiatic continent has been made responsible for the "burst" of the Indian summer monsoon and the cooling of the continent for the onset of the winter monsoon, more recent investigations reveal that it is not so much the thermal but the dynamic influence of the upper current which causes the suddenness of the weather change over India.

This line of reasoning has been initiated by a study made by Wagner (1931) in which the notion of a simple, closed circulation cell with an "anti-monsoon" aloft has been disproven. It was shown that the monsoonal flow itself reaches only up to a height of about 5 or 6 km. This has been confirmed since by many observations (Flohn, 1956*a*; India, 1942; Koteswaram, 1951, 1953, 1957; Mooley, 1956; Pakistan, 1952; Ramaswamy, 1952; Venkiteshwaran and Yegnanarayanan, 1951). On top of this monsoon current easterlies prevail during summer and westerlies during winter. Rodewald (1936) pointed out the importance of the flow patterns to the north of the Himalayas for the weather sequence over India (see also Petterssen, 1953*a*). Riehl (1954*c*) and his school further developed these aspects of a modern monsoon theory.

It has already been mentioned in Chapter 7.31 that the jet stream shows a tendency to split when impinging upon a large mountain range. Yeh (1950; and Koo-Chen-Chao, 1956; and Dao and Li, 1959) actually observed such a split jet stream over Eastern Asia during winter (see also Academia Sinica, 1957). The subtropical branch of the jet stream flows around the southern slopes of the Himalayas while the polar-front jet travels around the northern edges of the plateau of Tibet. This is clearly evident from a statistical study by Ramage (1952). Figure 7.413.1 contains the frequencies of jet-stream positions and the topography of the Himalayas along a cross section at 80° E. The "guiding" influence of the high mountain range upon the southernmost of the two jet-stream branches becomes clearly visible from this diagram. Both jet streams merge in a marked confluence zone over Eastern Asia.

As a result of an extensive study Yin (1949) found that the onset of the Indian summer monsoon is associated with the disappearance of the westerly jet stream along the southern slopes of the Himalayas. At the same time the long-wave trough shifts from its winter position at 85° or 90° E to its summer position at 75° E. This shift apparently is enforced by the topography of the plateau of Tibet. Upper-level easterlies appear over Northern India, and the intertropical convergence zone advances far toward the north into the Indian peninsula, carrying heavy monsoonal precipitation in its wake.

The transition from summer to winter monsoon follows a reversed pattern: The jet stream suddenly splits over the western slopes of the mountains, and the easterly upper flow over Northern India is replaced by a westerly jet stream (Yeh, Dao, and Li, 1959). The sudden change in the upper-flow pattern can be shown in Figure 7.413.2, which contains a time section of the rawinsonde of New Delhi for the months of September and October, 1954 (Reiter, 1959*a*; Reiter and Heuberger, 1960; see Koteswaram, 1958). Simultaneously with the intrusion of a westerly upper current over Northern India the intertropical convergence line and its associated monsoonal precipitation area are pushed to the south off the continent: the monsoonal rains suddenly cease.

The onset of the monsoon usually occurs in several stages, during which the equatorial convergence line retreats and advances successively several times. These retreats and advances are associated with temporary intrusions of westerlies to the south of the Himalayas. At last the final flow pattern of summer is established with its easterly component of flow along the southern slopes of the Himalayas (Chakravortty and Basu, 1957).

The "retreat" of the summer monsoon, however, seems to occur in only one stage (Ramage, 1952). It may be seen from Figure 7.413.2 that the westerly jet stream over New Delhi, once established, does not recede any more, but experiences a further

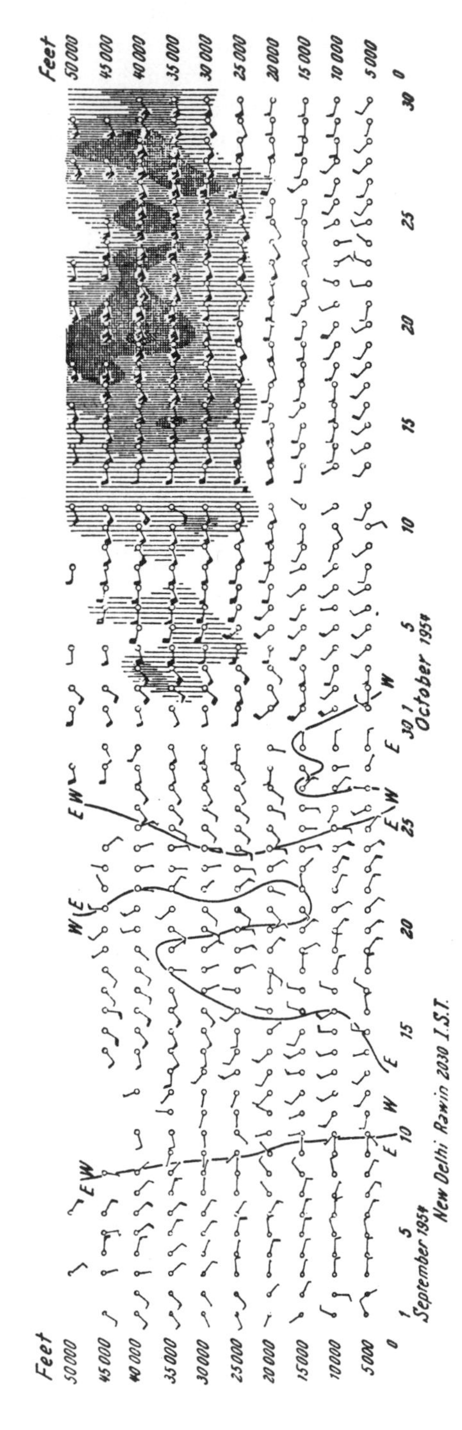

Fig. 7.413.2.—Time section of the New Delhi rawin, September and October, 1954. Solid lines indicate the division between easterly and westerly components of flow. Wind speeds > 40, 60, 80, 100 are marked by different hatching.

intensification during November. It appears to be a single jet maximum, which forces the break-through of the jet stream to the south of the Himalayas (Reiter, 1959*a*; Reiter and Heuberger, 1960).

This immediately raises two questions:

(1) Why do the burst and retreat of the monsoon and the jump of the jet stream across the Central Asiatic mountain ranges occur suddenly rather than gradually?

(2) Why is the winter flow pattern aloft apparently established during a single break-through, while the establishment of the summer regime succeeds only after several minor advances?

Chaudhury (1950) and Flohn (1957) tried to answer the first question. The observed splitting of the jet stream during winter—and especially the maintenance of this split—are considered to be an effect of the high-elevation radiating surface of the plateau of Tibet, which cools the overlying air masses more than does the free atmosphere over India. This reverses the north-south oriented temperature gradient of summer which caused the easterly upper current over Northern India. The jet stream, which so far has traveled to the north of the plateau, now suddenly jumps to the southern slopes. The thermal effect of the plateau as a cold source intensifies a baroclinic zone over Northern India, which otherwise would be located during winter at about 35° N, and weakens it over the plateau itself. (Only the southeastern parts of the plateau seem to act as a heat source during winter, due to the sinking motion of foehn winds which prevail there [Academia Sinica, 1958*a*].) Thus, two zones with a marked horizontal temperature gradient and with an associated jet stream are brought into existence: the one over Northern India and the other over the northern slopes of the plateau of Tibet, in the China-Mongolia region. This has been corroborated by temperature measurements taken by the Austrian Cho-Oyu Expedition of 1954 (Reiter and Heuberger, 1960): During September the baroclinicity over Northern India has been only slight, indicating a weak easterly component of flow in this region (the atmosphere over New Delhi was warmer than over Calcutta). During the latter part of September the plateau already showed lower mean temperatures than were measured at the same height in the Calcutta area. Thus, the high plateau became already thermally effective at this time. On 2 October, actually the jet stream began to penetrate south of the Himalayas (see Fig. 7.413.2).

In order to estimate the thermal influence of the whole mountain range correctly, one, of course, has to integrate over all local effects and their resulting small-scale circulations, like mountain and valley breezes, which become apparent from the diurnal variation of winds around the plateau (Academia Sinica, 1958*a*). Comparisons between neighboring mountain and valley observation sites may, at times, render a completely different picture of the thermal structure of the atmosphere over the mountains (Ramage, 1952).

Flohn (1953*a*, 1955, 1957, 1958*a*, 1959*d*) proved the existence of a thermal, quasi-stationary anticyclone over the plateau during summer whose pressure gradients cause the easterly flow pattern over Northern India (see also Dao and Chen, 1957; Academia Sinica, 1957).

There are three causes, therefore, which affect the burst and the retreat of the Indian monsoon:

(1) The seasonal fluctuations of the jet-stream position between higher and lower latitudes, and the fact that the Central Asiatic high mountain ranges are located *within the width of these fluctuations, close to their southernmost boundary.* The course of the weather sequences over India probably would be totally different, if the high plateau were located 10° of latitude farther to the north or to the south of its actual location.

(2) The tendency of the jet stream to split when impinging upon a large mountain range.

(3) The thermal effect of the elevated heat or cold source which the high plateau acts as in comparison to the conditions in the free atmosphere over Northern India.

Thus, it would primarily be the effect of the mountain ranges upon the jet stream, which causes the upper-flow patterns peculiar to the weather sequence of the monsoon, and not so much the size of the continent of Asia (Reiter, 1959*a*, *d*).

As far as the second of the two questions listed above are concerned—why the winter flow pattern establishes itself more easily than the summer pattern—more detailed synoptic and theoretical studies, taking into account the flow conditions around the whole hemisphere, will be necessary before an answer can be found.

If one proceeds from the characteristic upper-flow patterns over India in defining the summer and winter monsoon regime, it becomes apparent that many cases of precipitation which have been termed "monsoonal," have nothing to do with the equatorial convergence zone, but are caused by other kinds of disturbances. Flohn has pointed out that it may be misleading to identify the terms "monsoon" and "precipitation" with each other over the Indian subcontinent. Some of the precipitation in the latter part of the "monsoon season" falls under the influence of a westerly upper current.

The jet stream of winter, flowing along the southern slopes of the Himalayas, is characterized by great dryness, which indicates large-scale sinking motions. Occasionally precipitation occurs under the leading edge of jet maxima, which may at times yield rather large amounts along the mountain slopes due to a barrage effect. Especially the highlands of Deccan, however, remain dry during the winter. Only farther to the south, over Ceylon, does abundant precipitation fall also during this season, in connection with an upper easterly current. Koteswaram (1953, and Raman and Parthasarathy, 1953) showed that the maximum of sinking motion is located below the jet axis, which is in good agreement with the confluence mechanism, to which this jet stream owes its existence, and with Palmén's (1951*b*, 1954*a*) circulation scheme. This sinking motion merges into the strongly divergent current of the winterly northeast monsoon near the ground. The confluent region of the upper current is characterized by long-lived subsidence inversions and by fair weather, especially to the east of the plateau of Tibet (Y. Kao, 1958; Koo, 1955).

Even the monsoonal precipitation of *summer* is confined to local perturbations, which are associated with waves in the easterly jet stream (Koteswaram, 1956). This has been described in detail in Chapter 4.413. By temporary intrusions of a westerly upper current over Northern India, this jet stream is pushed toward the south. This causes the so-called monsoon breaks (Ramaswamy, 1958).

This easterly jet stream reaches its greatest intensity near the 100- or 150-mb level (Fig. 4.413.1 and 4.413.2; see also Krishna, 1952). Its quasi-stationary position apparently is caused by the elevated heating surface of the plateau of Tibet. The monsoonal precipitation which falls in the influence region of this jet stream and of the equatorial convergence zone associated with it, is in accordance with the vorticity theorem: upper divergence has to be expected in the region of decreasing cyclonic or increasing anticyclonic vorticity. Accordingly the monsoonal rains associated with wave disturbances fall mainly in the right rear and in the left front quadrant of the average jet maximum (Fig. 7.413.3). Between these rainy disturbances longer "monsoon breaks" may occur, as has already been mentioned (Raman, 1955).

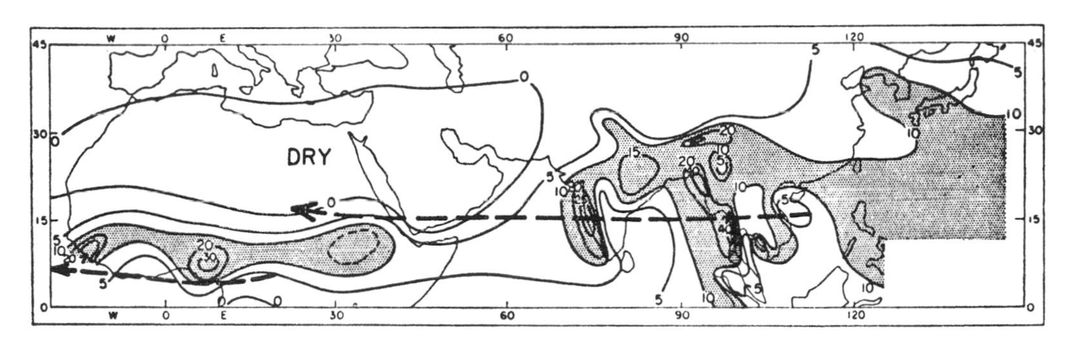

FIG. 7.413.3.—Mean July precipitation (in inches) and position of the easterly jet stream during August, 1955. (Koteswaram, 1956.)

From all that has been said so far it becomes evident that the Indian monsoon is a rather complex phenomenon which can only be understood in connection with the dynamic aspects of the upper-flow patterns.

Seasonal changes of the mean surface-wind conditions in other parts of the world sometimes have causes which may be quite different from the ones bringing about the Indian monsoon. One therefore should be rather cautious in using the term "monsoon." A most likely analogy may be found over West Africa. Flohn (1950*d*, 1951*a*) explains the West African "monsoon" as a part of the equatorial west wind zone, which may also be found over other regions (e.g., over the Philippines and to the north of New Guinea; see Riehl, 1954*c*). The existence of this west wind zone may be explained by a transgression of southern hemisphere air masses into the northern hemisphere: These air masses carry negative vorticity, which becomes apparent in the northern hemisphere by a clockwise (anticyclonic) turning. This circulation is especially clearly established over Africa, because during summer it reaches rather far to the north—probably due to the heating effect of the Sahara. Although no new subtropical anticyclones are formed here, as is the case over Tibet, an already existing anticyclone is pushed toward the north and it intensifies (U.S. Weather Bureau, 1952), thus bringing about essentially the same effect: The inner tropical convergence zone advances toward the north, and the air masses flowing toward the equator along the southeastern slopes of the subtropical high by conserving their absolute angular momentum give rise to the formation of another maximum of the tropical easterly jet (see Chapter 4.413). In its wake there is abundant precipitation.

The weather sequence over Eastern Asia is largely controlled by the jet stream north and south of the Himalayas and their seasonal fluctuations (Ozawa and

Tomatsu, 1956; Sorochan, 1957; Suda, 1955; Vitvitskii, 1956; Yeh, Dao, and Li, 1959). So for instance the precipitation of early summer in the Yangtze Valley may be observed almost simultaneously with the onset of the summer monsoon over India (Chinese *Mai-Yu*, Japanese *Bai-u*, "plum rains"). Over Japan and Korea this precipitation occurs somewhat later. It is associated with a frontal zone and with the jet stream, both of which are quasi-stationary to the lee of the Himalayas. A convergence zone is established between the trough over Eastern China and the subtropical high-pressure cell of the Western Pacific. The trough in the lee of the Himalayas, thus, intersects the subtropical high-pressure belt. One cell lies over Tibet and gives rise to the east wind regime of summer over India. The other cell over the western Pacific transports moist maritime air toward the north along its western slopes (this current frequently has been called the "southeast monsoon" of East Asia). This warm air is subject to large-scale ascending motions along the cold air masses imported from the northwest by the upper trough, causing widespread precipitation (Dao and Chen, 1957; Flohn, 1950*d*; Kamiko, 1956; Kobayashi, 1956; Saito, 1953; Suda, 1955). During the *bai-u* season, two jet streams are observed over Eastern Asia; the southernmost of the two is located at about 35° to 40° N and is associated with the *bai-u* front. The northern one lies at about 60° to 70° N over Siberia (Murakami, 1951, 1953; Nakamura and Arai, 1957). The end of the *bai-u* occurs with a northward shift of the jet stream (Chen, 1957).

7.42. The Atmospheric Circulation during Past Geological Periods

It has become the task of *paleo-climatology* to determine the mean weather conditions of past epochs for which we have no direct observational records available; we are left, therefore, with only indirect means of estimation. It would lead us too far afield if we attempted to discuss here the various methods of determining past climates (see Shapley, 1953). It should only be pointed out that certain physical and chemical methods enable us today to determine the age of various sediments directly (radioactive carbon isotopes, lead method, etc.), and to make inferences from these sediments on the temperature conditions under which certain organisms were living (oxygen-isotope method). By means of such methods one may draw conclusions on the order-of-magnitude climatological conditions during various periods of the earth's geological history. From the wealth of interesting problems we shall select only a few, which seem to be of importance in view of atmospheric jet streams.

One of the questions which has occupied the minds of paleo-climatologists for several decades, and which still cannot be considered solved, is the origin of the Ice Age and the climatic conditions prevailing during these periods. We shall not attempt here to pass critical judgment upon the various Pleistocene theories. Again, we shall primarily discuss the circulation problem.

The permo-carboniferous Ice Age will not be considered here either, since we do not have enough detailed information on the land masses of this epoch. It seems plausible that a position of the earth's pole of rotation different from today's may have been mainly responsible for the glaciation during this period and that the continental shelves have undergone a drifting motion during the subsequent geological periods (Jardetzky, 1948; Wegener, 1929). Brooks's (1950, 1951) assumption of cold oceanic currents in the southern hemisphere and of a distribution of continents similar to the one of today is inadequate in explaining an increasing glaciation, because one should expect a minimum of precipitation over a cold oceanic surface due to the resulting stabilization of the lower layers of the atmosphere.

We may assume that during the Pleistocene periods of glaciation *the continents and oceans existed in their present form.* Theories which use short periodic lifting and sinking of continental shelves to explain glaciation will have to be discarded as geophysically unreasonable, since they do not consider the nearly isostatic equilibrium of these continental shelves.

It has been shown in Chapter 4.43 that the large-scale atmospheric circulation is largely determined by the orography and the meridional temperature gradients.[1] The seasonal variations of the latter do not even seem to have enough influence upon the earth's atmosphere to shift drastically the planetary long-wave position, as may be seen from Figure 7.32.1. During summer there is some indication of a fourth wave, while during winter wave number 3 predominates on mean charts, and also the circumpolar vortex shows a relatively large eccentricity due to the Indian winter monsoon and the stationary position of the STJ over the southern slopes of the Himalayas.

The mean temperature at the earth's surface of the North Pole is −41° in January and −1° C in July, 26.4° and 26.6° C for the same months at the equator. During July the temperature maximum of 27.2° C is located at 20° N (Hann and Süring, 1939). The meridional temperature gradient therefore is much smaller during summer than during winter, even though it extends over a somewhat smaller latitude range during the warm season. The mean temperature of the northern hemisphere fluctuates between 8.1° C (January) and 22.4° C (July). The seasonal range of temperature of the total hemisphere (14.3° C) thus is much smaller than the one over the pole (*ca.* 40° C).

For the Pleistocene glacial periods one generally assumes a global mean temperature which is about 10° lower than the present-day mean temperature (Wexler, 1953). For this deterioration of climate one might reasonably assume a change in the radiation emission of the sun (Schell, 1959; Shapley, 1953). Although such a change in mean temperatures would lower the snow line by at least 500 m (assuming an average vertical temperature gradient of 0.5° C/100 m), the planetary circulation would not be changed by this. This may be concluded from the "dishpan" experiments (Chapter 4.43): The circulation pattern does not depend upon the mean temperature of the water contained in the rotating tank but on the *mean meridional temperature gradient* between equator and pole.

Under our present climatic conditions the winters are characterized by a strong meridional temperature gradient according to the data given above, and by a correspondingly high index of circulation which causes the already mentioned three-wave pattern.

During the Pleistocene we also have to count on a relatively high zonal index (Kosiba, 1949; Kraus, 1960*a*; Willett, 1953), because on the one hand there was a concentration of the temperature gradient along the ice shields which penetrated far to the south, and on the other hand we may conclude from sediment studies that

[1] Changes in the rate of rotation of the earth will hardly have to be considered.

the tropical latitudes have followed the cooling trend to a lesser degree than the polar regions (for an extensive bibliography see Charlesworth, 1957). Simpson (1959) even assumes that during the Ice Age the equatorial temperatures were somewhat higher than the present-day ones.

It is very difficult to find the ultimate causes for the advances of glaciers during the Quaternary. Apparently the periods during which the large ice shields were spreading out were characterized by increased amounts of precipitation in solid form, and by increased accumulation. Simpson's (1957, 1959; see Brooks, 1951; Wagner, 1940) assumption that the advance of the glaciers was preceded by a period of increased solar radiation, which led to higher rates of evaporation and to corresponding abundance of precipitation, seems to be quite intriguing in this connection, although it is contradicted by some observations from tropical regions. A warming of the tropics would have the same effect upon the circulation patterns of the atmosphere as a cooling of the poles. Duell and Duell (1948) and Craig and Hawkins (1951) found that the solar activity may have a certain influence upon the atmospheric circulation. So one may find an increase in the surface pressure of high latitudes and a pressure fall in temperate latitudes during winters following solar outbreaks. Increased solar activity on the other hand seems to cause a tendency for the formation of higher zonal indices of the atmospheric circulation, thus causing conditions favorable for glaciation (Willett, 1953). Correlations between weather sequence and sun-spot cycle sometimes are rather contradictory (see Macdonald and Roberts, 1958; Müller-Annen, 1960; Woodbridge and Davis, 1958). We cannot consider, therefore, the large number of literature references in this field.

The ice cover of the northern hemisphere during the Pleistocene shows two large main ice shields: one over North America and Greenland with its center over Hudson Bay, and the other over Northern Europe and Northwestern Russia. The rest of Asia, however, shows only little glaciation, mainly occurring along the mountain ranges.

Let us return to Figure 7.32.1. Because of their average "high index," the circulation patterns of winter seem to correspond closest to Pleistocene conditions. The well-developed trough in the lee of the Rocky Mountains brings about a confluence region along its eastern side, and therefore lets us expect a quasi-permanent precipitation maximum in this region. Under favorable temperature conditions it will cause accumulation of ice. As long as the assumption seems warranted that the wave pattern of winter, shown in Figure 7.32.1, established itself with great frequency and great persistence and that the global mean temperatures were low enough to cause a prevalence of solid precipitation in these latitudes, we will not have to postulate a shift of the rotation pole of the earth in order to explain the accumulation of ice. The prevalence of solid precipitation is promoted by the outbreaks of cold polar air masses occurring most often in the lee of the Rocky Mountains, which cause a bulge in the mean annual isotherms toward the south. The confluence between these cold air masses and maritime tropical air masses in the PFJ region even under the present climatic conditions brings about a precipitation maximum in the northeastern United States (Flohn, 1952*a*; Kraus, 1960*a*).

We should not be surprised, therefore, to find a *lowland glacier* over North America during the Pleistocene, *whose diverging ice masses have their center over Labrador and Hudson Bay* (Flint, 1957) and which show a direction of flow toward the *west* in central Canada. Only in the Rocky Mountain region itself do we find mountain glaciers, but their influence region does not reach far to the east under the relatively dry conditions to the lee of the main ranges.

In the Atlantic and European region a strongly developed high-pressure ridge may be recognized from Figure 7.32.1, which according to Figure 7.33.3 causes a frequency maximum of blocking weather patterns during the season of maximum zonal index, and which during the same season shifts its mean position farthest to the west. While Willett (1953) assumes a maximum of zonal index and a minimum of blocking frequency during periods of glaciation, it is evident from the studies described in Chapter 7.33 that the frequency of formation of Atlantic and Pacific blocks varies parallel rather than anti-parallel with the changes of zonal index. With increased zonal circulation, as it presently occurs during winter, we may expect that about 40 per cent of all days show a blocking high-pressure area in the East Atlantic region. Scandinavia, then, is under the influence of moist air masses, which come from the southwest Atlantic and travel around the high-pressure ridge. Supported by orographic influences, they bring abundant precipitation and may lead to glaciation in the lee of

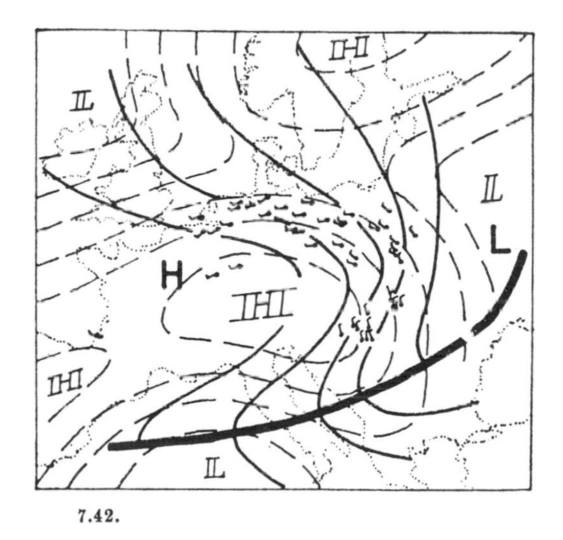

FIG. 7.42.—Winds and pressure distribution during the late Pleistocene. Dashed lines, interpretation according to Poser; solid lines, new interpretation.

the Scandinavian mountain ranges (Flint, 1957; Wexler, 1960*a*). From a study of summer and winter temperatures observed in Stockholm, Namias (1957) also arrives at the conclusion that a hemispheric "high-index" circulation is favorable for a glaciation of Scandinavia. It seems remarkable in this connection that the glaciers of the Alps during the Ice Age in no way matched the dimensions of the Scandinavian ice shield. Probably in the Central European region there was no excessively large supply of solid precipitation, as would otherwise be the case in markedly *zonal* weather patterns of winter (Rex,1 950*b*). Considering the slope direction of dunes from the late Pleistocene, Poser (1947; see Schwarzbach, 1950) arrives at mean wind directions over the Netherlands, Belgium, Germany, Poland, and Hungary. From this he reconstructed the pressure distribution, which calls for a branch of the Azores high to be located over Central Europe, with its center over the Alpine region. Over Scandinavia Poser assumed a glacial anticyclone. In Figure 7.42 Poser's interpretation of the pressure field has been entered with dashed lines. The full lines indicate another way of analyzing this data by considering *surface friction*. This pattern does *not* call for a glacial anticyclone. In interpreting this diagram one will have to consider, though, that it reconstructs the pressure distribution for weather with *strong* winds, and not necessarily for *average* conditions.

As may be seen from the present average pressure distribution over the northern hemisphere (U.S. Weather Bureau, 1952), the surface pressure pattern is decisively influenced by the upper flow. So, for instance, Greenland does not show anticyclonic conditions of surface pressure in the monthly means of any season. Instead, the core of the Icelandic low is located directly over the southern tip of Greenland during January. Especially during winter the surface pressure conditions reflect very impressively the position of the planetary long waves, except for a shift of the sea-level low-pressure centers with respect to the location of the same centers at the 700-mb surface by about 20° of longitude toward the east. If these findings are applied to the planetary wave pattern shown in Figure 7.32.1, one would have to expect a high-pressure ridge in the surface pressure distribution slightly to the west of the Greenwich meridian. The low-pressure center, however, would have to be sought near 50° to 60° E. The orientation of dunes shown in Figure 7.42 seems to agree well with this pressure scheme. Furthermore, if we consider that during an Atlantic blocking, such as is characteristic for weather patterns of winter, the low pressure activity in the Mediterranean tends to be above normal, the direction of dunes shown for Hungary becomes plausible, too. With all these considerations it cannot be emphasized enough, however, that we are only speculating without necessarily describing the actual conditions.

The small Pleistocene glaciation of Eastern Asia has to be attributed to the continentality of this region, which shows in the shortage of precipitation. From considerations made in Chapter 7.413 we will have to assume that the increased zonal circulation during the Pleistocene caused weather patterns characteristic of the winter monsoon over India for the larger part of the year, or maybe even for the whole year. According to this, the subtropical jet stream would have been located constantly to the south of the Himalayas, bringing moderate amounts of precipitation in the influence region of wave disturbances. That the Ice Age left only minor tracks in Southeastern Asia may be ascribed to the predominantly winter-monsoonal type of circulation pattern (see Charlesworth, 1957). The hypothesis that the Central Asiatic mountain ranges were considerably lower during the Pleistocene than they are today, thus showing only little glaciation at that time, does not seem to be very plausible (Klebelsberg, 1949).

One may see from Figure 7.32.1 that the Pacific anticyclone is very strongly developed during winter. It may be expected, therefore, that the trade wind circulation was intensified during the Pleistocene. This seems to be corroborated by studies of sediments from the tropical Pacific (Nyberg, 1951). The meridional extent of the subtropical high-pressure areas probably was smaller during the Ice Age than it is today, because Hadley's trade-wind cell decreases its dimensions with increasing zonal index. This seems to be in good agreement with the Pleistocene pluvial periods in subtropical and tropical latitudes, which occurred during the Ice Age (Flohn, 1952*a*, 1953*b*; Schwarzbach, 1950).

The atmospheric circulation patterns during ice-free epochs cannot be reasoned out too easily, because we do not have any analogon in our present weather occurrences. It may be assumed that the meridional temperature gradient was even smaller than what corresponds to our present summer conditions. The trade-wind circulation within the Hadley cell extended relatively far into the temperate latitudes of both hemispheres. The arid zones within the subtropical high-pressure belts also should have experienced a corresponding widening. The PFJ should have been relatively far poleward in both hemispheres.

As long as we may count upon the existence of mountain ranges which approximately correspond to the present forms, we will have to expect the presence of quasi-stationary long waves within the planetary circulation. During periods without any large elevated land masses, there still remains the land-sea distribution as an effective source of perturbations in the temperature and flow patterns. It is likely, however, that it was less effective than the dynamic influences of high mountain ranges. One could visualize pronounced trade-wind circulations on the average reaching much farther to the north than is the case even under present summer conditions. A relatively intensive jet stream, associated with a zone of abundant precipitation would have to be expected under these circumstances in subpolar latitudes (see Chapter 4.432).

8

JET STREAMS AS PART OF THE CIRCULATION OF THE ATMOSPHERE

In the preceding chapters we regarded the jet streams according to their different causes and effects. Because they constitute large-scale atmospheric processes of flow, they become a rather important part of the general circulation of the atmosphere. Since Bjerknes (1921) devised his circulation scheme in which the polar front played a dominant role, our knowledge about the development of flow patterns in the free atmosphere has vastly increased through the world-wide radiosonde network. It is beyond the scope of this book to describe in detail the different problems connected with the exploration of the general circulation. We shall only be concerned here with a short review of several viewpoints which contribute toward the understanding of the jet stream as a large-scale flow phenomenon. A lucid summary of the basic principles of the general circulation of the atmosphere has been given by Bolin (1952).

8.1. JET STREAMS FROM A PLANETARY APPROACH

The ultimate reason for processes of motion within the atmospheric shell is the latitude dependency of the heat budget (Wexler, 1955). The atmosphere has rightly been compared with a "heat engine" which receives heat energy from the sun by incoming radiation in low latitudes, and which looses energy at high latitudes by outgoing radiation. The *maximum* efficiency of this heat engine for a Carnot cycle amounts to 60/303, i.e. about 20 per cent, under the assumption of an equatorial mean temperature of $+30°$ C and a polar mean temperature of $-30°$ C.

According to Brunt (1944) the absorption of solar radiation amounts to about $1.1 \cdot 10^{17}$ watts. The dissipation of kinetic energy of the atmosphere (total amount approximately $3 \cdot 10^{20}$ joule) by friction is about $2.6 \cdot 10^{15}$ watts. Thus approximately 2 per cent of the absorbed solar energy is transformed into energy of motion. Therefore, the atmospheric "heat engine" has a *thermodynamic* efficiency (defined as the ratio of actual work output to work output under maximum efficiency) of about 2:20 or 10 per cent.

Wulf and Davis (1952) tried to prove that in reality the thermodynamic efficiency of the atmosphere lies near 60 per cent. This rather high efficiency would be brought about mainly by the fact that outgoing radiation occurs at lower temperatures than absorptive processes. Warm air masses would cool nearly adiabatically during up-gliding motions, while the dynamic heating during large-scale sinking processes is partly compensated by outgoing radiation. According to Lorenz (1960), the general circulation performs almost at its maximum possible intensity.

These conclusions actually seem to be corroborated by the circulation of the atmosphere. It has been shown in Chapter 6.122 that the main transformations of kinetic energy occur in the jet-stream region. The ascending motions which in addition release latent heat of condensation (Prandtl, 1949, 1950) are concentrated in relatively narrow zones, especially in the vicinity of jet streams and they occur rapidly enough to justify the assumption of (pseudo-) adiabatic conditions of flow. Large-scale sinking motions are mainly active in the wide anticyclonic areas, in which the radiation effect gains in importance because of the small vertical velocities.

Although in the stratosphere the vertical velocities will not reach the magnitudes which they attain in the troposphere, the resulting temperature changes nevertheless are large because of the stable stratification. Again it is the jet-stream region which is mainly affected. The assumption that the stratosphere is in a state of radiative equilibrium, proves not to be true; advective and dynamic effects largely influence the heat budget here (see Chapter 4.414).

The differences in the mean vertical temperature gradients of troposphere and stratosphere and the existence of the tropopause as a planetary phenomenon leads to the conclusion that in these two atmospheric layers different energy regimes dominate. The temperature distribution in the troposphere is mainly regulated by the earth's surface, i.e., by vertical exchange processes, while above the tropopause the radiation budget is of paramount importance. The amount of radiation energy available to the earth's surface depends on the angle of inclination and on the length of day, and it creates a maximum horizontal temperature gradient near approximately 60° N (Hofmeyr, 1950; Milankovitch, 1930). (The effects of cloudiness, of the thickness of the atmosphere and of the earth's albedo, etc., will not be considered here.) In the upper atmosphere, however, the available radiation energy is mainly controlled by the length of the day. From this consideration it would have to be expected that under summer conditions the meridional temperature gradient in the stratosphere should be reversed—which is actually observed—and the tropopause should at the same time become a surface of maximum wind (Arakawa, 1951*b*). The fact that the wind layer actually lies below the tropopause and the existence of the "tropopause break" both have to be attributed to dynamic effects.

During the winter months the part of the meridional temperature gradient in the stratosphere which is produced by radiation effects runs parallel to the mean gradient in the troposphere. Under this point of view the formation of the Arctic stratospheric jet stream of winter (Chapter 4.414) would be of *primary* importance, while the PFJ, which lies at the tropopause just as it does during summer, would constitute only a *secondary* wind-speed maximum, steered by the dynamics of the stratospheric jet stream. An eventual incorporation of the ASJ into long-range forecasting thus obtains a plausible justification.

From this line of reasoning it is evident that the tropopause has a decisive influence upon the vertical thickness of the jet stream and upon the location of the layer of maximum wind in space. In Chapter 4.415 it has been pointed out that jet streams in the upper atmosphere show a similar correlation to layers with marked changes in the vertical lapse rate (stratopause, etc.). Thus, the jet streams in their *vertical* structure seem to be a "pause" phenomenon, which is closely correlated with the thermal structure of the atmosphere (Pogosian, 1958; Zubian, 1952). The difficulties in a theoretical treatment result for the most part from the fact that the dynamic effects influencing the temperature distribution may not be strictly separated from the radiation effects.

For the *horizontal* structure of jet streams, however, the conservation of angular momentum and horizontal exchange processes must be considered essential. The "mixing theory" of the Chicago school (see Chapter 4.121) constitutes a relatively simple explanation (see also Berson, 1950*a*; Bolin, 1952; Grant, 1952; Ishimaru, 1954; Lucke, 1952; Queney, 1954). The poleward displacement of jet streams from winter to summer stands in agreement with the seasonal decrease of angular momentum in the summer hemisphere (Kasahara, 1950) and thus also complies with the "mixing theory". Arakawa (1953*d*) was able to expand the theory and to combine the velocity and vorticity distribution north and south of the jet axis into one single analytical expression.

The formation of jet maxima which are superimposed upon a homogeneous jet-stream belt has been attributed in Chapter 4.123 to the effect of inertia oscillations.

It would appear premature to consider the theoretical aspects of the jet streams as completely solved. Although individual phases of the life cycle of jet streams may be explained in a plausible manner, a general synthesis is still missing which would connect these individual phases into a continuous uninterrupted causal chain. The coexistence of various jet streams described in Chapter 4.41 also lacks a theoretical foundation.

8.2. JET STREAMS FROM A HYDRODYNAMIC APPROACH

Jet-stream research has received several valuable stimulations from hydrodynamics, although some of the conclusions drawn by analogy may not be quite applicable to the free atmosphere. Especially experiments trying to view the jet stream as "free jet phenomenon," as it would appear when a liquid is ejected from a nozzle, must be considered of questionable value. The atmospheric jet streams are "guided" currents in which the geostrophic and gradient wind determined by the pressure field contributes by far the largest part to the total wind field. The delta region of a jet maximum where ageostrophic components cause a strong deceleration of air particles might have the closest resemblance to a "free jet."

It would lead us too far afield if we would treat the various theoretical considerations leading to different jet-stream models in more detail.

Rossby (1951*b*) calculated the formation of a wind-speed maximum within a stable layer, which is bounded above and below by layers of constant potential temperature, using the assumption that the momentum transport per unit time which is associated with a constant mass transport should attain minimum values in the cross section under consideration. The vertical wind profiles computed by Rossby showed rather good agreement with actually observed profiles although the assumption of layers with constant potential temperature approximates only the *tropospheric* conditions below the level of maximum wind.

Rossby (1951*a*) also derived conditions for jet streams in the oceans which show a velocity maximum below the surface, again using the assumption of minimum momentum transport. It proved that below a critical uniform velocity the current will be concentrated in a relatively shallow layer close to the surface.

In a theoretical paper Freeman, Hurt, and Kasahara (1956) discussed several jet-stream models and their applicability to numerical weather forecasting (see also Queney, 1953). They start from the consideration that the jet stream essentially may be regarded as two-dimensional (see Battin, 1952). If the momentum is integrated along the vertical co-ordinate and if the values thus obtained are entered into charts, the analysis of the momentum integral approximately corresponds to the conditions of flow in the vicinity of the maximum wind layer.

8.3. PLANETARY WAVES

8.31. Stability of the Zonal Current

As has been shown in Chapter 3.251, the jet stream controls the propagation velocity of planetary waves which may be considered as perturbations of a zonal basic current. As Eady (1950) was able to show, the basic current is constantly regenerated so that in the general circulation the regenerating and the turbulent forces are in balance. That the baroclinicity which is connected with the jet stream at the same time is the cause for the formation of planetary waves may be gathered from the numerous papers on the stability of the zonal circulation in a baroclinic atmosphere (see Kuo, 1949; Holmboe, 1959). The amplification of a wave disturbance constitutes one of the central problems of weather prediction. As has been described in Chapter 6, from the change of jet-stream positions inferences may be drawn of the sequence of surface weather.

The computation of planetary waves and their instability is the basic concern of numerical weather prediction. We have already met one instability criterion in the condition $Q<0$ (Chapter 1.236). For cyclonic shear Arakawa (1951c, 1953e), obtained the instability criterion

$$-\frac{\partial u}{\partial y} > \frac{2u}{R}\, tg\, \varphi + \Omega \sin \varphi \qquad 8.31\ (1)$$

u is the zonal gradient wind, R is the earth's radius. Dugstad (1956) arrives at a similar criterion (see Reiter, 1960*b*).

Charney (1947) proved that baroclinic waves whose lengths are below a certain critical value are unstable and their amplitudes increase (Berson, 1950*b*; Gambo, 1950; Kuo, 1953*c*). The critical wave length corresponds approximately to the mean length of planetary long waves (Eady and Sawyer, 1951). As Spar (1957) could show, the instability of wave disturbances in a "thermotropic" model (in which the *direction* of the thermal wind is constant) depends on the shape of the vertical wind profiles. So, for instance, *concave* "jet stream" wind profiles (dashed-dotted line in Fig. 4.231.3) become unstable with larger wave length and therefore are more sensitive to disturbances than *convex* profiles (dashed line in Fig. 4.231.3).

If the zonal basic current is unstable with respect to *one* wave length, then it is generally unstable, because with the amplification of the respective wave disturbance the total current system will be changed. In an unstable wave pattern potential energy of the basic current will be transformed into kinetic energy of the perturbation (Pocinki, 1955).

Under the influence of the absolute vorticity of the basic current normally increasing toward the north, there is a tendency for cyclonic vorticies to migrate toward the north, anticyclonic vortices toward the south. Kuo (1950) was able to show that in the region of strong jet streams with a marked vorticity maximum to the north and a minimum to the south of the jet axis, the migration tendency of vortices may be reversed: cyclonic vortices migrate toward the south and lead to a "cutting-off" process, while anticyclones assume a blocking position far to the north (see also Arakawa, 1952*b*). In the lower layers of the atmosphere, where this reversed migration tendency does not appear, because of the lesser horizontal wind shear and the weaker established vorticity distribution, the high-tropospheric cut-off low may be accompanied by a surface anticyclone.

Masuda (1950) also obtained a blocking wave by considering a baroclinic disturbance in a *variable* zonal basic current (see also Izawa, 1950): the disturbance becomes unstable as soon as the basic current decreases below a critical threshold value. These considerations correspond to the synoptic experience whereby a blocking anticyclone is forming in the delta region of the jet maximum.

8.32. The Spectrum of Waves

The perturbations of a zonal basic current (which itself carries the wave number zero) may assume a whole spectrum of possible wave numbers which are superimposed upon each other and which may be separated by a Fourier analysis. Statistical investigations of the frequency and amplitude of the various waves render an interesting insight into the state of the atmospheric circulation (Saltzman, 1956, 1957).

The wave number $n=1$ constitutes the eccentricity of the circumpolar vortex. The preferred position of the circulation pole at about 155° W has already been pointed out in Figure 7.34.1 (La Seur, 1954; see theoretical treatment by Barrett, 1958). There is a linear correlation of the eccentricity of this pole with respect to the geographic pole (expressed in degrees of latitude) and the amplitude of the wave $n=1$ computed from a harmonic analysis.

The phase angle of this wave is determined by orographic effects (Himalaya and Rocky Mountains). The wave numbers $n=2$, 3, and 4 also show a certain geographic preference, which lets us surmise a resonance effect of the high mountain ranges (Eliasen, 1958; White and Cooley, 1956). As is clearly evident from Figure 7.32.1, these wave numbers appear even in the seasonal averages of the pressure conditions within the jet-stream zone, which points toward the quasi-permanent character of these waves. The quasi-stationary "centers of action" in the hemispheric surface weather charts are closely correlated with these wave numbers.

The wave numbers $n=5$ through 8 are associated with free planetary waves in a zonal basic current. Wave numbers >8 are connected with rapidly migrating small-scale cyclones and anticyclones. Wave numbers >12 have not been considered as significant because of errors in analysis which may be inherent in the weather charts (Syono, Kashara, and Sekiguchi, 1955).

Extensive statistical investigation has been due to Benton and Kahn (1958). Harmonic analyses have been carried out up to wave number 12 for winter and summer of 1949, and the "power spectra" of the meridional and zonal wind components have been computed. Furthermore, from these data, indications of the meridional transport of momentum, kinetic energy, and enthalpy could be obtained. The "power spectrum" of the zonal component shows a maximum in the yearly average at wave number $n=1$, as should be expected. When the harmonic analysis is performed for a single station only, the maximum lies with long periods (Chiu, 1959, 1960). Thus, maximum kinetic energy of the u component is carried by the zonal basic current, which may show a certain eccentricity of the pole of rotation.

The "power spectrum" of the v component shows maxima at wave numbers $n=3$ and $n=6$ (see Van Mieghem, Defrise, and Van Isacker, 1959). It is mainly these waves which are responsible for the kinetic energy of the meridional flow. The "co-power spectra" into which u and v components of the velocity enter and which indicate the meridional transport of angular momentum, of kinetic energy, and of enthalpy (see Panofsky and Wolff, 1957) show corresponding maxima at $n=1$, 3 and 6 (see Kubota and Iida, 1954). The contribution of the planetary long waves with small wave numbers, to the transport of these quantities attains surprisingly high magnitudes (Henry and Hess, 1957, 1958; Saltzman and Peixoto, 1957).

The maxima at $n=6$ are especially well pronounced in temperate and low latitudes, while they are shifted to lower wave numbers at high latitudes—probably because of the smaller circumference of the earth. The summer spectra show somewhat smaller amplitudes as compared to the spectra computed for winter. Not only is the zonal circulation somewhat less energetic in summer but so is the spectrum of the disturbances. The activity in higher wave numbers, however, seems to be increased as compared to the conditions prevailing during winter.

When computing the spectra of the yearly *mean* conditions of flow and comparing them with the averages computed from individual daily spectra, there does not seem to be much difference at low wave numbers (<4). This indicates that the mean flow already contains the larger part of the energy of the spectra and of the "co-spectra" in their *long wave* part. The energy contribution of the shorter wave lengths, however, is due to perturbations, which do not show up in the *mean* flow pattern.

If we consider the planetary waves in the jet-stream region as large-scale turbulence phenomena, as Defant (1921) did, the question arises whether the statistical theory of turbulence (see literature in Kolmogorov *et al.*, 1958), which assumes isotropic conditions, may be applied to these global flow patterns. From a study by Ogura (1958) it is evident that the condition of isotropy seems to be fulfilled for wave length between 60° and 20° of longitude at 20° and 70° N. In the region between 30° and 60° N, i.e., in the jet-stream region, the kinetic energy of the meridional *perturbation* components seems to be larger than the one of the zonal *perturbation* components.

Going back to the turbulence theory by Richardson (1920), we would have to assume that the turbulent motion draws its kinetic energy from the basic current. If the latter is stationary—which we may assume for the average conditions of the zonal circulation of the atmosphere—we will have to search for a mechanism which constantly replenishes the kinetic energy of the basic current, since the latter would be stopped completely by frictional influences within five or six days (Sutcliffe, 1949, see also Lettau, 1954). (We will not consider here, for the time being, the seasonal fluctuations of kinetic energy. As Spar [1949] was able to show, the increase of kinetic energy from summer to winter is paralleled by a decrease in potential and internal energy [see also Haurwitz, 1949].) It is rather obvious to look for this mechanism in a transformation of potential energy, whose decrease again will be compensated by non-adiabatic processes (radiation, condensation) (Čadež, 1949; Defant, 1951; Neis, 1950; Van Mieghem, 1952*b*, 1955). As has been shown in Chapter 6.122 the main transformations of potential into kinetic energy take place in the influence region of wave disturbances and are again found in the close vicinity of the jet-stream level (see Lorenz, 1955; Mintz, 1947). *Thus, the perturbations may at times be largely responsible for the supply of kinetic energy to the basic current*, and the classical concept of turbulence should not be applied to these large-scale global considerations.

The reasoning given above has been subject to many investigations. Charney (1953), Kuo (1951*c*, 1953*a*), Platzman (1952), Saltzman (1959), Yeh (1957*b*), among others, have proven that transition of kinetic energy from the perturbations into the basic current is possible. This is mainly the case when the basic current is stable and when the kinetic energy of the perturbations is maintained by other processes. Thus we may assume the following "energy cycle" which dominates the large-scale motions in the jet-stream region (Arakawa, 1957; Van Mieghem, 1952*c*):

1. Transformation of internal and potential energy into kinetic energy of the perturbation motion.

2. Transformation of the kinetic energy of perturbations into kinetic energy of the basic current.

3. Dissipation of both forms of kinetic energy by friction.

The transport of *angular momentum* caused by the large-scale (horizontal) turbulence elements is directed over large distances against the gradient of angular momentum of the basic current. Thus, angular momentum will be supplied to the basic current (Lorenz, 1956).

The basic current will experience an intensification through perturbations if it is originally weakly established and if it shows only little detail. If it is, however, rather intense and shows sharp profiles, a destabilization may result and perturbations will originate. Thus, the basic current may give off kinetic energy to the perturbations (Lorenz, 1953). In this theoretical reasoning the mechanism of the *index cycle*, which has been described in Chapter 3.251, is reflected (see also Arakawa, 1953*g*; Blakadar, 1950; Bolin, 1952; Syono and Aihara, 1957; Wippermann, 1956).

From investigations by Saltzman (1958; and Fleisher, 1960) it becomes evident that waves with the wave number 3 are the main suppliers of kinetic energy to the zonal basic current, while the waves $n=5$ to 8, at times, may draw kinetic energy from the basic current and, at times, may supply energy to the current. Thus, it would mainly be the latter waves which express themselves especially well during an index cycle. Wiin-Nielsen (1959*b*) obtains a further maximum in the production of kinetic energy at wave numbers $n=6$ and 7 during January and April, 1959 (wave lengths approximately 4700 and 4000 km). These correspond to the unstable baroclinic waves. The kinetic energy of these cyclone waves seems to contribute on the one hand to long waves ($n=1$ through 5) and to the basic zonal current ($n=0$), and on the other hand to the short waves ($n=11$ through 15) (Saltzman and Fleisher, 1960).

Arakawa (1953*f*) also was able to prove a transition of kinetic energy into the basic current by using observational data from the northern hemisphere (Starr and White, 1952*a*; see also Möller, 1952). According to his conclusions, the energy of motion is supplied to the jet stream on its southern side from the subtropical and tropical regions, while the dissipation of kinetic energy occurs on the cyclonic side of the jet stream.

Starr (1953*a*) considers a regeneration of the kinetic energy of the basic current from perturbation energy possible within two weeks; this period corresponds in order of magnitude to the transition from low to high index stages.

8.4. THE ENERGY BUDGET OF THE ATMOSPHERIC CIRCULATION

In the preceding section it has been shown that the basic current is in a mutual exchange of kinetic energy with the superimposed disturbances, which may be observed as an "index cycle." The question arises where at last this energy comes from, how it is transported, and how it is finally dissipated.

The atmosphere with its energy budget is not a closed system. On the one hand there is a continuous heat transfer by radiation, and on the other hand a momentum exchange with the rotating earth is given by surface friction. According to recent investigations, Palmén (1960) obtains for the dissipation of kinetic energy by friction north of the 30th parallel at least $60 \cdot 10^{10}$ kilojoule per second. Since from a large-scale point of view the atmospheric circulation may be considered stationary (the fluctuations which have been discussed in Chapter 7.411 will not be considered here), the sources and sinks in the momentum exchange between earth and atmosphere will have to be in equilibrium (Ferrel, 1889) and there has to be a transport mechanism which transfers momentum from the source areas into the sink area (White, 1951; see Reuter, 1960). The same also holds for the energies of sensible and latent heat.

As has been pointed out in Chapter 4, the source regions for westerly angular momentum are the trade wind zones and the region of polar easterlies. Here by surface friction easterly angular momentum is dissipated and westerly momentum is produced. The sink of westerly angular momentum is located in the zone of westerlies. Thus, in this area westerly momentum has to be transported out of the jet-stream region toward the surface (Kao, 1960; Sheppard, 1954*a*; Widger, 1949). This is mainly accomplished in the area of sinking motion to the rear of cyclones, i.e., in the form of large-scale *vertical* exchange processes (Starr, White, and Lorenz, 1950; White and Cooley, 1952).

A *mean meridional circulation*, described in Chapter 4.412, accomplishes part of the transport of angular momentum and heat from the tropics into temperate latitudes. The circulation cells shown in Figure 4.412.1 are justified by the existence of *ageostrophic* flow processes, which are easy to observe in the friction layer near the ground but which also have to be present in the free atmosphere (Palmén, 1950; Priestley, 1950; Queney, 1959*b*). As has, however, been shown in Chapter 4.433, the effect of this circulation cannot be estimated unambiguously, since it decidedly depends upon the choice of the co-ordinate system. It is advisable, therefore, to consider meridional circulations only in connection with the second transport mechanism—the large-scale horizontal exchange processes.

In numerous studies the significance of these two mechanisms for heat and momentum transport and thereby for the maintenance of the general circulation of the atmosphere has been pointed out. The numerical results of the various investigations sometimes are strongly divergent because of the rather fragmentary observation network, especially over the oceans, which may introduce a bias with respect to certain circulation patterns caused by orography and land-sea distribution. On the other hand, many of these investigations cover relatively short periods of time in which again certain dominating circulation patterns may have biased the statistics.

In spite of these many shortcomings several results of the circulation research will be pointed out here, because they supplement the picture so far obtained on the mechanism of jet streams in a large-scale view.

Starr and White (1952*a*) investigated the seasonal variation of the meridional transport of angular momentum across the 30th northern parallel. Figure 8.4 shows the results of their computations. According to this, the momentum transport by horizontal exchange processes, given by $\overline{(u^*v^*)}$, is about twice as large in winter as in summer (see also Yeh, 1957*a*). According to Bjerknes (1951*b*) and Mintz (1951), the northward transport of angular momentum during winter at this latitude circle amounts to about $5 \cdot 10^{26}$ g cm^2 sec^{-2} (see also Starr and White, 1951). Any contributions of the mean meridional circulation toward the momentum transport, according to the study by Starr and White, is of inferior significance (see Eady, 1953; Kuo, 1951*c*; Starr 1951*a*, *b*; Starr and White, 1954*b*; Van Mieghem, 1956*b*). The jet-stream level shows a remarkable maximum in the transport of this quantity (Kao, 1954; Mintz, 1951; Pisharoty, 1954; Starr and White, 1952*b*). Only one-fifth of the total meridional momentum transport occurs below the 500-mb level (Van Mieghem, 1956*c*). This is not surprising because a maximum of momentum is concentrated in the upper troposphere.

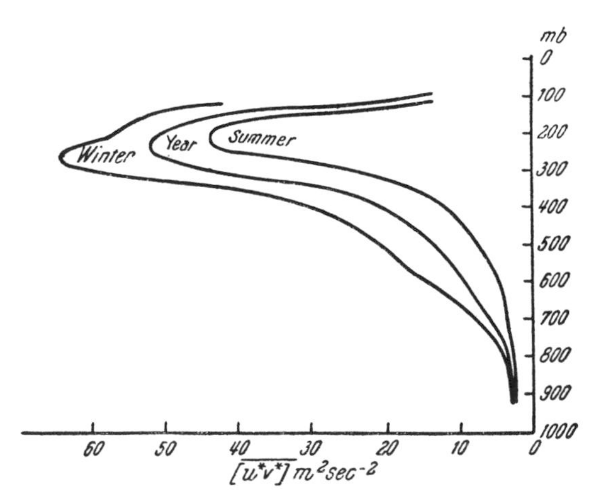

FIG. 8.4.—Vertical profiles of momentum transport by large-scale eddy exchange processes. (Starr and White, 1952*a*.)

Since on the average the trough axes are tilted from northeast toward southwest, a correlation between u^* and v^* has to be expected, such that more westerly momentum is flowing northward on the east side of the troughs than is transported southward on the west side of troughs. Yeh and Yang (1956) found that this momentum transport is not constant but is mainly concentrated in periods with "low index," in which the planetary waves show especially large amplitudes.

Since the angular momentum which is transported northward in the upper troposphere by means of horizontal vortices has to come from the friction layer near the surface of the earth, a "direct" vertical circulation cell ("Hadley" cell) has to be effective (Palmén, 1954*b*; Palmén and Alaka, 1952; Yeh, 1958). Palmén (1956) computed the mass transport within this circulation cell to be $2.2 \cdot 10^{14}$ g sec^{-1} during winter. Convective processes during disturbed weather situations, which cause the formation of cumulo-nimbi reaching all the way up to the tropopause level, may contribute substantially to the vertical transport of momentum (Sheppard, 1954*b*).

The mean meridional circulation is difficult to obtain from wind observations only, because the velocity components involved are small (according to theoretical investigations by Kuo [1956*a*], they have an order of magnitude of cm/sec) and the accuracy of the measurements still leaves much to be desired. Some results from more recent and larger statistical material indicate the existence of such a circulation, however (Mintz and Lang, 1955*a*; Priestley and Troup, 1954; Tucker, 1957, 1959). Starr and White (1954*a*) estimate the contribution of the mean meridional circulation toward the total momentum transport at about 11 per cent (see also Chapter 4.412). This magnitude is much smaller than the one obtained from older estimates (Priestley, 1951). With increasing geographic latitude the effect of horizontal vortices upon the transport processes dominates (Yeh, 1951).

Non-adiabatic radiation effects seek to establish a single direct circulation cell between equator and pole in the earth's atmosphere which would correspond to the Hadley regime in the dishpan experiments (Chapter 4.432). In the atmosphere, however, we observe a breakdown of the circulation into three cells (Fig. 4.412.1): a direct polar and a direct tropical circulation cell encloses an indirect cell (also called Ferrel cell). Kuo (1956*a*) explains this split into three cells in a plausible manner by the effect of horizontal exchange processes and of friction (see A. Arakawa, 1957).

9

JET STREAMS AND AERONAUTICS

With the advance of civil and military aeronautics into higher and higher air spaces, the jet streams of the upper troposphere and lower stratosphere, i.e., mainly the polar-front jet and the subtropical jet, became the subject of very practical considerations. At first, the existence of jet streams created a number of navigational problems. But also difficult flight conditions, as for instance clear-air turbulence, demand the attention of meteorological research. It should not be surprising, therefore, if in this field of applied meteorology a wealth of literature has accumulated during the last decade. Here we shall only attempt a survey of the problems involved. As far as the field of aircraft engineering is concerned our knowlecge on jet streams is far from complete, because of the ever-changing flight conditions encountered by the various modern aircraft types.

9.1. NAVIGATIONAL PROBLEMS

9.11. The Optimum Flight Level

Neglecting more refined distinguishing characteristics, present air traffic has four types of propellants available:

1. piston engines,
2. turbo-jet engines with propeller drive,
3. ram-jet engines,
4. rockets.

Because 1 to 3 utilize the oxygen of the air for the combustion process, they can only be used within the atmosphere. Type 4 carries all chemical reactors along and therefore is suited for flights outside the earth's atmosphere. In types 1 and 2 the force for driving the aircraft is transmitted by propellers, whereas types 3 and 4 are based on the reaction principle.

It becomes apparent that the effectiveness of jet aircraft depends largely on air density or—approximately—on pressure altitude and temperature (National Advisory Committee for Aeronautics, 1955; Alabaster, 1953). This is evident from a rapid increase of true air speed with height, and, on the other hand, from an increase of the ratio of distance flown to fuel consumption, expressed in n.mi./gallon (Reiter, 1957*b*). The conditions of vertical wind shear influence to a certain extent the effectiveness of the aircraft (Tolefson, 1956), expressed in ground speed or miles flown per gallon. One may distinguish between two principal types of airborne operations: operations with minimum fuel consumption, and operations under maximum continuous power. The first kind of operation is mainly applicable to civil aeronautics, while the latter kind may be important for military tasks.

It proves that the two kinds of operations have different sensitivity to upper-wind conditions. They will be described briefly, therefore, in the following.

9.111. Operations under Minimum Fuel Consumption

Under calm conditions and in horizontal flight the fuel consumption of the training aircraft T-33A at about 26,000 ft amounts to only half of the consumption at sea level. The consumption of Boeing 707 decreases in a similar way. If one neglects the additional fuel burn-off during climb-out, the most economic flight level lies close to the

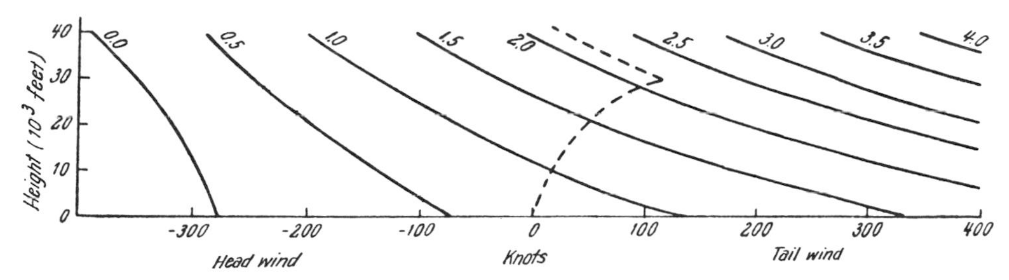

FIG. 9.111.—Fuel consumption, n.mi./gallon (USAF T-33A) as a function of pressure height and wind conditions. Dashed line, hypothetical vertical wind profile.

operational ceiling of the respective aircraft type. Since the ceiling continuously advances to greater heights with decreasing wing load of the aircraft (due to fuel burn-off), economical flight plans for jet aircraft usually allow a gradual increase in flight level. So, for instance, the T-33A reaches the optimum flight level after climb out at about 30,000 ft, and keeps climbing continuously to about 42,000 ft. Such continuous ascents can hardly ever be made, however, because of safety reasons in a dense air traffic pattern.

From a diagram containing the effectiveness (n.mi./gal.) of the aircraft as a function of height (ordinate), and taking into account the wind speed (abscissa), the effects of vertical wind shears upon the optimum flight level may be seen immediately (Fig. 9.111). If a vertical wind profile is entered in this diagram with the same scale—corresponding to the wind-speed values indicated along the abscissa—an ascent to higher levels is advisable only as long as this wind profile still indicates an increase in effectiveness (n.mi./gal.). In the example of a tail-wind profile (dashed line) this will be the case up to about 30,000 ft. Beyond this, the wind profile runs parallel to the lines of constant effectiveness. Further climbing, therefore, would not improve the effectiveness of the aircraft.

Figure 9.111 indicates that in the case of the T-33A only very well-pronounced jet-stream weather situations will show vertical wind shear conditions that might influence the optimum flight level. Conditions are similar with the Boeing 707. Only near the 40,000 ft level, which is not far from the ceiling of this aircraft type, the vertical wind shears seem to gain importance at times. In general we may, however, conclude that in planning the optimum flight level for present-day jet aircraft the jet stream will hardly ever have to be considered (Kelly and Kaster, 1954).

9.112. Operations under Maximum Continuous Power

Operations which have to be planned with respect to maximum ground speed rather than thrifty flying, the jet stream in its vertical structure is of far greater importance. Figure 9.112 shows the vertical distribution of true air speed (TAS) together with various wind profiles. Since in considering the effect of vertical wind profiles upon the optimum flight level, only a relative TAS scale (abscissa) suffices, the TAS curves for the respective aircraft have been shifted arbitrarily. (The actual performance of the T-33A under normal load conditions would be described, if in Figure 9.112*a* the TAS values were increased by about 300 knots.) The maximum values

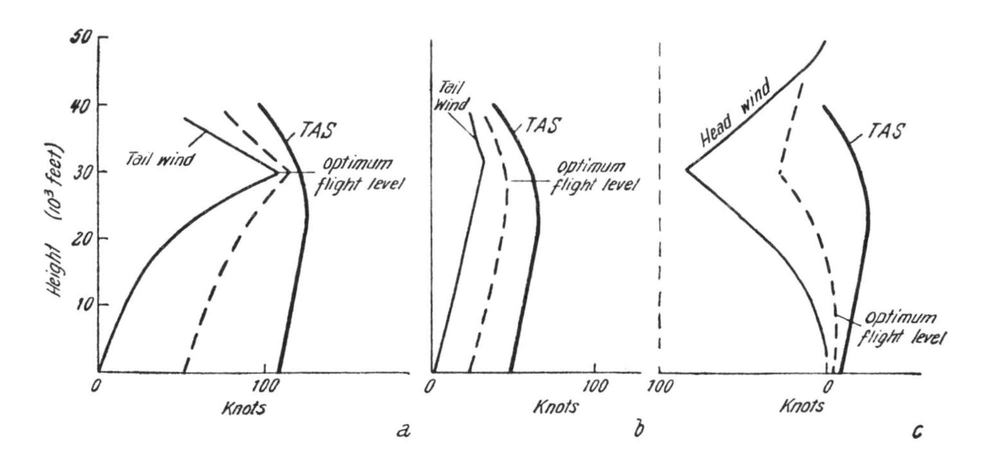

Fig. 9.112.—Determination of optimum flight level for maximum ground speed under different wind conditions.

along the dashed lines indicate the optimum flight level for maximum ground speed. It may easily be seen from this diagram that for flights in strong jet-stream tail winds (*a*) the optimum flight level lies in the jet core; in weaker jet streams (*b*), however, the optimum level lies between the level of maximum wind and the level of maximum TAS. Head-wind conditions may, at times, produce two optimum levels (*c*); because of the lesser fuel consumption the final choice will usually be with the higher of these two levels.

9.113. Optimum Flight Level Determination in Routine Flight Briefing

As has been pointed out in Chapter 9.111, the vertical structure of the jet stream is of little influence upon the choice of the level of minimum fuel consumption of civilian airliners. In order to estimate the influence of the jet stream upon airborne operations, maps of the kind shown in Figure 3.246.2 may be of great aid. If Figures 9.111 or 9.112 are prepared in the form of small foil overlays, having the same scale as the small wind profiles of Figure 3.246.2, the optimum flight level in various parts of the jet-stream region may be read off immediately, and from a combination of the values thus obtained the flight level of the operation may be adjusted to optimum conditions.

The existing air traffic control regulations do not permit a jet aircraft to follow its theoretically determined optimum flight level, which would incorporate a continuous rise due to fuel burn-off. With the increasing density of air traffic at jet-stream level, it became necessary to subdivide the air space into layers approximately 2000 ft thick, which are alternately reserved for traffic in one direction, either out-bound or in-bound. If for long-range flights the shift of the optimum flight level to greater heights should be taken into account properly, this is done best by dividing the route into two or more legs, each of which is flown at constant but successively higher altitude. Thus, instead of a continuous climb, e.g., from 30,000 to 42,000 ft, a stair-step climb by 4000 ft increments is advocated between the more or less equidistant flight legs. It may readily be seen that this kind of flight planning—should it yield greater economy in flying under the presently valid air traffic regulations—will have to rely more than ever upon accurate high-level wind forecasts. As may be gathered from Figure 9.111, the fuel consumption of jet aircraft is rather large. If fuel can be saved by utilizing *reliable* upper-wind forecasts, payload may be carried instead.

9.12. Pressure Pattern Flying

Pressure pattern flying is the utilization of the forecast wind field between take-off and landing in navigating the aircraft. (For detailed literature see U.S. Air Weather Service, 1954*c*; Great Britain Meteorological Office, 1949; Davies, 1950.)

The influence of the jet stream upon the optimum flight *level* of minimum fuel consumption has been proven small or even negligible. The *horizontal* structure of the wind field is, however, of much greater importance in the choice of the optimum flight *route* (Buxton and Chandler, 1955). The influence of the upper-flow pattern will be the smaller, the faster the aircraft is flying. For operational planning of short-range jet aircraft, like the T 33A, the general opinion prevails that the jet stream will hardly ever have to be considered in laying out the flight track, because the flying time of this type of aircraft is relatively short, and its speed is more than twice as great as the wind speed in strong jet streams. Thus, for some time, optimum route planning has been confined to slow-flying, long-range aircraft equipped with piston engines.

For modern intercontinental air traffic this reasoning needs some revision. Figure 9.12 shows the increase ΔS of the distance traveled between two points A and B, if instead of the great circle route L between A and B a triangle is flown in the fashion indicated in the inset diagram. From this figure one may see that, depending on the position of the point in this triangle at which the course is changed (given by the distance x of its projection onto the line L, measured from A), departures of more than 20 per cent of L are permissible (given by the height h of the triangle), without increasing the total distance traveled by more than 10 per cent ($\Delta S < 10$ per cent of L). If in the course of this detour more favorable wind conditions are encountered, which help to increase the ground speed by more than 10 per cent in comparison to a flight along the great circle, this departure from the great circle route will be well warranted.

From the horizontal structure of the polar-front jet described in Chapter 4.1 it may be seen that the horizontal wind shear along the cyclonic side of the jet stream is larger than the one along the anticyclonic side. Therefore, if a head-wind flight along the jet axis has to be planned, a departure into the cold-air side would be most profitable. It may readily be seen from Figure 9.12 and from what has been said in Chapter 4.1 that for short flights a departure is unremunerative as long as the increase in distance is larger than the increase in ground speed. During strongly developed jet-stream weather situations one may expect a horizontal wind shear of about 40 knots/100 km

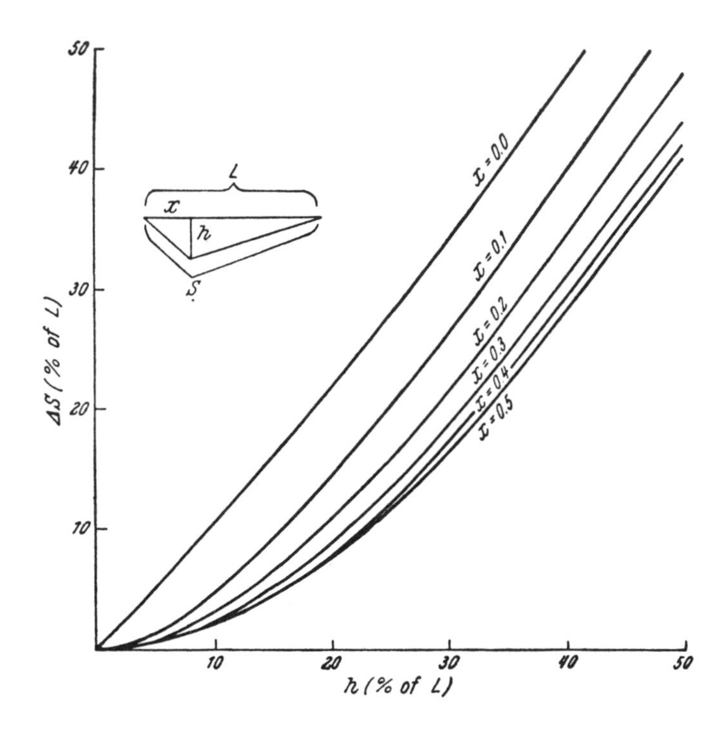

FIG. 9.12.—Increase of distance flown (ΔS) with departure from great circle route L (see text).

on the cyclonic side near the jet axis. Let us assume, for simplicity's sake, that this gradient in speed is linear. Let the wind speed in the jet axis be 100 knots. During a head-wind flight along the jet axis a departure of 100 km toward the cold side in form of a triangular track as indicated in Figure 9.12 would render a mean wind speed along the whole route of about 80 knots. If the true air speed (TAS) of the aircraft is 400 knots, the avoidance of 20 knots of head winds would correspond to about 5 per cent of TAS. A departure from the great circle course by $h = 100$ km would only be profitable if $\Delta S < 5$ per cent of L. Let us further assume that the aircraft flies along the isosceles of a triangle ($x = 0.5$ in Fig. 9.12); in this case h could amount to 15 per cent of L. The great circle route L, therefore, would have to be at least 670 km long for a course departure under the above conditions to be justified for economical reasons.

This order-of-magnitude computation has been made under relatively extreme conditions of horizontal shear. At some distance from the jet axis, especially on its anticyclonic side, one has to expect much smaller shears (see Fig. 4.122.1). Let us assume a horizontal wind shear of only 10 knots per 100 km under otherwise similar conditions. This would render a mean wind speed along the detour route of 95 knots or a saving of 5 knots, i.e., 1.25 per cent of TAS. $h=100$ should then amount to only 7 per cent of L, which means that L would have to be at least 1430 km.

These estimates have been made under the assumption that the jet axis runs along the great circle route. For practical purposes this will hardly ever be the case, but the streamlines of the upper current will intersect the planned flight route under a certain angle. For the mean wind conditions along the detour route, therefore, smaller shear values will apply than the ones assumed above for a cyclonic and anticyclonic case. Furthermore, the mean wind speeds will be different for different portions of the flight. The problem of computing an optimum flight path, therefore, is much more complicated. From what has been said so far it may be gathered, however, that for long flights, of more than 1000 km, the computation of an optimum flight path which departs from the great circle route should be considered by all means, especially since the savings in fuel may be directly applied to payload. Reliable forecasts of the upper-wind conditions are, however, a prerequisite (International Air Transport Association, 1955; Chadwick, 1955).

Several methods may be applied in considering the upper winds in flight planning. They will be discussed briefly in the following.

9.121. "Single-Heading" Flight

The single-heading method is the simplest navigational procedure which takes the upper-wind field into account. From a contour analysis of the millibar level at or near which the flight will be conducted, one determines the height difference Δh of the topography between departure and destination points A and B which are located at a distance Δl from each other. This height difference amounts to a geostrophic cross-wind component of

$$V_{\text{cross}}=\frac{g}{f}\frac{\Delta h}{\Delta l} \qquad 9.121\ (1)$$

in m/sec if Δh and Δl are given in m [see Eq. 1.222 (7)]. This cross-wind component is taken into account once and forever in the aircraft's course after reaching flight altitude. Since V_{cross} describes only the *mean* conditions between A and B, and since V generally varies along the flight route, the aircraft will *not* follow the shortest connecting line between A and B, but it will fly a curve, the shape of which will depend upon the local wind conditions.

Since with this flight plan a course setting will have to be computed only once—at the beginning of the flight ("single heading")—this method calls for a *minimum* of navigational efforts. With respect to fuel consumption and flying time this method is not the most economic, however (Corwin, 1955).

Investigations of a number of flights made with the B-47 (425 knots TAS) revealed that the error in the drift correction near 40° N amounts to about 7.6 nautical miles per each 100 ft forecasting error in the height difference between departure and destination points of the route. In a statistical study over the United States and over the Eastern Pacific the mean forecasting error turned out to be 203 ft. One therefore has to expect a mean error in the drift computations of about 15.4 nautical miles (Strategic Air Command Headquarters, 1954). Because of the large horizontal pressure gradients in the jet-stream region even small errors in the prediction of the jet axis will result in large forecasting errors of the height differences between two points say at the 300-mb level. Therefore especially in the jet-stream region one will have to expect relatively large errors in drift corrections.

9.122. The Minimum Flight Path

In 1944 two groups of Coronado Flying Boats were dispatched in more than 100 Atlantic crossings between Newfoundland and Northern Ireland. While one group followed the great circle route, the other group applied minimum flight plans. It turned out that the latter of the two groups was able to carry on the average 10 per cent more payload than the former group. Flights across the North Atlantic near the 500-mb level showed maximum savings in flying time of about 33 per cent when following minimum flight plans (Davis, 1954; Fraser, 1951; see Polson, 1957; Reynolds and Chandler, 1958).

Since then minimum flight plans have found widespread application in air navigation. Especially the "time-front" method lends itself to almost universal application.

"Time fronts" are lines on which an aircraft of a certain TAS would be located after a certain time (1, 2, 3 hours, etc.) under arbitrary but constant course, and by taking into account the upper-wind field. They are constructed in the following manner: At the point of departure one draws a circle, the radius of which corresponds to the TAS of the aircraft. In the case of tail-winds one adds to (in the case of head-winds one subtracts from) this arc graphically the *mean* wind vectors which are observed along the various radius-vectors, thus arriving at the first time front T_1. To this time front one, again, adds TAS increased by the mean wind vector. In this fashion one obtains the other time fronts T_2, T_3, etc. The minimum flight path is found by plotting the wind vector backwards in the point of destination, and by constructing a line normal to the previous time front from the end point Q of this reversed wind vector, thus arriving at an intersection point P which lies on this previous time front. PQ gives the course of the aircraft (which may have to be corrected by the magnetic declination to arrive at the magnetic course). The distance between P and destination indicates the ground-speed vector. One proceeds in this way until all course segments have been constructed backwards to the departure point. The sequence of all ground-speed vectors gives the minimum flight-path.

Naturally, for the construction of the minimum flight path the wind conditions at the *time of the flight* will have to be considered. A detailed and dependable wind forecast will be needed, therefore. Cook Research Laboratories (1954*a*, *b*, 1955, 1956; Bellamy, 1954; Burkett and Gringorten, 1956) propose the use of a geostrophic computation scheme. One starts from the contour analysis of the millibar surface closest to the flight level. To facilitate aeronavigation the anlysis is prepared in terms of D values (altimeter correction values) (Bellamy, 1945*b*; Woolcock, 1952), where

$$D = z - z_p \qquad 9.122\ (1)$$

is the anomaly of the respective contour value z of the isobaric surface as compared with the standard atmosphere (z_p). If the flight is not carried out at a standard isobaric level, the vertical wind shear between neighboring standard pressure levels is assumed to be linear and is given by the thermal wind, which may be expressed by an analysis of the mean specific temperature anomaly $S = (T^* - T_p)/T_p$. The subscript p

again indicates conditions in the standard atmosphere. T^* is the virtual temperature at the respective level.

The time variation of the wind field is taken into account by an analysis of the τ-value, which gives the field distribution of the predicted hourly changes of the D values.

The use of nomographs and plotting machines has been proposed in computing time fronts and flight routes in routine operations (Burkett and Gringorten, 1956; Cook Research Laboratories, 1956; Corwin, 1953; De Jong, 1956; and Bik, 1953; Powell, 1957).

If the predicted winds are not verified during the flight, several possibilities of correction are available:

1. If the new wind forecast seems to be more reliable the navigator may make a computation of new time fronts, which give a minimum flight path from the present position of the aircraft (Burkett and Gringorten, 1956; Peel, 1953).
2. If the destination has almost been reached, one may proceed after a single-heading plan, since for short distances it departs only little from a minimum flight path (De Jong and Bik, 1953).
3. If, at the point of destination, one measures the angle between the actual position of the aircraft and the position predicted according to the minimum flight-path computations, the resulting angle of correction may be applied to the remaining headings of the old optimum flight plan (De Jong and Bik, 1953).

The only critical comments which may be made against this otherwise rational and reliable method are the following:

1. This method is based upon the assumption of an accurately predictable wind field. This assumption is not warranted under the presently available methods of measurement and forecasting, especially over the oceans, for flight plans which lead into the vicinity of jet axes. It would be desirable, therefore, if more upper-wind observations taken by aircraft would be made available to weather services (Gartineau, 1951). One will have to expect, therefore, that changes in flight plans will have to be made while the flight is in progress, which might either call for abandoning the optimum flight plan altogether (items 2 and 3 above), or which will make new computations necessary which require quite a bit of skill and time on the navigator's part.
2. The present Air Traffic Control regulations call for fixed flight routes. They also specify danger areas which are closed to air traffic, so that a minimum flight-path computed in the fashion described above may at times be difficult to carry through, or may have to be modified drastically (Gringorten, 1955; Williams, 1957).
3. The time-front method gives as a direct result the flying time rather than the fuel consumption, which would be of primary interest to airlines as it is needed for computing the payload.

9.123. Flight Planning along Standardized Flight Tracks

Successful attempts to consider points 1 and 2 may be found in a flight-planning method which has been applied profitably by the Pacific Division of Pan American World Airways (Stiefelmaier, 1955). Standardized flight tracks have been constructed between Tokyo and Honolulu, which are then chosen for a flight depending on the position of the jet stream. This method would by all means be worth further development. It would make it possible for commercial airlines to utilize optimum flight paths with small computational efforts. Meeker (1954) also describes a method which allows the choice of the most suitable of a number of routes by means of a nomograph.

The author (1957*b*) has outlined a procedure, too, which will be explained briefly in the following:

Figure 9.123 is a schematic diagram of the navigational problem: Let AB be the flight route along the great circle, which is subdivided into a number of rhumb lines. TAS is the vector of true air speed of the aircraft at flight level, U is the wind vector and GS_i is the ground speed vector between C_i and D_i outlining the ith flight leg. GSR_i is the projection of the vector GS_i onto a line parallel to the rhumb line which approximates the great circle. d indicates the wind direction relative to the heading of the flight, and the "track angle" T is the angle between the optimum route GS_i—which still has to be determined—and the rhumb line GSR_i. We have to find an equation which gives GSR_i as a function of U, d, T, and TAS. It may be obtained from Figure 9.123 by simple trigonometric considerations.

$$GSR = \cos T \cdot (B + \sqrt{B^2 - U^2 + TAS^2}) \qquad 9.123\ (1)$$

where

$$B = U\cos(d - T).$$

One of the four variables may be eliminated by expressing all speeds in fractions of TAS. If $GSR' = GSR/TAS$, and $B' = B/TAS$ as well as $U' = U/TAS$, we arrive at an equation with three variables:

$$GSR' = \cos T \cdot [B' + \sqrt{B'^2 + (1 - U'^2)}]. \qquad 9.123\ (2)$$

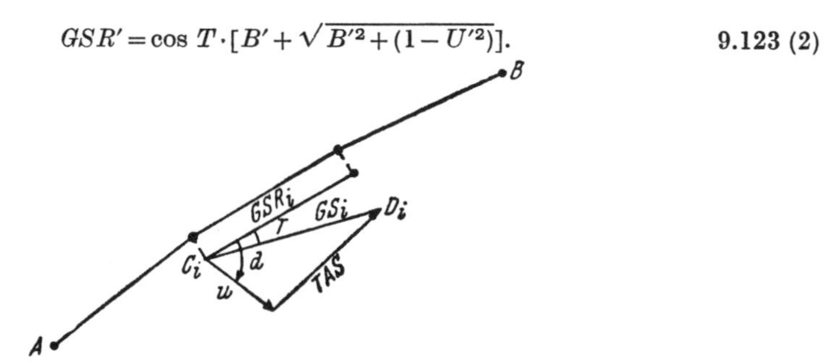

FIG. 9.123.—Computation of optimum flight path (see text).

The pilot, however, is not so much interested in the improvements of ground speed as in savings of flying time and fuel. The desired quantity, therefore, would be

$$t' = t_a/t_{gc}. \qquad 9.123\ (3)$$

t_a is the time actually required for traveling the respective flight leg while t_{gc} is the time which is needed to cover the projection of this flight leg onto the great circle (or the approximating rhumb line) during *calm* conditions. If L is the length of the section of the great circle (or its rhumb line) under consideration, we have

$$t_a = L/GSR \qquad 9.123\ (4)$$

and

$$t_{gc} = L/TAS. \qquad 9.123\ (5)$$

Therefore,

$$t' = 1/GSR'. \qquad 9.123\ (6)$$

It is recommended that the reciprocal values of 9.123 (2) be computed in tables as functions of U', d, and T. $(100 - 100t')$ gives immediately a comparison of flying time along the alternate route expressed in per cent of the flying time along the great circle under calm conditions. This quantity will be positive for time savings, negative for losses.

If the flight legs L_i of the total route are chosen of *equal length*, the arithmetic mean of the t'_i will give the total change of flying time along the whole alternate route as compared to a great circle flight under calm conditions. If the individual flight legs are *not* equidistant their resulting per cent values of flying time changes will have to be multiplied with weighting factors which allow for the specific lengths of the individual flight legs.

Once the somewhat complicated work of computing the tables is finished, the savings in flying time may be obtained immediately in per cent for arbitrary upper wind conditions and for a number of alternate routes. Practical experience indicates (Reiter, 1957*b*) that sometimes several flight routes show hardly any difference in the computed flying time. In the final choice of the flight route, therefore, one may consider the *confidence* in the upper-wind forecast. If, for instance, the position of the jet axis is not known exactly, one will choose a more conservative alternate route closer to the great circle for a flight plan which should run in the vicinity of this jet axis.

For scheduled intercontinental flights, Eq. 9.123 (2 and 6) could be tabulated in such a fashion that the routes prescribed by Air Traffic Control regulations are already considered in the angle T.

If the fuel *consumption* should be computed along the various alternate routes, instead of the flying time, a factor could be included in the tabulated per cent numbers, which considers the flying time (decreased fuel load due to continuous burn-off) and the power setting (temperature dependent). In most cases it will suffice, however, to interpret directly the savings (excess consumption) in fuel from the savings (loss) in flying time.

9.124. Methods for Locating the Jet Stream

With the strict regulations imposed by Air Traffic Control nowadays it is rarely possible to hunt the jet stream. Nevertheless hints on the position of the jet stream, which the pilot could gather en route, would be of great value. They will enable him to estimate in advance whether his flight plan will verify, and what corrections he should expect in flying time and fuel consumption.

During flights below the level of maximum wind careful observation of the temperature indicator may give valuable clues (Jacobs, 1955) on position, for strongest winds may be found on the *warm* side of the frontal zone.

Above the jet-stream level another baroclinic zone is well established (see Fig. 4.112.3); here, however, the strongest winds are found along the cold side of the frontal zone. The maximum horizontal wind shear above as well as below the jet-stream level lies within the baroclinic zone. If from the flight temperature observations one finds that the route intersects the frontal zone, small changes in course—if compatible with Air Traffic Regulations—will result in drastic changes of wind speeds.

If careful upper-level weather analyses are available for the particular flight level, the mean isotherm along the position of the jet stream may be correlated directly with temperature observations en route, thus allowing a correction of the upper-air map while the flight is in progress.

At jet-stream level "isentrope hump" and "isentrope trough" may serve as indicators of the jet-stream position (Reiter, 1961*e*). As long as detailed research is not able to provide us with usable chemical or other methods of jet-stream detection, clouds (see Chapter 6.3) may be taken as an aid in locating the jet axis (Frost, 1953).

9.125. Climatology of Long-Range Air-Traffic Routes

The procedures described above serve in choosing the most favorable route from a variety of possibilities under the given upper-flow conditions. With the presently valid Air Traffic Control regulations the applicability of these procedures is rather limited, as has already been mentioned. Therefore in planning intercontinental air traffic routes the climatology of upper-air flow patterns should be considered (Durst and Davis, 1949; Graystone, 1956; Haldiman and Tanck, 1959; Henry, 1957; Lahey and Bryson, 1960; Robert, 1960; Tanck, 1960). The flights of Scandinavian Airlines System to the United States are routed over the north pole, not for publicity, but for economy (Reiter, 1959*g*).

Certainly in the field of jet-stream climatology there are a number of computations which could be especially useful to airlines. Computing "equivalent head-winds" along certain flight routes has already proved valuable (Coyle, 1950; Crossley, 1949; Cruchter, 1956; Durward and Jones, 1955; Gabites and Porter, 1951, 1952; Great Britain Meteorological Office, 1950; Harley, 1952; Kuhlbrodt, 1952*b*; O'Byrne and Connaughton, 1957; Sawyer, 1950*a*; U.S. Navy, 1954). From a frequency distribution of the winds aloft the mean head and tail winds are computed, which one has to expect when flying any of these routes. From this frequency distribution one may see at the same time which safety factors will have to be included in the fuel load in order to be able to fly the route even under extreme conditions. For jet air traffic which in addition to the winds is sensitive to the temperature conditions, the latter may be included in the statistics in the form of apparent head or tail winds (Crossley, 1956*a*).

The persistence of the jet-stream pattern is of primary interest in planning an air route. So for instance flights from Tokyo to Honolulu may count with great probability upon the presence of strong tail winds. Today this distance is traversed in non-stop flights with conventional aircraft, while the return flight usually calls for a re-fuel stop at Midway or Wake Island. Without doubt jet air traffic will make possible non-stop flights from Tokyo to San Francisco which will follow a more northerly route, utilizing the presence of the polar-front jet. The return flights will most economically follow a more southerly route, trying to stay clear of the jet stream.

In Trans-Atlantic air traffic conditions are less favourable because of the greater variability of the jet stream. Statistics on the frequency of jet stream incidence in various meridians have been published (Buxton and Chandler, 1955) which show that jet streams may fluctuate over the whole region between Greenland and the Azores. It is not immediately apparent, therefore, that a Central European airline would be more economically routed via Iceland and Newfoundland on its westbound flights, rather than following a direct route. Seasonal fluctuations in the mean jet-stream position would have to be considered, which, perhaps, would indicate west-bound flights should be directed during summer along a more southerly route, as for instance via the Azores. For decisions of this kind one probably would have to consult frequency distributions of minimum flight paths (see Bundesanstalt für Flugsicherung, 1959; Buxton and Chandler, 1955). Airlines which have to consider only a small scattering of the minimum flight paths around the great circle route will be much safer in the computation of payload and fuel reserves than lines which find large deviations from the great circle beneficial. Such a wide scattering would be an indication of an unstable upper-wind regime. So for instance during October, 1954, the width of scatter of the minimum flight paths about the great circle route was about 7.5° of latitude for westbound flights from Keflavik, Iceland, to Idlewild, New York, while the scatter amounted to 18° of latitude during the same period of time for flights from London to Idlewild.

Air traffic conditions are less favorable in the southern hemisphere than in the northern. There are no weather ships and therefore no upper-wind reports over the vast expanses of the oceans. The only sources of information are island stations and pilot reports. A climatological treatment of jet streams over these areas would be of eminent importance (Phillpot and Reid, 1952).

9.2. CLEAR-AIR TURBULENCE AS AN AERONAUTICAL PROBLEM

Besides the above-mentioned navigational problems which the age of jet air traffic brings about, the phenomenon of *clear-air turbulence* (CAT) is another challenge for the aircraft designer as well as for the pilot. Even though the bumpiness in flight may be within tolerable limits from the point of view of passenger comfort, it causes additional stresses in the material that may lead to "metal fatigue," thus shortening the life of the plane (Reiter, 1959*g*, 1960*b*). The demand for reliable turbulence forecasts therefore is by all means justified, although cases of severe CAT are relatively rare.

It has been shown in Chapter 4.312, by means of meteorological factors which may cause the formation of CAT, that the turbulence zones have meso-structural characteristics and therefore are rather difficult to grasp in a direct forecast. Turbulence is most frequent in the vicinity of jet streams but it seems an exaggeration to designate every jet stream automatically as a "turbulence zone" in the upper-level weather charts and to stress avoiding it. It may be seen from Figure 4.312.1 that the largest turbulence frequencies mainly occur in stable baroclinic layers, with other layers of relatively laminar flow interspersed. If one attempted to utilize the jet stream successfully by applying the navigational methods described above, one would have to develop an additional procedure for avoiding these stable zones. Since these zones are of a meso- or micro-structural character, however, they are difficult to account for in a forecast. The "jet-stream front" may be an exception, since it appears as a zone of great turbulence frequency in nearly all jet-stream traverses.

At present one has to rely mainly upon the following statistical information when issuing turbulence warnings although it does not have to apply in each individual case (Reiter, 1960*b*, 1961*e*).

1. The probability of occurrence of CAT is about three times larger near the jet stream than in areas of weak winds.

2. One has to expect lee waves and associated turbulence over hilly terrain, where upper winds blow approximately parallel to winds at mountain-peak level, the latter having a strong component normal to the mountain ridges, and if the stability of the atmosphere decreases with height. Such weather situations are frequently found in the jet-stream region. Maximum wave amplitudes should be expected within layers of maximum stability. A routine computation of the Scorer parameter over mountain stations close to the air traffic routes is recommended. One has to consider that even small ground elevations may produce waves under favorable circumstances.

3. In the jet-stream region there are three main areas with excessive turbulence frequency and with unstable flow conditions (see Fig. 4.312.1):

(*a*) on the anticyclonic side of the jet stream, approximately at the level of the jet axis;

(*b*) on the cyclonic side of the jet axis near the tropopause;

(*c*) below the jet axis in the region of the baroclinic and thermally stable layer of the "jet-stream front."

Of these three areas, *c* is most readily evident from radiosonde ascents, because the "jet-stream front" usually is somewhat thicker than the other stable zones. Its position relative to the jet core fluctuates, however, so that in mean cross sections area *c* is less conspicuous than the areas *a* and *b*. This gives rise to the hope that from carefully executed cross section analyses—at least over the continents—some indications may be obtained which would permit an effective turbulence forecast.

4. Along discontinuity surfaces (fronts, inversions, stable layers, haze layers, tropopause) one has to expect increased turbulence frequencies, especially when these discontinuities are associated with a wind shear in the vertical. More severe CAT seems to be connected with "isentropic troughs."

5. In agreement with the theoretical investigations by Sekera (1948) gravity waves in the region of strong vertical wind shears are oriented in bands parallel to the wind direction; with weak shears, however, they lie normal to the wind direction. One would have to expect therefore that in an area of weak vertical wind shears flights conducted parallel to the jet axis would experience more turbulence than flights oriented normal to the wind direction. This would primarily hold for turbulence area *a* and partly also for area *b*. With strong vertical wind shear one should experience turbulence mainly during flights normal to the jet axis. This holds mainly for area *c*, partly also for area *b*.

From what is known so far about CAT one may propose the following avoidance measures if they are compatible with the existing Air Traffic Control regulations and if they seem advisable in the interest of passenger comfort.

1. Reduction of air speed. By this the acceleration Δn will be reduced for an equally strong gust velocity W_{de}, according to Eq. 4.312 (1).

2. For flights parallel to the jet stream: change of altitude by about 200–300 m.

For flights normal to the wind direction: change of altitude by about 200–300 m in turbulence area *b*, where isentropic surfaces and thereby also the stable zone are approximately horizontal. Elsewhere one will have to consider the slope of the isentropic surfaces: for flights from the anticyclonic (warm) to the cyclonic (cold) side a *descent* will be preferred, while for a reversed flight direction an *ascent* is advisable.

If turbulence is associated with a temperature change, the turbulent zone will in all probability be traversed in short time, if the present course is maintained. If, however, turbulence is experienced with constant free air temperature, one should consider a change of course, since the original flight route probably runs parallel to a stable zone (see Fig. 4.312.2).

3. In the region of strong lee waves near mountain ranges one should consider a change of course which brings the aircraft into an oblique angle against the wind. In

most of these cases the cloud pattern will give a clue to the most favorable direction to be taken by the flight.

For air safety's and passenger comfort's sake the collection and the processing of a large number of CAT reports is of interest. Most of all, however, the micro-structure of the atmosphere should receive increased attention, so one may find out more about the mechanisms which lead to the formation of CAT.

BIBLIOGRAPHY

ABBREVIATIONS

ACSI	Atti del Congresso Scientifico Internazionale sulle Correnti a Getto (Jet-stream) e Ondulatorie; Torino (Italia) 4–6 Giugno 1959
AER	Aeronautical Engineering Review
AFS	U.S. Air Force, Bambridge Research Center, Air Force Surveys in Geophysics
AGR	Annali di Geofisica, Roma
AM	Annalen der Meteorologie, Hamburg
AMGBA	Archiv für Meteorologie, Geophysik und Bioklimatologie, Serie A, Wien
AMGBB	Archiv für Meteorologie, Geophysik und Bioklimatologie, Serie B, Wien
AMMM	Australian Meteorological Magazine, Melbourne
AMO	Antarctic Meteorology, Proceedings of the Symposium held in Melbourne, February 1959. Oxford: Pergamon. 1960
AMS	American Meteorological Society
AMSP	Acta Meteorologica Sinica, Peking
AMST	American Meteorological Society, Proceeding of the Toronto Meteorological Conference, September 1953
AWS	Air Weather Service
A & M	Texas, Agricultural and Mechanical College, Department of Oceanography and Meteorology
BAMS	Bulletin of the American Meteorological Society, Boston
BDW	Berichte des Deutschen Wetterdienstes, Offenbach
BDWUS	Berichte des Deutschen Wetterdienstes in der U.S.-Zone, Bad Kissingen
BPA	Beiträge zur Physik der (freien) Atmosphäre, Frankfurt a. M.
CM	Compendium of Meteorology, American Meteorological Society, Boston
CP	Royal Meteorological Society, Centenary Proceedings 1950, London
DFS	Deutsche Forschungsanstalt für Segelflug, München
GA	Geografiska Annaler, Stockholm
GBG	Gerlands Beiträge zur Geophysik, Leipzig
GH	Geophysica, Helsinki
GM	Great Britain Meteorological Office, Geophysical Memoirs
GMOPN	Great Britain Meteorological Office, Professional Notes
GMT	Geophysical Magazine, Tokyo
GP	Geofysiske Publikasjoner, Oslo
GPA	Geofisica Pura e Applicata, Milano
GRD	Geophysics Research Directorate, Air Force Cambridge Research Center
GRP	U.S. Air Force, Cambridge Research Center, Geophysical Research Papers
IB	Idöjárás, Budapest
IJMG	Indian Journal of Meteorology and Geophysics, Delhi
ISG	Izvestiia, Ser. Geof. Akademiia Nauk S.S.S.R.
IUGG	I. U. G. G., Association of Meteorology, Rome, September 1954, Scientific Proceedings. London: Butterworth. 1956

JATP	Journal of Atmospheric and Terrestrial Physics, London
JGR	Journal of Geophysical Research, Washington, D.C.
JINL	Journal of the Institute of Navigation, London
JM	Journal of Meteorology, Boston
JMRT	Journal of Meteorological Research, Tokyo
JMSJ	Journal of the Meteorological Society of Japan
LM	La Météorologie, Paris
MA	Meteorologiske Annaler, Oslo
MAB	Meteorologische Abhandlungen, Institut für Meteorologie und Geophysik, Freie Universität Berlin
MDW	Mitteilungen des Deutschen Wetterdienstes, Offenbach
MG	Meteorologiia i Gidrologiia, Leningrad
MIT	Massachusetts Institute of Technology
MM	Meteorological Monographs, AMS Boston
MML	Meteorological Magazine, London
MNM	Météorologie Nationale, Monographies, Paris
MR	Meteorologische Rundschau, Offenbach
MRP	Great Britain, Meteorological Research Committee, Meteorological Research Paper
MU	Meddelande, Uppsala Universitet, Meteorologiska Institutionen
MWR	Monthly Weather Review, Washington, D.C.
MZ	Meteorologische Zeitschrift, Braunschweig
N	Navigation, Los Angeles
NACA	National Advisory Committee for Aeronautics
NWRF	U.S. Navy Weather Research Facility, Norfolk, Virginia
NYU	New York University, College of Engineering
PMGT	Papers in Meteorology and Geophysics, Tokyo
QJRMS	Quarterly Journal of the Royal Meteorological Society, London
RM	Research Memorandum (NACA)
RMA	Rivista di Meteorologia Aeronautica, Roma
RMV	Rossby Memorial Volume: The Atmosphere and Sea in Motion, B. Bolin, Editor, New York 1959
RP	Research Paper
SAR	Schweizer Aero Revue, Bern
T	Tellus, Stockholm
TAGU	Transactions of the American Geophysical Union, Washington, D.C.
TAT	Tateno, Journal of the Aerological Observatory
TN	Technical Note
TP	Technical Paper
TR	Technical Report
UAL	United Air Lines, Denver
UCLA	University of California at Los Angeles
U of C	University of Chicago
USAWS	U.S. Air Weather Service
USWB	U.S. Weather Bureau

W	Weather, London
WMO	World Meteorological Organization
WW	Weatherwise, Boston
ZM	Zeitschrift für Meteorologie, Berlin

Numbers in parentheses following references refer to *Meteorological Abstracts and Bibliography* or *Meteorological and Geoastrophysical Abstracts*, in which the respective paper has been listed.

ABBÈ, C., 1907: Projections of the globe appropriate for laboratory methods of studying the general circulation of the atmosphere. BAMS 13: 502–506.

Academia Sinica, Peking, 1957: On the general circulation over Eastern Asia. I. T 9 (4): 432–446.

— 1958*a*: On the general circulation over Eastern Asia. II. T 10 (1). 58–75.

— 1958*b*: On the general circulation over Eastern Asia. III. T 10 (3): 299–312.

ALABASTER, R. C., 1953: The operation and navigation of jet airliners. JINL 6 (3): 213–237. (6.10–46.)

ALAKA, M. A., 1955: Case study of an easterly jet stream in the tropics. U of C, Contr. N6ori-02036, TR. (7.10–152.)

— 1958*a*: A case study of an easterly jet stream in the tropics. T 10 (1): 24–42.

— 1958*b*: Aviation aspects of mountain waves. WMO-No. 68. TP. 26.

ALLEN, R. A., R. FLETCHER, J. HOLMBOE, J. NAMIAS, and H. C. WILLETT, 1940: Report on an experiment in five-day weather forecasting. Papers in Physical Oceanography and Meteorology, MIT 8 (3): 51–53.

ALLINGTON, K., B. W. BOVILLE, and F. K. HARE, 1960: Midwinter ozone variations and stratospheric flow over Canada, 1958–1959. T 12 (3): 266–273.

ALT, J., P. ASTAPENKO, and N. J. ROPAR Jr., 1959: Some aspects of the Antarctic atmospheric circulation in 1958. IGY World Data Center A (Nat. Acad. Sci. Wash. D.C.). IGY General Report Series No. 4, 28 pp. (10.11–18.)

AMBLE, O., 1945: Evaluation of the gradient wind. MA 2 (7): 247–262. (1.11–11.)

American Meteorological Society, 1950–60: Meteorological Abstracts and Bibliography. AMS Boston, Vol. 1–11.

ANDERSON, A. D., 1952: Meteorological trajectory study for test flights to be made from San Francisco. U.S. Naval Research Laboratory, NRL Memorandum Report No. 23, May 21. (4 G–88.)

— 1955*a*: Estimate of the tracking effectiveness of high frequency radio direction finding for transosonde balloons. U.S. Naval Research Laboratory, NRL Memorandum Report 502, Sept. (7.10–79.)

— 1955*b*: A study of the accuracy of winds derived from transosonde trajectories. U.S. Naval Research Laboratory, NRL Memorandum Report No. 498. (7.3–88.)

— 1956: Experiments using window to measure high-altitude winds. BAMS 37 (9): 454–457, U.S. Naval Research Laboratory, NRL Report No. 4682, Jan. 10. (9.3-207.)

— 1957*a*: Comments on "Upper-air wind measurements with small rockets". JM 14: 473–474.

— 1957*b*: Free-air turbulence. JM 14: 477–494.

— H. J. MASTENBROOK, and H. D. CUBBAGE, 1955: The transosonde: a new meteorological data gathering system. U.S. Naval Research Laboratory, NRL Report No. 4649, Nov. 3. (7.10–80.)

— and H. J. MASTENBROOK, 1956: A new upper air data system, the transosonde. BAMS 37 (7): 342–350. (8.4–105.)

ANDERSON, R., B. W. BOVILLE, and D. E. MCCLELLAN, 1955: An operational frontal contour analysis model. QJRMS 81: 588–599. (7.3–167.)

ANDERSON, W. L., 1958: A low elevation angle radar refraction check. 7th Weather Radar Conference, Miami Beach, Florida, Nov. 17–20, 1958, Proceedings, Ser. E.: 44–49. (11.1–143.)

ANGELL, J. K., 1957: Application of routine transosonde data to analysis and forecasting. USWB, Training Paper No. 13. (9.10–30.)

— 1958*a*: An analysis of routine 300-mb transosonde flights from Japan. MWR 86: 335–343.

— 1958*b*: Lagrangian wind fluctuations at 300 mb derived from transosonde data. JM 15 (6): 522–530.

— 1958*c*: Some evidence for tidal oscillations obtained from 300-mb transosonde data. JM 15 (6): 566–567.

— 1959*a*: Estimating the frictional force at 300 mb by means of transosonde and radiosonde data. JM 16 (2): 216–217.

— 1959*b*: A summary of Navy-sponsored 300-mb constant level balloon (transosonde) flights from Japan in 1957–1958. Wash., D.C., USWB, 53 pp. A summary of Navy-sponsored 250-mb constant level balloon (transosonde) flights from Japan in 1958–1959. Wash., D.C., USWB, 53 pp. (11.4–200.)

— 1960*a*: An analysis of operational 300-mb transosonde flights from Japan in 1957–1958. JM 17: 20–35.

— 1960*b*: A climatological analysis of two years of transosonde flights from Japan. MWR 87 (12): 427–439.

Anonymous, 1938: Fireball shows superstratosphere winds blow at 200 m.p.h. BAMS 19 (9): 413. (4 G–130.)

— 1950: Constant height balloons. W 5 (10): 356. (2.2–19.)

— 1951: Operation "Moby Dick". WW 4 (6): 123. (4 F–82.)

— 1952: Forecasting winds at 30,000–40,000 ft and above. MML 81 (975): 79–85. (3.9–69.)

— 1953: Cloud forms of the jet stream. Shell Aviation News, London, No. 180: 4–6. (6.7–240.)

— 1956: Three-front model MML 85 (1005): 83–88. (7.8–86.)

— 1960: Tiros I concludes mission; Tiros II readied. WW 13 (4): 159–161, 180.

APPLEMAN, H., 1952: The forecasting of jet aircraft condensation trails. AER 11 (8): 30–32. (4.3–82.)

— 1953: The formation of exhaust condensation trails. BAMS 34: 14–20.

ARAKAWA, A., 1957: On the mean meridional circulation in the atmosphere. JMSJ, 75th Anniversary Volume, p. 230–236.

ARAKAWA, H., 1941: Stabilitäts- und Böigkeitsbedingungen der allegemeinen Zirkulation der Atmosphäre. MZ 58: 381–384 (7.4–196.)

— 1942: Stabilitätskriterien der atmosphärischen horizontalen Turbulenz. GBG 58: 3–10.

— 1951*a*: The criterion of dynamic stability of zonal motion including the vertical shear. GPA 20: 56–61. (3.9–91.)

— 1951*b*: Tropopause in a steady zonal wind field. JMSJ, 2nd. ser., 29 (3): 86–89. (4 G–58.)

— 1951*c*: Possible heavy turbulent exchange between the extratropical tropospheric air and the polar stratospheric air. T 3 (3): 208–211. (4.8–99.)

— 1952*a*: Basic principles of the balloon bomb. Met. Res. Inst. Suginami, Tokyo. (5 E–126.)

— 1952*b*: Kinematics of meandering and blocking action of the westerlies. PMGT 3 (1): 12–18. (4.5–93.)

ARAKAWA, H., 1952*c*: Severe turbulence resulting from excessive wind-shear in tropical cyclones. JM 9: 221–223.

— 1953*a*: The anticyclonic eddies just south of the jet stream. AMGBA 5 (1): 1–4. (4 G–89.)

— 1953*b*: Tilted-trough model as an interaction between low- and high-latitude disturbances. JM 10 (1): 64–66. (4.8–96.)

— 1953*c*: Vorticity waves in the tropical latitudes. PMGT 3 (4): 269–276. (5.2–109.)

— 1953*d*: Zonal wind-profile between the pole and the equator given by a single expression. AMGBA 5 (2): 129–135. (4.4–108.)

— 1953*e*: Clear-air turbulence near the jet stream. QJRMS 79 (339): 162–163. (4 G–120.)

— 1953*f*: On the time rate of work done by the eddy stresses in the free air, and the maintenance of westerlies in middle latitudes. JM 10 (5): 392–393. (5.3–132.)

— 1953*g*: On the maintenance of the westerlies and tropical revolving wind systems. JMSJ, 2nd ser., 31 (6): 195–205. (5.10–165.)

— 1953*h*: Baroclinicity along some meridional cross sections through the atmosphere. AMGBB 6 (1): 53–58. (5.2–106.)

— 1956*a*: Basic principles of the balloon bomb. PMGT 6 (3/4): 239–243. (9.9–116.)

— 1956*b*: Characteristics of the low level jet stream. JM 13: 504–506.

— 1957: On the maintenance of zonal mean flow. PMGT 8 (1): 39–54. (10.6–182.)

— 1959: The worlds strongest winds as revealed by Tateno-Relay-Method Soundings. BAMS 40 (7): 343–347. (11.6–317.)

ARIZUMI, N., 1950: A diagrammatic method of computing vertical motion in the atmosphere and its applications. GMT 22 (2): 131–141. (2.6–89.)

ARMSTRONG, C. L., and R. D. GARRETT, 1960: High altitude wind data from meteorological rockets. MWR 88 (5): 187–190.

ARNOLD, A., 1956: Representative winds aloft. BAMS 37 (1): 27–30. (8.3–92.)

ASTAPENKO, P. D., 1960*a*: Problems of the circulation of the atmosphere in the Antarctic. AMO: 241–255.

— 1960*b*: Atmospheric processes in the high latitudes of the southern hemisphere. Academy of Sciences, U.S.S.R. Moscow Committee of the International Geophysical Year.

ATTMANNSPACHER, W., 1959: Extreme der horizontalen Windgeschwindigkeit und Vertikalwind. MR 12 (4): 112–117.

— 1960*a*: Nullschicht und Wetter. MDW No. 20: 28–49.

— 1960*b*: Über die Existenz einer hochstratosphärischen Nullschicht 1. Art. MR 13 (2): 38–45.

AUBERT, E. J., and J. S. WINSTON, 1951*a*: A study of atmospheric heat-sources in the northern hemisphere for monthly periods. JM 8 (2): 111–125. (4 G–59.)

— — 1951*b*: Comparison of monthly geostrophic and gradient winds with resultant rawins. JM 8 (2): 126–127. (2.11–117.)

AUFM KAMPE, H. J., 1956: Upper-air wind measurements with small rockets. JM 13 (6): 601–602. (8.5–149.)

— 1960: Meteorological rocket network for measuring atmospheric parameters up to 250,000 ft. WW 13 (5): 192–195.

AUSTIN, E. E., 1952: Upper winds of Aden. QJRMS 79: 528–532. (4 F–91.)

— and J. K. BANNON, 1952: Relation of the height of the maximum wind to the level of the tropopause on occasions of strong wind. MML 81 (965): 321–325. (4 G–90.)

— and D. DEWAR, 1953: Upper winds over the Mediterranean and Middle East. MRP 811. (5.2–178.)

AUSTIN, J. M., 1954: The forecasting significance of the Reed-Sanders article. JM 11 (3): 253–254. (6.3–101.)

AUSTIN, J. M., and L. KRAWITZ, 1956: 50-mb patterns and their relationship to tropospheric changes. JM 13: 152–159.

BADNER, J., and M. A. JOHNSON, 1957: Relationship of tropopause and jet streams to rainfall in southeastern United States, Feb. 4–9, 1957. MWR 85 (62–68). (9.4–117.)

BAILEY, R. E., 1958: Forecasting of heavy snowstorms associated with major cyclones. Eastern Airlines, Inc., Met. Dept., Contract AF 19 (604)–2073, Scientific Report No. 1, p. 142–157. (11.3–49.)

BAIRD, G. H., 1956: Composite charts of some synoptic features of squall lines. NYU, Res. Div. Dep. of Meteorology and Oceanography, Contract AF 19 (604)–1387, Scientific Report No. 1. (8.4–135.)

BALZER, M. E., and H. T. HARRISON, 1959: The nature of high level clear air turbulence. UAL Meteorology Circular No. 48.

BANNON, J. K., 1951*a*: Meteorological aspects of turbulence affecting aircraft at high altitude. GMOPN No. 104. (4 G–60.)

— 1951*b*: Severe turbulence encountered by aircraft near jet streams. MML 80 (951): 262–269. (3 K–163.)

— 1952: Weather systems associated with some occasions of severe turbulence at high altitude. MML 81 (958): 97–101. (5 D–201.)

— 1953*a*: Note on the structure of the high altitude wind belt in the Middle East in winter. MRP 821 (5.2–180.)

— 1953*b*: Some aspects of the mean upper-air flow over the earth. AMST 109–121. (6.3–191.)

— 1954*a*: Note on the structure of the high altitude strong-wind belt in the Middle East in winter. QJRMS 80 (344): 218–221. (5.9–206.)

— 1954*b*: Note on the subtropical jet stream in January and April 1951. MML 83 (987): 257–263. (6.2–127.)

— 1955: The mean wind at 60 mb. MRP 925. (7.5–191.)

— 1958: Stratospheric temperatures over the Antarctic. QJRMS 84 (362): 434–436. (10.5–63.)

— B. C. FROST, and T. H. KIRK, 1956: Some meteorological aspects of high level navigation. JINL 9 (3): 282–309. (7.10–49.)

— and M. P. JACKSON, 1953: Relation between tropopause and level of maximum wind at Gibraltar. MML 82 (970): 100–102. (4 E–250.)

BARBÉ, G. D., 1956: Données numériques sur quelques courants "jets" mesurés au-dessus de la région Parisienne au cours de l'année 1956. LM, Ser. 4, No. 44: 339–354. (10.1–207.)

— 1957: Mesure précise du vent en altitude a l'aide de sondages rapprochés dans le temps. MNM No. 3. (9.1–17.)

— 1958: Sur l'étude expérimentale des courants jet atmosphériques. Académie des Sciences, Paris, Comptes Rendus 247 (2): 230–233.

— 1959: Sur l'établissement du régime d'été de la circulation stratosphérique entre 20 et 30 km au voisinage de la latitude 45° N. Caractère anormalement précoce de l'année 1959. Paris, Academie des Sciences, Comptes Rendus, 248 (22): 3196–3198. (11.3–149.)

BARFORD, N. C., *et al.*, 1954: High altitude free balloon flying. JATP 5 (4): 219–229. (6.2–50).

BARNETT, M. A. F., 1951: Mean circulation at high levels over New Zealand. JM 8 (3): 202. (4 F–65.)

BARR, W. C., 1960: Theoretical evaluation of cylindrical chaff as a wind sensor at high altitude. U.S. Army Signal Research and Development Laboratory. TR 2138, 22 July 1960.

BARRETT, E. W., 1958: Eccentric circumpolar vortices in a barotropic atmosphere. T 10 (3): 395–400.

BASSUS, K. VON, 1906–07: Über die Windverhältnisse in der oberen Inversion. BPA 2: 92–95 (5 D–9.)

BATTIN, R. H., 1952: Investigation of the dynamics of the general circulation. MIT, Contract AF-19-122-153, Gen. Circ. Proj., Scientific Report No. 4. (5.2–105.)

BAUR. F., 1936: Die Bedeutung der Stratosphäre für die Großwetterlage. MZ 53: 237–247. (2 A–79.)

— 1947: Musterbeispiele europäischer Großwetterlagen, 35 pp. Wiesbaden: Dietrich.

BEAMER, C. C., and S. M. SEREBRENY, 1953: Pacific jet stream research, for the period 1 Febr.–30 April 1953. Pan. Am. World Airw., Inc., Pac. Alaska Div., Bur. Aeron., Project Arowa, Contr. N 189s–90981, Prog. Rep. No. 1, 1953. (4 I–279.)

BEDEL, B., 1954: Les observations météorologiques de la Station du Groenland 70° 55′ 03″ N–40° 38′ 22″ W–Altitude 2993 m: Conditions atmosphériques en altitude du 17 septembre 1949 au 10 août 1951. Expéditions Polaires Françaises, Exp. Arctiques, Résultats Scientifiques, Ser. N. V. Paris. (8.9–31.)

BEEBE, R. G., and F. C. BATES, 1955: A mechanism for assisting in the release of convective instability. MWR 83 (1): 1–10.

BEELITZ, P., 1958: Bearbeitung der Ergebnisse der Radiosondenaufstiege anläßlich des zweiten Weltvergleiches von Radiosonden in Payerne (Schweiz), 1956. MAB 7 (4): 120 pp.

BEHR, K., 1960: Über markante Erwärmungen in der Stratosphäre, Entdeckung, Beispiele, Theorien. MAB 9 (2): 57 pp.

— 1960*a*: Tägliche Höhenkarten der 25-mb-Fläche für das Internationale Geophysikalische Jahr 1958. Teil II, 2. Vierteljahr. MAB 10 (2). Tägliche Höhenkarten der 50-mb-Fläche für das Internationale Geophysikalische Jahr 1958. Teil II, 2. Vierteljahr. MAB 12 (2).

— *et al.*, 1960*b*: Tägliche Höhenkarten der 25-mb-Fläche für das Internationale Geophysikalische Jahr 1958. Teil I, 1. Vierteljahr. MAB 10: H. 1.

— *et al.*, 1960*c*: Tägliche Höhenkarten der 10 mb-Fläche für das Internationale Geophysikalische Jahr 1958. Teil II, 2. Vierteljahr. MAB 13 (2).

BELL, G. J., and L. H. KWAI, 1953: Upper winds determined by radar 1949 to 1951. Hong Kong Roy. Obs., TN No. 5 (4 E–251, 5 B–304.)

BELLAMY, J. C., 1945*a*: Slide rule for constant vorticity trajectories. Appendix in: U of C. Dep. of Meteorol. Miscell. Rep. No. 19.

— 1945*b*: The use of pressure altitude and altimeter corrections in meteorology. JM 2 (1): 1–79.

— 1949: Objective calculations of divergence, vertical velocity and vorticity. BAMS 30 (2).

— 1951: Models and techniques of synoptic representation. CM 1951, pp. 711–714. (3.8–2.)

— 1954: Four dimensional flight planning. N 4 (3): 105–113. (6.7–91.)

BENTON, G. S., and A. B. KAHN, 1958: Spectra of large-scale atmospheric flow at 300 mb. JM 15 (4): 404–410.

BERENGER, M., and J. HEISSAT, 1959*a*: Contribution a l'étude statistique et météorologique de la turbulence. MNM 17, 21 pp.

— — 1959*b*: Contribution à l'étude de la variation saisonnière des jets. LM Ser. 4, No. 53: 11–23. (11.6–314.)

BERG, H., 1949: Die Höhenwindverhältnisse über Westdeutschland. Wetter und Klima 2 (3/4): 97–103. (4 E–166.)

— 1953: Zur Blockierung der Westwinddrift. GPA 25: 92–100. (5.4–103.)

— 1956: Windmessungen in großen Höhen. BDW No. 22: 72–82. (8.7–110.)

BERGERON, T., 1956: Multiple frontal systems as links in the general atmospheric circulation (summary). IUGG, p. 289. (10.1–208.)

— 1959: Methods in scientific weather analysis and forecasting. An outline in the history of ideas and hints at a program. RMV: 440–474.

BERGGREN, R., 1952: The distribution of temperature and wind connected with active tropical air in the higher troposphere and some remarks concerning clear air turbulence at high altitude. T 4 (1): 43–53. (4 E–227.)

— 1953*a*: On frontal analysis in the higher troposphere and the lower stratosphere. MU No. 29. (5 D–220.)

— 1953*b*: On temperature frequency distribution in the free atmosphere and a proposed model for frontal analysis. T 5: 95–100. (5.2–146, 5 D–242.)

— B. BOLIN, and C.-G. ROSSBY, 1949: An aerological study of zonal motion, its perturbation and breakdown. T 1 (2): 14–37. (4 G–18.)

— W. J. GIBBS, and C. W. NEWTON, 1958: Observational characteristics of the jet stream. A survey of the literature. WMO, TN No. 19.

BERGTHORSSON, P., and B. R. DÖÖS, 1955: Numerical weather map analysis. T 7 (3): 329–340.

BERKES, Z., and J. BORSOS, 1955: A ciklonképzödési helyek eloszlása az északi félgömbön. (Distribution of locations of cyclogenesis over the Northern Hemisphere.) IB 59 (6): 321–330. (8.8–209.)

BERKOFSKY, L., 1952: Stationary mountain perturbations. JM 9 (1): 72–75. (3.11–114.)

BERRY, F. A., W. H. HAGGARD, and P. W. WOLFF, 1954: On the analysis of 500-mb zonal wind profiles and index cycles. JM 11 (5): 380–386. (6.3–107.)

BERSON, A., 1910: Bericht über die aerologische Expedition des Königl. Aeronautischen Observatoriums nach Ostafrika im Jahre 1910. Ergebn. d. Arb. d. Preuß. Aeronaut. Observat. Lindenberg, Braunschweig 1910.

BERSON, F. A., 1950*a*: On the role of long-wave instability in the general circulation; a study of five-day means in Nov. 1948. Svenska Meteorol. och Hydrolog. Inst. Medd. Ser. A. No. 3. (4 G–31.)

— 1950*b*: On the factors controlling the instability of long waves in zonal currents. Arkiv för Geofysik 1 (9): 187–236. (3.1–78.)

BESSEMOULIN, J., 1956: Erreurs introduites par l'inexactitude de la radiosonde sur le calcul de l'altitude d'une surface isobare. LM, Ser. 4, No. 41: 21–27. (8.9–136.)

— and A. VIAUT, 1958: Courant-jets et front polaire. Académie des Sciences, Paris, Comptes Rendus, 246 (14): 2154–2156. (10.1–275.)

— *et al.*, 1960: Rapport préliminaire du groupe de travail de la Commission de Météorologie Synoptique sur les réseaux. WMO TN No. 30, WMO No. 94. TP 38.

BEYNON, W. J. G. (editor), 1960: Some ionospheric results obtained during the International Geophysical Year. Proceedings of a symposium organized by the URSI/AGI Committee, Brussels 1959. Amsterdam: Elsevier. 401 pp.

BIELINSKI, L. S., 1960: Location of jet maxima. BAMS 41 (7): 368–371.

BILANCINI, R., 1950: La "corrente a getto". RMA 10 (3): 3–13. (4 G–32.)

BINDON, H. H., 1951: Clear-air gusts in the upper troposphere over Eastern Canada. W 6 (5): 152–153. (3 K–165.)

BJERKNES, J., 1951*a*: Extratropical cyclones. CM 577–598.

— 1951*b*: The maintenance of the zonal circulation in the atmosphere. Adresse Presidentielle, U. G. G. I. AIM 9c, Bruxelles.

— 1953*a*: Maintenance of the zonal circulation of the atmosphere. Presidential address, I. U. G. G. Association of Meteorology, Brussels 1951. Procès-Verbaux des Séances, Mémoires et Discussions, pp. I–XXIII. (7.6–118.)

BJERKNES, J., 1953*b*: The flux of angular momentum and heat in the general circulation. AMST 122–123. (6.3–111.)

— 1954: The problem of cyclogenesis from Helmholtz's time to present. AMST 133–138. (6.3–116.)

— 1960: Ocean temperatures and atmospheric circulation. WMO Bulletin 9 (3): 151–157.

— and J. HOLMBOE, 1944: On the theory of cyclones. JM 1 (1/2): 1–22. (3.5–155.)

— and E. PALMÉN, 1937: Investigation of selected European cyclones by means of serial ascents. GP 12 (2): 62 p. (4 E–87, 5 D–91.)

BJERKNES, V., 1898: Über die Bildung von Zirkulationsbewegungen. Videnskabsselskabets Skrifter, Oslo 1898.

— 1921: On the dynamics of the circular vortex with applications to the atmosphere and atmospheric vortex and wave motion. GP 2 (4): 88 p.

— 1926: Die atmosphärischen Störungsgleichungen. BPA 13: 1–14.

— 1929: Über die hydrodynamischen Gleichungen in Lagrangescher und Eulerscher Form und ihre Linearisierung für das Studium kleiner Störungen. GP 5 (11): 1–43.

— *et al.*, 1933: Physikalische Hydrodynamik. 797 pp. Berlin: Springer. (4 G–2.)

— and H. SOLBERG, 1921: Meteorological conditions for the formation of rain. GP 2: 60 pp.

BLACKADAR, A. K., 1950: The transformation of energy by the large scale eddy stress in the atmosphere. NYU, Meteorol. Papers, 1 (4). (5.5–93.)

— 1957: Boundary layer wind maxima and their significance for the growth of nocturnal inversions. BAMS 38: 283–290.

BLEEKER, W., 1949: The relation between fronts and jet stream. BAMS 30 (5): 190–191.

— 1950: The structure of weather systems. CP, pp. 66–80.

BLEICHRODT, J. F., W. BLEEKER, and F. H. SCHMIDT, 1960: Changes in the radioactivity regime during the passage of a cold front over the Netherlands. T 12 (2): 188–194.

BÖHME, W., 1956: Der Impulsaustausch in der oberen Troposphäre und der Nullschichteffekt. ZM 10 (1): 12–22. (7.9–132.)

BOFFI, J. A., 1949*a*: Efecto de la Cordillera de los Andes en la circulación general del aire sobre la Republica Argentina. Sociedad Cientifica Argentina, Anales 147 (3): 126–140. (2.2–67.)

— 1949*b*: Effect of the Andes Mountains on general circulation over the southern part of South America. BAMS 30 (7): 242–247. (2.7–76.)

BOLIN, B., 1950: On the influence of the earth's orography on the general character of the westerlies. T 2 (3): 184–195. (2.2–60.)

— 1952: Studies of the general circulation of the atmosphere. Advances in Geophysics, New York, 1: 87–118. (4.8–3.)

— and H. NEWTON, 1952: Report on a conference on the application of numerical methods in forecasting atmospheric flow patterns. T 4 (2): 141–144. (5.2–63.)

BOND, H. G., 1953: Easterly jet streams over Darwin. W 8 (8): 252–253. (5.1–135.)

BOOGARD, H. M., v. D., 1954: Jet Stream between Pretoria and Maun. South Africa, Weather Bureau, News Letter, No. 63: 8. (6.4–144.)

BOOKER, H. G., 1957: Turbulence in the ionosphere with applications to meteor trails, radio star scintillation, auroral radar echoes, and other phenomena. Polar Atmosph. Symposium, Pt. 2, pp. 52–81. London: Pergamon.

— 1959: Summary lecture on motions in the E and F layer. BAMS 40 (12): 627.

BOSSOLASCO, M., 1949: Variazioni del moto polare della terra e loro correlazioni meteorologiche. GPA 14 (3–4): 197–202. (2.7–77.)

Boutet, R., 1950: Sondage optique de l'atmosphere par mesure de la scintillation. Annales de Geophys. 6 (4): 322–330. (3.6–119.)

Boville, B. W., W. S. Creswick, and J. J. Gillis, 1955: A frontal-jet stream cross section. T 7 (3): 314–321. (7.10–153.)

— — and R. J. Reed, 1957: Comments on "A study of a characteristic type of upper-level frontogenesis". JM 14: 91–93.

Bracelin, P., 1952: Notes on jet streams and turbulence at high levels. Great Britain, Naval Weather Service, Circular No. 15/52, NWS 161/52. (5 D–203.)

Bradbury, D., and E. Palmén, 1953: On the existence of a polar front at the 500-mb level. BAMS 34, 56–62. (5.1–145.)

Brandtner, E., 1948: Der Staubfall in Westeuropa am 29. März 1947. MR 1 (7–8): 222–226. (1.4–38.)

Brasefield, C. J., 1950: Winds and temperatures in the lower stratosphere. JM 7 (1): 66–69. (4 F–50.)

Breiland, J. G., 1958: Meteorological conditions associated with the development of instability lines. JM 15 (3): 297–302. (11.3–53.)

Breistein, P. M., 1954: Investigation of cyclone development, Storm 2. U of C, Dep. of Met., Contr. AF 19 (604): 390, TR No. 6. (6.8–212.)

— and S. J. Smebye, 1952: En anvendelse av prinsippet om hvirvlingens bevarelse til beregning av rygger og trågs forflytning i 500 mb.-nivået. (Application of the principle of conservation of vorticity to the calculation of movements of ridges and troughs at the 500-mb level.) Det Norske Videnskaps-Akademi i Oslo. Institutt for Vaer-og Klimaforskning, Report No. 3. (9.6–132.)

Brewer, A. W., 1949: Evidence for a world circulation provided by the measurements of helium and water vapor distribution in the stratosphere. QJRMS 75 (326): 351–363. (5 D–147.)

— 1959: Ozone and water vapor. BAMS 40 (12): 629.

Brezowsky, H., 1952: Säkuläre Schwankungen der Zirkulation. BDWUS 35: 48–50. (3.10–117.)

— H. Flohn, and P. Hess., 1951: Some remarks on the climatology of blocking action. T 3 (3): 191–194. (3.11–115.)

Brindley, J., 1960: Stability of flow in a rotating viscous incompressible fluid subjected to differential heating. Phil. Trans. Roy. Soc. Ser. A, Vol. 253, A. 1020.

Britton, G. P., and H. H. Lamb, 1956: A study of the general circulation of the atmosphere over the far South. Pt. I and II. W 11 (9): 281–291; 11 (11): 339–354. (8.2–122.)

Brombacher, W. G., 1936: Wind direction and wind velocity derived from the travel of the balloon "Explorer III." National Geographic Society, Washington, Contributed Technical Papers, Stratosphere Series, No. 2: 144–146. (4 F–15.)

Brooks, C. E. P., 1932: The movement of volcanic dust over the globe. MML 67: 81–86. (1 F–26.)

— 1950: Climate through the ages, 2. Aufl. London: Benn.

— 1951: Geological and historical aspects of climatic change. CM, pp. 1004–1018.

— *et al.*, 1950: Upper winds over the world. GM, No. 85. QJRMS 72: 55–73. (4 E–186.)

— and N. Carruthers, 1953: Handbook of statistical methods in meteorology. London: H.M. Stationery Office.

— and T. M. Hunt, 1930: The zonal distribution of rainfall over the earth. Mem. Roy. Meteorol. Soc., Vol. 3 (28).

Brundidge, K. C., 1956: Analysis of selected Project Jet Stream flight data. A & M, Contract AF 19 (604)–559, Scientific Report No. 10. (8.7–174.)

BRUNDIDGE, K. C., 1958: A preliminary study of eleven Project Jet Stream flights; 1956–1957 phase. A & M, Contract No. AF 19 (604)–1565. Final Report "Wind Field near the Tropopause" 86–108.

— and J. L. GOLDMAN, 1958: Some new jet stream models. A & M, Final Report "Wind Field near the Tropopause," Contract No. AF 19 (604)–1565, p. 109–126.

BRUNT, D., 1930: The present position of theories of the origin of cyclonic depressions. QJRMS 56, 345–350. Reprinted in: Some problems of modern meteorology, RMS, London 1934.

— 1944: Physical and dynamical meteorology. Cambridge: University Press.

BUGAEV, V. A., 1947: B. L. Dzerdzeevskii. Tsirkuliatsionnye skhemy v troposfere tsentral'-noi Arktiki. (B. L. Dzerdzevskii. Circulation patterns in the troposphere of the Central Arctic.) MG No. 3: 84–85. (2.9–76.)

— 1955: Plantetarnye vysotnye frontal'nye zony i tsiklogenez. (Planetary high-altitude frontal zones and cyclogenesis.) Akademiia Nauk Uzbekskoi SSR. Institut Matematiki i Mekhaniki, Meteorologiia i gidrologiia v Uzbekistane. Tashkent. (9.11–185.)

BULL, G. A., 1951: Blue sun and blue moon. MML 80 (943): 1–4. (2.7–186.)

Bundesanstalt für Flugsicherung, Deutscher Wetterdienst, Deutsche Lufthansa, 1959: Paper-Jet. Teil A. Offenbach, Frankfurt, Hamburg.

BUNDGAARD, R. C., 1956*a*: Estimating vorticity advection. BAMS 37 (9): 465–472. (8.7–170.)

— 1956*b*: Computation of streamlines from the pressure field. JM 13 (6): 569–582. (8.4–82.)

BURKETT, T. L., and I. I. GRINGORTEN, 1956: Integration of weather forecasting, flight planning and flight watch. Inst. of Aeronaut. Sciences, Preprint No. 590. (9.8–59.)

BUROLEAU, M., 1937: Note sur les courants aériens à Dakar. Comité d'Etudes Historiques et Scientifiques de l'Afrique Occidentale Française, Publications Ser B., No. 3: 35–40. (4 F–17.)

BUXTON, E. B., and C. L. CHANDLER, 1955: Weather forecasts for jet airliners on the North Atlantic. Pan American World Airways, New York, Meteorological Office.

BYERS, H. R., 1959: General Meteorology. 3rd ed. 540 pp. New York: McGraw Hill.

BYRAM, G. M., 1954: Atmospheric conditions related to blowup fires. Station Paper No. 35, Southeast Forest Experiment Station, Asheville, N.C.

ČADEŽ, M., 1949: O pretvaranju energije u atmosferi. (On the formation of energy in the atmosphere.) Izdan'a Savezne uprave Khidrometeoroloshke sluzhbe pri Vladi FNRJ, Rasprave i studije, 2, Belgrade. (2.1–68.)

— 1956: Über die orographische Zyklogenese und Antizyklogenese. BDW 4 (22): 109–113. (9.4–132.)

CALDER, K. L., 1949: The criterion of turbulence in a field of variable density, with particular reference to conditions in the atmosphere. QJRMS 75: 71–88.

California Institute of Technology, 1948: Evaluation of Forecast Aids. Contr. AFW 28-099 ac–430, Prelim. Report. (3.1–53.)

CALSTEAD, E. M., 1953: A study of constant absolute vorticity trajectories on isentropic surfaces. JM 10 (5): 356–361. (5.3–98.)

CARLIN, A. V., 1953: A case study of the dispersion of energy in planetary waves. BAMS 34 (7): 311–318. (5.9–130.)

CARMICHAEL, H., and E. G. DYMOND, 1939: Upper air investigations in North-west Greenland. Royal Soc. of London, Proceeding, Ser. A, 171 (946): 345–359. (4 F–18.)

CHADWICK, R. H., 1955: Operating and flight planning techniques for the Viscount. JINL. 8 (4): 331–343 (7.3–64.)

CHAKRAVORTTY, K. C., and S. C. BASU, 1957: The influence of "western disturbances" on the weather over northeast India in monsoon months. IJMG 8 (3): 261–272. (9.4–128.)

CHAPMAN, S., 1950: Upper atmospheric nomenclature. BAMS 31 (8): 288–290. JGR 55 (4): 395–399, JATP 1 (2): 121–124; 1 (3): 201, 1951. (2.3–49.)

— 1951: The earth's magnetism. London: Methuen.

CHARLES, B. N., 1959*a*: Lag correlations of upper winds. JM 16 (1): 83–86.

— 1959*b*: Empirical models of interlevel correlation of winds. JM 16 (5): 581–585. (11.6–313.)

— 1959*c*: On some limitations of upper wind records. JGR 64 (3): 343–346. (11.2–227.)

CHARLESWORTH, J. K., 1957: The quaternary era. 2 volumes. London: Arnold.

CHARNEY, J. G., 1947: The dynamics of long waves in a baroclinic westerly current. JM 4 (5): 135–162. (2.11–71.)

— 1948: On the scale of atmospheric motions. GP 17 (2): 1–17.

— 1953: On baroclinic instability and the maintenance of the kinetic energy of the westerlies. International Union of Geodesy and Geophysics, Association of Meteorology, Brussels, August 1951, Assemblée Générale, Mémoires et Discussion, p. 47–63. (8.1–192.)

— and A. ELIASSEN, 1949: A numerical method for predicting the perturbations in middle-latitude westerlies. T 1 (2): 38–54. (1.2–48.)

— B. GILCHRIST, and F. G. SHUMAN, 1956: The prediction of general quasi-geostrophic motions. JM 13 (5): 489–499. (8.2–92.)

CHAUDHURY, A. M., 1950: On the vertical distribution of wind and temperature over Indo-Pakistan along the meridian 76° E in winter. T 2 (1): 56–62. (4 G–34.)

CHEN, LUNG-SHUN, 1957: The variation of wind field along 140° E during the last stage of Mai-Yü. AMSP 28 (4): 294–302. (10.2–288.)

CHIU, WAN-CHENG, 1958: The observed mean monthly wind fields in the lower stratosphere and upper troposphere over North America. JM 15 (1): 9–16.

— 1959: The spectra of large-scale turbulent transfer of momentum and heat. NYU Research Div., Dept. of Meteorology and Oceanography, Contract AF 19 (604)–1755, Scientific Report No. 8. (11.5–272.)

— 1960: The wind and temperature spectra of the upper troposphere and lower stratosphere over North America. JM 17: 64–77. (11.4–223.)

CHVOSTIKOV, E. A., 1952: Serebristye oblaka. (Noctilucent clouds.) Priroda, Moskau 5: 49–59. (4 F–106.)

CLAPP, PH. F., 1944: Empirical studies of the motion of long waves in the westlerlies. USWB, RP No. 20. (2 A–123.)

— and J. S. WINSTON, 1951: A case study of confluence as related to the jet stream. JM 8 (4): 231–243. (4 G–63.)

CLARKE, R. H., 1956: A study of cyclogenesis in relation to the contours of the 300-mb surface. AMMM No. 12: 1–21. (8.5–163.)

— 1960: An attempt to deduce the effect of Antarctica on the temperature of middle latitudes by a controlled model experiment. AMO 221–231.

CLARKSON, L. S., 1951: Evidence for a stratospheric circulation in vertical meridional planes between polar and equatorial regions in winter. MML 80 (953): 309–318. (5 D–179.)

— 1956: Analysis of winds at 40,000 feet and 50,000 feet over Singapore. MML 85: 1–9. (7.7–185.)

— 1958: Variation with time and distance of high-level winds over Malaya. MML 87 (1031): 143–151. (11.3–89.)

— and L. W. LITTLEJOHNS, 1958: A cross-section of equatorial upper winds at 103° E. MML 87 (1030): 105–107. (10.11–151.)

CLAUSS, J., 1957: Die Schwankungen des subtropischen Hochdruckgürtels als Indikator langanhaltender Trockenzeiten in Mitteleuropa, insbesondere langanhaltender Sommertrockenheit in Deutschland. MAB 5 (2). (9.11–16.)

CLAYTON, H. H., 1941: The zonal index and solar activity. TAGU: 420–423. (2 B–164.)

CLEM, LEROY, H., 1955: Clear-air turbulence near the jet stream maxima. BAMS 36 (2): 53–60. (7.4–197.)

— 1957: Clear-air turbulence from 25,000 to 45,000 ft over the United States. USAWS, TR No. 105–147. (10.5–270.)

— D. COLSON, and L. P. HARRISON, 1954: Corrections of the upper level wind computations for effect of earth's curvature. BAMS 35 (8): 357–362. (6.7–113.)

CLINE, D. E., 1957: Rocket-beacon wind-sensing system. U.S. Signal Engineering Lab., Ft. Monmouth, N.J., Engineering Report E-1205. (10.11–110.)

CLODMAN, J., 1953: High level turbulence. Met. Branch., Dep. of Transport, Toronto, Technical Circular, TEC 160, CIR 2332.

— 1954: The interrelationship between wind-speed maxima, fronts and certain contour heights on isobaric surfaces. BAMS 35 (10): 464–467. (7.5–181.)

— 1958: Contrail dissipation and high level turbulent diffusion. Met. Branch., Dep. of Transport, Toronto, Technical Circular TEC 227, CIR 3088.

— and J. T. BALL, 1959: Clear-air turbulence. NYU, Research Division. Final Report under Contract No. AF 19 (604)–3068.

— G. M. MORGAN, and J. T. BALL, 1960: High level turbulence. NYU Research Div., Final Report under Contract No. AF 19 (604)–5208, 84 pp.

COLE, R. O., and L. W. CHAMBERLAIN, 1958: Vertical wind shears near the core of the jet stream over the Northeastern United States, August 1–2, 1958. MWR 86: 319–327. (10.7–106.)

COLON, J. A., 1951: On the wind structure above the tropopause over Puerto Rico. BAMS 32 (2): 52–53. (4 F–68.)

— 1954: Case study of the high tropospheric wind field. U of C, Dep. of Met., Contr. N 6ori–02036, Project No. 085,003, Report on Research. (6.7–241.)

COLSON, D., 1949: Air flow over a mountain barrier. TAGU 30 (6): 818–830. (2.7–79.)

— 1950: Effect of a mountain range on quasi-stationary waves. JM 7 (4): 279–282. (2.1–72.)

CONNER, W. C., 1956: Structure of the 500-mb-jet in major tornado-genesis. USWB Jan. 9, 1956. (9.3–180.)

CONOVER, J. H., 1959: Cloud patterns and related air motions derived by photography. Harvard Univ., Blue Hill Met. Observ., Final Report, Contract No. AF 19 (604)–1589, June 1959.

— 1960: Cirrus patterns and related air motions near the jet stream as derived by photography. JM 17 (5): 532–546.

— and J. C. SADLER, 1960: Cloud patterns as seen from altitudes of 250 to 850 miles—preliminary results. BAMS 41 (6): 291–297.

— and C. J. WENTZIEN, 1955: Winds and temperatures to 40 kilometers. JM 12 (2): 160–164. (6.9–190.)

Cook Research Laboratories, Skokie, Ill., 1954*a*: Computing paths for minimum flight time on vorticity charts. Contract AF 33 (038)–23324, Interim Progress Report PR 17–23. (7.6–50.)

— 1954*b*: Four dimensional flight planning. Contract AF 33 (038)–23324, Atmospheric Reconnaissance system studies, Interim Progress Report No. PR 17–19. (6.10–192.)

— 1955: Integration of weather forecasting, flight planning and flight watch. Contract AF 33 (038)–23324, Interim Progress Report PR 17–16. (7.9–54.)

Cook Research Laboratories, Skokie, Ill., 1956: Project Wind Rider. Optimum flight planning and its meteorological aspects. Interim Manual IB 49–1, Contract No. AF 19 (604)–1504.

CORBY, G. A., 1957: The air flow over mountains. Notes for forecasters and pilots. Met. Rep. No. 18, pp. 53. London: H.M. Stationery Office.

— 1961: Some experiments in the objective analysis of contour charts. QJRMS 87 (371): 34–42.

— and C. E. WALLINGTON, 1956: Airflow over mountains: the lee wave amplitude. QJRMS 82 (353): 266–274. (7.11–234.)

CORN, J., and D. FULTZ, 1955: Synoptic analysis of convection in a rotating cylinder. GRP No. 34. (7.3–150.)

CORWIN, H. G., 1953: Flight planning based on prognostic charts. Trans World Airlines Inc., Met. Dep. (8.7–85.)

— 1955: Pressure pattern flight planning: a comparison of the time front method with single average drift correction technique. Trans World Airlines, Inc., Meteorological Technical Bulletin No. 55–5. (10.1–96.)

COUDRON, J., 1952: Le jet et les courves de variation de la vitesse moyenne du vent avec l'altitude. Journal Scientifique de la Météorologie, Paris, 4 (16): 143–148. (5 D–247.)

COURT, A., 1949: Meteorological data for Little America III. Tabular and graphical results of observations made at the West Base of the United States Antarctic Service Expedition of 1939–41. MWR, Supplement No. 48. (4 F–40.)

COYLE, J. R., 1950: The nature of sub-stratospheric conditions on the Buenos Aires-London air route. Panair do Brasil, Meteorological Service, Brasilian Weather Study. (4 G–35.)

CRAIG, R. A., 1950: The observations and photochemistry of atmospheric ozone and their meteorological significance. MM No. 2.

— and D. HAWKINS, 1951: Atmospheric pressure changes and solar activity. Special Report No. 38. A.M.C. Contract W 19–122ac–17.

— and W. S. HERING, 1957: The stratospheric warming of January-February 1957. JM 16 (2): 91–107.

CRARY, A. P., 1950*a*: Investigation of stratospheric winds and temperatures from acoustical propagation studies. GRP No. 5. (4 F–53.)

— 1950*b*: Stratospheric winds and temperatures from acoustical propagation studies. JM 7 (3): 233–242. (1.8–146.)

— 1952: Stratosphere winds and temperatures in low latitudes from acoustical propagation studies. JM 9 (2): 93–109. (4 F–92.)

— 1953: Annual variations of upper air winds and temperatures in Alaska from acoustical measurements. JM 10 (5): 380–389. (5.3–226.)

— and V. C. BUSHNELL, 1955: Determination of high altitude winds and temperatures in the Rocky Mountain area by acoustic soundings Oct. 1951. JM 12 (5): 463–471. (7.3–301.)

CRESSMAN, G. P., 1948: On the forecasting of long waves in the upper westerlies. JM 5 (2): 44–57. (4 G–9.)

— 1949: Some effects of wave-length variations of the long waves in the upper westerlies. JM 6 (1): 56–60. (1.4–53.)

— 1950: Variations in the structure of the upper westerlies. JM 7 (1): 39–47. (4 G–36.)

— 1953: An application of absolute vorticity charts. JM 10 (1): 17–24. (4.8–59.)

— 1959: An operational objective analysis system. MWR 87 (10): 367–374.

CROCKER, A. M., 1949: Synoptic application of the frontal contour chart: the motion of selected lows, 5–7 Nov., 1946. QJRMS 75: 57–70.

CROCKER, A. M., 1952: Jet stream in eastern North America on the afternoon of May 20, 1952. Canada Met. Div., Cir., 2153, Tec. 119. (4 G–91.)

— W. L. GODSON, and C. M. PENNER, 1947: Frontal contour charts JM 4: 95–99.

CROSSLEY, A. F., 1949: Equivalent head winds on air routes. JINL 2: 195–209.

— 1956*a*: Temperature-compensated equivalent head-winds for jet aircraft. Great Brit. Met. Office, Meteorological Reports 3 (17). (8.6–66.)

— 1956*b*: Errors in the estimation of geostrophic winds. MML 85 (1012): 311–313. (8.2–200.)

— 1961: Ice accretion and turbulence on North Atlantic air routes. QJRMS 87 (371): 55–64.

CRUTCHER, H. L., 1956: Route equivalent winds, BAMS 37 (1): 14–18. (8.5–103.)

CULKOWSKI, W. M., 1956: Tropopause analysis and surface forecasting. BAMS 37 (5): 199–204. (8.1–171.)

CUNNINGHAM, N. W., 1956*a*: A study of thermal wind in the vicinity of a jet stream. A & M Scientific Report No. 8, Contr. AF 19 (604)–559. (8.6–199.) 75th Anniversary Volume JMSJ, 165–172. A & M, Contributions in Oceanogr. and Meteorology 4 (No. 96): 51–58.

— 1956*b*: The frequency distribution of high velocity wind currents over Texas. The Texas Journal of Science, 8 (No. 4). A & M, Contributions in Oceanography and Meteorology No. 71, Vol. 3: 157–169.

— 1958: A study of the duration of clear-air turbulence near the jet stream and its relation to horizontal temperature gradient. A & M, Final Report "Wind Field near the Tropopause"; Contr. No. AF 19 (604)–1565, p. 75–85.

CURTIS, R. C., and H. A. PANOFSKY, 1958: The relation between large-scale vertical motion and weather in summer. BAMS 39 (10): 521–531.

CZAPSKI, U., 1952: Über den „cut-off" Vorgang und die Wiederherstellung der Viererdruckfelder. AM 5 (7–12): 321–327.

DAHLER, H., 1954: Neue Anschauungen über die wetterwirksamen Vorgänge in der Troposphäre und deren Vorhersage. Teil II: Die großräumigen anisobaren Vertikalbewegungen. Abschließende Betrachtung und Ausblick. ZM 8 (11–12): 323–352. (7.10–141.)

— 1955: Über die Winddrehung mit der Höhe und ein neuer Nachweis des Nullschichteffekts. MR 8 (11/12): 180–181. (7.7–133.)

— 1957: Zur Entstehung des jet stream und einige Folgerungen. MR 10 (3): 93–101. (10.1–209.)

— 1960: Die Bedeutung der Temperaturadvektion für die Bildung und Verlagerung von Strahlstrom und Tropopause. MDW No. 20: 12–13. ZM 13 (9/10): 205–211.

DALZIEL, K., 1955: Rawin measurements at Heard Island. AMMM 10: 47–56. (7.8–72.)

DANIELSEN, E. F., 1959: The laminar structure of the atmosphere and its relation to the concept of a tropopause. AMGBA 11 (3): 293–332.

DAO, SHIH-YEN, and LUNG-SHUN CHEN, 1957: The structure of general circulation over continent of Asia in summer. JMSJ, 75th Anniversary Volume, 215–229. (10.6–187.)

DARLING, E. M., JR., 1953: Winds at 100 mb and 50 mb over the United States in 1952. BAMS 34 (10): 458–461. (5.8–178.)

DAVIES, D. A., and H. W. SANSOM, 1952: Easterly jets over East Africa. W 7 (11): 343–344. (4 G–92.)

DAVIES, D. M., 1950: Atmospheric winds. Royal Aeronautical Soc., Journal 54 (477): 602–605. (4 G–37.)

Davies, T. V., 1952: The flow of a liquid which is heated from below. MIT, Contr. AF 19-122-153, General Circulation Project, Scientific Report No. 12. (5.2-104.)

— 1956: The forced flow due to heating of a rotating liquid. Roy. Soc. of London, Philosophical Transactions, Ser. A 249 (958): 27-64. (8.5-188.)

Davis, N. E., 1951: The mean position of the jet stream. MRP 615. (4 G-64.)

— 1954: A successful transatlantic crossing in a jet stream. MML 83 (987): 268-271. (6.2-128.)

Dean, G. A., 1956: Examples of the mean three-dimensional wind circulation over the tropical North Pacific Ocean. MWR 84 (3): 87-102. (8.7-175.)

Decca Radar Ltd., 1957: Decca windfinding radar. London. (9.2-164.)

Defant, A., 1921: Die Zirkulation der Atmosphäre in den gemäßigten Breiten der Erde. GA 3: 209-266.

— 1949: Neuere Ansichten über die allgemeine Zirkulation der Atmosphäre in mittleren Breiten. AMGBA 1 (3/4): 273-294. (4 G-19.)

— and F. Defant, 1958: Physikalische Dynamik der Atmosphäre. Frankfurt a. M.: Akademische Verlagsgesellschaft.

Defant, F., 1951: Die Änderung des meridionalen Windprofils durch Kondensationswärme und Turbulenzvorgänge. AMGBA 4: 156-175. (4 G-65.)

— 1952: A kinematic-graphical method for the 24 hour prognosis of the 500-mb chart. BAMS 33 (2): 83. (3 E-235.)

— 1953: On the mechanism of index changes. U of C, Dep. of Met., Contract N 6ori-20, Task Order 11, Project No. 082,003, Technical Report. (5 D-248.)

— 1954: Über den Mechanismus der unperiodischen Schwankungen der allgemeinen Zirkulation der Nordhalbkugel. Über charakteristische Meridionalschnitte der Temperatur für High- und Low Index-Typen der allgemeinen Zirkulation und über die Temperaturänderungen während ihrer Umwandlungsperioden. AMGBA 6 (3/4): 253-279, 280-296. (5.8-110.)

— 1956*a*: Über die Struktur hochtropospärischer Düsenströme, insbesondere des subtropischen Strahlstroms über Nordamerika. BDW 4 (22): 126-133. (8.7-152.)

— 1956*b*: Characteristic meridional temperature profiles and their changes during high- and low-index types of the general circulation. IUGG, p. 302-304. (10.1-210.)

— 1958: Die allgemeine atmosphärische Zirkulation in neuerer Betrachtungsweise. GH 6 (3-4): 189-217.

— 1959*a*: Die Westwärts-Intensivierung des Polarfront-Jetstream in den Winkel zwischen Polarfront und Tropopause an der Ostseite eines plaren Kälteausbruches, eine Erweiterung des klassischen Grenzflächenproblems von Margules. AMGBA 11 (2): 197-217.

— 1959*b*: On hydrodynamic instability caused by an approach of subtropical and polar-front jet stream in northern latitudes before the onset of strong cyclogenesis. RMV p. 305-325.

— and H. Taba, 1957: The threefold structure of the atmosphere and the characteristics of the tropopause. T 9 (3): 259-274.

— — 1958*a*: The details of wind and temperature field and the generation of the blocking situation over Europe (Jan. 1-4, 1956). BPA 31 (1/2): 69-88.

— — 1958*b*: The strong index change period from Jan. 1 to Jan. 7, 1956. T 10 (2): 225-242.

— — 1958*c*: The breakdown of zonal circulation during the period January 8 to 13, 1956, the characteristics of temperature field and tropopause and its relation to the atmospheric field of motion. T 10 (4): 430-450.

Defrise, P., *et al.*, 1960: Les représentations graphiques en météorologie. WMO TN No. 31, OMM No. 95, TP 39.

De Jong, H. M., 1956: Theoretical aspects of aeronavigation and its application in aviation meteorology. Netherlands, Meteorologisch Instituut, Mededeelingen en Verhandelingen, No. 64 (9.5–64.)

— 1958: Errors in upper level wind computations. JM 15 (2): 131–137.

— and F. C. Bik, 1953: A report on the theory and application of the minimum flight path. Schiphol Airport, Amsterdam.

Denver University, Institute of Industrial Research, 1951: Determination of atmospheric winds and temperatures in the 30- to 60 km-region by acoustic means. Contract AF 19 (122)–252, Quarterly Progress Report No. 2. (4 F–69.)

— 1953: Determination of atmospheric winds and temperatures in the 30- to 60 km-region by acoustic means. Contract AF (122)–252, Quarterly Progress Reports No. 8, 9, 10, 11. (6.3–185.)

De Pasquale, O., 1955: Idee ed applicazioni precorritrici di oltre 30 anni addietro sulle "correnti a getto". (Ideas and applications of the jet stream theory 30 years ago.) RMA 15 (2): 32–34. (8.1–198.)

De Q. Robin, G., 1957: Upper wind over an antarctic station. QJRMS 83: 533–536.

Desai, B. N., 1957: Comments on C. Ramaswamy: On the subtropical jet stream and its role in the development of large-scale convection. Reply by Ramaswamy. T 9 (1): 135–136. (9.4–127.)

Deutscher Wetterdienst, Bad Kissingen, 1957: Symposium über numerische Wettervorhersage in Frankfurt a. M. vom 23. bis 28. Mai 1956. BDW No. 38 (Bd. 5).

Di Benedetto, F., 1953: Su alcune proprietà notevoli del rotore del vento di gradiente. (Some remarkable properties of the curl of the gradient wind.) AGR 6 (4): 511–532. (6.2–110.)

Dickson, R. R., 1955*a*: A case study of the jet stream. BAMS 36 (5): 195–203. (7.4–1944.)

— 1955*b*: Aids to jet stream forecasting. U.S. Office of Naval Operations, NAVAER, 50–1 P-533. (8 C–67.)

Dieterichs, H., 1950: Über die Entstehung der Perlmutterwolken. MR 3 (9–10): 208–213. (2.2–155.)

— 1952: Schablone zum Zeichnen von Isohypsenabständen. ZM 6 (3): 89. (3.9–31.)

Dietrich, G., 1957: Allgemeine Meereskunde. Berlin: Borntraeger.

Dietzius, R., 1917: Die Geschwindigkeit des Windes in großen Höhen über Wien. BPA 7 (3): 174–184. (4 E–155.)

Dines, W. H., 1911: The vertical temperature distribution in the atmosphere over England, and some remarks on the general and local circulation. Phil. Trans. Roy. Soc. London, Ser. A., 211: 277–300.

— 1912: Total and partial correlation coefficients between sundry variables of the upper air. GM 2.

— 1919: The characteristics of the free atmosphere. GM 13.

— 1925: The correlation between pressure and temperature in the upper air with a suggested explanation. QJRMS 51: 31–38.

Dobson, G. M. B., 1920: Winds and temperature gradients in the stratosphere. QJRMS 46 (193): 54–62. (4 F–4.)

Döös, B. R., 1956: Automation of 500 mb forecasts through successive numerical map analysis. T 8 (1): 76–81.

— 1958: Effect of the vertical variation of wind and stability on mountain waves. Florida State University, Tallahassee, Dept. of Met., Contract Nonr-1600 (00). TR No. 13, Dec. 30 (10.11–207.)

— and M. A. Eaton, 1957: Upper air analysis over ocean areas. T 9 (2): 184–194.

DOPORTO, M., 1951: The computation of atmospheric pressure at the 8 km level of constant air density. Eire, Met. Service, Geophysical Publications 3 (4). (7.8–54.)

— and W. A. MORGAN, 1947: The significance of the isopycnic level. QJRMS 73: 384–390.

DOUGLAS, C. K. M., 1922: Observation of upper cloud drift as an aid to research and weather forecasting. QJRMS 4: 342–356.

— 1925: On the relation between the source of the air and the upper air temperature up to the base of the stratosphere. QJRMS 51: 229–238. (5 D–50.)

DROESSLER, E. G., 1950: "Skyhook" plastic balloons for high altitude soundings. BAMS 31 (6): 191–193. (1.8–16.)

DROUILHET, P. R., 1958: Transosonde balloons flying on a routine basis. BAMS 39 (2): 96–97. (10.11–107.)

DUELL, B., and G. DUELL, 1948: The behavior of atmospheric pressure during and after solar particle invasions and solar ultraviolet invasions. Smithsonian Miscell. Coll. 110 (No. 8.)

DUE ROJO, A., 1954: El "Jet Stream" o rio aereo estratosferico. (The jet stream or stratospheric river of air.) Granada, Observatorio de Cartuja. Trabajos Scientificos, Ser. B. 8 (66). (6.10–136.)

DUGSTAD, I., 1956: A generalization of Richardson's criterion of turbulence. A & M Sci. Rep. No. 11, Contr. AF 19 (604)–559.

DU JONCHAY, I., and V. MIRONOVICH, 1953: Les courants aeriens de l'hémisphère sud. I. U. G. G., Association of Met., Brussels 1951, Procès-Verbaux des Séances, Mémoirs et Discussion, p. 81–85, Brussels (7.7–137.)

DUNCAN, P. F., 1951: Wind measurement at great heights. Aeroplane, London 80 (2066): 234–235. (4 F–71.)

DUNNING, H. H., and N. E. LA SEUR, 1955: An evaluation of some condensation trail observations. BAMS 36: 73–79. (6.9–218.)

DURSI, M., and V. EDGARDO, 1954: Corriente de "chorro." (Jet stream.) Revista Nacional de Aeronautica, Buenos Aires, 14 (145): 54–55. (6.2–129.)

DURST, C. S., 1948: The fine structure of wind in the free air. QJRMS 74: 349–360. (1.2–132.)

— 1952: The variation of wind in short periods of time between 30,000 and 35,000 feet, Jan. 1950 to Jan. 1952. MRP 745. (4 E–231.)

— 1954: The accuracy of route wind forecasts for aviation. JINL 7 (1): 28–43. (6.10–102.)

— 1960. The statistical variation of wind with distance. QJRMS 86 (370): 543–549.

— and N. E. DAVIS, 1949: Jet streams and their importance to air navigation. JINL 2 (3): 210–218. (4 G–20.)

— — 1957: Accuracy of geostrophic trajectories. MML 86 (1019): 138–141. (8.9–208.)

— and G. H. GILBERT, 1950: Constant-height balloons—calculation of geostropic departures. QJRMS 76: 75–88.

DURWARD, J., 1921: Diurnal variation of wind velocity and direction at different heights. GMOPN 15.

— 1925: The investigation of the winds in the upper air from information regarding the place of fall of pilot balloons and the distribution of pressure. GMOPN No. 42. (4 G–1.)

— 1936: Upper winds at Wadi Hafa (Sudan). GMOPN 72.

— 1937: Upper winds measured at MIY Imperia, Mirabella Bay, Crete. GMOPN 79.

— and D. C. E. JONES, 1955: Weather phenomena at high levels. Aeroplane 88: 18–21. (6.9–151.)

DWYER, W. N., 1955: Cloud forms associated with "jet stream". AMMM No. 8: 55. (7.7–200.)

DYER, A. J., and S.-A. YEO, 1960: A radio-active fall-out study at Melbourne, Australia. T 12 (2): 195–199.

DZHORDZHIO, V. A., 1956*a*: Struinoe techenie. (Jet stream.) MG No. 6: 49–60. (8.9–171.)

— 1956*b*: O postroenii srednikh vertikal'nykh razrezov s tsel'iu izucheniia struinogo techeniia i drugikh osobennostei obshchei tsirkuliatsii atmosfery. (Construction of mean vertical cross sections for studying the jet stream and other characteristics of general atmospheric circulation.) Tashkent. Geofizicheskaia Observatoriia, Trudy No. 11/12: 87–112. (10.10–127.)

EADY, E. T., 1949: Long waves and cyclone waves. T 1 (3): 33–52. (1.2–84.)

— 1950: The cause of the general circulation of the atmosphere. CP 156–172. (2.3–61.)

— 1951: The quantitative theory of cyclone development. CM 464–469. (3.7–4.)

— 1953: The maintenance of the mean zonal surface currents. AMST 124–128. (6.3–156.)

— and J. S. SAWYER, 1951: Reviews of modern meteorology. 3. Dynamics of flow patterns in extra-tropical regions. QJRMS 77 (334): 531–551. (3.4–114, 4 G–66.)

EBDON, R. A., 1960: Notes on the wind flow at 50 mb in tropical and subtropical regions in January 1957 and January 1958. QJRMS 86 (370): 540–542.

EDWARDES, H. N., 1950: High altitude meteorological balloon techniques. Australia Commonwealth Scientif. and Industr. Research Organ. Div. of Radiophysics, RPR 107. (3.1–39.)

— 1952: Some measurements of velocity of high altitude winds at Sidney, N. S. W. BAMS 33 (2): 56–59. (4 F–94.)

EDWARDS, H. D., J. F. BEDINGER, and E. R. MANRING, 1956: Emission from a sodium cloud artificially produced by means of a rocket. (In: The airglow and the aurorae: a symposium. London: Pergamon.) (8.7–198.)

EKHART, E., 1940: Zur Kenntnis der Windverhältnisse in der oberen Stratosphäre. Reichsamt für Wetterdienst. (4 F–20.)

ELIASEN, E., 1958: A study of the long atmospheric waves on the basis of zonal harmonic analysis. T 10 (2): 206–215.

ELIASSEN, A., and W. E. HUBERT, 1953: Computations of vertical motion and velocity budget in a blocking situation. T 5 (2): 196–206. (5.2–107.)

— J. S. SAWYER, and J. SMAGORINSKY, 1960: Upper air network requirements for numerical weather prediction. WMO TN No. 29, WMO No. 94, TP 38.

ELLIOTT, R. D., 1955: Study of vorticity injections. Astrophysics Research Foundation, Santa Barbara, Calif. Contract N 189s–99279, Report 55–1. (9.5–146.)

— 1956: Low latitude vorticity injections and the development of large-scale anomalous circulation patterns. BAMS 137 (6): 270–275. (8.9–167.)

— and T. B. SMITH, 1949: A study of the effects of large blocking highs on the general circulation in the Northern Hemisphere westerlies. JM 6 (2): 67–85.

ELLISON, T. H., and C. D. WALSHAW, 1955: The evaluation of some regression coefficients for estimating the 150-mb wind at Liverpool. QJRMS 18 (349): 480–483. (6.11–154.)

ELSAESSER, H. W., 1957: Errors in upper-level wind forecasts. BAMS 38: 511–517.

ELSE, C. V., 1955: Wind finding trials of Radar A. A. No. 3 Mk. VII (Second series). MRP 922. (7.6–85.)

ELSLEY, E. M., 1951: Alberta forest fire smoke—24 September 1950. W 6 (1): 22–24. (2.7–56.)

EMERY, P. F., 1956: Strong winds at high levels in the equatorial zone of the Far East. MML 85 (1011): 275–277. (8.2–128.)

ENDLICH, R. M., 1953: A study of vertical velocities in the vicinity of jet streams. JM 10 (6): 407–415. (5.6–117.)

ENDLICH, R. M., 1954: A note on pressure at the tropopause. BAMS 35 (3): 131–132. (6.3–98.)

— P. HARNEY, *et al.*, 1954: Project Jet Stream. The observation and analysis of the detailed structure of the atmosphere near the tropopause. BAMS 35: 143–153. (6.5–121.)

— and G. S. MCLEAN, 1957: The structure of the jet stream core. JM 14: 543–552.

— — 1960*a*: Geostrophic and gradient departures in jet streams. JM 17 (2): 135–147.

— — 1960*b*: Analyzing and forecasting meteorological conditions in the upper troposphere and lower stratosphere. AFS No. 121.

— and R. M. RADOS, 1959: The meteorological measurements and field program of project jet stream from 1956 to 1958. GRP No. 64.

— S. B. SOLOT, and H. A. THUR, 1955: The mean vertical structure of the jet stream. T 7 (3): 308–313. (7.9–144.)

EPSTEIN, E. S., 1959: An empirical study of vertical velocities in the lower stratosphere. MWR 87 (3): 91–96.

ERIKSON, M., 1954: Study of turbulence and vertical motion in the upper atmosphere derived from the ascensional rates of the rubber balloons. GH 4 (4): 153–179. (7.4–198.)

ERTEL, H., 1936: Die Arten der Unstetigkeit des Windfeldes an der Tropopause. MZ 53 (12): 450–455. (5 D–83.)

— 1939: Singuläre Advektion und Zyklonenbewegung. MZ 56 (11): 401–407. (5 D–98.)

— 1942: Ein neuer hydrodynamischer Wirbelsatz. MZ 59 (9): 277–281.

ERVET, P., 1958: Utilisation de la distance oblique dans les sondages vent au radar. LM Ser. 4, No. 51: 209–221. (11.1–136.)

— and A. ROBUCHON, 1959: Mesure fin du vent en altitude à l'aide de deux radars à poursuite automatique. LM Ser. 4, No. 54: 121–128. (11.5–258.)

ESSENWANGER, O., 1953: Statistische Untersuchungen über die Zirkulation der Westdrift in 55° Breite. BDW No. 7. (5.11–87.)

ESTOQUE, M. A., 1950: On the properties of two-dimensional wave-motions in an atmosphere which is characterized by zonal winds. NYU, Met. Papers Vol. 1, No. 5.

— 1955: The mechanism of vorticity change associated with a selected cyclone. U of C, Dep. of Met., Contract AF 19 (604)–1293, TR No. 4. (7.8 118.)

— 1956: A prediction model for cyclone development integrated by Fjørtoft's method. JM 13: 195–202.

— 1957*a*: A graphically integrable prediction model incorporating orographic influences. JM 14: 293–296.

— 1957*b*: Graphical integrations of a two-level model. JM 14: 38–42.

— 1958: Some characteristics of turbulence at high altitudes. Geophysics Research Directorate, GRD Research Notes No. 4, AFCRC-TN-58-624.

EWING, R. A., 1949: The determination of upper winds by electronic means. Sixth Pacific Science Congress 1947, Proceedings Roy. Soc. of New Zealand, Transactions, 77 (5): 76–78. (2.6–22.)

EXNER, F., 1925: Dynamische Meteorologie, 2. Aufl. Wien.

FALCONER, R. E., 1953: A correlation between atmospheric electrical activity and the jet stream. General Electric Research Lab., Schenectady, N.Y., Report No. RL-900. (4 G–137.)

— and J. SCHAEFER, 1954: Cloud and atmospheric-electric observations of the formative stages of the Worcester, Massachusetts, Tornado. BAMS 35: 437–440.

FALLER, A. J., 1956: A demonstration of fronts and frontal waves in atmospheric models. JM 13 (1): 1–4. (7.8–136.)

FARKAS, E., 1955: Upper winds over Invercargill. New Zealand Met. Service, Technical Note 121. (7.9–186.)

FARTHING, E. D., 1959: Analysis of high level PIREPS during the period Oct. 6–Nov. 6, 1958. Kansas City, Mo., Trans World Airlines, Inc., Meteor. Section, 1959. (11.1–239.)

FAUST, H., 1953: Die Nullschicht, der Sitz des troposphärischen Windmaximums. MR 6 (1/2): 6–15. (4 E–253.)

— 1954*a*: Die Strahlströme als Erscheinung der Nullschicht. MR 7 (9/10): 161–166. (6.2–130.)

— 1954*b*: Nullschichteffekt und Frontalzonen. AMGBA 6 (3/4): 334–369. (5.8–89.)

— 1955*a*: Der Nullschichteffekt als Funktion der Schärfe des Maximums in der vertikalen Windverteilung. MR 8 (3/4): 48–50. (6.10–137.)

— 1955*b*: Übergradientische Winde in der Nullschicht und das Problem der Strahlströme. AMGBA 8 (1/2): 45–71. (6.8–10.)

— 1955*c*: Vertikale Änderung der Windgeschwindigkeit und Luftdruckänderungen. MR 8 (1/2): 19–23. (6.10–123.)

— 1959*a*: Bemerkungen zum Aufsatz: „Zum Problem der Nullschicht" von E. REITER. MR 12 (3): 96–97.

— 1959*b*: Nullschichteffekt und allgemeine Zirkulation. GPA 44: 257–264.

— 1960: Die Schwachwindschicht in der unteren Stratosphäre als Nullschicht. MR 13 (3): 77–85.

FAWCETT, E. B., and L. W. SNELLMAN, 1959: 300-mb isotach analysis. BAMS 40 (2): 78–84. (11.3–39.)

FAY, R., 1958: A note on the mid-tropospheric wind maximum. BAMS 39 (7): 360–362. (11.3–40.)

FEA, G., M. MONTALTO, and A. GAZZOLA, 1957: Analisi obiettiva, a scala sinottica, dei campi di velocità troposferici. RMA 17 (1): 3–30. (8.10–195.)

FERENCE, M., 1951: Instrumentation and techniques for meteorological measurements. CM 1207–1222.

FERRARI, G., 1958: Carte des zones d'ascendance de nature ondulatoire, par trasmontane dans le Latium (Italie centrale). OSTIV Publication V, und SAR 1960/1.

FERREL, W., 1889: A popular treatise on the winds. New York.

FETNER, M. W., 1956: Summary of location and extents of turbulent areas encountered during flight investigations of the jet stream from October 1953 to May 1954 and November 1954 to July 1955. NACA RML 55H04a.

FETT, W., 1956: Ein neues Höhenwind-Auswertgerät. ZM 10 (7): 207–216. (8.2–61.)

FETTE, H., 1933: Strömungsversuche im rotierenden Laboratorium. Z. techn. Physik 14 (7): 257–266.

FISHER, E. L., 1956: Vertical motion and cyclogenesis. NYU, Research Division, Dep. of Met. and Ocean., Contr. Nonr-285 (09), Technical Paper No. 6. (8.6–269.)

FJØRTOFT, R., 1951: Stability properties of large-scale atmospheric disturbances. CM 454–463. (3.8–3.)

— 1952: On a numerical method of integrating the barotropic vorticity equation. T 4: 179–194.

FLEAGLE, R. G., 1947: The fields of temperature, pressure and three-dimensional motion in selected weather situations. JM 4: 165–185.

— 1957: On the dynamics of the general circulation. QJRMS 83 (355): 1–20. (8.4–20.)

— 1958: Inferences concerning the dynamics of the mesosphere. JGR 63 (1): 137–146. (9.11–161.)

— and R. M. ENDLICH, 1954: Comments on "A study of vertical velocities in the vicinity of jet streams." JM 11 (6): 513–514. (6.5–116.)

FLEAGLE, R. G., and Y. IZUMI, 1955: Empirical and theoretical studies of baroclinic instability. Washington (State) Univ., Dep. of Met. and Climat., Contr. AF 19 (604)-314, Scientific Report No. 1. (9.4–125.)

FLEISHER, A., 1959: Some spectra of turbulence in the free atmosphere. JM 16 (2): 209–211.

FLETCHER, R. D., 1953: The association of wind speed with height of upper-air constant-pressure surface. BAMS 34 (4): 155–159. (4 G–131.)

FLINT, R. F., 1957: Glacial and pleistocene geology. New York: Wiley.

FLOHN, H., 1944: Die Intensität der zonalen Zirkulation in der freien Atmosphäre außertropischer Breiten. GBG 60: 196–209.

— 1950*a*: Die planetarische Zirkulation der Atmosphäre bis 30 km Höhe. BDWUS No. 12: 156–161. (4 F–56.)

— 1950*b*: Grundzüge der allgemeinen atmosphärischen Zirkulation auf der Südhalbkugel. AMGBA 2 (1): 17–64. (4 F–55.)

— 1950*c*: Neue Erkenntnisse über die Monsunzirkulation. MR 3 (7–8): 176. (1.11–103.)

— 1950*d*: Studien zur allgemeinen Zirkulation der Atmosphäre. BDWUS No. 18. (2.5–72.)

— 1950*e*: Neue Anschauungen über die allgemeine Zirkulation der Atmosphäre und ihre klimatische Bedeutung. Erdkunde 4: 141–162.

— 1951*a*: Allgemeine Zirkulation und natürliche Klimaeinteilung. AM 4 (1–6): 76–77. (3.3–107.)

— 1951*b*: Die Zirkulation der Atmosphäre in den Polargebieten. Polarforschung 3 (1): 58–64. (3.3–108.)

— 1952*a*: Allgemeine atmosphärische Zirkulation und Polarklimatologie. Geol. Rundschau 40: 153.

— 1952*b*: Atmosphärische Zirkulation und erdmagnetisches Feld. BDWUS No. 38: 46–51. (4.2–106.)

— 1952*c*: Probleme der großräumigen Synoptik. BDWUS No. 35: 12–23. (3.10–72.)

— 1953*a*: Hochgebirge und allgemeine Zirkulation. II. Die Gebirge als Wärmequellen. AMGBA 5 (3): 265–279. (4.6–101).

— 1953*b*: Studien über die atmosphärische Zirkulation der letzten Eiszeit. Erdkunde 7 (4): 266–275.

— 1955: Zur vergleichenden Meteorologie der Hochgebirge. AMGBA 6: 193–206.

— 1956*a*: Der indische Sommermonsun als Glied der planetarischen Zirkulation der Atmosphäre. BDW 4 (22): 134–139. (8.9–221.)

— 1956*b*: Investigations on the general atmospheric circulation especially in lower latitudes. IUGG 431–442. (8.8–202.)

— 1957: Large-scale aspects of the "summer-monsoon" in South and East Asia. JMSJ, 75th Anniversary Volume, 180–186.

— 1958*a*: Beiträge zur Klimakunde von Hochasien. Erdkunde 12 (4): 294–308.

— 1958*b*: Luftmassen, Fronten und Strahlströme (Grundbegriffe der synoptischen Meteorologie). MR 11 (1): 7–13.

— 1959*a*: Aktuelle Probleme der aerologischen Synoptik. (Einleitendes Referat.) BDW No. 51: 82–95. (11.3–41.)

— 1959*b*: Probleme der geophysikalisch-vergleichenden Klimatologie seit Alexander von Humboldt. BDW No. 59: 9–31.

— 1959*c*: Meteorologische Probleme bei der Ausbreitung radioaktiven Aerosols. GPA 44: 271–286.

— 1959*d*: Bemerkungen zur Klimatologie von Hochasien. Aktuelle Schneegrenze und Sommerklima. Akademie der Wissenschaften und der Literatur, Mainz, Abhandlungen der math.-naturw. Klasse, Jg. 1959, Nr. 14: 309–331.

FLOHN, H., 1960a: Mehrfachbildung der Tropopause und Windfeld im äquatorialen Pazifik. MDW No. 20: 50–57.

— 1960b: Strahlströme in der Stratosphäre. Wetterkarte des Seewetteramtes, Hamburg. Jahrg. 8, No. 76–78.

— and K. HINKELMANN, 1952: Äquatoriale Zirkulations-Anomalien und ihre klimatische Auswirkung. BDWUS 42: 114–121.

— R. HOLZAPFEL, and H. OECKEL, 1959: Untersuchungen über die stratosphärische Ostströmung, auf der Sommerhalbkugel. BPA 31: 217–243. (11.1–206.)

FLOWERS. E. G., 1960: The atmosphere from the surface to 50 mb over the South Pole during 1957. AMO 453–462.

— and H. HANSEN, 1959: Comparison of various conditioning methods for rawinsonde balloons. MWR 87 (7): 261–267.

FÖRCHTGOTT, J., 1956: Active turbulent layer downwind of mountain ridges. OSTIV Publication IV. und SAR 1957 (6).

FORSDYKE, A. G., 1951: Zonal and other indices. MML 80 (948): 156–161. (3.2–17.)

FORTAK, H., 1959: Das Eindringen hochstratosphärischer Erwärmungen in die untere Stratosphäre als Austauschproblem. GBG 67 (1): 66–78.

— 1960: Gradientwindbestimmung aus Karten in stereographischer Projektion. BPA 32 (3/4): 249–256.

FOSTER, R. L., and E. F. ROBINSON, 1953: The strong jet over the Southwestern Plain States, Nov. 24–25, 1953. MWR 81 (11): 374–378. (5.11–88.)

FOTHERINGHAM, R. R., 1953: High altitude winds at O. W. S. "Polar Front". MRP 812. (5.2–181.)

Frankfurt a. M., Wetterdienststelle, 1932: Synoptische Bearbeitungen Nr. 1–5, Okt. 1932. Stratosphärische Steuerung. Frankfurt a. M. (2 A–72.)

FRASER, D. O., 1951: Optimum flight paths. JINL 4 (2): 178–200. (3.1–16.)

FREEMAN, J. C., 1953: A jet stream model. Abstract in: American Met. Soc., 120th National Meeting, Program, New York City, Jan. 26–29, 1953. p. 395. (4 G–122.)

J. T. HURT, and A. KASAHARA, 1956: Barotropic models of the planetary jet stream. A & M Contract AF (604)–559, Scient. Report No. 12. (8.6–2.)

FRENCH, J. E., and K. R. JOHANNESSEN, 1954: Forecasting high clouds from high-level constant-pressure charts. AMST: 160–171. (6.3–75.)

FRENZEN, P., 1955: Westerly flow past an obstacle in a rotating hemispheric shell. BAMS 36 (5): 204–210. (7.6–119.)

— *et al.*, 1956: Experimental apparatus and techniques. In: D. FULTZ: Studies in experimental hydrodynamics applied to large-scale meteorological phenomena. Final Report, Part I, Contract AF 19 (122)–160. pp. C-2 bis C-36.

— and N. E. LA SEUR, 1956: Criteria for the occurrence of an eccentric circumpolar vortex in the atmosphere inferred from model experiments. JM 13 (1): 124–126. (7.8–127.)

FRITZ, S., 1959: On observing the atmosphere from satellites. I. Cloud observations. WW 12 (4): 139–144, 163–165.

— and H. WEXLER, 1960: Cloud pictures from satellite Tiros I. MWR 88 (3): 79–87.

FROST, B. C., 1953: Flying in jet stream winds. Shell Aviation News, London, No. 186: 4–8. (5.9–203.)

— 1954: More about the jet stream. Shell Aviation News, London, No. 195: 14–18. (7.7–62.)

FROST, R., 1952: The upper air circulation in low latitudes and its relation to certain climatological discontinuities. MRP 706. (4 G–94.)

— 1953: Upper air circulation in low latitudes in relation to certain climatological discontinuities. GMOPN No. 7 (107). (5.1–132.)

FUGLISTER, F. C., 1951: Multiple currents in the Gulf Stream system. T 3: 230–233.

— and L. V. WORTHINGTON, 1951: Some results of a multiple ship survey of the Gulf Stream. T 3 (1): 1–14. (2.11–196.)

FUJITA, T., 1955: Results of detailed synoptic studies of squall lines. T 7: 405–436.

— H. NEWSTEIN, and M. TEPPER, 1956: Mesoanalysis, an important scale in the analysis of weather data. USWB, Washington, D.C., RP No. 39.

FUKUOKA, J., 1958: The variations of the Kuroshio current in the sea south and east of Honshu (Japanese main island). The Oceanographical Magazine, Japan Meteorological Agency, 10 (2): 201–213.

FULKS, J. R., 1951: The instability line. CM 647–652. (3.8–4.)

FULTZ, D., 1945: Upper-air trajectories and weather forecasting. U of C, Miscell. Rep. No. 19.

— 1949: A preliminary report on experiments with thermally produced lateral mixing in a rotating hemispherical shell of liquid. JM 6 (1): 17–33. (1.3–43.)

— 1950*a*: Experimental studies of a polar vortex I. T 2 (3): 137–149. (2.2–61.)

— 1950*b*: Experimental studies related to atmospheric flow around obstacles. GPA 17 (3–4): 88–93. (2.5–60.)

— 1951*a*: Experimental analogies to atmospheric motions. CM 1235–1248.

— 1951*b*: Experiments combining convection and rotation and some of their possible implications. Midwestern Conference on Fluid Mechanics, Univ. of Illinois, May 12–13, 1950. Proceedings, Publ. Ann Arbor 1951. (7.7–139.)

— 1951*c*: Non-dimensional equations and modeling criteria for the atmosphere. JM 8 (4): 262–267. (3.5–138.)

— 1952: On the possibility of experimental models of the polar-front wave. JM 9 (6): 379–384. (4.11–131.)

— 1956*a*: A survey of certain thermally and mechanically driven systems of meteorological interest. U.S. Office of Naval Research, Proceedings of the First Symposium on the use of models in Geophysical Fluid Dynamics, Sept. 1953. (9.4–172.)

— 1956*b*: Studies in experimental hydrodynamics applied to large-scale meteorological phenomena. Part I, II. Final Report. Contract AF 19 (122)–160.

— 1960: Experimental models of rotating fluids and possible avenues for further research. In: Dynamics of Climate; Editor: R. L. PFEFFER, pp. 71–77. New York.

— and P. FRENZEN, 1955: A note on certain interesting ageostrophic motions in a rotating hemispherical shell. JM 12 (4): 332–338.

— and R. KAYLOR, 1959: The progagation of frequency in experimental baroclinic waves in a rotating annular ring. RMV p. 359–371.

— and R. LONG, 1951: Two-dimensional flow around a circular barrier in a rotating spherical shell. T 3 (2): 61–68. (3.2–71.)

— *et al.*, 1956: Studies of thermal convection in a rotating cylinder with some implications for large-scale atmospheric motions. U of C, 64 pp. (10.6–185.)

— *et al.*, 1959: Studies of thermal convection in a rotating cylinder with some implications for large-scale atmospheric motions. MM No. 21 (Vol. 4).

GAALSWYK, A., 1958: Suggested uses of meteorological data collected by constant-pressure level balloon systems. General Mills, Inc., Mechanical Div., Contract AF 19 (604)–2170, Scientif. Report No. 1. (9.10–115.)

GABITES, J. F., 1952: Mean westerly wind flow between the 700- and 100 millibar levels over the New Zealand region. New Zealand Meteorological Service, TN No. 90. (4 G–95.)

— 1953: Mean westerly wind flow in the upper levels over the New Zealand region. New Zealand Journal of Science and Technology, Ser. B, 34 (5): 384–390. (4 G–123.)

GABITES, J. F., 1954: Drift of radioactive dust from the British nuclear bomb tests in October 1953. New Zealand Met. Office, Note No. 40. (7 E–88.)

— and E. M. PORTER, 1951: Equivalent head winds at 30,000 ft on South Pacific air routes during 1951. New Zealand Met. Service, TN No. 83. (4 E–234.)

— — 1952: Equivalent head winds on air routes leading to New Zealand. New Zealand Met. Service, TN 86. (4 E–234.)

GALES, D. M., 1955: Air Weather San Francisco-Cheyenne. Trans World Air Lines Inc. (7.3–63.)

GALLOWAY, J. L., 1958: Three-front model: its philosophy, nature, construction and use. W 13 (1): 3–10. (10.3–237.)

GAMBO, K., 1950: The criteria for stability of the westerlies. Tokyo Univ., Geoph. Inst., Geophysical Notes 3 (29). (2.10–70.)

— 1951: Notes on the energy dispersion in the atmosphere. JMSJ Ser. 2, 29 (7): 215–232. (3.7–95.)

— 1956: The topographical effect upon the jet stream in the westerlies. JMSJ Ser. 2 34 (1): 24–28. (9.5–258.)

GARDINER, A. J., *et al.*, 1956: Optical studies of atmospheric turbulence. Flagstaff Arizona, Lowell Observatory, Contr. AF 19 (604)–953, Final Report 1956. (9.5–268.)

GARRIOCK, A., 1957: Forecasting upper winds. AMMM No. 19: 1–14. (9.11–143.)

GARRIOTT, E. B., 1954: Long-range weather forecasts. BAMS 35: 62.

GARTINEAU, A., 1951: Routes aériennes de durée minimum. LM 4th ser. No. 22: 113–127. (4.7–54.)

GAZZOLA, A., 1954: Le jet stream dans une situation de bloquage. IUGG 44–49.

— 1955: La corrente a getto durante una situazione di blocco. RMA 15 (1): 25–31. (8.1–193.)

— 1956: Sur la variabilité avec l'altitude du paramètre l^2 lors de la formation d'ondes de relief. RMA 16 (3): 21–30. (10.3–272.) SAR 32 (4): 217–220.

General Mills, 1951: The General Mills Aeronautical Research Laboratories. BAMS 32 (3): 111–112. (3.1–38.)

GENÈVE, R. and G. JACQUEMARD, 1957: Coupe méridienne de l'atmosphère au-dessus du Nord-Ouest de l'Afrqiue. (Meridional section of the atmosphere over northwestern Africa.) Académie des Sciences, Paris, Comptes Rendus 244 (6): 793–796. (9.8–166.)

GEORGI, J., 1950: Hochstürme über der Dänemarkstraße. Deutsche Hydrograph. Zeitschrift 3 (1/2): 136–143. (4 G–39.)

GEORGII, W., 1953: Problemas de la corriente ondulatoria y de chorro en la Argentina. (Problems of the air current and the jet stream in Argentina.) Revista Nacional de Aeronautica, Buenos Aires, 13 (131): 33–37. (5.7–128.)

— 1956*a*: Beiträge zum Problem der Turbulenz der Strahlströme. DFS, Bericht No. 1.

— 1956*b*: Flugmeteorologie. Frankfurt a. M.: Akademische Verlagsgesellschaft. (9.8–5.)

— 1957: Strahlströme und Böenlinien. SAR 32 (6): 319–324. (10.3–228.)

— 1958*a*: Forschungsflüge in alpiner Wellenströmung. SAR 33 (6): 307–314. (11.2–93.)

— 1958*b*: Problemi riguardanti la struttura e la turbolenza del corrente a getto. RMA 18: 3–17. (11.1–241.)

— 1960: Monographie der Strahlströme, Teil 2. DFS Forschungsbericht No. 6.

— M. REINHARDT, and M. SCHURER, 1957: Beiträge zum Problem der Turbulenz der Strahlströme. DFS, Bericht No. 3.

GERBIER, N., 1959: Écoulement de l'air au voisinage immédiat du relief. ACSI 88–93.

— and M. BERENGER, 1960*a*: Les ondes de ressaut. Ministère des Travaux Publics et des Transports, Secrétariat Générale à l'Aviation Civile & Commerciale. Service de la Formation Aeronautique, du Travail Aérien et des Transports.

GERBIER, N., and M. BERENGER, 1960*b*: Études expérimentales des ondes dues au relief. MNM No . 20.

— — 1961: Experimental studies of lee waves in the French Alps. QJRMS 87 (371): 13–23.

GERSON, N. C., 1952: Unsolved problems in physics of the high atmosphere. Advances in Geophysics 1: 156–242. New York.

— and J. KAPLAN, 1951: Nomenclature of the upper atmosphere. JATP 1 (3): 200. (2.9–63.)

GIÃO, A., 1956: Introduction à la climatologie dynamique de l'Amérique du nord, de l'Atlantique nord et de l'Europe. GPA 34: 101–150. (8.6–343.)

GIBBS, W. J., 1952: Notes on the mean jet stream over Australia. JM 9 (4): 279–284. (4 G–96.)

— 1953: A comparison of hemispheric circulations with particular reference to the western Pacific. QJRMS 79 (339): 121–136. (4 G–124.)

— 1955: 200-mb divergence associated with rapid and intense cyclogenesis. AMMM 11: 17–35. (9.6–126.)

GIFFORD, F. A., 1952: The breakdown of a low-level inversion studied by means of detailed soundings with a modified radiosonde. BAMS 33: 373–379.

— 1955: The height of scintillation-producing disturbances. BAMS 36 (1): 35–36. (6.11–351.)

— and A. H. MIKESELL, 1953: Atmospheric turbulence and the scintillation of starlight. W 8 (7): 195–197. (4.11–178.)

GILCHRIST, A., 1953: Upper winds in the tropics and subtropics. MRP 795. (5.2–179.)

— 1955: Winds between 300 and 100 mb in the tropics and subtropics. Great Brit. Met. Office, Met. Reports No. 16. (7.4–141.)

GILES, K. C., and R. E. PETERSON, 1956: Velocity departures from geostrophic flow as measured from constant level balloon data. General Mills, Inc. Mechanical Div., Contract AF 19 (604)–1180, Scientific Report No. 1. (8.11–120.)

— — 1957: A study of wind velocities measured from constant-pressure balloons. JM 14 569–572.

GIRS, A. A., 1955: K voprosu ob izuchenii obshchei tsirkuliatsii atmosfery. (Investigation of the general circulation of the atmosphere.) ISG No. 4: 16–28. (7.10–149.)

GODSKE, C. L., *et al.*, 1957: Dynamic meteorology and weather forecasting. AMS Boston, Carnegie Inst., Wash. (8.7 5.)

GODSON, W. L., 1950*a*: The structure of North American weather systems. CP: 89–106.

— 1950*b*: Generalized criteria for dynamic instability. JM 7 (4): 268–278. (2.2–62.)

— 1950*c*: Synoptic significance of dynamic instability. JM 7 (5): 333–342. (2.3–35.)

— 1952: The relative accuracy of rawins and contour-measured winds. Canada, Met. Division, Circular 2076. (4 E–236.)

— 1955*a*: Arctic jet streams and high-level turbulence. In: RUSSEL, P., and M. B. BALLABON: Informal papers in Arctic Meteorology. McGill Univ., Arctic Met. Group, Contract AF 19 (604)–1141, Scientific Report No. 1. (8.4–179.)

— 1955*b*: The relative accuracy of rawins and contour-measured winds in relation to performance criteria. WMO No. 51. TP 20, TN No. 15.

— 1957: The arctic winter stratospheric jet stream (abstract). Polar Atmosph. Sympos. Pt. 1, London: Pergamon.

— 1960: Total ozone and the middle stratosphere over arctic and subarctic areas in winter and spring. QJRMS 86 (369): 301–317.

— and R. LEE, 1958: High level fields of wind and temperature over the Canadian Arctic. BPA 31 (1/2): 40–68.

GÖTZ, F. W. P., 1931: Das atmosphärische Ozon. In: Ergebnisse der kosmischen Physik, edited by V. CONRAD and L. WEICKMANN, p. 180–235. Leipzig.

— 1938: Die vertikale Verteilung des atmosphärischen Ozons. In: Physik der Atmosphäre. (Gerlands Beiträge zur Geophysik, 3. Supplementband.) Editor: V. CONRAD, p. 253–325. Leipzig.

— 1949: Der Stand des Ozonproblems. BDWUS No. 11: 7–13.

GOLD, E., 1953: The variation of wind near the tropopause. MML 82 (973): 194–198. (4.11–192.)

GOLDIE, A. H. R., 1937: Kinematic features of depressions. GM No. 72.

— 1939: Depressions as vortices. GM 79.

— 1947: The upper atmosphere. Estimated distribution of temperature, pressure and wind up to the 45 km level. MRP 360.

— 1950: The average planetary circulation in vertical meridian planes. CP 175–180. (4 F–58.)

— 1952: The global circulation of stratosphere air and the mechanism of change of tropopause level. MRP 734. (5 D–208.)

— 1953: Global circulation of air at high level and mechanism of change of tropopause level. MML 82 (973): 198–210. (5 D–225.)

— J. G. MOORE, and E. E. AUSTIN, 1958: Upper air temperatures over the world. GM 13, No. 101.

GOODY, R. M., 1954: The physics of the stratosphere. Cambridge: University Press. (5 D–231.)

GOULD, R. C., 1956: An investigation of rawinsonde data techniques for computing winds aloft. U.S. Naval Ordnance Test Station, China Lake, Calif., NAVORD Report, 5318. (9.1–122.)

GRAF. F., 1940: Untersuchungen über die Höhenwindverhältnisse benachbarter aerologischer Stationen. Univ. Berlin, Met. Inst., Veröffentlichungen, 3 (6): 1940. (7.3–90.)

GRAHAM, R. D., 1955: An empirical study of planetary waves by means of harmonic analysis. JM 12: 298–307.

GRANDOSO, H. H., and J. E. NÚÑEZ, 1955: Análisis de una situación de bloqueo en la parte austral de América del Sur. (Analysis of a blocking situation in the southern parts of South America.) Meteoros, Buenos Aires, 5 (1/2): 35–54. (7.10–151.)

GRANT, A., 1952: A re-examination of the zonal-wind profile under conditions of constant vorticity. JM 9 (6): 439–441. (4.7–73.)

GRAY, R., and N. CARRUTHERS, 1951: Upper air over the Falkland Islands. MML 80: 125–130. (2.11–181.)

GRAYSTONE, P., 1954: Estimation of mean winds and standard deviations at high levels. MML 83 (989): 325–329. (6.3–34.)

— 1956: Equivalent head-wind statistics for variable tracks. MRP 987. (8.1–120.)

Great Britain Meteorological Office, 1940: (a) Variations of wind with distance. (b) Variation of wind with time. Meteor. Office Monogr. 389, 8 pp.

— 1945: Meteorological Report on the Ryukyu Islands. Great Britain, Met. Office, Aviation, Met. Report No. 28. (4 E–136.)

— 1949: Theoretical aspects of pressure pattern flying. Compiled by J. S. SAWYER. London: H.M. Stationery Office. (1.3–82.)

— 1950: Equivalent head winds on some of the principal air routes of the world. Met. Reports No. 7. London: H.M. Stationery Office. (1.11–116.)

Great Britain, Patent Office, 1955: Improvements in or relating to a method of forming a load-carrying balloon and the resulting product. Patent Specification 735, 614. (7.11–118.)

GREENHOW, J. S., 1959: Radio meteoritic phenomena. BAMS 40 (12): 627.
— and E. L. NEUFELD, 1956: The height variation of upper atmospheric winds. Philosoph. Magazine, Ser. 8, 1 (12): 1157–1171. (8.4–245.)
GRIMMINGER, G., 1941: The intensity of lateral mixing in the atmosphere as determined from isentropic charts. BAMS 22: 227–228.
GRINGORTEN, I. I., 1955: Conditional minimum flight paths. N 4 (7): 274–278. (8.3–78.)
GROVES, G. V., 1956*a*: Effect of experimental errors on determinations of wind velocity, speed of sound and atmospheric pressure, in rocket-grenade experiments. JATP 9 (5/6): 237–261. (8.4–81.)
— 1956*b*: Introductory theory for upper atmosphere wind and sonic velocity determination by sound propagation. JATP 8 (1/2): 24–38. (7.8–280.)
— 1956*c*: Theory of the rocket-grenade method of determining upper atmospheric properties by sound propagation. JATP 8 (4/5): 189–203. (7.10–126.)
GRÜNEWALD, G., 1955: Allgemeine Betrachtungen über die mitteltroposphärische Zirkulation der Nordhemisphäre in Hinblick auf europäische Witterungsumstellungen. DDR Met. und Hydr. Dienst, Abhandlungen 4 (29). (8.9–173.)
GUSTAFSON, A. F., 1949: Final Report on the upper wind project. Dep. of Met., UCLA.
— 1954: The error in rawin computations due to neglecting the earth's curvature. BAMS 35 (7): 295–300. (6.6–57.)
GUTENBERG, B., 1932: Die Schallausbreitung in der Atmosphäre. In: B. GUTENBERG, Handbuch der Geophysik, p. 89–145. Berlin: Borntraeger.
— 1946: Physical properties of the atmosphere up to 100 km. JM 3 (2): 27–30. (4 F–31.)

HAARLÄNDER, H., 1957: Eine kinematische Methode zur Vorhersage wahrer Luftbahnen mit Beispielen, I. BDW No. 31. (9.1–151.)
— 1959: Zum Problem der Verfrachtung radioaktiver Spurenstoffe in der Atmosphäre. BDW No. 55.
HAGE, K. D., 1957: On summer cyclogenesis in western Canada associated with upper cold lows. U of C, Dep. of Met., Contr. AF 19 (604): 2179. Scientific Report No. 1. (9.3–9.)
HAIG, T. O., 1954: Plastic balloons for high altitude research. Journal of Aviation Medicine, St. Paul, Minn., 25 (4): 351–353. (6.7–125.)
HALDIMANN, F., and H.-J. TANCK, 1959: Meteorological route description Europe-Dakar-Rio de Janeiro-Buenos Aires-Santiago, Chile. TR, Swiss Air and Lufthansa, Flight Operations, Meteorology, Zürich, Hamburg, 26 pp.
HALTINER, G. J., and Y. P. HSIEH, 1951: Upper-level vortices and the turbulent transfer of momentum, JM 8 (3): 202–204. (3.7–96.)
— and F. L. MARTIN, 1957: Dynamical and physical meteorology. New York: McGraw-Hill.
HAMILTON, R. A., and J. W. ARCHBOLD, 1945: Meteorology of Nigeria and adjacent territory. QJRMS 71: 231–264.
HAMMOND, R., 1955: Rockets for atmospheric research. Instrument Practice 9 (5): 427–430. (6.11–119.)
HANN, J., and R. J. SÜRING, 1939: Lehrbuch der Meteorologie, 5. Aufl. Leipzig: Keller. 1943. (4 F–26.)
HANSON, K. J., 1960: A case study of the explosive stratospheric warming over the Antarctic, October 1958. AMO: 128–137.
HARDING, J., 1955: The profile of jet streams in the Middle East. MRP 932. (7.5–121.)
HARE, F. K., 1960*a*: The disturbed circulation of the arctic stratosphere. JM 17: 36–51.
— 1960*b*: The summer circulation of the arctic stratosphere below 30 km. QJRMS 86 (368): 127–143. 86 (370): 576–578.

HARLEY, D. G., 1952: Equivalent tail winds on the Shannon to Gander route. JINL and MRP 749.

HARMANTAS, L., and S. G. SIMPLICIO, 1958: A suggested approach to the problem of providing high-altitude wind forecasts for jet transport operations. BAMS 39 (5): 248–252. (11.3–90.)

HARRISON, D. N., 1955: Radar wind comparisons on the Ocean Weather Ships (second series). MRP 928. (7.5–66.)

HARRISON, H. T., 1956: Synoptic features of the mountain wave at Denver, Colorado. UAL Meteorology Circular No. 41.

— 1957*a*: Forecasting the mountain wave at Denver, Colorado. UAL Meteorology Circular No. 42. (11.3–22.)

— 1957*b*: Mountain wave zones in the United States. UAL Meteorology Circular No. 43.

— 1959: The use of horizontal wind shear in forecasting high level clear air turbulence. UAL Meteorology Circular No. 49. (10.11–72.)

HARSÁNYI, E., 1960: Nullschicht und Drucktemperaturkurven. MR 13 (3): 85–86.

HARTMANN, W., 1950: Die Genauigkeit der Ermittlung des Höhenwindes aus den Karten der absoluten Topographie. AM 3 (1–2): 27–34. (1.7–12.)

HAURWITZ, B., 1941: Dynamic Meteorology. New York: McGraw-Hill.

— 1949: Report on studies of atmospheric energy. NYU, Dep. of Met. (3.2–73.)

— 1950: Atmospheric oscillation. NYU, Contract AF 19 (122)–49, Progress Reports, Nos. 122-04 to 122-08. (4 F–74.)

— 1954: Zonal wind field in the upper atmosphere. NYU, Contract AF 19 (122)–49, Scientific Report No. 7. (6.9–223.)

— and H. A. PANOFSKY, 1950: Stability and meandering of the Gulf Stream. TAGU 31 (5), Pt. 1: 723–731. (2.8–189.)

HAVENS, J. M., and W. A. BAUM, 1956: Frequency distributions of predominant tropopause heights along 80° W in summer. BAMS 37 (3): 87–93. (7.11–156.)

HAWKINS, H. F., 1955: The weather and circulation of June 1955, illustrating a circumpolar wave. MWR 83 (6): 125–131. (8.1–194.)

HAY, R. F. M., 1952*a*: Wind at high levels over Hong Kong. MRP 778. (4 E–239.)

— 1952*b*: Wind at high levels over Singapore (1950–52). MRP 770. (4 F–101.)

— 1953: High-level strong easterlies over Singapore and Hong Kong, W 8 (7): 206–208. (4.11–194.)

HEATH-SMITH, J. R., 1955: Turbulence encountered by Comet 1 aircraft. Farnborough, England. Royal Aircraft Establishment, Report Structures 179. (7.11–70.)

HELLIWELL, R. A., 1958: Whistlers and very low frequency emissions. "Geophysics and the IGY," Am. Geoph. Union, Publ. No. 590. p. 35–44.

HELMHOLTZ, H. VON, 1873: Über ein Theorem, geometrisch ähnliche Bewegungen flüssiger Körper betreffend, nebst Anwendung auf das Problem, Luftballons zu lenken. Monatsber. K. Akad. Wiss., Berlin, 501–504.

HENDL, M., 1960: Entwurf einer genetischen Klimaklassifikation auf Zirkulationsbasis. ZM 14 (2): 46–50.

HENRY, R. M., and S. L. HESS, 1957: A study of large-scale spectra of atmospheric kinetic energy, wave speed, momentum flux, and heat flux. Florida State Univ., Dep. of Met., Contr. Nonr-1600 (00). Project NR-082-071, Techn. Report No. 9. (9.5–145.)

— — 1958: Study of large-scale spectra of some meteorological parameters. JM 15 (4): 397–403. (10.6–186.)

HENRY, T. J. G., 1957: Maps of upper winds over Canada. Toronto, Meteorol. Branch, Dept. of Transport. (10.11–204.)

HENRY, T. J. G., and G. R. ARMSTRONG, 1949: Aerological data for northern Canada. Toronto, Met. Division. (4 E–172.)

HERBST, W., and K. PHILIPP, 1953: Wanderweg eines atomtechnischen Aerosols. Naturwissenschaften 40 (2): 54. (7 E–69.)

— R. NEUWIRTH, and K. PHILIPP, 1954: Betrachtungen über die Eignung radioaktiver atomtechnischer Aerosole als Markierungsmittel bei Arbeiten auf dem Gebiet der meteorologischen Strömungsforschung. Naturwissenschaften 41: 156–160. (5.8–276, 7 E–68.)

HERING, W., 1955: Verfahren zur Bestimmung der Aufstiegsgeschwindigkeit der Radiosonde, Modell Lang. ZM 9 (5): 153–155. (6.10–76.)

— 1956: Betrachtungen über die Veränderlichkeit der Aufstiegsgeschwindigkeit der Radiosondenballone. ZM 10 (2): 57–62. (7.11–119.)

HESS, P., and H. BREZOWSKY, 1952: Katalog der Großwetterlagen Europas. BDWUS No. 33, 39 pp.

HESS, S. L., 1948: Some new mean meridional cross-sections through the atmosphere. JM 5 (6): 293–300. (4 G–10.)

— 1953: Variable vorticity trajectories. Florida State Univ., Dep. of Met., Contr. Nonr-988 (01), Project NR 082-071. TR. (6.1–224.)

HESSELBERG, TH., 1913: Die Luftbewegung im Cirrusniveau. Veröffentl. Geophys. Inst. Univ. Leipzig, Ser. 2, Bd. 1, 17–73.

HEYWOOD, G. S. P., 1933: The upper winds of Hong Kong from observations made with pilot balloons 1921–1932. Hong Kong, Royal Observ. (4 F–9.)

HIDE, R., 1953: Some experiments on thermal convection in a rotating liquid. QJRMS 79: 161.

— 1956: Geomagnetism: fluid motion in the earth's core and some experiments of thermal convection in a rotating liquid. Proceed. First Sympos. Geophys. Models, Baltimore, 1953, pp. 101–116. Washington: U.S. Government Printing Office.

HILDEBRANDSSON, H. H., 1898: Études internationales des nuages 1896–1897. Observations et mesures de la Suède. Uppsala. (4 E–251.)

HINKELMANN, K., 1956: Ein Beitrag zur Theorie der Zyklonenentwicklung. BDW No. 22: 92–107.

HISLOP, G. S., 1951: Clear-air turbulence over Europe. Royal Aeronaut. Society, Journal 55 (484): 185–225. (5 D–188.)

HÖILAND, E., and K. PEDERSEN, 1954: Some computations of changes of kinetic energy and of momentum during a cyclone development. Norske Videnskaps-Akademi i Oslo. Institutt for Vaer- og Klimaforskning, Report No. 4. (7.6–121.)

HOFMEYR, W. L., 1950: Remarks on the theory of the jet stream. JM 7 (3): 245. (4 G–41.)

— 1952: A statistical analysis of radar winds over Pretoria in winter. Notos (South Africa, Weather Bureau). 1 (4): 186–192. (4 F–124.)

— 1953: A statistical analysis of Radar winds over Pretoria in summer. Notos 2 (3): 144–148. (5.8–181.)

— 1954: A statistical analysis of radar winds over Maun in summer. Notos 3 (3): 192–195. (7.8–183.)

— 1957: Upper air over the Antarctic. In: VAN ROOY, Meteorology of the Antarctic, Pretoria, pp. 183–184.

HOINKES, H., 1940: Regeneration und Teilung langlebiger Drucksteiggebiete. Sitzungsbericht der Akad. d. Wiss., Wien. Math. nat. wiss. Klasse, Abteilung IIa. Bd. 149 (H. 7 und 8), 367–391.

— 1951: Frontenanalyse mit Hilfe von Bergbeobachtungen. Ein Beitag zur Frage des Voreilens der Kaltluft in der Höhe. AMGBA 4: 238–262.

HOLLMANN, G., 1953: Beitrag zur Zyklonentheorie. MR 6 (3/4): 41–45. (4.10–113.)
— 1954: Zur Frage des Nullschichteffekts und der Strahlströme. MR 7 (9/10): 166–170. (6.2–133.)
— 1955*a*: Über die Beziehung zwischen Wind- und Druckfeld in Abhängigkeit von der geographischen Briete. MR 8: 79–82.
— 1955*b*: Über- und untergradientische barokline Zonalströmung als Lösung der hydrodynamischen Gleichungen. MR 8 (7/8): 105–107. (7.3–152.)
— 1958: Transformation der Grundgleichungen der dynamischen Meteorologie in Koordinaten der stereographischen Projektion zum Zwecke der numerischen Vorhersage. BPA 31 (3/4): 162–176.
— 1959*a*: Über die Nullschichteigenschaft von Flächen extremer Windstärke. MR 12 (6): 170–173.
— 1959*b*: Zur Frage des Vorzeichenwechsels der Vertikalbewegung beiderseits isobarer Flächen extremer Windgeschwindigkeit. MR 12 (5): 137–138.
— and K. O. WEGNER, 1958: Approximative Berechnung der Vertikalbewegung ausgewählter Wetterlagen. BPA 31 (3/4): 200–216.
HOLMBOE, J., 1959: On the behavior of baroclinic waves. RMV: 333–349.
HOLZAPFEL, R., 1954: Zur Einflußhöhe der Alpen auf die allgemeine Strömung. MR 7 (5/6): 92–95. (6.1–325.)
— 1956*a*: Ergebnisse aerologischer Beobachtungen in Deutschland. BDW No. 27. (8.5–21.)
— 1956*b*: Zum Einfluß von Gebirgen auf die allgemeine Zirkulation. BDW No. 22: 140–142.
— 1958: Über die Luftbewegung bis 30 km Höhe über Berlin. MR 11 (1): 34–36.
HOOPER, A. H., 1957: Radiosonde Trials at Payerne, 1956. MML 86 (1016): 33–36. (8.7–111.)
HOPPER, V. D., and J. E. LABY, 1960*a*: High altitude studies with meteorological balloons. BPA 32 (3/4): 237–248.
— — 1960*b*: Importance of global wind study in the 30 km region. AMO 466–480.
HORROCKS, H., 1942: Winds at high levels relative to the fronts and occlusions of typical depressions. London, Met. Office. M. O. M. 431. (4 F–23.)
HOUSE, D. C., 1959: The mechanism of instability-line formation. JM 16 (2): 108–120.
HOVMÖLLER, E., 1948: North-south cross section showing distribution of temperature, relative humidity and wind in a well-marked zonal current over Western Europe. JM 5 (2): 67–69. (4 G–11.)
— 1949: The trough-and-ridge diagram. T 1 (2): 62–66. (1.2–49.)
— 1950: Zonal and meridional air currents in the stratosphere over Europe. GPA 17 (3/4): 112–120. (4 E–194.)
HOYLE, H. D., 1955*a*: The sub-tropical jet stream of the eastern North Pacific in January and April 1952. MRP 924. (7.5–122, 9.1–183.)
— 1955*b*: Unusual behaviour of a depression, April 17–23, 1954. MML 84 (1000): 307–313. (7.3–161.)
HSIEH, Y.-P., 1949: An investigation of a selected cold vortex over North America. JM 6 (6): 401–410. (3–46.)
— 1950*a*: On the formation of shear lines in the upper atmosphere. JM 7 (6): 382–387. (2.4–74.)
— 1950*b*: The mean wind and temperature distribution through a flat upper ridge in winter. T 2 (2): 130–133. (4 G–42.)
HUBERT, L. F., 1949: High tropospheric westerlies of the equatorial West Pacific Ocean. JM 6 (3): 216–224. (4 F–41.)
— S. FRITZ, and H. WEXLER, 1960: Pictures of the earth from high altitudes and their meteorological significance. Proceedings COSPAR Space Symposium, January 1960.

Hubert, W. E., 1953: A case study of variations in structure and circulation about westerly jet streams over Europe. T 5 (3): 359–372. (5.7–86.)

— and Y. Dagel, 1955: Upper mean flow over tho North Atlantic during January 1952. T 7 (1): 111–117. (6.10–193.)

Hughes, G. D., and R. Foster, 1954: The tropopause during a major change in circulation over the Western United States, Nov. 25 to 28, 1954. MWR 82 (11): 343–354. (6.11–172.)

Hughes, L. A., E. S. Jordan, and R. J. Renard, 1952: On the computation of upper-level winds from constant pressure charts. U of C, Report to Office of Naval Research (unpublished).

Hughes, R. F., 1959: Meteor trains. Smithsonian Contributions to Astrophysics 3 (8): 79–94.

Hulburt, E. O., 1952: Physical characteristics of the upper atmosphere of the earth. U.S. School of Aviation Medicine, Randolph Field, Texas: Physics and Medicine of the Upper Atmosphere, Albuquerque. (5.1–114.)

Hurst, G. W., 1952: The profile of a jet stream observed 18th January 1952. MRP 722. (4 G–98.)

— 1953: The profile of a jet stream observed 1st September, 1952. MRP 772. (4 G–97.)

— 1955: Wind derivations from vertical photographs. JINL 8 (3): 250–255. (6.11–97.)

Hutchings, J. W., 1950: A meridional atmospheric cross-section for an oceanic region. JM 7 (2): 94–100. (4 G–43.)

— 1952: The winter jet stream in the Southern Hemisphere. W 7 (3): 73–77. (4 G–99.)

Hwang, S. S., 1955: Basic factors determining the main features of the general circulation of the atmosphere. AMSP 26 (1/2): 35–64. (8.9–168.)

Hyde, E. A., 1954*a*: High altitudo air turbulence. Flight 65 (2360): 492–493.

— 1954*b*: Clear-air turbulence and its allied phenomena. Shell Aviation News, No. 192: 14–15. (6.7–222.)

Iakobi, N. O., 1929: Svecha krasnogo ognia dlia nochnykh sharopilotnykh nabliudenii v poliarnykh oblastiakh. (Use of a red light for observations of pilot balloons at night in Polar Regions.) Meteorologicheskii Vestnik, Leningrad, 39 (9/12): 268–271. (7.1–28.)

Ichiye, T., 1960: On critical regimes and horizontal concentration of momentum in ocean currents with two-layered system. T 12 (2): 149–158.

Imai, I., 1954: On the ascensional rate of a balloon. JMSJ Ser. 2, 32 (7/8): 183–191. (7.6–70.)

India, Met. Department 1942: Normals of upper air data. India, Met. Department, Upper air data 12, Pt. B. (4 F–24.)

International Air Transport Association (IATA), 1955: Long distance flights: a condensed record of discussions of operational problems of long distance flights (held during the 8th Annual Technical Conference of IATA, Puerto Rico, Apr.–May 1955). IATA Document Général 1537, Montreal. (9.6–73.)

International Civil Aviation Organization, 1956: Aeronautical Telecommunications. ICAO 1956, Annex 10.

International Meteorological Organization, 1950, 1951: État d'advancement du dépouillement des expériences pour la comparaison mondiale des radiosondes à Payerne, 1950, par la Délégation Suisse. Zurich Nov. 6, 1950. (3.10–62.) Comparaison mondiale des radiosondes: acte final de la première expérience à la Station Aérologique de Payerne, Suisse, 8 au 30 mai, 1950. v. 1 et 2, Feb. 1951. (3.10–63.)

Iselin, C. O'D., 1936: A study of the circulation of the western North Atlantic. Pap. Phys. Ocean. and Met. 4 (4), 101 pp.

ISELIN, C. O'D., 1950: Some common characteristics of the Gulf Stream and the atmospheric jet stream New York Acad. of Science, Transactions, 2nd Ser., 13 (2): 84–86. (4 G–44.)

ISHIMARU, Y., 1954: On the zonal circulation and its perturbation. (Mechanism of the earth's atmosphere, 5th communication.) GMT 25 (1/2): 123–149. (5.9–127.)

ISRAËL, H., 1957: Atmosphärische Elektrizität. Leipzig.

— 1959: Luftelektrische Wirkungen des jet stream ACSI, p. 23–24.

IZAWA, T., 1950: On the upper disturbances in the westerlies whose mean circulation have longitudinal wind gradient. JMSJ 2nd ser., 28 (7): 224–232. (2.7–80.)

JACOBS, L. E., 1955: Navigational aspects of the jet stream. N 4 (7): 242–249. (7.4–145.)

JAMES, D. G., 1955: Investigations relating to cirrus clouds. MRP 933. (7.5–100.)

JAMES, R. P., and G. C. HOLZWORTH, 1954: Some fluctuations in the jet stream and tropopause associated with cyclonic development and movement, Febr. 18–21, 1954. MWR 82 (2): 64–72. (6.6–173.)

JAMES, R. W., 1951*a*: A February cross-section along the Greenwich meridian. MML 80 (954): 341–346. (4 G–68.)

— 1951*b*: The structure of mean circulation. T 3 (4): 258–267. (4.1–98.)

— 1952: On the vertical structure of pressure and wind fields. AMGBA 5 (1): 17–35. (3.10–112.)

JANSÁ, G., and M. JOSÉ, 1956: La ecuación del viento térmico y la corriente a chorro. (The thermal wind equation and the jet stream.) Revista de Geofisica, Madrid 15 (59): 323–344. (9.5–152.)

JANZ, B., 1954: Tropopause analysis. Canada, Met. Division, Cir.-2496 TEC-188. (6.10–65.)

JARDETZKY, W., 1948: Bewegungsmechanismus der Erdkruste. Österr. Akad. d. Wiss., Math. naturwiss. Klasse, Denkschriften 108 (3).

JENISTA, C. O., 1953: A statistical study of precipitation distribution as related to various types of mean zonal motion. BAMS 34: 10–13. (4.11–220.)

JENKINS, C. F., 1952*a*: A survey of available information on winds above 30,000 ft. AFS No. 24, 35 pp. (4 F–103.)

— 1952*b*: Forecasting the mountain wave. AFS No. 15. (5.1–211.)

— and J. KUETTNER, 1953: Flight aspects of the mountain wave. AFS No. 35.

JENKINS, K. R., and W. L. WEBB, 1959: High-altitude wind measurement. JM 16 (5): 511–515.

JENKINSON, A. F., 1954: Upper winds from nephoscope observations. MML 83: 174–175. (5.9–207.)

— 1955: Average vector wind distribution of the upper air in temperate and tropical latitudes. MML 84 (995): 140–147. (6.10–197.)

JENRETTE, J. P., 1960: An objective application of vorticity principles to precipitation forecasting. BAMS 41 (6): 317–323.

JOHANNESSEN, K. R., 1956*a*: Some theoretical aspects of constant pressure trajectories. AWS, Manual 105–47, Washington Hq. AWS (86 pp.).

— 1956*b*: Three-dimensional analysis of the jet stream through shear charts. Proceedings of the Workshop on Stratospheric Analysis and Forecasting, Feb. 1–3, 1956. (11.2–186.)

— and G. P. CRESSMAN, 1952: Verification of an equation for trough and ridge movement. BAMS 33 (7): 267–270. (4.11–79.)

JOHNSON, D. H., 1952: Further notes on the wind field of middle latitudes. MRP 761. (4 G–102.)

— 1953*a*: A further study on the upper westerlies; the structure of the wind field in the eastern North Atlantic and Western Europe in January 1950. QJRMS 79 (341): 402–407. (4.11–193.)

JOHNSON, D. H., 1953b: Jet stream of October 28, 1952. MML 82 (972): 178–182. (4 G–133.)
— 1953c: The jet stream. Part I and II. W 8 (9, 11): 270–274, 325–329. (5.4–163.)
— 1955: The success achieved in forecasting upper winds by orthodox and statistical techniques. MRP 953. (7.10–109.)
— and S. M. DANIELS, 1953: Rainfall in relation to the jet stream. MRP No. 803. (5 H–96. QJRMS 80: 212–217 (1954).
JOHNSON, N. K., 1946: Wind measurements at 30 km. Nature, London, 157: 24. (4 F–33.)
JONES, E. E., 1949: Radar as an aid to the study of the atmosphere. Journal of the Royal Astronautical Society, 53: 437–448.
— J. E. N. HOOPER, and N. L. ADLER, 1951: The radar-sonde system for the measurement of upper wind and air data. Institution of Electrical Engineers, London, Proceedings 98, Pt. II (64): 461–469. (3.10–64.)
JONES, F. E., and H. S. W. MASSEY, 1956: Rocket exploration of the upper atmosphere. Nature, London, 177 (4510): 643–645. (7.9–89.)
JULIAN, P. R., L. KRAWITZ, and H. A. PANOFSKY, 1959: The relation between height patterns at 500 mb and 100 mb. MWR 87 (7): 251–260. (11.6–315.)
JUNGE, CH., 1938; Turbulenzmessungen in den höheren Atmosphärenschichten. Annalen der Hydrogr. und maritimen Meteorol. 66: 104–109. (3K–48.)

KAISER, T. R., 1954: A new technique in upper atmosphere research. In: BOYD, R. L. F. u. a.: Rocket exploration of the upper atmosphere, pp. 108–111. London: Pergamon. (8 H–104.)
KAMATA, T., and G. HORIUCHI, 1955: Stratospheric easterlies over Tateno. JMRT 7 (1): 34–39. (7.7–142.)
KAMIKO, T., 1956: Seasonal changes of long waves and belts of maximum westerlies in the Far East. JMRT 8 (2): 69–76. (8.5–197.)
KANITSCHEIDER, R., 1932–39: Beiträge zur Mechanik des Föhns. I. BPA 18: 27–49 (1932); II. BPA 24: 26–44 (1938); III. BPA 25: 49–58 (1939).
KAO, S. K., 1954: The meridional transport of kinetic energy in the atmosphere. JM 11 (5): 352–361. (6.4–8.)
— 1958: Planetary waves and jet streams in the atmosphere. TAGU 39 (4): 620–623.
— 1960: Transfer of momentum vorticity and the maintenance of zonal circulation in the atmosphere. JM 17 (2): 122–129.
— and M. NEIBURGER, 1959: Oscillations and trajectories of air particles in some pressure systems. JGR 64 (9): 1283–1291.
KAO, Y.-H., 1958: On the high autumn clear weather in China. AMSP 29 (2): 83–92. (10.6–269.)
KASAHARA, A., 1950: On the dynamical mechanism of the high tropospheric jet stream. Tokyo Univ., Geophys. Inst., Geophysical Notes 3 (31). (4 G–45.)
— 1956: Three-dimensional structure of small-scale atmospheric perturbations aloft. A & M Contract AF 19 (604)–559, Scientific Report No. 7. (8.6–201.)
KATS, A. L., 1955: Kolichestvennaia kharakteristika gorizontal'nykh sostavliaiushchikh obshchei tsirkuliatsii atmosfery v severnom polusharii. (Quantitative evaluation of the horizontal characteristics of the general circulation of the atmosphere in the Northern Hemisphere.) MG No. 2: 7–12. (7.3–154.)
KAUFMANN, P., 1958: Atmosphärische Strömungsquerschnitte. GPA 40: 187–199.
KAWAMURA, A., 1956: Monthly mean winds aloft over Tateno in 1950 through 1953. JMRT 8 (1): 8–19. (8.6–267.)
KAWATA, Y., 1958: The influence of the Rocky Mountains on non-steady isobaric height patterns. In: Vortex. Collected Papers of Numerical Weather Prediction Group in Tokyo.

Kazès, I., and J. L. Steinberg, 1957: Etude de la scintillation du soleil observée avec plusieurs antennes sur la longeur d'onde de 3.2 cm. Académie des Sciences, Paris, Comptes Rendus, 245 (7): 782–785. (10.1–344.)

Kaznacheeva, V. D., 1958: K voprosu dinamiki frontogeneza. (Problem of frontogenesis dynamics.) Akademiia Nauk Uzbekskoi SSR, Tashkent, Izvestiia, Ser. Fiziko-Matematicheskikh Nauk, No. 1: 47–64. (10.10–244.)

Keller, G., 1952: Astronomical "seeing" and its relation to atmospheric turbulence. Ohio State Univ., Research Foundation, Contract AF 19 (604)–41, TR No. 1. (8.1–243.)

Kellogg, W. W., 1952: Diffusion of smoke in the stratosphere. Calif. UCLA, Institute of Geophysics, Contract AF 19 (122) 246, Air Transport Project, Final Report. (3 K–196.)

— 1956: Very high level observations. Proceedings of the Workshop on Stratospheric Analysis and Forecasting. USWB, Washington, D.C., 84–97.

— and G. F. Schilling, 1951: A proposed model of the circulation in the upper stratosphere. JM 8 (4): 222–230. (4 F–76.)

Kelly, R. D., and H. B. Kaster, 1954: Simulated jet transport operation. Society of Automotive Engineers, N.Y., SAE Preprint No. 298. (6.7–92.)

Kennedy, W. B., L. Brogan, N. J. Sible, *et al.*, 1954: Diurnal variations of atmospheric winds and temperatures in the 30- to 50-km region over southwestern New Mexico by acoustical propagation studies, Oct. 20–24, 1952. Denver Univ., Denver Research Inst. Contract AF 19 (122)–252, Scientific Report No. 4. (6.3–187.)

— — — 1955: Further acoustical studies of atmospheric winds and temperatures at elevations of 30 to 60 kilometers. JM 12 (6): 519–532. (7.5–261.)

— — — and A. C. Auten, 1954: Atmospheric winds and temperatures in the 30- to 60-km region over Eastern Colorado as determined by acoustical propagation studies 31 Oct. 1951 to 28 Aug. 1952. Denver Univ., Denver Research Inst., Contract AF 19 (122)–252, Scientific Report No. 3. . . . studies Oct. 20–24, 1952. Scientific Report No. 4 (6.3–186, 187.)

— — — and R. A. Brown, 1953: Atmospheric winds and temperatures to 55 km altitude over southwestern New Mexico as determined by acoustical propagation studies 0600–1020 MST 22 October 1952. Denver Univ., Denver Research Inst., Contract AF 19 (122)–252, Scientific Report No. 2. (6.4–216.)

Kessler, E., 1954: Curvature corrections for radiowind reports. BAMS 35 (7): 328–330. (6.11–102.)

Kikuchi, T., 1957: The advection of jet stream core and the heavy rainfall. JMRT 9 (8): 560–565. (9.5–122.)

Kimpara, A., 1953: Atmospherics due to fronts in the upper atmosphere. Nagoya Univ., Research Inst. of Atmospherics, Proc. 1, 45–49. (4 K–263.)

Kirkman, R. A., and J. M. LeBedda, 1948: Meteorological radio direction finding for measurement of upper winds. JM 5 (1): 28–37. (1.5–14.)

Klebelsberg, R. v., 1949: Handbuch der Gletscherkunde und Glazialgeologie. 2. Band. Wien: Springer.

Klein, W. H., 1951: A hemispheric study of daily pressure variability at sea level and aloft. JM 8: 332–346.

— 1956: Principal tracks and mean frequencies of cyclones and anticyclones in the Northern Hemisphere. USWB. (8.9–29.)

— 1958: The frequency of cyclones and anticyclones in relation to the mean circulation. JM 15 (1): 98–102.

Kleinschmidt, E., 1935: Handbuch der meteorologischen Instrumente. Berlin: Springer.

KLEINSCHMIDT, E., JR., 1941*a*: Stabilitätstheorie des geostrophischen Windfeldes. Ann. Hydrogr., Berlin, 69: 305–325.

— 1941*b*: Zur Theorie der labilen Anordnung. MZ 58: 157–163.

— 1950: Über Aufbau und Entstehung von Zyklonen. MR 3 (1–2): 1–6. MR 3 (3–4): 54–61. (1.11–70.)

— 1951: Über Aufbau und Entstehung von Zyklonen. MR 4 (5–6): 89–96. (3.1–93.)

— 1955: Die Entstehung einer Höhenzykone über Nordamerika. T 7 (1): 95–110. (7.11–178.)

— 1959: Nicht-adiabatische Abkühlungen im Bereich des Jetstream. BPA 32 (1/2): 94–108. (11.4–225.)

— 1960: Antwort auf vorstehende Bemerkungen. BPA 32 (3/4): 274–276.

KLUG, W., 1956: Der Mechanismus der Steuerung von hochreichenden Zyklonen. MAB 3 (2), 42 pp.

KNEPPLE, R., 1960: Die Breitenabhängigkeit der Maximalwindhöhe. MR 13 (5): 156–158.

KNIGHTING, E., 1954: Upper winds over the world. QJRMS 80 (344): 239–240. (6.9–81.)

KOBAYASHI, S., 1956: On the asymmetry of circumpolar currents. JMRT 8 (8): 503–507. (9.7–162.)

KOBAYASHI, Y., 1950: On the zonal component of upper wind at Tateno. TAT 5 (1): 37–41. (4 F–77.)

KOCHANSKI, A., 1954: Thermal structure and vertical motion in the lower stratosphere. AWS, TR 105–129, Washington, D.C.

— 1955: Cross section of the mean zonal flow and temperature along 80° W. JM 12 (2): 95–106. (6.8–202.)

— 1956: Horizontal temperature gradient at 200 mb and adjacent levels. BAMS 37(2): 47–54. (8.3–190.)

— 1957: Some objective methods for forecasting 300-mb und 200-mb winds: a preliminary report. US AWS TR 105–136. (11.3–91.)

— 1958: Ageostrophic deviations and wind prognosis. JM 15 (1): 84–90.

— 1959: Temperatures and winds at 25–30 km over Russia in July 1957. US AWS, Climatic Center, Technical Memorandum to the Director, CLIM CEN TM-59-1. (11.5–296.)

— and P. E. WASKO, 1956*a*: Daily wind flow at the 50- and 25-mb levels. BAMS 37 (1): 8–13. (9.3–206.)

— — 1956*b*: Mean wind flow at the 50- and 25-mb levels. BAMS 37 (2): 61–69. (8.9–234.)

KOENIGSFELD, L., 1955: Study of the variation of potential gradient with altitude and correlated meteorological conditions. GRP No. 42: 21–26.

KOEPPE, C. E., and G. C. DE LONG, 1958: Weather and Climate. New York: McGraw-Hill.

KÖPPEN, W., 1931: Grundriß der Klimakunde, 2. Aufl. Berlin: de Gruyter.

— and R. GEIGER, 1953: Klima der Erde. Wandkarte. Neu bearbeitet von R. GEIGER und W. POHL. Darmstadt.

KOLMOGOROV, A. N., *et al.*, 1958: Sammelband zur statistischen Theorie der Turbulenz. Herausgeber: H. GOERING. 228 pp. Berlin: Akademie-Verlag.

KOMABAYASI, M., *et al.*, 1955: The quantitative forecast of precipitation with the numerical prediction method. JMSJ Ser. 2, 33 (5): 205–216. (9.5–123.)

KOO, CH.-CH., 1955: A Tibeti-fennsik dinamikus hatása a keletázsiai légkörzésre. (Der dynamische Einfluß des Hochlandes von Tibet auf die ostasiatische Zirkulation.) IB 59 (4): 204–211. (8.3–160.)

KOPCEWICZ, T., 1954: Cirkulációs indexek, ciklonkeletkezés és ciklonpályák Európában. (Indices of circulation, cyclogenesis and cyclone tracks in Europe.) IB 58 (6): 397–406. (7.7–138.)

KORSHOVER, J., 1954*a*: Mean winds over the Marshall Islands, April 1951. UCLA, Inst. of Geophysics, Oahu Research Center, Contract AF 19 (604): 546, Scientific Report No. 8. (7.6–168.)

— 1954*b*: Mean winds over the Marshall Islands, March 1951. UCLA, Inst. of Geophysics. Oahu Research Center. Contract AF 19 (604)–546, Scientific Reports No. 1, 4 and 6. (6.2–41.)

KOSCHMIEDER, H., 1951: Dynamische Meteorologie, 3. Aufl. Leipzig: Akademische Verlagsgesellschaft.

KOSIBA, A., 1949: Niektore zagadnienia ogolnej cyrculacji atmosferycznej. (Some problems of atmospheric circulation.) Czasopismo Geograficzne, Lodz, Polen. 20 (1–4): 59–80. (2.3–60.)

KOSLOWSKI, G., 1958: Überlegungen zu einem Geschwindigkeitsdiagramm in der Atmosphäre. MAB 4 (2).

KOTESWARAM, P., 1951: Physical properties of the upper atmosphere over India. IJMG 2 (2): 101–112. (4 F–78.)

— 1953: An analysis of the high tropospheric wind circulation over India in winter. IJMG 4 (1): 13–21. (4 G–125.)

— 1956: Easterly jet stream in the tropics. U of C, Dep. of Met., Contract N6ori-02036, Project NR 082–120, Report. (8.6–202.)

— 1957: Mean zonal wind circulation over India. IJMG 8 (3): 346–347. (9.9–161.)

— 1958: The easterly jet stream in the tropics. T 10 (1): 43–57.

— and C. A. GEORGE, 1958: On the formation of monsoon depressions in the Bay of Bengal. IJMG 9 (1): 9–22. (9.10–180.)

— and S. PARTHASARATHY, 1954: The mean jet stream over India in the pre-monsoon and post-monsoon seasons and vertical motions associated with sub-tropical jet streams. IJMG 5: No. 2.

— C. R. V. RAMAN, and S. PARTHASARATHY, 1953: The mean jet stream over India and Burma in winter. IJMG 4 (2): 111–122. (4 G–134.)

— and V. SRINIVASAN, 1958: Thunderstorms over Gangetic West Bengal in the pre-monsoon season and the synoptic factors favorable for their formation. IJMG 9 (4):301–312.

Krakatoa Committee of the Royal Society of London, 1888: The eruption of Krakatoa. G. J. SYMONS, Ed. London: Trübner. (1 F–35.)

KRAUS, E. B., 1960*a*: Synoptic and dynamic aspects of climatic change. QJRMS 86 (367): 1–15, 86 (370): 569–575.

— 1960*b*: Problems of long term interaction between the Antarctic and temperate latitudes. AMO 145–152.

KRISHNAMURTI, T. N., 1959*a*: The subtropical jet stream of winter. Res. Report, Contract No. N6ori–02036, NR 082–120, U of C.

— 1959*b*: Vertical cross section through the "polar-night" jet stream. JGR 64 (11): 1835–1844. (11.6–269.)

KRISHNA RAO, R. P., 1952: Probable regions of jet streams in the upper air over India. Current Science, Bangalore, 21 (3): 63–64. (4 G–104.)

KRUHL, H., 1952: Über Warmfrontwellen und zur Dynamik warmer Hochdruckgebiete. AM 5 (1–2): 15–29.

KUBOTA, S., and M. IIDA, 1954: Statistical characteristics of the atmospheric disturbances. PMGT 5 (1): 22–34. (8.4–188.)

KÜHN, U., 1956: Die kalten Höhenzyklonen der Nordhalbkugel. GBG 65 (3): 246–262. (8.2–133.)

— 1957: Ein Beitrag zum Verhalten kalter Höhentiefs über Nordamerika. GBG Bd. 66: 330–348.

KUEI, P.-L., and Z.-SH. WANG, 1959: An analysis of the mechanism of development of a cyclone in northeastern China. AMSP 30 (2): 150–164. (11.6–274.)

KUETTNER, J., 1952*a*: Note on high level turbulence encountered by a glider. AFS No. 29. (6.2–204.)

— 1952*b*: On the possibility of soaring on travelling waves in the jet stream. Soaring, Memphis, Tenn., 16 (3): 9–14. (4 G–105.)

— 1955: The exploration of the jet stream by sailplanes. Soaring, Dallas, 19 (3): 11–13, 16–17. (7.7–143.)

— 1959*a*: The rotor flow in the lee of mountains. USAF, Cambridge Research Center GRD, Research Notes No. 6. Also: SAR 1958 (4) and OSTIV Publication No. IV. (9.11–86), (11.1–230.)

— 1959*b*: The band structure of the atmosphere. T 11 (3): 267–294.

— and G. MCLEAN, 1958: Vertical motions in the jet stream. In: OSTIV Publication V. and SAR 1960/4.

KUHLBRODT, E., 1952*a*: Hochtropospharische Winde über dem tropischen Atlantik. AM 5 (7–12): 274–280.

— 1952*b*: Höhenwinde auf dem Seeweg Kapverdenregion—La Plata. GPA 21: 19–31. (3.11–164.)

KUKHTO, A. P., 1956: K voprosu ob otklonenii fakticheskogo vetra ot geostroficheskogo. (Problem of the deviation of the actual wind from the geostrophic.) MG No. 2: 19–21. (8.9–235.)

KUO, H.-L., 1949: Note on the inertial stability of geostrophic zonal flow. JM 6 (5): 356–358. (1.2–76.)

— 1950: The motion of atmospheric vortices and the general circulation. JM 7 (4): 247–258. (2.2–66.)

— 1951*a*: Dynamical aspects of the general circulation and the stability of zonal flow. T 3 (4): 268–284. (4.10–115.)

— 1951*b*: Vorticity transfer as related to the development of the general circulation. JM 8 (5): 307–315. (3.4–122.)

— 1951*c*: A note on the kinetic energy balance of the zonal wind systems. T 3 (3): 205–207. (3.11–109.)

— 1953*a*: On the production of mean zonal currents in the atmosphere by large disturbances. T 5 (4): 475–493. (5.10–110.)

— 1953*b*: On convective instability of a rotating fluid. Symposium on Hydrodyn. Model Experiments, Johns Hopkins Univ., Baltimore, Sept. 1–4.

— 1953*c*: The development of quasi-geostrophic motions in the atmosphere. GRP No 24: 27–52.

— 1954*a*: Energy releasing processes and stability of thermally driven motions in a rotating fluid. MIT, Dep. of Met., Contract AF 19 (604)–1000, General Circulation Project, Scientific Report No. 1. and JM 13 (1): 82–101. (8.4–181.)

— 1954*b*: Symmetrical disturbances in a thin layer of fluid subject to a horizontal temperature gradient and rotation. JM 11 (5): 399–411. (6.3–104.)

— 1955: On convective instability of a rotating fluid with a horizontal temperature contrast. J. Marine Research 14: 14–32.

— 1956*a*: Forced and free meridional circulations in the atmosphere. JM 13 (6): 561–568. (8.4–182.)

— 1956*b*: Energy-releasing processes and stability of thermally driven motions in a rotating fluid. JM 13 (1): 82–101. (7.8–120.)

— 1957: Further studies of thermally driven motions in a rotating fluid. JM 14: 553–558.

KUO, H.-L., 1960: Theoretical findings concerning the effects of heating and rotation on the mechanism of energy release in rotating fluid systems. In: Dynamics of climate, Editor: R. L. PFEFFER, pp. 78–85. New York.

LAGOW, E. H., R. HOROWITZ, and J. AINSWORTH, 1958: Rocket measurements of the Arctic upper atmosphere. Annales de Géophysique, Paris, 14 (2): 131–139. (10.6–39.)

LAHEY, J. F., and R. A. BRYSON, 1960: Atlas of 300-mb wind characteristics for the Northern Hemisphere. Wisconsin, Univ. Dept. of Met., Contract AF (604)–2278, Final Report Pt. 1. (11.5–13.)

LAIRD, H. B., 1958: Fallout forecast program for civil defense. BAMS 39 (7): 377.

LAKE, H., 1956: Meteorological analysis of clear-air turbulence: a report on the U.S. Synoptic High-Altitude Gust Program. GRP No. 47. (8.5–24.)

LAL, D., 1959: Cosmic ray produced radioisotopes for studying the general circulation in the atmosphere. IJMG 10 (2): 147–154. (11.4–234.)

LAMB, H. H., 1952: The jet stream in the Southern Hemisphere. W 7 (8): 258. (4 G–106.)

— 1957: Some interesting properties of the "nullschicht" or maximum-wind layer. MML 86 (1019): 142–145. (8.9–157.)

— 1958: Differences in the meteorology of the northern and southern polar regions. MML 87 (1938): 364–379. (11.4–235.)

— 1959: The southern westerlies: a preliminary survey; main characteristics and apparent association. QJRMS 85: 1–23 and 299–301.

— *et al.*, 1957: Jet streams over North Africa and the Central Mediterranean in Jan. and Feb. 1954. MML 86 (1018): 97–111. (8.8–203.)

— and A. I. JOHNSON, 1959: Climatic variation and observed changes in the general circulation. GA 41 (2–3): 94–134.

— and J. ROBINSON, 1957: Forecasting weather in the Mediterranean. MML 86 (1021): 214–217. (9.11–187.)

LAMP, W., 1958: Geostrophischer und zyklostrophischer Gradientwindzirkel. Benutzbar für Analysen auf Wetterkarten der Lambert-Projektion mit eniem Maßstab $1:5 \cdot 10^6$. MR 11 (2): 57–60.

LANDERS, H., 1955*a*: Analysis of some "project jet stream" data. BAMS 36 (8): 371–378. (7.9–145.)

— 1955*b*: A three-dimensional study of the horizontal velocity divergence. JM 12 (5): 415–427.

— 1956: Vorticity distribution and advection in the lower and middle troposphere. JM 13: 511–520.

— 1957: A small-scale feature in the field of motion. BAMS 38 (3): 130–133. (10.1–199.)

LANDSBERG, H. E., 1958: Trends in Climatology. Science 128 (3327): 749–758.

LANDOLT-BÖRNSTEIN, 1952: Zahlenwerte und Funktionen aus Astronomie und Geophysik. Berlin-Göttingen-Heidelberg: Springer.

LARSEN, S. H. H., 1959: Measurements of atmospheric ozone at Spitzbergen (78° N) and Tromsö (70° N) during the winter season. GP 21 (5), 8 pp.

LARSSON, L., 1958: A method to study the structure of standing lee waves and rotors. In: OSTIV Publication V. and SAR 1960/5.

LA SEUR, N. E., 1954: On the asymmetry of the middle-latitude circumpolar current. JM 11 (1): 43–57. (5.7–87.)

LEE, J. T. and J. G. GALWAY, 1956: Preliminary report on the relationship between the jet at the 200-mb level and tornado occurrence. BAMS 37 (7): 327–332. (8.4–183) (10 B–106).

— — 1958: The jet chart. BAMS 39 (4): 217–223. (10 B–149.)

LEE, M. A., 1955: Loran in polar regions. N 4 (8): 323–326. (8.1–33.)

LEE, R., 1954: A method of jet stream analysis at 300 mb. Canada, Met. Div., CIR-2565, TEC-198. (8.10–144.)

— 1955: Synoptic evidence for a direct circulation about a jet stream. QJRMS 81 (349): 462–468. (6.11–201.)

— 1956: An example of shear-line formation in the upper troposphere. Canada, Met. Div., CIR-2558, TEC-195. (8.10–182.)

— and W. L. GODSON, 1957: The Arctic stratospheric jet stream during the winter of 1955/56. JM 14 (2): 126–135. (8.8–45.)

LEESE, H., 1957: Synoptisch-statistische Untersuchungen über den Zusammenhang zwischen Höhenströmung und Luftdruckänderung am Boden. MAB 5 (3).

LETTAU, H., 1947: Über maximale Gegensätze des Luftdruckes als Funktion der Erdrotation. MR 1 (3–4): 99–100.

— 1948: Maximalwerte der Windgeschwindigkeit als Funktion der Erdrotation. MR 1 (15/16): 451–453. (4 E–159.)

— 1954: A study of the mass, momentum and energy budget of the atmosphere. AMGBA 7: 133–157. (5.11–78.)

— 1955: Turbulence in the stratosphere. BAMS 36 (4): 178–179. (7.11–217.)

— 1956: Theoretical notes on the dynamics of the equatorial atmosphere. BPA 29 (2): 107–122.

LEVITON, R., 1954*a*: A method of correcting tabulated rawinsonde wind speeds for curvature of the earth. AFS No. 53. (8.1–116.)

— 1954*b*: Height errors in a rawin system. AFS No. 60. (8.1–143.)

LILLER, W. and F. L. WHIPPLE, 1954: High-altitude winds by meteor-train photography. In: Rocket exploration of the upper atmosphere. London: Pergamon. (6.8–266.)

LIST, R. J., 1954: On the transport of atomic debris in the atmosphere. BAMS 35 (7): 315–325. (7 E–99.)

— 1958: Smithsonian Meteorological Tables. 6th revised edition. Smithsonian Institution.

LOCKHART, L. B. Jr., and R. L. PATTERSON Jr., 1960: Measurements of the air concentration of gross fission product radioactivity during the IGY July 1957–December 1958. T 12 (3): 298–307.

LOEWE, F., and U. RADOK, 1950: A meridional aerological cross-section in the South-West Pacific. JM 7 (1): 58–65. (4 G–46.)

LONG, R. R., 1951*a*: A theoretical and experimental study of the motion and stability of certain atmospheric vortices. JM 8 (4): 207–221. (3.6–78.)

— 1951*b*: Research on experimental hydrodynamics in relation to large-scale meteorological phenomena. U of C, Progress Report No. 5 (2.9–72.)

— 1952: The flow of a liquid past a barrier in a rotating spherical shell. JM 9 (3): 187–199. (4.2–102.)

— 1955: Sources and sinks at the axis of a rotating liquid. Johns Hopkins Univ., Dep. of Civil Engineering. Contract Nonr-248 (31). Project NR 082-104. TR No. 5 (8.3–167.)

LONGLEY, R. W., 1956: The rate of ascent of pilot balloons and the variation of wind as determined by them. Suffield Experimental Station, Ralston, Canada. Suffield TP No. 96. (9.2–158.)

LORENZ, E. N., 1953: The interaction between a mean flow and random disturbances. T 5 (3): 238–250. (5.8–105.)

— 1955: Available potential energy and the maintenance of the general circulation. T 7 (2): 157–167. (7.10–145.)

— 1956: A study of the general circulation and a possible theory suggested by it. IUGG 457–462. (8.10–141.)

LORENZ, E. N., 1960: Generation of available potential energy and the intensity of the general circulation. In: Dynamics of Climate, Editor: R. L. PFEFFER, pp. 86–92. New York.

LOWELL, S. C., 1951: The boundary conditions at the tropopause T 3 (2): 78–81. (5 D–191.)

LOWENTHAL, M., and A. ARNOLD, 1955: Signal Corps Air Weather Service high-altitude radiosonde flights, Aug. 1954. U.S. Signal Corps Engineering Labs., Ft. Monmouth, N.J. Techn. Memorandum M-1711. (8.4–25.)

LUCKE, O., 1952: Über die allgemeine Zirkulation in der unteren Atmosphäre im Lichte der Hydrodynamik. ZM 6 (7): 202–215. (4.9–88.)

LUDLAM, F. H., 1957: Noctilucent clouds. T 9 (3): 341–364.

LUGEON, J., 1960: L'échosondage de l'atmosphère. Annalen der Schweizerischen Zentralanstalt, 1959: 1–7.

LUNZ, P., 1943: Mittlere Höhenwinde aus Registrierballonflugbahnen Lindenberg und München 1906–1938. MZ 60: 132–136. (4 F–27.)

LYONS, H., J. J. FREEMAN, and D. E. HEBERLING, 1947: Radar pulse repeaters for upper-air wind sounding. Paper presented at Amer. Met. Soc. Meeting Jan. 1947.

LYRA, G., 1940: Über den Einfluß von Bodenerhebungen auf die Strömung einer stabil geschichteten Atmosphäre. BPA 26: 197–206.

— 1943: Theorie der stationären Leewellenströmung in freier Atmosphäre. Zeitschrift für angewandte Mathematik und Mechanik 23 (1): 1–28.

MCCABE, J. T., and TH. D. POTTER, 1959: A method for the construction of climatological fallout-dose patterns. BAMS 40 (11): 561–565.

MCCLAIN, E. P., 1960: Thermal conditions in the Arctic stratosphere near 80 W in January. JM 17 (4): 383–389.

MCCLELLAN, D. E., 1954: Jet stream analysis. Canada, Met. Div., CIR-2425 TEC-179. (6.2–72.)

MACDONALD, N. J., and H. T. HARRISON, 1960: Some observations of the mountain wave in Eastern Colorado. BAMS 41 (11): 627–632.

— and W. O. ROBERTS, 1958: The relationship of 300-mb circulation changes to geomagnetic disturbances from 1952 to 1958. BAMS 39 (7) 377 and Univ. of Colorado, High Altitude Observ., Institute for Solar-Terrestrial Research, TR No. 6 (11.1–203.)

MACHTA, L., 1959: Transport in the stratosphere and through the tropopause. Advances in Geophysics 6: 273–288.

— *et al.*, 1956: World-wide travel of atomic debris. Science, Wash. D.C., 124 (3220): 474–477. (8.8–106.)

— *et al.*, 1957: Airborne measurements of atomic debris. JM 14 (2): 165–175. (8.8–105.)

MCINTYRE, D. P., 1955: On the baroclinic structure of the westerlies. JM 12 (3): 201–210. (6.9–155.)

— 1958: The Canadian 3-front, 3-jet stream model. GH 6 (3–4): 309–323.

— and R. LEE, 1953: Jet streams in middle and high latitudes. AMST 172–181. (6.3–109.)

MCLEAN, G. S., 1957: Cloud distribution in the vicinity of jet streams. BAMS 38: 579–583.

— and R. M. RADOS, 1955: Project Jet Stream observation of a small-scale high-level vortex. BAMS 36 (9): 469–474. (7.11–181.)

MCTAGGART-COWAN, P. D., 1950: The jet stream. Roy. Met. Soc., Canadian Branch (Publications). 1 (1). (4 G–47.)

Madagascar, Service Météorologique, 1948: Moyennes de vent et température en altitude. Tananarive 1948. (4 E–160.)

MAEDE, H., 1956: Über einige Beziehungen zwischen der Lage des Kältepols und der Zirkulation über Mitteleuropa. ZM 10 (7): 193–206. (8.2–171.)

MAGATA, M., 1957: On the topographical effect upon the perturbations of the middle latitude westerlies. PMGT 8 (1): 25–38.

MAINE, R., and C. PIERREHUMBERT, 1955: Constant absolute vorticity trajectories. AMMM No. 8. 37–47. (7.11–141.)

MALET, L. M., 1954: Diverses experiences de comparaison de radiosondes. WMO No. 35, TP 11, TN No. 5 (7.2–93.)

— 1955: Comparaison régionale des radiosondes, Bruxelles, 4-XI-54–19-XI-54, Tome I. Belgium, Institut Royal Météorologique, Publications Ser. A. No. 3. (8.6–144.)

MALKUS, J. S., and C. RONNE, 1954*a*: Concerning the structure of some cumulus clouds which penetrate the high tropical troposphere. TR No. 27, Woods Hole Oceanogr. Inst.

— — 1954*b*: On the structure of some cumulonimbus clouds which penetrated the high tropical troposphere. T 6: 351–366.

MALONE, T., 1951: Compendium of Meteorology, Boston, AMS. (3.3–1.)

MALZEV, V., 1926: Luminous night clouds. Nature, London, 118 (2975): 14–15. (4 F–6.)

MANTIS, H. T., 1957: Accuracy of the Signal Corps transponder system of balloon positioning. Minnesota, Univ. School of Physics, Contr. Nonr 710 (22). TR. (9.8–15.)

— 1959: Winds and wind structure at 100,000 feet from constant altitude balloon trajectories. Minnesota, Univ. School of Physics, Contract AF 19 (604)–2207, Final Scientific Report (Technical Report) 84 pp.

— 1960: On a diurnal variation of stratospheric winds. JM 17 (4): 465–468.

MARC, V., H. TREUSSART, and A. DARMAGNAC, 1959: Détermination des erreurs accidentelles affectant les mesures effectuées au moyen d'un radar WF_1 modifié "Omera." LM Ser. 4, No. 54: 129–145. (11.5–259.)

MARTIN, F. L., 1955: Generalization of constant absolute vorticity trajectories. U.S. Naval Postgraduate School, RP No. 7 (7.2–128.)

MASTENBROOK, H. J., 1956: Transosonde flights for 1955, data report. U.S. Naval Res. Lab., NRL Memorandum Report, No. 612, 523, 628. (9.7–112.)

— and A. D. ANDERSON, 1953: Evaluation of the transosonde system. Report for period Jan. 1952–March 1953. Data report for period April–Aug. 1953. U.S. Naval Res. Lab., NRL Memorandum Reports No. 171 and 240. (5 E–141.)

— — 1954: The transosonde. WW 7 (4): 79–81. (6.7–124.)

MASUDA, Y., 1950: Dynamics of baroclinic disturbances in the upper troposphere. PMGT 1 (2–4): 188–197. (2.11–72.)

MASUZAWA, J., 1960: Statistical characteristics of the Kuroshio Current. The Oceanographical Magazine, Japan Meteorological Agency, 12 (1): 7–15.

MATSUHASHI, S., and K. FURUKAWA, 1954: Comparison of geostrophic and observed winds. TAT 5 (4): 337–343. (6.11–271.)

MATSUMOTO, S., H. ITOO, and A. ARAKAWA, 1953: On the monthly mean distribution of temperature, wind and relative humidity of the atmosphere over Japan from March 1951 to Febr. 1952. JMSJ 31: 248–258. (5.10–42.)

MATTHEWMAN, A. G., 1950: Variation of geostrophic wind with potential temperature in the horizontal and in the vertical, with application to vertical cross-section diagrams. MML 79 (934): 97–102. (1.7–10.)

MATTHEWS, L. S., 1956: A direct-reading geostrophic wind scale. MML 85 (1011): 263–267. (8.2–63.)

MEANS, L. L., 1944: The nocturnal maximum occurrence of thunderstorms in the Midwestern States. U of C Miscellaneous Reports No. 16.

— 1952: On thunderstorm forecasting in the central United States. MWR 80: 165–189.

— 1954: A study of the mean southerly wind maximum in low levels associated with a period of summer precipitation in the Middle West. BAMS 35 (4): 166–170. (6.4–145.)

MEEKER, R. I. Jr., 1954: A simple rapid method for approximating least time flight tracks. Amer. Airlines, Inc., Los Angeles. (6.9–224.)

MEISINGER, F., 1958: On the criterion for hydrodynamic instability of permanent, horizontal, isobaric motion. Rasprave (Papers) Beograd. 2: 18–25.

MEURERS, J., 1952: Zur Aerodynamik der Pilotballone. BDWUS 35: 143–149. (3.10–52.)

MEYER, H. K., 1957: Betrachtungen über Höhenvorhersagekarten. BDW 6 (40): 20 pp.

— 1960: Die kalte arktische Stratosphäre im Dezember 1959 und die Auswirkung auf die Strömungsverhältnisse in Mitteleuropa. MR 13 (4): 106–111.

MIDDLETON, W. E. K., 1943: Meteorological Instruments, 2nd edition. Toronto: University Press. (2.1–29.)

MILANKOVITCH, M., 1930: Mathematische Klimalehre und astronomische Theorie der Klimaschwankungen. In: Handbuch der Klimatologie von W. KÖPPEN und R. GEIGER, Band I, Teil A. Berlin.

MILDNER, P., 1933: Über die Turbulenz des Windes, beobachtet mit Hilfe von doppelt und einfach visierten Pilotballonen. BPA 20: 114–126. (3 K–36.)

— 1954: Über den Zusammenhang zwischen der Polarfront in den höheren Schichten der Troposphäre und der Entwicklung und Bewegung der Bodendruckgebilde. MAB 2 (3): 105–116. (7.10–154.)

MILES, M. K., 1954: A kata-front of notable structure. MML 83 (988): 289–293. (6.3–119.)

MILLER, A., and J. VEDERMAN, 1951: Blocking action over the Northeast during the latter half of Febr. 1951. MWR 79 (2): 39–44. (2.9–81.)

MILLER, J. E., 1948*a*: On the concept of frontogenesis, JM 5: 169–171.

— 1948*b*: Studies of large-scale vertical motions of the atmosphere. NYU Met. Paper 1 (1): 40–44.

MINTZ, Y., 1947: On the kinematics and thermodynamics of general circulation of the atmosphere in the higher latitudes. TAGU 28 (4): 539–544. (3.1–87.)

— 1951: The geostrophic poleward flux of angular momentum in the month of Jan. 1949. T 3: 195–200.

— 1953: The observed planetary circulation of the atmosphere. UCLA, Dep. of Met., Contr. AF (122)–48, Scientific Report No. 3. (6.4–146.)

— 1954: The observed zonal circulation of the atmosphere. BAMS 35 (5): 208–214. (6.7–167.)

— 1955: The mean geostrophic poleward flux of angular momentum and of sensible heat in the winter and summer of 1949. Calif. UCLA, Dep. of Met., Contr. AF 19 (122)–48, Scientific Report No. 7 and Final Report. (6.11–191.)

— and G. DEAN, 1952: The observed mean field of motion of the atmosphere. GRP No. 17. (4.6–9.)

— and J. LANG, 1955: A model of mean meridional circulation. UCLA, Dep. of Met., Contr. AF 19 (122)–48, General Circulation Project, Final Report. (8.6–203.)

MIRONOVITCH, V., 1953*a*: Essai d'une coupe aérologique verticale à travers les deux hémisphères de 0 à 22 km. Ann. Geophysique 9: 285–290.

— 1953*b*: Répresentation de la circulation atmosphérique générale pour une coupe aérologique méridienne à travers les deux hémisphères. Académie des Sciences, Paris, Comptes Rendus 236 (4): 404–406. (4 G–126.)

— 1956: Les poles de la circulation atmospherique general et les poles magnetiques terrestres. BPA 29 (2): 123–128.

— and A. VIAUT, 1938: Turbulence et navigation aérienne dans la substratosphere. L'Aéronautique, Paris, 20: 202–206. (5 D–96.)

— and R. VIART, 1958: Interruption du courant zonal en Europe Occidentale et sa liaison avec l'activité solaire. MAB 7 (3).

MÖLLER, F., 1952: Die Aufrechterhaltung der Westwinddrift durch Großaustausch. BDWUS 35: 135–138. (3.10–115.)

MOHRI, K., 1953: On the fields of wind and temperature over Japan and adjacent waters during winter of 1950–1951. T 5 (3): 340–358. (5.9–131.)

— 1956: An analysis of jet streams over Japan on Nov. 3, 1952. JMSJ Ser. 2, 34 (1): 29–33. (9.7–163.)

— 1957: A note on an extremely strong jet stream on February 8, 1953. JMSJ 75th Anniversary Vol.: 173–175.

— 1958*a*: An example of upper frontogenesis over the Far East. GH 6 (3–4): 325–333.

— 1958*b*: Jet streams and upper fronts in the general circulation and their characteristics over the Far East, Pt. 1. GMT 29 (1): 45–126. (11.1–207.)

MOIR, R. W., 1950: A brief note on the upper winds at 30,000 ft over Nandi, Fiji. New Zealand Met. Service, Circular Note No. 59. (4 E–196). (4 I–210.)

MONTALTO, M., 1959: Correnti verticali a scala sinottica. ACSI: 136–140.

MONTGOMERY, R. B., 1937: A suggested method for representing gradient flow in isentropic surfaces. BAMS 18 (6–7).

MOOK, C. P., 1954: On the normal monthly variation of blocking patterns over the North Atlantic. BAMS 35 (8): 379–380. (6.9–153.)

— 1959: A preliminary meteorological study of the origin of whistlers. JGR 64 (7): 715–718.

MOOLEY, D. A., 1956: Zonal wind circulation and vertical temperature distribution along the Indian longitudes during monsoon and winter seasons. IJMG 7 (2): 113–128. (8.6–263.)

— 1957: Role of "western disturbances" in the production of weather over India during different seasons. IJMG 8 (3): 253–260. (9.9–163.)

MOORE, C. B., *et al.*, 1948: Constant level balloons. NYU TR No. 1. (1.1–43.)

— J. R. SMITH, and A. GAALSWYK, 1954: On the use of constant-level balloons to measure horizontal motions in the atmosphere. JM 11 (3): 167–172. (6.2–118.)

— — — 1955: Ein neues Hilfsmittel der Wettervorhersage: Ballone, die in einer bestimmten Höhe driften. Umschau 55 (9): 261–262. (6.10–74.)

MOORE, J. G., 1956: Cross-sections of the mean zonal component of geostrophic wind. MML 85 (1008): 167–171. (7.10–150.)

MORASCA, N., 1953: Le componenti verticali del vento nella libera atmosfera determinate mediante il sondaggio con due teodoliti ed errori dei comuni sondaggi per effetto di tali componenti. RMA 13 (4): 19–25. (7.5–80.)

MORELAND, W. B., 1956: The 100-mb and 50-mb map project—analysis problems and some 50-mb circulation features. Proceedings of the Workshop on Stratospheric Analysis and Forecasting. Washington, D.C. 58–77.

— 1960: Antarctic stratospheric circulation and ozone observations. AMO 394–409.

MORLEY, K. T., 1953: Investigation of the validity of the geostrophic wind flow assumptions in tropical areas of Australia. AMMM No. 4: 39–47. (7.6–166.)

— 1957: The use of a jet stream nomogram. AMMM 10: 29–35. (9.11–188.)

MÜLLER, H. G., 1944: Ein neues elektrisches Höhenwindmeßverfahren. Deutschland, Reichsamt für Wetterdienst, Forschungs- und Erfahrungsberichte, Ser. B, No. 20. (2.10–31.)

MÜLLER-ANNEN, H., 1960: Über Schwankungen der Zonalzirkulation: Teil I: Die Zonalzirkulation und die Höhe der Sonnenfleckenzyklen. MR 13 (6): 169–172. Teil II: Die Zonalzirkulation und ihre Beziehungen zu den Sonnenflecken-Relativzahlen und der Solarkonstante. MR 13 (6): 172–178.

Mulky, G. R., 1955: Kinematic analysis of upper wind fields. IJMG 6 (2): 163–170. (8.3–124.)

Munk, W., 1950: On the wind-driven ocean circulation. JM 7 (2): 79–93.

— G. W. Groves, and G. F. Carrier, 1950: Note on the dynamics of the Gulf Stream. Journal of Marine Research 9 (3): 218–238. (2.8–190.)

— and R. L. Miller, 1950: Variation in the earth's angular velocity resulting from fluctuations in atmospheric and oceanic circulation. T 2 (2): 93–101. (1.11–59.)

Murakami, T., 1951: On the study of the change of upper westerlies in the last stage of Bai-u Season (Rainy Season in Japan). JMSJ 2nd ser. 29 (5): 162–175. (4 G–71.)

— 1953: On the seasonal variation of upper flow patterns. Part I: From winter to spring. JMSJ 31 (5): 173–193. (5.9–204.)

— 1956: The topographical effect upon the stationary upper flow patterns. PMGT 7 (2): 69–89. (10.3–274.)

Murgatroyd, R. J., 1955: Wind and temperature to 50 km over England. Anomalous sound propagation experiments 1944–55. GM No. 95. (7.11–205.)

— 1956: Meteorological Research in Aircraft. MRP 995. (8.2–74.)

— 1957: Winds and temperatures between 20 km and 100 km—a review. QJRMS 83 (358): 417–458. (9.2–27.)

— 1959: Jet stream flight of 6th March 1959. Unpublished Report.

— 1960: Some characteristic properties of jet streams over Northwestern Europe as shown by measurements from aircraft (Abstract). MDW No. 20: 4–5.

— and C. J. B. Clews, 1949: Wind at 100,000 ft over southeast England; observations and a discussion of the monsoon theory of wind at great heights. GM No. 83. (4 F–44.)

— and N. C. Helliwell, 1957: The measurement of wind at altitude by airborne instruments. MRP 1070. (10.6–237.)

Murray, R., 1951: Practical value of the contour chart as a method of representing upper winds. Summary of results. MRP 663.

— 1952: The jet streams over the British Isles during June 14, 1951. MML 82 (971): 129–140 and: MRP 743. (4 G–135.)

— 1953. The upper troposphere and lower stratosphere near jet streams: an examination of observations made by the Meteorological Research Flight, Farnborough. MRP 813. (5.3–143.)

— 1954: On the accuracy of contour charts in forecasting upper winds. GMOPN 7 (110). (5.8–69.)

— 1956: Some features of jet streams as shown by aircraft observations. GM No. 97. (7.6–9.)

— and S. Daniels, 1951: Transverse flow at entrance and exit to jet streams. MRP 690. (4 G–72.)

— and D. J. Johnson, 1952: Structure of the upper westerlies; a study of the wind field in the eastern Atlantic and Western Europe in September 1950. QJRMS 78 (336): 186–199. (4 G–108.)

Murray, W. D., C. S. Schneider, and J. R. Smith, 1950: Development and utilization of constant-level balloons. TAGU 31 (6): 843–848. (2.5–27.)

Nabeshima, Y., 1957: On the structure of atmosphere near the tropopause and the numerical prediction at the 300-mb level. JMSJ 75th Anniversary Vol.: 280–288.

Nagai, T., and Y. Matuoka, 1949: On the tropopause at Tateno, 1st report. TAT 4 (4): 129–137. (5 D–153.)

Nakamura, S., and E. Arai, 1957: An upper air wind analysis during the latter stage of "Bai-u" in 1952. TAT 6 (1): 9–16. (9.11–137.)

NAKAYAMA, A., 1957: Thermodynamic and dynamic effects on the development of strong thunderstorms. JMRT 9 (3): 157–161. (9.8–173.)

NAMIAS, J., 1947*a*: Extended forecasting by mean circulation methods. U.S. Weather Bureau (2 A–140.)

— 1947*b*: Physical nature of some fluctuations in the speed of the zonal circulation. JM 4 (4): 125–133. (4 G–7.)

— 1950: The index cycle and its role in the general circulation. JM 7 (2): 130–139. (1.7–41.)

— 1952*a*: The annual course of month-to-month persistence in climatic anomalies. BAMS 33 (7): 279–285.

— 1952*b*: The jet stream. Scientific American 187 (4): 26–31. (4 G–109.)

— 1953: Quasi-periodic cyclongenesis in relation to the general circulation. AMST p. 154. (6.6–176.)

— 1954: Quasi-periodic cyclogenesis in relation to the general circulation. T 6 (1): 8–22. (6.2–147.)

— 1957: Characteristics of cold winters and warm summers over Scandinavia related to the general circulation. JM 14: 235–250.

— 1958: Synoptic and climatological problems associated with the general circulation of the Arctic. TAGU 39 (1): 40–51.

— and PH. CLAPP, 1944: Studies of the motion and development of long waves in the westerlies. JM 1 (3/4): 57–77.

— — 1949: Confluence theory of the high tropospheric jet stream. JM 6 (5): 330–336. (4 G–22.)

— — 1951: Observational studies of general circulation patterns. CM 551–567.

NAN'NITI, T., 1958: Relation between the vorticity and the location of the front of the Kuroshio off the Tohoku District. The Oceanographical Magazine, Japan Met. Agency 10 (2): 185–192.

National Academy of Sciences, 1958*a*: Oceanography Program: First twelve months. IGY Bulletin No. 16, p. 1–7.

— 1958*b*: Second and third U.S.-IGY satellites. IGY-Bulletin 11: 13–16.

National Advisory Committee for Aeronautics, 1955: Meteorological problems associated with commercial turbojet-aircraft operation. NACA, RM 54L29.

NEIBURGER, M., and J. K. ANGELL, 1956: Meteorological applications of constant-pressure balloon trajectories. JM 13 (2): 166–194. (7.9–86.)

— *et al.*, 1948: On the computation of wind from pressure data. JM 5 (3): 87–92. (5.1–207.)

NEIS, B., 1950: Zum Begriff der allgemeinen Zirkulation der Atmosphäre. ZM 4 (3): 72–77. (1.10–66.)

NEUBER, H., 1959: Ein Flugzeug für die Erforschung der hohen Atmosphäre. ACSI p. 122–128.

NEUWIRTH, R., 1954: Die Anwendung der horizontalen Scherzahlen („Scherungsvorticity") in synoptischen, biometeorologischen und Strahlungsuntersuchungen. MR 7 (5–6): 88–92. (6.2–120.)

— 1955: Meteorologische Auswertung von Messungen der künstlichen Radioaktivität der Luft und des Niederschlages. GPA 32: 147–158. (7 E–159.)

NEVIÈRE, E., 1959: Relations entre les courants rapides at les types de temps en Afrique équatoriale. MNM No. 14.

NEWELL, H. E. JR., 1955: Rocket data on atmospheric pressure, temperature, density and winds. Annales de Géophysique, Paris, 11 (2): 115–144. (7.10–81.)

NEWTON, C. W., 1950: Structure and mechanism of the prefrontal squall line. JM 7: 210–222.

NEWTON, C. W., 1954: Frontogenesis and frontolysis as a three-dimensional process. JM 11 (6): 449–461. (6.5–139.)

— 1955: Investigation of cyclone development, Storm No. 5. U of C, Dep. of Met., Contract AF 19 (604)–1293, TR No. 3. (7.10–158.)

— 1956*a*: Mechanism of circulation change during a lee cyclogenesis. JM 13 (6): 528–593. (8.4–194.)

— 1956*b*: Observational studies of squall line behavior, and effects of environmental wind field. U of C, Dep. of Met., Contract Cwb 8613, TR. (9.4–164.)

— 1958: Variations in frontal structure of upper level troughs. GH 6 (3–4): 358–375. (10.10–241.)

— 1959*a*: Axial velocity streaks in the jet stream: ageostrophic "inertial" oscillations. JM 16: 638–645.

— 1959*b*: Synoptic comparisons of jet stream and Gulf Stream systems. RMV p. 288–304.

— and J. E. CARSON, 1953: Structure of wind field and variations of vorticity in a summer situation T 5 (3): 321–339. (6.1–212.)

— and H. R. NEWTON, 1959: Dynamical interactions between large convective clouds and environment with vertical shear. JM 16 (5): 483–496.

— *et al.*, 1951: Structure of shear lines near the tropopause in summer. T 3 (3): 154–171. (4 G–74.)

NICOLET, M., 1950: Propositions pour une nomenclature de la haute atmosphere. Annales de Géophysique 6 (4): 318–321. (3.1–70.)

NOJIMA, H., 1954: The jet streams over Honjo and Tateno in the winter season 1951–1952. TAT 5 (3): 219–232. (8.4–184.)

NYBERG, A., 1945: Synoptic-aerological investigation of weather conditions in Europe 17–24 April 1939. Statens Met. Hydrogr. Anstalt, Stockholm, Comm., Ser. of pap. No. 48, 122 pp.

— 1949: An aerological study of large-scale atmospheric disturbances. T 1 (1): 44–53. (4 G–23.)

— 1950: A study of vertical motion and formation of fronts and jet streams. CP pp. 81–89. (4 G–49.)

— 1951: On the variation of the general circulation of the atmosphere during past ages. In: Reports of the Swedish Deep-Sea Expedition 1947–1948. Vol. V/II. Royal Society of Arts and Sciences, Göteborg, 1951–1960.

— and H. RIEHL, 1953: Note on "A further study on the relation between the jet stream and cyclone formation." T 5 (3): 316–317. (5.7–88.)

OBERBECK, A., 1877: Über diskontinuierliche Flüssigkeitsbewegungen. Ann. Phys. N.S. 2: 1–16.

O'BYRNE, J. W., and M. J. CONNAUGHTON, 1957: An analysis of the wind components at the 300-mb level along the great circle track between Shannon and Gander. Eire, Met. Service, TN No. 24. (9.5–87.)

O'CARROLL, F. M., 1955: Investigation into the accuracy of wind forecasts prepared at Shannon airport for the Great-Circle Route Shannon–Gander. Eire, Met. Service, TN No. 20. (7.11–73.)

OCKENDEN, C. V., 1939: High altitude pilot balloon ascents at Habbaniya, Iraq. QJRMS 65 (282): 551–553. (4 F–19.)

OGURA, Y., 1958: On the isotropy of large-scale disturbances in the upper troposphere. JM 15 (4): 375–382. (10.6–195.)

O'HARE, J. E., Q. H. CARLSON, and W. E. TAMBLYN, 1954: Some results of a tanker survey of the Gulf Stream. TAGU 35 (3): 420–430. (6.7–90.)

OHNSORG, F., 1957: Error estimates from constant-level balloon tracking. JM 14 (1): 81–83. (8.6–132.)

OHRING, G., 1958: The radiation budget of the stratosphere. JM 15 (5): 440–451.

— and H. S. MUENCH, 1960: Relationships between ozone and meteorological parameters in the lower stratosphere. JM 17 (2): 195–206.

OOI, S., S. MATSUMOTO, and H. ITOO, 1951: A study on westerly troughs near Japan (I). PMGT 2 (3/4): 219–233. (4.11–116.)

ORIHATA, J., 1956: On the dynamical analysis of upper-air pressure pattern over Japan area. Met. Notes Ser. 2, No. 5, Met. Res. Inst., Kyoto Univ.

— 1957: High-level cyclones south of the subtropical jet stream. JMSJ Ser. 2, 35 (1): 45–51. (9.9–162.)

OTSUKA, R., and K. SHIMADA, 1954: On the upper currents in low latitudes of the Northwestern Pacific Ocean at the beginning of March 1954 (Meteorological investigation on the explosion at Bikini Island, Pt. 1). JMSJ Ser. 2, 32 (7/8): 225–239. (8.8–169.)

— — 1955: On the vertical structure of upper wind in low latitudes. JMRT 6 (12): 581–583. (7.7–183.)

OZAWA, T., and K. TOMATSU, 1956: On the mechanism of warm and cold weather in summer in the neighborhood of Japan. JMRT 8 (8): 495–502. (9 C–89.)

PAETZOLD, H.-K., 1956a: Das heutige Bild der Stratosphäre. Umschau 56 (17): 528–531. (8.1–178.)

— 1956b: Die Meteorologie der Stratosphäre. BDW No. 22: 43–54.

— and F. PISCALER, 1959: Vertikale Ozonverteilung und Synopsis. BDW 51: 101–104. (11.6–257.)

— and H. ZSCHÖRNER, 1955: Beobachtung eines „Ozonloches" über den Alpen. ZM 9 (8): 250–251. (8.2–113.)

Pakistan, Meteorological Department 1952: Upper air data, 1948. Monthly means of pilot balloon data (Karachi 1952). (4 F–111.)

PALM, E., 1958: Two-dimensional and three-dimensional mountain waves. GP 20 (3). (10.11–176.)

— and A. FOLDVIK, 1960: Contribution to the theory of two-dimensional mountain waves. GP 21 (6): 30 pp.

PALMÉN, E., 1935: Registrierballonaufstiege in einer tiefen Zyklone. Finska Vetenskaps-Societeten, Helsinki, Commentationes Physico-Mathematicae, 8 (3): 1–32. (5 D–79.)

— 1948a: Discussion of problems concerning frontal analysis in the free atmosphere. Societas Scientiarum Fennica, Helsinki, Commentationes Physico-Mathematicae. 8 (8). (2.6–31.)

— 1948b: On the distribution of temperature and wind in the upper westerlies. JM 5 (1): 20–27. (4 G–12.)

— 1949: Origin and structure of high-level cyclones south of the maximum westerlies. T 1 (1): 22–31. (4 G–24.)

— 1950: Contribution to the theory of the general atmospheric circulation. Finska Vetenskaps-Societeten, Helsingfors, Commentationes Physico-Mathematicae 5 (4). (10.1–205.)

— 1951a: The aerology of extratropical disturbances. CM 599–620. (5 D–239.)

— 1951b: The role of atmospheric disturbances in the general circulation. QJRMS 77 (333): 337–354. (4 G–75.)

— 1954a: Über die atmosphärischen Strahlströme. MAB 2 (3): 35–50. (6.9–156.)

— 1954b: On the relationship between meridional eddy transfer of angular momentum and meridional circulations in the earth's atmosphere. AMGBA 7: 80–84. (5.11–81.)

PALMÉN, E., 1956: The mean vertical-meridional circulation in low latitudes of the Northern Hemisphere. IUGG 409–412. (8.10–142.)

— 1958: Vertical circulation and release of kinetic energy during the development of Hurricane Hazel into an extratropical storm. T 10 (1): 1–23. (10.3–234.)

— 1959: On the maintenance of kinetic energy in the atmosphere. RMV 212–224.

— 1960: One generation and frictional dissipation of kinetic energy in the atmosphere. Univ. of Helsinki, Inst. of Meteorology, Mitteilungen.—Papers No. 87, 15 pp.

— and M. A. ALAKA, 1952: On the budget of angular momentum in the zone between equator and 30° N. T 4 (4): 324–331. (5.1–128.)

— and K. M. NAGLER, 1948: An analysis of the wind and temperature distribution in the free atmosphere over North America in a case of approximately westerly flow. JM 5 (2): 58–64. (4 G–13.)

— — 1949: The formation and structure of a large-scale disturbance in the westerlies. JM 6 (4): 227–242. (4 G–25.)

— and C. W. NEWTON, 1948: A study of the mean wind and temperature distribution in the vicinity of the polar front in winter. JM 5 (5): 220–226. (4 G–14.)

— — 1951: On the three-dimensional motions in an outbreak of polar air. JM 8 (1): 25–39. (2.8–65.)

— H. Riehl, and L. A. VUORELA, 1958: On the meridional circulation and the release of kinetic energy in the tropics. JM 15 (3): 271–277.

PALMER, C. E., 1953: The Central Pacific Project. California Univ., Institute of Geophysics, Contract AF 19 (122)–414, 1st Quarterly Report, Append. A, Oct. 1951. Final Report March 1953. (4 F–127.)

— 1954: The general circulation between 200 mb and 10 mb over the equatorial Pacific. W 9 (11): 341–349. (6.3–110.)

— 1956: Solar radio noise and high-level zonal wind shear over the Central Pacific Ocean. JM 13 (3): 315–316. (7.10–210.)

— 1959: The stratospheric polar vortex in winter. JGR 64 (7): 749–764.

— and R. C. TAYLOR, 1960: The vernal breakdown of the stratospheric cyclone over the South Pole. JGR 65 (10): 3319–3329.

— *et al.*, 1955: The practical aspects of tropical meteorology. UCLA, Oahu Res. Center, Spec. Report No. 2 (AFCRC-TN-55-460) AWSM 105–48 (195 pp.).

PALOMARES, C. M., 1956: Efectos de la corriente aerea en chorro sobre las capas atmosféricas inferiores. (Effects of the jet stream on the lower atmospheric layers.) Revista de Geofisica, Madrid, 15 (58): 167–172. (9.1–187.)

PANOFSKY, H. A., 1944: The effect of vertical motion on local temperature and pressure tendencies. BAMS 25: 271–275.

— 1946: Methods of computing vertical motion in the atmosphere. JM 3: 45–49.

— 1951: Large-scale vertical velocity and divergence. CM 639–646. (3.8–7.)

— 1956: Flow patterns at 100 mb and above. Proceedings of the Workshop on Stratospheric Analysis and Forecasting, Washington, D.C., pp. 146–155.

— and P. WOLFF, 1957: Spectrum and cross-spectrum analysis of hemispheric westerly index. T 9 (2): 195–200.

PANT, P. S., 1955: Circulation in the upper atmosphere. NYU, Research Div., Contract AF 19 (604)–1006, Scientific Report No. 1. (7.3–212.)

— 1956: Circulation in the upper atmosphere. JGR 61 (3): 459–474. (8.3–229.)

PARTL, W., and H.-J. TANCK, 1960: Die Bestimmung der Tropopause vom Strahlturbinenflugzeug aus. MR 13 (6): 178–180.

PATON, J., 1949: Luminous night clouds, MMI 78 (930): 354–357. (1.3–140.)

PATON, J., 1953: Direct evidence of vertical motion in the atmosphere at a height of about 80 km provided by photographs of noctilucent clouds. AMST: 31–33. (6.3–200.)

PAULY, J., and R. MENIN, 1954: Formule approchée donnant la vitesse maximum du vent dans un "jet." Journal Scient. de la Météorologie, Paris, 6 (22): 69–72. (8.11–121.)

PEEL, R., 1953: The use of pressure pattern flying by Trans-Canada Airline. JINL 6 (1): 15–28. (4.9–131.)

PENN, S., 1955: A possible high-level thunderstorm mechanism in the case of August 20, 1951, over New Zealand. BAMS 36 (6): 278–288. (7.2–145.)

PEPPLER, A., 1914: Zur Kenntnis der Luftströmungen in großen Höhen über Zyklonen und Antizyklonen. BPA 6: 73.

PERNTER, J. M., 1889: Der Krakatau-Ausbruch und seine Folgeerscheinungen. MZ 6: 329–339, 409–418, 447–466. (1 F–38.)

PETERS, B., 1959: On the use of cosmic ray produced isotopes for studying large-scale circulations in the atmosphere. Advances in Geophysics 6: 289–296.

PETERSON, R. E., 1956: A comparison of relative vorticities computed from geostrophic and observed winds. NYU Research Division, Contract Nonr-285 (09), TP No. 5. (8.3–152.)

— 1957: Comparative studies of relative vorticities computed from geostrophic and observed winds. JM 14 (4): 367–374. (8.11–163.)

PETTERSSEN, S., 1949: Associations between the vorticity of large-scale air currents and the occurrence of subsidence and convection. BAMS 30 (5): 191–192. (2.5–64.)

— 1950: Some aspects of the general circulation of the atmosphere. CP 1950: 120–155. (2.3–62.)

— 1952: On the propagation and growth of jet stream waves. QJRMS 78 (337): 337–353. (4 G–110.)

— 1953*a*: On the dynamics of the Indian monsoon. Indian Acad. of Science, Bangalore, Proceedings, Ser. A. 37 (2): 229–233. (5.1–197.)

— 1953*b*: On the relation between vorticity, deformation and divergence and the configuration of the pressure field. T 5 (3): 231–237. (5.4–98.)

— 1955*a*: Investigation of cyclone development. U of C, Dep. of Met., Contract AF 19 (604)–390. Final Report 1955. (7.3–160.)

— 1955*b*: On the magnitude of cyclone development and the possibility of large-scale modification. National Acad. of Sciences, Wash. D.C., Proceedings, 41 (11): 815–819. (9.7–144.)

— 1955*c*: A general survey of factors influencing development at sea level. JM 12: 36–42.

— 1956: Weather analysis and forecasting. Vol. 1, 2. New York: McGraw-Hill. (7.8–4.)

— and D. BRADBURY, 1954: An investigation of cyclone development. Storm No. 1. U of C, Dep. of Met., Contr. AF 19 (604)–390, TR No. 5. (6.8–211.)

— G. DUNN, and L. L. MEANS, 1955: Report of an experiment in forecasting of cyclone development. JM 12 (1): 58–67. (6.5–72.)

— M. A. ESTOQUE, and L. A. HUGHES, 1957: An experiment in prognostication. JM 14: 191–205.

— and W. C. SWINBANK, 1947: On the application of the Richardson criterion to large-scale turbulence in the free atmosphere. QJRMS 73: 335–345.

PHILLIPS, N. A., 1950: The behavior of jet streams over eastern North America during January and February 1948. T 2 (2): 116–124. (4 G–50.)

— 1956: The general circulation of the atmosphere: a numerical experiment. QJRMS 82 (352): 123–129. (7.9–142.)

PHILLPOT, H. R., 1959: Winds at 30,000 and 40,000 ft in the Australia–New Zealand–Fiji area. Bureau of Met., Melbourne, Project Report 59/2645.

PHILLPOT, H. R., and D. G. REID, 1952: Equivalent head winds on Australian air routes. Comm. Australia Bur. Met., Melbourne, Bull. No. 41, 24 pp.

PINUS, N. Z., 1957: Atmospheric turbulence of dimensions which affect aircraft. ISG No. 3: 395–400.

PIPER, H., 1956: Beitrag zum Verhalten der kinetischen Energie bei Zyklonenvertiefung. MR 9 (9/10): 157–158. (8.2–134.)

PISHAROTY, P. R., 1954: The kinetic energy of the atmosphere. Calif. Univ. at Los Angeles, Dep. of Met., Contract AF 19 (122)–48, Scientific Report No. 6. (5.7–9.)

— 1955: General Circulation Project. Univ. of Calif., Final Report XIV.

— and B. N. DESAI, 1956: "Western Disturbances" and Indian Weather. IJMG 7 (4): 333–338. (8.10–147.)

PLAGGE, H., and L. B. SMITH, 1956: Project Rawijet: A study of the wind variability in space and time at the Salton Sea Test Base. Sandia Corporation, Research Report SC-3880 (TR). (9.1–230.)

PLATZMAN, G. W., 1947: Some remarks on the measurement of curvature and vorticity. JM 4 (2): 58–62.

— 1952: The increase or decrease of mean-flow energy in large-scale horizontal flow in the atmosphere. JM 9 (5): 347–358. (4.2–98.)

POCINKI, L. S., 1955: Stability of a simple baroclinic flow with horizontal shear. GRP No. 38. (8.4–185.)

POGOSIAN, KH. P., 1957*a*: Futóáramlások mozgó légnyomási képzödmények rendszerében. (Jet streams within the systems of moving pressure formations.) IB 61 (6): 401–407. (10.3–226.)

— 1957*b*: Vysotnye frontal'nye zony i struinye techeniia v atmosfere. (High frontal zones and jet streams in the atmosphere.) MG 7: 3–11. (10.10–242.)

— 1957*c*: Sezonnye osobennosti raspredeleniia struinykh technii v severnom polusharii. (Seasonal characteristics of the distribution of jet streams in the northern hemisphere.) MG 9: 3–14. (11.1–208.)

— 1958: O nekotorykh osobennostiakh struinykh techenii v atmosfere. (Some characteristics of jet streams in the atmosphere.) ISG No. 4: 515–526. (10.6–188.)

— 1959*a*: Obshchaia tsirkuliatsiia atmosfery. (The general circulation of the atmosphere.) Leningrad: Gidrometoizdat, 259 pp. (10.11–9.)

— 1959*b*: Stratosfernoe struinoė techenie v kholodnoe polugodie. (The stratospheric jet stream in the cold half-year.) MG 2: 15–21. (11.6–270.)

POLSON, R. K., 1957: The case for flexible air navigational tracks on the North Atlantic. N 5 (7): 337–344. (10.4–84.)

PONCELET, L., 1935: Sur des mouvements de turbulence dans la stratosphère décelés par un ballon-sonde. Académie Royale des Sciences de Belgique, Bulletin de la classe des Sciences, Ser. 5, 21 (2): 195–215. (3 K–42.)

PÔNE, R., 1953: Resultats provisoires d'une méthode d'analyse en altitude utilisée en France. (Preliminary results of a method used in France for high-level analysis.) IUGG Association of Met., Brussels, Procès-Verbaux des Séances, Mémoires et Discussion, p. 104–105. (7.11–136.)

PORTER, E. M., 1951: Some observations of a "jet stream" in the New Zealand region. New Zealand Met. Service, Wellington, Circular Note No. 74 (4 G–76.)

— 1952*a*: Upper winds over Invercargill. New Zealand Met. Office, TN No. 94. (4 F–113.)

— 1952*b*: Upper winds over Nandi and Auckland. New Zealand Met. Office, TN No. 92. (4 F–114.)

— 1953: The westerly wind flow at 300 mb across Australia and New Zealand. New Zealand Met. Office, TN No. 98. (5.4–165.)

Poser, H., 1947: Dauerfrostboden und Temperaturverhältnisse während der Würmeiszeit im nichtvereisten Mittel- und Westeuropa. Naturwissenschaften 34 (8).

— 1948: Boden- und Klimaverhältnisse in Mitteleuropa während der Würmeiszeit. Erdkunde 2: 53–68.

Pothecary, I. J. W., 1956: Comments on "A study of a characteristic type of upper-level frontogenesis." JM 13 (3): 316–317. (7.10–216.)

— and R. J. Murgatroyd, 1953: The use of aircraft to measure wind shear by observation of vertical smoke trails. MRP 810. (6.11–99.)

Powell, P. G., 1957: Route analysis and flight planning with isotachs. JINL 10 (3): 264–270. (8.10–58.)

Prandtl, L., 1926: Este Erfahrungen mit dem rotierenden Laboratorium. Naturwissenschaften 14 (19): 245.

— 1949: Wettervorgänge in der oberen Troposphäre. Akademie der Wissenschaften in Göttingen, Math.-Phys. Kl., Math.-phys.-chem. Abteilung. Nachrichten No. 2: 13–18. (4 G–26.)

— 1950: Dynamische Erklärung des Jet-Stream-Phänomens. BDWUS 12: 198–200. (1.10–63.)

— 1956: Strömungslehre. Braunschweig: Vieweg.

Pratt, K. G., 1953: A revised formula for the calculation of gust loads. NACA TN 2964.

Press, H., M. H. Schindler, and J. K. Thompson, 1953: Summary of pilots' reports of clear-air turbulence at altitudes above 10,000 ft. NACA RM L 52L30a. (8.6–248.)

Preusche, W., 1952: Ein Modell zur Veranschaulichung der Vertikalbewegung in der Jet-Zone. BDWUS No. 38: 42–46. (4 G–111.)

Priestley, C. H. B., 1950: On the dynamics of the general atmospheric circulation. Australian Journal of Scientific Research, Ser. A, Physical Sciences, 3 (1): 1–18. (4 G–51.)

— 1951: Physical interaction between tropical and temperate latitudes. QJRMS 77 (332): 200–214. (2.6–48.)

— and A. J. Troup, 1954: Further studies of the physical interaction between tropical and temperate latitudes. Australia, Commonwealth Scientific and Industrial Research Organization, Section of Met. Physics, TP No. 1. (6.1–135.)

Primault, B., 1951: Des cartes en altitude et de leur influence sur le calcul des temps de vol. (Upper level charts and their role in calculation of flight time.) LM 4th Ser., No. 24: 250–258. (3.10–33.)

Project Jet Stream, 1959: Flight data pertaining to jet streams. Project Jet Stream, GRD, Air Force Cambridge Research Center ARDC and Data Reduction Laboratory, Univ. of Dayton, Ohio.

Protheroe, W. M., 1955: Determination of shadow band structure from stellar scintillation measurements. Optical Soc. of Am., N.Y., Journal 45 (10): 851–855. (7.8–256.)

Proudman, J., 1953: Dynamical Oceanography. London: Methuen.

Prudhomme, A., 1949: Les vitesses ascensionelles des ballons de radiosondage. Annales de Géophysique 5 (3): 225–232. (2.2–18.)

— 1950: Le rôle de l'activité solaire dans les phenomenes atmosphériques. LM Ser. 4, No. 18: 85–98. (2.3–5.)

Queney, P., 1941: Ondes de gravité produites dans un courrant aérien par une petite chaine de montagnes. Comptes Rendus de l'Académie des Sciences de Paris, pp. 213–588.

— 1947: Theory of perturbations in stratified currents with applications to air flow over mountain barriers. U of C, Dep. of Met., Miscell. Report No. 23.

— 1948: The problem of air flow over mountains: A summary of theoretical studies. BAMS 29 (1): 16–26.

QUENEY, P., 1952: Les ondes atmosphériques considérées comme associées aux discontinuités du tourbillon. (Atmospheric waves associated with vorticity discontinuities.) T 4 (2): 88–111. (4.8–89.)

— 1953: Phénomènes de résonance et d'instabilité dans les écoulements barotropes, avec application aux ondes atmosphériques de grande échelle. Annales de Géophysique 9: 185–226. (6.4–129.)

— 1954: Les grandes mouvements de l'atmosphére. LM Ser. 4, No. 35: 195–207. (6.11–195.)

— 1959*a*: Ondes de relief dans un vent variable. ACSI 96–104.

— 1959*b*: Explication dynamique de la circulation générale de l'atmosphère sur la base des idées de Rossby. RMV 225–229.

— *et al.*, 1960: The airflow over mountains. WMO TN No. 34, WMO-No. 98. TP 43, 135 pp.

QUIRING, H., 1953: Höhenwind und Keplerbewegung. Zeitschrift für Naturforschung 8a (6): 395–396. (4.10–181.)

RADOK, U., and R. H. CLARKE, 1958: Some features of the subtropical jet stream. BPA 31 (1/2): 89–108. (11.1–209.)

— and A. GRANT, 1951: A note on cross-section technique. Weather Development and Res. Bull. Melbourne, No. 17: 39–48. (3.6–86.)

— — 1957: Variations in the high tropospheric mean flow over Australia and New Zealand. JM 14 (2): 141–149. (8.8–257.)

RAETHJEN, P., 1925: Zur Mechanik der Pilotballone. Ann. d. Hydrogr. u. Marit. Met. 53 (1925): 273–284.

— 1949: Zyklogenetische Probleme. AMGBA 1: 295–346.

— 1950: Über den Dualismus der atmosphärischen Druckfelder. BDWUS 12: 185–197. (1.11–60.)

— 1951: Das planetarische Zirkulationssystem. AM 4 (1–6): 65–75. (5 D–193.)

— 1953*a*: Dynamik der Zyklonen. Probleme der kosmischen Physik, 384 pp. (5.3–10.)

— 1953*b*: The five types of vorticity variation and cyclogenesis. IUGG Association of Met., Brussels 1951, Procès-Verbaux des Séances, Mémoires et Discussion. (7.5–114.)

— 1954: Zirkulation der Atmosphäre. (Kurzer Abriß der Meteorologie, dynamisch gesehen, Teil 3.) Geophys. Einzelschriften No. 3, Hamburg. (8.1–6.)

— 1955: General circulation and cyclogenesis. New York Academy of Sciences, Transactions, Ser. 2, 18 (2): 144–160. (8.6–198.)

— 1956: The two types of sudden frontal cyclogenesis. IUGG p. 497–500. (9.5–161.)

— 1957*a*: Die Entstehung des jet-stream und seiner Turbulenz. AM 8 (3/4): 108–114.

— 1957*b*: Über die Entstehung des „jet-stream" und seiner Turbulenz. SAR 32 (7): 384–388. (10.2–252.)

— 1958*a*: Trägheitsellipse und jet stream. GH 6 (3/4): 439–453. (11.1–256.)

— 1958*b*: Ähnlichkeitsbedingungen für geohydrodynamische Modellexperimente in rotierender Schale. AMGBA 10 (2/3): 178–193. (10.11–156.)

— 1959: Über die Bedeutung der Konvektion für die Entstehung des jet-stream und seiner Trogstörungen. ACSI 25–34.

— 1960: Über den „Scale."-Unterschied vertikaler und horizontaler Störbewegungen. BPA 32 (3/4): 257–264.

RAFTERY, T. J., and H. J. PLAGGE, 1957: Survey of fast-rising balloons and rawin reflectors, Sandia Corp., Albuquerque, N.M., Technical Memorandum 142-57-52. (11.1–154.)

RAHMATULLAH, M., 1952: Synoptic aspects of the monsoon circulation and rainfall over Indo-Pakistan. JM 9: 176–179.

RAMAGE, C. S., 1952: Relationship of general circulation and normal weather over southern Asia and the Western Pacific during the cool season. JM 9 (6): 403–408. (4.6–104.)

RAMAKRISHNAN, K. P., S. PARTHASARATHI, and N. C. APHALE, 1957: Some high pilot balloon ascents at Poona. IJMG 8 (3): 273–288. (9.4–170.)

RAMAMURTHI, K. M., 1955: A "jet stream" over northern India revealed by a "Comet" debriefing report. IJMG 6 (3): 277–278. (8.6–264.)

RAMAN, C. R. V., 1955: Breaks in Indian southwest monsoon and typhoons in Southwest Pacific. Current Science, Bangalore, 24 (7): 219–220. (8.6–253.)

RAMANATHAN, K. R., 1954: Atmospheric ozone and the general circulation of the atmosphere. IUGG Scientific Proc., Intern. Ass. of Met., Rome, pp. 3–24.

— 1955: On upper tropospheric easterlies and the travel of monsoon and post-monsoon storms and depressions. In: UNESCO Symposium on Typhoons, Tokyo, Nov. 9–12 1954, Proceedings. (7.2–135.)

— and R. N. KULKARNI, 1960: Mean meridional distributions of ozone in different seasons calculated from *umkehr* observations and probable vertical transport mechanisms. QJRMS 86 (368): 144–155.

RAMASWAMY, C., 1952: Winds at 40,000 ft and above over Calcutta during the southwest monsoon period. IJMG 3 (2): 157–158. (4 F–116.)

— 1956: On the subtropical jet stream and its role in the development of large-scale convection. T 8 (1): 26–60. (8.1–202.)

— 1958: A preliminary study of the behaviour of the Indian southwest monsoon in relation to the westerly jet stream. GH 6 (3/4): 455–477.

RAMSEY, B., 1955: Upper winds in the South-east-Asia–West Australia region. MML 84 (1002): 372–377. (7.6–167.)

RAND, W. M. JR., 1956: Dewey and Almy Chemical Company—manufacturers of meteorological balloons. BAMS 37 (3): 118–120. (9.1–133.)

RAPP, R. R., 1960: The accuracy of winds derived by radar tracking of chaff at high altitudes. JM 17 (5): 507–514.

RATNER, B., 1955*a*: The high wind over Philadelphia, Pa. January 23, 1955. MWR 83 (1): 31. (7.4–218.)

— 1955*b*: Winds and fallout: a climatological appraisal. Wash. D.C., USWB (7 E–164.)

REED, J. W., 1954: The representativeness of winds-aloft observations. BAMS 35 (6): 253–256. (6.11–100.)

REED, R. J., 1951: A study of atmospheric vorticity. MIT TR No. 10, Research on atmospheric pressure changes, 20 pp.

— 1953: Large-scale eddy flux as a mechanism for vertical transport of ozone. JM 10 (4): 296–297. (5.2–186.)

— 1955: A study of characteristic types of upper-level frontogenesis. JM 12: 226–237; 13: 316–317; 14: 91–93.

— 1957*a*: Arctic weather analysis. Polar Atmosph. Symposium, Part I. London: Pergamon.

— 1957*b*: Detailed wind structure in an intense frontal zone. BAMS 38 (6): 357–359. (8.10–183.)

— 1960*a*: Some comments on "hodograph analysis as applied to the occurrence of clear-air turbulence." JM 17 (4): 476–477.

— 1960*b*: Principal frontal zones of the northern hemisphere in winter and summer. BAMS 41 (11): 591–598.

— and E. F. DANIELSEN, 1959: Fronts in the vicinity of the tropopause. AMGBA 11: 1–17. (10.10–243.)

— and B. A. KUNKEL, 1960: The Arctic circulation in summer. JM 17 (5): 489–506.

REED, R. J., and F. SANDERS, 1953: An investigation of the development of a mid-tropospheric frontal zone and its associated vorticity field. JM 10 (5): 338–349. (5.3–138.)

— and W. G. TANK, 1956: Miscellaneous studies of polar vortices. Wash. State Univ., Dep. of Met. and Climat., Contract AF 19 (604)–1298, Occasional Report No. 4, Scientific Report No. 1. (8.7–176.)

REGER, J., 1938: Doppelanschnitte von Registrierballonen am Observatorium Lindenberg in den Jahren 1936–1937. Deutschl., Reichsamt f. Wetterdienst, Wissenschaftliche Abhandlungen 5 (4): 1938. (2.6–20.)

REGULA, H., 1934: Seismische Untersuchungen des Geophysikalischen Institutes in Göttingen. XVI. Schallausbreitung in der Atmosphäre. Zeitschrift für Geophysik 10 (3/4): 167–185. (4 F–10.)

— 1949: Erforschung der Hochstratosphäre durch Schallwellen. MR 2 (9–10): 263–267. (1.4–40.)

REGULA, W., 1949: Temperaturen und Winde in der oberen Stratosphäre. MR 2 (9/10): 267–270. (4 F–45.)

REIDAT, R., 1930: Gewitterbildung durch Kaltlufteinbruch in der Höhe. BPA 16 (4): 291–297. (1 H–34.)

REINECKE, I., 1950: Untersuchungen über die Abweichungen vom Gradientwind in der oberen Troposphäre. MAB 1 (1). (2.8–73.)

— 1951: Abweichungen vom Gradientwind in der oberen Troposphäre. AM 4 (1–6): 226. (3.7–145.)

— 1952: Fronten in der Stratosphäre? AM 5 (7/12): 346–352. (5.5–114.)

REINHARD, H., 1951: Höhenwindverhältnisse im Gebiete des Ärmelkanals. AMGBB 3: 110–122. (3.2–127.)

REITER, E. R., 1957*a*: An aid for accurate wind plotting, BAMS 38: 617–618.

— 1957*b*: Jet stream and jet aircraft operations. N 5: 267–278.

— 1957*c*: The layer of maximum wind. Final Report, U of C, Contr. Noas-55-262-C with Project AROWA, U.S. Navy.

— 1957*d*: Warum ein Geophysikalisches Jahr? Die Pyramide 5 (9/10 und 11/12): 127–134, 157–163.

— 1958*a*: Die Verwendung von Kontinuitätsdiagrammen in der nordalpinen Wetterprognose. AMGBA 10: 161–177.

— 1958*b*: Klima von Innsbruck 1931–55. (Anhang 1956 und 1957.) Statistisches Amt der Landeshauptstadt Innsbruck, 2. Sonderveröffentlichung.

— 1958*c*: The layer of maximum wind. JM 15 (1): 27–43.

— 1959*a*: Das Ende des Indischen Sommermonsuns 1954 mit Daten der österreichischen Cho-Oyu-Expedition. BDW 54: 293–297.

— 1959*b*: Die Mesostruktur der Strahlströme aus Project-Jet-Stream-Flügen No. 16 und 14. Zwischenbericht No. 1 an die Deutsche Lufthansa, Projekt „Streckenplanung," Publ. des Inst. f. Met. und Geophysik, Innsbruck, No. 95.

— 1959*c*: Entgegnungen zu vorstehenden Bemerkungen von Dr. HEINRICH FAUST. MR 12 (3): 97–98.

— 1959*d*: Neuere Ansichten über den indischen Monsun. Die Pyramide 7 (2): 51–52.

— 1959*e*: The layer of maximum wind as an aid in flight briefing. ACSI 35–47.

— 1959*f*: Zum Problem der Nullschicht. MR 12 (3): 95–96.

— 1959*g*: Flugzeuge im Strahlstrom. Die Pyramide 7, 89–90.

— 1960*a*: Turbulenz im wolkenfreien Raum. (Clear-Air Turbulence.) MDW No. 20: 8–9.

— 1960*b*: Turbulenz im wolkenfreien Raum. (Clear-Air Turbulence.) BDW No. 61.

REITER, E. R., 1960*c*: Auswertung von amerikanischen Flugbeobachtungen über die Feinstruktur von Strahlströmen. Teil II: Auswertung der Project-Jet-Stream-Flüge No. 22, 24, 29, 30, 31, 32. Zwischenbericht No. 2 an das Zentralamt des Deutschen Wetterdienstes. Publ. des Inst. f. Met. und Geophysik, Innsbruck, No. 96.

— 1960*d*: The detailed structure of the atmosphere near jet streams. Publ. des Inst. f. Met. und Geophysik, Innsbruck, No. 102.

— 1960*e*: The detailed structure of the atmosphere near jet streams. GPA 46: 193–200.

— 1961*a*: Die nordamerikanische Strahlstromwetterlage vom 23. bis 27, Januar 1957 an Hand von Forschungsflügen des ,,Project Jet Stream." BPA 33: 244–279.

— 1961*b*: Project Jet Stream Research Flight No. 30, April 8, 1957. QJRMS 87(373): 332–345.

1961*c*: Der Einfluß der Hochgebirge auf das Klima. Die Pyramide 9 (1): 16–22.

— 1961*d*: The detailed structure of the wind field near the jet stream. JM 18 (1): 9–30.

— 1961*e*: Die vertikale Struktur des Strahlstromkernes aus Forschungsflügen des Project Jet Stream. BDW No. 80.

— 1961*f*: The meso-structure of jet streams. SAR No. 10.

— and E. F. DANIELSEN, 1960: Bemerkungen zu E. KLEINSCHMIDT: ,,Nicht-adiabatische Abkühlung im Bereich des jet stream." BPA 32 (3/4): 265–273.

— and H. HEUBERGER, 1960: Jet stream and retreat of the Indian summer monsoon and their effect upon the Austrian Cho-Oyu-Expedition 1954. GA 42 (1): 17–35.

— *et al.*, 1961: Analyse dreier Forschungsflüge des Project Jet Stream. AMGBA 12 (2): 183–221.

— H. RIEHL, and J. W. HINKELMAN JR., 1957: Jet stream and maximum wind level studies. Paper given at the 150th National Meeting of the AMS, Jan. 28–31, 1957, N.Y. BAMS 37 (10): 536.

— and E. SZEKERES, 1960: Witterungskalender. Meteorologischer Rückblick, Herbst 1959. Die Pyramide 8 (1): 27–28.

REUTER, H., 1954: Methoden und Probleme der Wettervorhersage, Wien: Springer.

— 1955: Bodendruckänderung und Winddivergenz auf isobaren Flächen. AMGBA 8 (4): 321–331. (7.2–103.)

— 1960: Zum gegenwärtigen Stand der Theorie der Allgemeinzirkulation. Wetter und Leben 12 (9–10): 177–191.

— and F. HUBER, 1956: Über den Anteil verschiedener Höhenschichten am Zustandekommen von Bodendruckänderungen. BDW 4 (22): 108. (11.3–28.)

REX, D. F., 1950*a*: Blocking action in the middle troposphere and its effects upon regional climate. I. Aerological study of blocking action. T 2 (3): 196–211. (2.2–68.)

— 1950*b*: Blocking action in the middle troposphere and its effect upon regional climate. II. Climatology of blocking action. T 2 (4): 275–301. (2.8–64.)

— 1951: The effect of Atlantic blocking action upon European climate. T 3 (2): 100–111. (3.1–89.)

REYMANN, G., 1960: Die Strahlströme in der synoptischen Praxis. MDW No. 20: 14–27.

REYNOLDS, P. R. J., and C. L. CHANDLER, 1958: Flying the jet stream. Canadian Aeronautical Journal. Ottawa 4 (3): 86–93. (10.7–104.)

REYNOLDS, S. E., 1955: Thunderstorm charge structure and suggested electrification mechanism. GRP No. 42: 162–168.

RICHARDSON, J. M., and W. B. KENNEDY, 1952: Atmospheric winds and temperatures to 50 km altitude as determined by acoustical propagation studies. Acoustical Society of America, Journal. 24 (6): 731–741. (4 F–117.)

RICHARDSON, L. F., 1920: The supply of energy from and to atmospheric eddies. Proc. Roy. Soc. London, A, 97: 354–373.

RICHTER, K. H., 1952: Ergebnisse aus Radar-Höhenwindmessungen in Hannover-Langenhagen. BDWUS No. 42: 331–338. (4 F–118.)

RIEHL, H., 1945: Subtropical flow patterns in summer. U of C, mimeographed report. (1 H–154.)

— 1948*a*: Jet stream in upper troposphere and cyclone formation. TAGU 29 (2): 175–186. (4 G–15.)

— 1948*b*: On the formation of typhoons. JM 5: 247–264.

— 1951: Aerology of tropical storms. CM 902–913. (4.2–13.)

— 1954*a*: Comments on quasi-periodic oscillation of the Norfolk rawin. U.S. Navy Bureau of Aeronautics, Project AROWA, unpublished.

— 1954*b*: Jet Stream Flight, March 23, 1953. AMGBA 7: 56–66. (5.11–89.)

— 1954*c*: Tropical Meteorology, New York: McGraw-Hill.

— 1956: On the atmospheric circulation at 500 mb in the auroral belt. JGR 61 (3): 525–534.

— 1959: On the production of kinetic energy from condensation heating. RMV pp. 381–399.

— *et al.*, 1952: Forecasting in middle latitudes. U of C, Dep. of Met. (2.11–39) and MM No. 5 (80 pp.).

— *et al.*, 1953: The jet stream. Techn. Rep. under Contract between Project AROWA and U of C, NAVAER 50-1 R-249.

— *et al.*, 1954: The jet stream. MM 2 (7) (6 B–201).

— F. A. BERRY, and H. MAYNARD, 1955: Exploration of the jet stream by aircraft during the 1952–1953 winter. JM 12 (1): 26–35. (6.5–123.)

— and D. FULTZ, 1957: Jet stream and long waves in a steady rotating-dishpan experiment: structure of the circulation. QJRMS 83 (356): 215–231 and 84: 186–187. (8.8–259.)

— — 1958: The general circulation in a steady rotating-dishpan experiment. QJRMS 84: 389–417.

— W. H. HAGGARD, and R. W. SANBORN, 1956: On the prediction of 24-hour hurricane motion. JM 13 (5): 415–420.

— and R. HIGGS, 1960: Unrest in the upper-stratosphere over the Caribbean Sea during January 1960. JM 17 (5): 555–561.

— and C. O. JENISTA, 1952: A quantitative method for 24-hour jet stream prognosis. JM 9 (3): 159–166. (4.3–81.)

— N. E. LA SEUR, *et al.*, 1952: Forecasting in middle latitudes. MM 1 (5), (5.5–58.)

— and H. MAYNARD, 1954: Exploration of the jet stream by aircraft during the winter of 1953. U of C, Dep. of Met., Contract N 189 s-88360, Final Report. (6.2–136.)

— K. S. NORQUEST, and A. L. SUGG, 1952: A quantitative method for the prediction of rainfall patterns. JM 9 (5): 291–298. (4.5–76.)

— and S. TEWELES JR., 1953: A further study on the relation between the jet stream and cyclone formation. T 5 (1): 66–79. (4 G–127.)

— — 1954: Rainfall and vorticity advection. JM 11 (5): 425–428. (6.3–81.)

— T.-CH. YEH, and N. E. LA SEUR, 1950: A study of variations of the general circulation. JM 7 (3): 181–194. (4 G–52.)

RINK, H., 1957: Der plastische Ballon, ein neues Hilfsmittel zur Untersuchung der oberen Atmosphäre. ZM 11 (12): 371–376. (11.2–135.)

ROACH, F. E., 1959: Airglow motions. BAMS 40 (12): 628.

ROBERT, J., 1960: Étude météorologique sur le trajet aérien Tontouta-Nandi (Nouvelle-Calédonie-Fidji). MNM No. 21.

ROBERTS, O. F. T., 1923: The theoretical scattering of smoke in a turbulent atmosphere. Proc. Roy. Soc. London A. 104: 640–654.

ROBERTSON, D. S., D. T. Liddy, and W. G. ELFORD, 1953: Measurements of winds in the upper atmosphere by means of drifting meteor trails. Pt. 1. JATP 4 (4/5): 255–270. (7.5–65.)

ROBERTSON, G. W., and H. Cameron, 1952: A planimetric method for measuring the velocity of the upper westerlies. BAMS 33 (9): 387–389. (4.9–30.)

ROBINSON, E. F., and E. J. JOSEPH, 1955: The effect of a blocking high on two consecutive lows over the central United States, June 7–11, 1955. MWR 83 (6): 132–136. (8.1–195.)

ROBUCHON, A., and P. ERVET, 1958: La mesure du vent en altitude à l'aide d'un radar. LM Ser. 4, No. 51: 153–159. (11.1–142.)

RODEWALD, M., 1935: Das norddeutsche Hochdruckgewitter vom 19. August 1932. Annalen der Hydrogr. und maritimen Met., 63: 23–29. 64: 143–153. (1936). (1 H–56.)

— 1936: Bemerkungen zu: KARL WIEN, Die Wetterverhältnisse am Nanga Parbat während der Katastrophe auf der deutschen Himalaja-Expedition 1934. MZ 53: 182–186.

— 1952: Die blaue Sonne vom 27. September 1950. Naturwiss. Rundschau 5 (1): 8–15. (3.4–248.)

RODRIGUEZ, F. P., 1955: Notas sobre las corrientas de chorro. (Notes on the jet stream.) Revista de Geofisica, Madrid, 14 (56): 313–346. (8.6–204.)

ROGERS, R. R., 1957: Radar measurement of gustiness. MIT Weather Radar Research Report No. 29.

ROSSBY, C.-G., 1926: On the solution of problems of atmospheric motion by means of model experiments. MWR 54 (6): 237–240.

— 1938: On the mutual adjustment of pressure and velocity distributions in certain simple current systems. II. J. Marine Research I: 239–263.

— 1940: Planetary flow patterns in the atmosphere. QJRMS 66, Suppl.: 68–87. (5 F–5.)

— 1945*a*: Kinematic and hydrostatic properties of certain long waves in the westerlies. Dep. of Met., U of C, Miscellaneous Report No. 5, 37 pp.

— 1945*b*: On the propagation of frequencies and energy in certain types of oceanic and atmospheric waves. JM 2 (4): 187–204.

— 1947: On the distribution of angular velocity in gaseous envelopes under the influence of large-scale horizontal mixing processes. BAMS 28 (2): 53–68. (4 E–149.)

— 1948: On displacement and intensity changes of atmospheric vortices. J. Marine Research 7: 175–187.

— 1949*a*: Dispersion of planetary waves in a barotropic atmosphere. T 1 (1): 54–58.

— 1949*b*: On a mechanism for the release of potential energy in the atmosphere. JM 6 (2): 163–180.

— 1949*c*: On the nature of the general circulation of the lower atmosphere. In: KUIPER, "The atmospheres of the earth and planets." Chicago: University Press. (4 G–27.)

— 1950: On the dynamics of certain types of blocking waves. Chinese Geophysical Society, Nanking, Journal 2 (1): 1–13. (4 G–53.)

— 1951*a*: On the vertical and horizontal concentration of momentum in air and ocean currents. I. Introductory comments and basic principles with particular reference to the vertical concentration of momentum in ocean currents. T 3 (1): 15–27. (4 G–77.)

— 1951*b*: Über die Vertikalverteilung von Windgeschwindigkeit und Schwerestabilität in Freistrahlbewegungen der oberen Troposphäre. AMGBA 4: 3–23. (4 G–78.)

— 1953: A comparison of current patterns in the atmosphere and the ocean basins. I.U.G.G. Association of Meteorology, Brussels 1951, Procès-Verbaux des Séances, Mémoires et Discussion. (7.8–125.)

— *et al.*, 1937: Isentropic analysis. BAMS 18: 201.

ROSSBY, C.-G., *et al.*, 1939: Relations between variations in the intensity of the zonal circulation of the atmosphere and the displacement of the semipermanent centers of action. J. of Marine Research 2 (1): 38–55. (2 A–93.)

— and V. P. STARR, 1945: Basic principles of weather forecasting. Appendix by C. G. ROSSBY: Forecasting of flow patterns in the free atmosphere by a trajectory method. New York: Harper & Brothers.

— and H. C. WILLET, 1948: The circulation of the upper troposphere and lower stratosphere. Science, New York. (108): 643–652. (4 G–16.)

ROSSI, V., 1957: A simple method for the computation of wind values from the Finnish radio theodolite record. GH 6 (2): 121–125.

ROTH, A. L., and A. H. PALMER, 1911: Charts of the atmosphere for aeronauts and aviators. 98 pp., New York: Wiley.

ROUAUD, A., 1957: Erreur dans la détermination du vecteur vent. Journal Scientifique de la Météorologie, Paris, 9 (33): 1–13. (11.2–126.)

ROUSE, H., 1951: Model techniques in meteorological research. CM 1249–1254. (4.9–8.)

ROW, A. L., 1951: Upper winds over Auckland. New Zealand Met. Serv., Circular Note No. 78, 1 p. (4 D–266) (4 E–247).

Royal Meteorological Society and Royal Astronomical Society, 1954: Stellar Scintillation, Joint Discussion, Dec. 16, 1953. QJRMS 80 (344): 241–260. (5.10–10.)

RUBIN, M. J., 1955: An investigation of relationships between Northern and Southern Hemisphere parameters. Notos 4 (2): 122–126. (8.1–205.)

— and H. VAN LOON, 1954: Aspects of the circulation of the Southern Hemisphere. JM 11: 68–76. (5.4–101.)

RUDLOFF, W., 1950: Zur jährlichen Schwankung der Erddrehung. (Vorläufige Mitteilung.) AM 3 (11–12): 376–378. (2.8–61.)

— 1951: Die Driftzahl oder der atmosphärische Drehimpuls als Zirkulationsmaß. AM 4 (1–6): 14–26. (3.4–116.)

RUNGE, H., 1951: Blaue Sonne, Blauer Mond. ZM 5 (2): 60–62. (2.5–193.)

RUTHERFORD, G. T., 1954: A profile of the jet stream, 9th August 1953. AMMM 7: 13–25. (7.4–143.)

— 1955: Comparison of forecast winds with those reported by aircraft on high altitude flights. AMMM No. 8: 33–36. (7.4–82.)

— 1956: The accuracy of forecast and found winds. AMMM 12: 43–60. (8 C–78.)

RYAN, P., 1958: 40,000 ft winds Singapore-Darwin. AMMM No. 20: 66–70. (10.11–202.)

SAITO, T., 1951: Dynamics of the jet stream. PMGT 2 (2): 132–149. (4 G–79.)

— 1955: Preliminary study of blocking in the Far East. JMRT 7 (2): 81–83. (8.3–161.)

SAITO, N., 1953: An aerological study of the cold vortex and stationary front in summer in the Far East. JMSJ 31 (2): 51–59. (5.4–59.)

SAITO, S., and J. NARIKAWA, 1954: Report on cooperative observations of high clouds in West Japan. JMRT 6 (8): 299–314. (7.2–218.)

SALMELA, H. A., and N. SISSENWINE, 1959: A note comparing 1 km vertical wind shears derived from simultaneous AN/GMD-1 A and AN/GMD-2 winds-aloft observations. GRD Research Notes No. 22.

SALTZMAN, B., 1956: Equations for the study of the energetics of the larger scales of atmospheric turbulence. MIT, Dep. of Met., Contract AF 19 (604)–1000, Scientific Report No. 5. (8.4–224.)

— 1957: Equations governing the energetics of the larger scales of atmospheric turbulence in the domain of wave number. JM 14: 513–523.

— 1958: Some hemispheric spectral statistics. JM 15 (3): 259–263.

SALTZMAN, B., 1959: On the maintenance of the large-scale quasi-permanent disturbances in the atmosphere. T 11 (4): 425–431.

— and A. FLEISHER, 1960*a*: Spectrum of kinetic energy transfer due to large-scale horizontal Reynolds stresses. T 12 (1): 110–111.

— — 1960*b*: The exchange of kinetic energy between larger scales of atmospheric motion. T 12 (4): 374–377.

— and J. P. PEIXOTO, 1957: Harmonic analysis of the mean Northern-Hemisphere wind field for the year 1950. QJRMS 83 (357): 360–364. (8.10–199.)

SANDERS, F., and E. KESSLER, 1955: A test of the application of vorticity charts. BAMS 36 (6): 251–255. (7.2–104.)

SANDERS, R. A., 1953: Blocking highs over the eastern North Atlantic and Western Europe. MWR 81 (3): 67–73.

SANFORD, T. E., 1958: A further study of jet stream turbulence. A & M Final Report, Contract No. AF 19 (604)–1565, pp. 127–134.

SASAKI, Y., 1958: A theory and analysis of clear-air turbulence. A & M Scientific Report No. 1, Contract AF 19 (604)–1565.

SAUCIER, W. J., 1955: Principles of meteorological analysis. Chicago: University Press. (7.3–7.)

— 1956*a*: Exploration of the jet stream by aircraft during the 1952–1953 winter. A & M, Contributions in Oceanography and Meteorology, No. 60–89, Vol. 3.

— 1956*b*: Project Jet Stream B-47 Flights 2, 6, 9, 11 and 14. A & M Final Report, Contract AF 19 (604)–559, pp. 30–78.

— 1958*a*: Additional jet stream studies. A & M Final Report. Contract AF 19 (604)–1565, pp. 135–137.

— 1958*b*: A summary of wind distribution in the jet streams of the Southeast United States investigated by Project Jet Stream. A & M Final Report, AF 19 (604)–1565, pp. 6–57.

— 1958*c*: Background information regarding Project Jet Stream. A & M Final Report, Contract AF 19 (604)–1565, pp. 1–3.

— 1958*d*: An error analysis of geostrophic 300-mb numerical wind-speed forecasts. U.S. AWS TR 105–148.

— and K. C. BRUNDIDGE, 1956: Variability of wind direction in relation to wind speed. BAMS 37 (9): 462–464.

— and H. RIEHL, 1956: Exploration of the jet stream by aircraft during the 1953 winter. JM 13 (3): 312–314. (7.10–155.)

SAWYER, J. S., 1950*a*: Equivalent headwinds. Application of upper-wind statistics to air-route planning. 20 pp. London: H.M. Stationery Office. (2.1–21.)

— 1950*b*: The movement of jet streams and the wind hodograph. MML 79 (942): 357–358. (4 G–54.)

— 1951*a*: Day to day variations in the tropopause. Their causes and significance. MRP 612. (5 D–194.)

— 1951*b*: The dynamical systems of the lower stratosphere. QJRMS 77 (333): 480–483. (5 D–195.)

— 1953: The free atmosphere in the vicinity of fronts—analysis of observations by the Meteorological Research Flight (1950–52). MRP 807. (5.5–113.)

— 1954: Day to day variations in the tropopause. GM 11 (92). (5 D–232.)

— 1955: The free atmosphere in the vicinity of fronts: analysis of the observations by the Meteorological Research Flight 1950–1952. GM No. 96. (8.8–215.)

— 1957: Jet stream features of the earth's atmosphere. W 12 (11): 333–344. (9.1–188.)

SAWYER, J. S., 1958: Temperature, humidity and cloud near fronts in the middle and upper troposphere. QJRMS 84 (362): 375–388; 85 (365): 295–297.

— 1960: Numerical calculation of the displacement of a stratified airstream crossing a ridge of small height. QJRMS 86 (369): 326–345.

— 1961: Quasi-periodic wind variations with height in the lower stratosphere. QJRMS 87 (371): 24–33.

— and B. ILETT, 1951: The distribution of medium and high clouds near the jet stream. MML 80 (952): 277–281. (4 G–81.)

SCHAEFER, V. J., 1953*a*: Cloud forms of the jet stream. T 5 (1): 27–31. (4 G–128.)

— 1953*b*: The use of clouds for locating the jet stream. Aeroplane, London, 85 (2206): 599–602. (5.9–205.)

— 1953*c*: Track jet streams by cloud motions. Sci. News Letter, 63: 83–84. (5.1–137.)

— 1955*a*: Atmospheric electricity associated with jet streams. GRP 42: 59–66. (8.5–331.)

— 1955*b*: Jet Stream and Project Skyfire. Munitalp Foundation, Inc., N.Y., Occasional Paper No. 0006. (9.5–153.)

— 1955*c*: Jet streams, thunderstorms and Project Skyfire. AMGBA 8: 265–282. (6 J–332.)

— 1955*d*: Thunderstorms and Project Skyfire. New York Academy of Sciences, Transactions, Ser. 2, 17 (6): 470–473. (7.2–277.)

— 1955*e*: Gewitter, Strahlströme und ,,Skyfire-"Projekt. AM 7 (1/2): 149–151. (7.6–125.)

— 1957: Relationship of jet streams to forest wildfires. Journal of Forestry, Wash., D.C., 55 (6): 419–425. (10.10–232.)

— and W. E. HUBERT, 1955: A case study of jet stream clouds. T 7 (3): 301–307. (7.9–146.)

SCHEDLER, A., 1917: Über den Einfluß der Lufttemperatur in verschiedenen Höhen auf die Luftdruckschwankungen am Erdboden. BPA 7: 88–101.

SCHELL, I. I., 1959: On the nature and the origin of changes in climate. BAMS 40 (12): 632.

SCHERHAG, R., 1936: Bemerkungen zur Divergenztheorie der Zyklonen. MZ 53: 84–90.

— 1948*a*: Beispiel einer stratosphärischen Steuerung. MR 1 (9–10): 287–290. (1.4–27.)

— 1948*b*: Neue Methoden der Wetteranalyse und Wetterprognose. Berlin: Springer. (1–52.)

— 1952: Die explosionsartigen Stratosphärenerwärmungen des Spätwinters 1951/52. BDWUS 6 (38): 51–63.

— 1957: The role of the tropospheric cold-air poles and of stratospheric high-pressure centers in the Arctic weather. Polar Atmosph. Symposium, Pt. 1: 101–117, London: Pergamon and JATP, Special Supplement, Pt. 1.

— 1960: Stratospheric temperature changes and the associated changes in pressure distribution. JM 17 (6): 575–582.

SCHINZE, G., and R. SIEGEL, 1943: Die luftmassenmäßige Arbeitsweise. Reichsamt für Wetterdienst (Luftwaffe), Wissensch. Abh.

SCHMIEDEL, K., 1937: Stratosphärische Steuerung und Wellensteuerung. Univ. Leipzig. Geophys. Inst., Veröffentlichungen Ser. 2., 9 (1): 1–102. (2 A–87.)

SCHMITT, W., 1952: Two intensive polar outbreaks in the southern oceans. Notos 1 (4): 193–201. (4 G–116.)

SCHNEIDER-CARIUS, K., 1956: Grundschicht und Nullschicht, zwei polare Schichtbildungen in der Troposphäre. AMGBA 9 (3): 305–323. (8.2–111.)

— and H. FAUST, 1953: Grundschicht und Nullschicht der Atmosphäre. GPA 26: 119–126. (5.11–136.)

SCHULTE-VENNBUR, H., 1953: Niederschlagsstrukturen von Zyklonen in Nordamerika. GPA 26: 97–111. (6.6–178.)

SCHULZE, W., 1950: Platzhöhen von Radiosondenballonen und Ozongehalt der freien Atmosphäre. AM 3 (1–2): 42–48. (1.6–13.)

SCHUMACHER, N. J., 1955: Upper air temperature over an Antarctic station. T 7 (1): 87–95.

SCHWARZBACH, M., 1950: Das Klima der Vorzeit. Stuttgart: Enke.

SCHWERDTFEGER, W., 1960a: Der südliche Polarwirbel. MR 13 (3): 89–93.

— 1960b: The seasonal variation of the strength of the southern circumpolar vortex. MWR 88 (6): 203–208.

SCORER, R. S., 1949: Theory of waves in the lee of mountains. QJRMS 75: 41–56.

— 1951a: Clear-air turbulence over Europe. W 6 (2): 59–60. (3 K–177.)

— 1951b: Gravity waves in the atmosphere. AMGBA 4: 176–193.

— 1951c: On the stability of stably stratified shearing layers. QJRMS 77 (331): 76–84. (2.7–73.)

— 1952: High-level winds and temperatures for jet aircraft operations. Discussion. QJRMS 78: 449.

— 1953a: Forecasting mountain and lee waves. MML 82 (974): 232–234. (5.1–91.)

— 1953b: Theory of airflow over mountains. II. The flow over a ridge. QJRMS 79: 70–83.

— 1954: Turbulence generated in standing waves. QJRMS 80 (346): 629–630. (6.3–160.)

— 1955: Turbulence generated in standing waves. QJRMS 81 (350): 619. (7.5–174.)

— 1956: Airflow over and in the lee of an isolated hill. In: OSTIV Publication IV. and SAR 1957 (2).

— 1957: Clear air turbulence in the jet stream. W 12 (9): 275–282. (9.2–212.)

— 1958a: Natural aerodynamics. London: Pergamon.

— 1958b: Airflow over mountains: indeterminacy of solution. QJRMS 84 (360): 182–183. (10.6–242.)

— 1959: Turbulence produced in waves of large amplitude. ACSI 117–120.

— and H. KLIEFORTH, 1959: Theory of mountain waves of large amplitude. QJRMS 85 (364): 131–143.

SCRASE, F. J., 1949: Wind and temperature measurements up to 30 km. Nature, London, 164 (4170): 572. (4 F–46.)

— 1951: Radiosonde and radarwind measurements in the stratosphere over the British Isles. QJRMS 77 (333): 483–488. (4 F–85.)

— 1954: Turbulence in the upper air, as shown by radar-wind and radiosonde measurements. QJRMS 80 (345): 369–376. (5.11–123.)

SEILKOPF, H., 1939: Maritime Meteorologie. Handbuch der Fliegerwetterkunde, Bd. II. Berlin: Radetzki.

— 1952: Modelle der atmosphärischen Großzirkulation. BDWUS 35: 68–71. (3.10–77.)

SEKERA, Z., 1948: Helmholtz waves in a linear temperature field with vertical wind shear. JM 5: 93–102.

— 1949: The distribution of kinetic energy in certain steady barotropic currents. JM 6 (5): 321–329. (4 G–28.)

SELLICK, N. P., 1950: High winds over Southern Rhodesia. W 5: 67. (4 E–267.)

SEREBRENY, S. M., 1951: Some preliminary considerations of the jet stream over Japan. Pan American World Airways, Inc., Pacific Alaska Div., TR No. 41. (4 G–82.)

— 1955: The jet stream structure over the Pacific. N 4 (6): 231–241. (7.5–125.)

— and E. J. WIEGMAN, 1953: Characteristic properties of the jet stream over the Pacific. Case history No. 1, Pt. 1. Pan American World Airways, Inc., Pacific-Alaska Div., Contr. N 189 s–90981, TR No. 1. (5.7–11.)

— — 1954: Certain characteristic features of the jet stream and their application to airline operations. Met. Section, Pan American World Airways, Inc., Pac.-Al.-Div., 37 pp. (6.7–173.)

SEREBRENY, S. M., E. J. WIEGMAN, and W. F. CARLSON, 1954*a*: Characteristic properties of the jet stream over the Pacific. Case history No. 1, Pt. 2. Pan American World Airways, Inc., Pac.-Al.-Div., Met. Dep. Contract N 189 s–96835, TR No. 4. (7.5–124.)

— — — 1954*b*: Characteristic properties of the jet stream over the Pacific. Case history No. 2, Pt. 1. Pan American World Airways, Inc., Pacific-Al.-Div., Met. Dep. Contract N 189 s–96835, TR No. 2. (6.7–172.)

— — and R. G. HADFIELD, 1957: Study of jet stream conditions in the Northern Hemisphere during summer. Pan American World Airways, Inc., Met. Dep. Contract N 600 (188)–44188 (Project AROWA), TR No. 6. (9.7–32.)

— — — 1960: Models of jet stream structure. Pan American World Airways, Inc., Pacific Alaska Division, Meteorology Dept., TR No. 9. U.S. NWRF, Contract No. N 189 (188) 42246A NWRF 20-0160-031.

SERRA, A., 1955: Su alcune caratteristiche stagionale delle correnti atmosferiche nell'alta troposfera e bassa stratosfera sull'isola di Sardegna e sul Mediterraneo occidentale. RMA 15 (3/4): 3–22. (8.4–243.)

SHAFFER, R., 1957: On the existence of a systematic error in the measurement of winds aloft. BAMS 38 (3): 138–139. (8.9–117.)

SHAPIRO, R., 1956: Further evidence of a solar-weather effect. JM 13: 335–340.

— 1959: A comparison of the response of the North American and European surface pressure distributions to large geomagnetic disturbances. JM 16 (5): 569–572.

— and F. WARD, 1960: The time-space spectrum of the geostrophic meridional kinetic energy. JM 17 (6): 621–626.

SHAPLEY, H., 1953: Climatic change, evidence, causes and effects. Cambridge: Harvard Univ. Press.

SHAW, W. N., 1904: On the general circulation of the atmosphere in middle and higher latitudes. MWR 32: 264–267.

SHAW, Sir N., and E. AUSTIN, 1928: Manual of Meteorology. Vol. II.: Comparative Meteorology. Cambridge. (4 E–32.)

SHEPPARD, P. A., 1951: The jet stream and related phenomena. Science Progress 39 (155): 483–495. (4 G–83.)

— 1954*a*: Momentum flux and meridional motion in the general circulation. AMST: 103–108. (6.3–112.)

— 1954*b*: The vertical transfer of momentum in the general circulation. AMGBA 7: 114–124. (5.11–82.)

— 1959: Dispersione di particelle radioattive nell'atmosfera. RMA 19 (3): 3–14.

SHERMAN, L., 1952: On the scalar-vorticity and horizontal-divergence equations. JM 9: 359–366.

— 1953: Estimates of the vertical velocity based on the vorticity equation. JM 10 (5): 399–400. (5.6–128.)

— 1954: A note on extrapolation. BAMS 35 (5): 234–235. (6.7–141.)

— and H. RIEHL, 1953: On the propagation of isolines. JM 10 (3): 231–232. (4.11–78.)

SHIMADA, Y., 1958: Jet stream in the Far East. JMRT 10 (3): 217–221. (10.2–253.)

SHIMIZU, T., 1958: Upper wind pattern of extratropical cyclone at sea in the Far East. JMRT 10 (5): 383–396. (11.2–193.)

SHOWALTER, A. K., 1943: The tornado: an analysis of antecedent meteorological conditions. Washington, D.C., USWB, 161 pp.

— 1956: A simple technique for measuring radius of curvature of streamlines. BAMS 37 (7): 368–369. (9.5–92.)

— and J. R. FULKS, 1943: Preliminary report on tornadoes. Washington, D.C., USWB. (1 E–88.)

SIELAND, K., 1951: Scherungswindnomogramme. AM 4 (7/9): 399–402. (3.9–30.)

SILVESTER, R., 1955: Method of obtaining the gradient wind from the geostrophic wind. MML 84 (1001): 348–350. (7.4–83.)

SIMPSON, G. C., 1957: Further studies in world climate. QJRMS 83: 459–485.

— 1959: World temperature during the Pleistocene. QJRMS 85 (366): 332–349.

SINHA, K. L., 1958: A method of working out the rate of ascent of the balloon from the value of the coefficient of aerodynamic resistance. BPA 30 (4): 297–303.

— 1959: Evaluation of the constant of the balloon-ascent formula at different Reynolds numbers from the value of the coefficient of aerodynamic resistance JM 16: 692.

SINHA, M. C., 1960: Upper air standing waves over Kabul valley. BPA 32 (3/4): 215–236.

SITTKUS, A., 1958: Beobachtungen an radioaktiven Schwaden von atomtechnischen Versuchen im Hinblick auf atmosphärische Transport- und Austauschprobleme. BPA 30 (2/3): 200–206.

SMAGORINSKY, J., 1953: The dynamical influence of large-scale heat sources and sinks on the quasi-stationary mean motions of the atmosphere. QJRMS 79: 342–366.

SMEYBE, S. J., 1958: Computation of precipitation from large-scale vertical motion. JM 15 (6): 547–560.

SMITH, C. D., 1950: The widespread smoke layer from Canadian forest fires during late September 1950. MWR 78 (9): 180–184. (2.9–60.)

SMITH, J. R., 1958: Project Skyhook. Raven Industries, Inc., Sioux Falls, S. Dak., Contract Nonr 2358 (00) Report, May 1, 1957, and May 1, 1958. (11.2–136.)

SMITH, L. B., 1954: A study comparing winds aloft measuring equipment at Salton Sea test base. Sandia Corporation, Albuquerque. N.M., Report SC-3512 (TR). (9.7–127.)

— 1960: The measurement of winds between 100,000 and 300,000 ft by use of chaff rockets. JM 17 (3): 296–310.

SNELLMAN, L. W., 1953: On changes in the zonal wind profile and their relation to forecasting. BAMS 34 (3): 91–100. (5.6–83.)

SOLBERG, H., 1930: Das Zyklonenproblem. Verh. III. Intern. Kongreß für techn. Mechanik.

— 1939: Le mouvement d'inertie de l'atmosphère stable et son rôle dans la théorie des cyclones. Procès-Verbaux, Mét., Un. Géod. Géophys. Intern., Edinburgh 1936. II. 66–82.

SOOS, E., 1959: Windmaxima mit und ohne Nullschichtcharakter. MR 12 (4): 118–120.

SOROCHAN, O. G., 1957: Nekotorye soobrazheniia o periode letnego mussona Vostochnoi Azii. (Some considerations on the nature of summer monsoon in Eastern Asia.) Leningrad, Glavnaia Geofizicheskaia Observatoriia, Trudy, No. 71: 184–208.

South Africa, Department of Transport, Weather Bureau, 1950: Upper winds in Southern Africa, 282 pp. Pretoria. (4 E–200.)

SPANGENBERG, W. W., 1949: Über die leuchtenden Nachtwolken der Jahre 1932–1941. Wetter und Klima 2 (1–2): 15–23. (1.3–139.)

SPAR, J., 1949: Energy changes in the mean atmosphere. JM 6 (6): 411–415. (1.3–50.)

— 1950: Synoptic studies of the potential energy in cyclones. JM 7 (1): 48–53. (1.5–43.)

— 1956: Vorticity development in the cyclone of Nov. 6, 1953. NYU, Res. Div., Dep. of Oceanogr. and Met., Contr. Nonr-285 (09), Progress Report No. 3. (7.10–161.)

— 1957: A note on the stability of baroclinic waves. JM 14 (2): 146–140. (8.8–196.)

— *et al.*, 1955: Vorticity changes in an east coastal cyclone. NYU, Res. Division, Contr. Nonr-285 (09), Progress Report No. 2 (8.1–186.)

— and S. PETTERSSEN, 1956: Comments on "A general survey of factors influencing development at sea level." JM 13 (1): 123–124. (7.8–138.)

SPRENGER, K., 1960: Die jahreszeitlichen Anomalien der Driftrichtung in der tiefen Ionosphäre nach Beobachtungen auf 245 KHz. ZM 14 (1): 6–16.

STALEY, D. O., 1957: A study of tropopause formation. BPA 29 (4): 290–316.

— 1960: Evaluation of potential-vorticity changes near the tropopause and the related vertical motions, vertical advection of vorticity, and transfer of radioactive debris from stratosphere to troposphere. JM 17 (6): 591–620.

STARAS, H., 1955: Forward scattering of radio waves by anisotropic turbulence. Institute of Radio Engineers, Proc. IRE. 43 (10): 1374–1380.

STARK, P., 1957: The weather and circulation of Jan. 1957: a month with a persistent block in the Gulf of Alaska. MWR 85 (1): 19–27. (9.9–159).

STARR, V. P., 1948*a*: Essay on the general circulation of the earth's atmosphere. JM 5 (2): 39–43. (7.8–128.)

— 1948*b*: On the production of kinetic energy in the atmosphere. JM 5 (5): 193–196. (8.1–187.)

— 1951*a*: Applications of energy principles to the general circulation. CM 568–576. (3.5–10.)

— 1951*b*: The physical basis for the general circulation. CM 541–550. (3.8–9.)

— 1953*a*: Note concerning the nature of the large-scale eddies in the atmosphere. T 5 (4): 494–498. (5.10–148.)

— 1953*b*: Some aspects of the dynamics of cyclones. GRP No. 24: 9–17.

— 1954: Commentaries concerning research on the general circulation. T 6: 268–272.

— 1959: Note concerning the influence of rotation on convection. T 11 (3): 360–363.

— 1960: Questions concerning the energy of stratospheric motions. AMGBA 12 (1): 1–7.

— and R. R. LONG, 1953: The flux of angular momentum in rotating model experiments. GRP 24: 103–113. (6.1–139.)

— and R. M. WHITE, 1951: A hemispherical study of atmospheric angular momentum balance. QJRMS 77 (332): 215–225. (2.6–52.)

— — 1952*a*: Note on the seasonal variation of the meridional flux of angular momentum. QJRMS 78 (335): 62–69. (3.4–121.)

— — 1952*b*: Schemes for the study of hemispheric exchange processes. QJRMS 78: 407–410. (3.10–116.)

— — 1954*a*: Two years of momentum flux data for 13° N. MIT, Dep. of Met., Contr. AF 19 (122)–153. Studies of the atmospheric circulation, Final Report, Pt. 1. (8.1–196.)

— — 1954*b*: Balance requirements of the general circulation. GRP No. 35. (7.8–129.)

— — and E. LORENZ, 1950: Preliminary studies of the eddy momentum flux evaluated from observed wind soundings. MIT, General Circulation Project, Report No. 5. (3.5–148.)

STARRETT, L. G., 1949: The relation of precipitation patterns in North America to certain types of jet streams at the 300-mb level. JM 6 (5): 347–352. (4 G–29.)

STEVENS, A. W., 1936: The first photograph ever made showing the division between the troposphere and the stratosphere and also the actual curvature of the earth—photographed from an elevation of 72,395 feet, the highest point ever reached by man. Nat. Geographic Magazine. (5 D–90.)

STEWART, C. D., 1924: The measurement of upper wind velocities by observations of artificial clouds. GMOPN No. 38.

STEWART, N. G., 1960: Radioaktive Indikatoren in der Atmosphäre. Endeavour 19 (76): 197–201.

STIEFELMAIER, C. A., 1955: Operational aspects of the jet stream. N 4 (6): 227–231. (7.5–126.)

STÖRMER, C., 1935: Measurements of luminous night clouds in Norway, 1933 and 1934. Astrophysica Norvegica, Oslo, 1 (3): 87–114. (4 F–12.)

STOLOV, H. L., 1955: Tidal wind fields in the atmosphere. JM 12 (2): 117–140. (6.8–267.)

STOMMEL, H., 1951: Determination of the lateral eddy diffusivity in the climatological mean Gulf Stream. T 3 (1): 43. (2.11–200.)

— 1954: Circulation in the North Atlantic Ocean. Nature, No. 173.

STOREBØ, P. B., 1960: The exchange of air between stratosphere and troposphere. JM 17 (5): 547–554.

Strategic Air Command Headquarters, 1st Weather Group, 1954: Forecasting Manual for SAC Operations. Offutt Air Force Base, Nebraska.

STREIFF-BECKER, R., 1942: Neue Untersuchungen über Föhn in den Schweizer Alpen. Schweizerische Naturforschende Gesellschaft, Denkschriften 74 (4): 244–278. (1.11–104.)

SUDA, K., 1955: On the cold wave of January 1954 in the Far East. GPA 32: 159–169. (8.3–223.)

— 1956: A persistent cold-outbreak in the Far East related to the blocking situation. JMSJ Ser. 2, 34 (3): 137–146. (8.7–189.)

— 1957: A large-scale upper level cyclone over eastern Siberia and its effect on the Far Eastern weather. GMT 28 (1): 9–20. (9.11–193.)

— and T. ASAKURA, 1955: A study on the unusual "Bai-u" season in 1954 by means of northern hemisphere upper air mean charts. JMSJ 33 (6): 233–244.

SUGIMOTO, T., 1957: Fluctuation of jet stream in the Far Eastern Asia. JMRT 9 (7): 463–466. (9.9–217.)

— 1958: Fluctuation of jet stream in the Far East Asia. Pt. 2. JMRT 10 (7): 554–561. (10.6–239.)

SUMNER, E. J., 1954: A study of blocking in the Atlantic-European sector of the Northern Hemisphere. QJRMS 80 (345): 402–416. (5.11–97.)

SUTCLIFFE, R. C., 1938: On development in the field of barometric pressure. QJRMS 64: 495–504.

— 1939: Cyclonic and anticyclonic development. QJRMS 65: 518–524.

— 1940: Rapid development where cold and warm air masses move toward each other. Synopt. Div. Techn. Mem. No. 12, Air Min. Great Brit.

— 1947: A contribution to the problem of development. QJRMS 73: 370–383.

— 1949: The general circulation of the atmosphere. QJRMS 75 (326): 417–434. (1.2–81.)

— 1950: Variations in the length of the day. MML 79 (942): 353–354. (2.8–62.)

— 1951: Mean upper contour patterns of the Northern Hemisphere—the thermal synoptic view-point. QJRMS 77 (333): 435–440. (2.11–74.)

— 1960: The Mediterranean in relation to the general circulation. MAB 9 (1): 125–133.

— and J. K. BANNON, 1956: Seasonal changes in the upper air conditions in the Mediterranean-Middle East area. IUGG pp. 322–334. (8.7–177.)

— and A. G. FORSDYKE, 1950: The theory and use of upper air thickness patterns in forecasting. QJRMS 76 (328): 189–217. (1.6–21.)

— and J. S. SAWYER, 1954: Forecasting winds up to the 100-mb level by the contour-chart technique. AMST: 155–159. (6.3–78.)

SUTTON, O. G., 1932: A theory of eddy diffusion in the atmosphere. Proc. Roy. Soc. London A 135 (826): 143–165.

— 1953: Micrometeorology. London: McGraw-Hill.

SVERDRUP, H. U., 1952: Oceanography for Meteorologists. London: Allen & Unwin.

SYONO, S., and M. AIHARA, 1957: Some characteristic features of barotropic disturbances. Pt. 1. JMSJ Ser. 2, 35 (1): 12–18. 35 (2): 128–136. (9.11–132.)

— A. KASAHARA, and Y. SEKIGUCHI, 1955: Some statistical properties of the atmospheric disturbance at the 500-mb level. JMSJ Ser. 2, 33: 23–30.

TABA, H., 1959: The horizontal and vertical wind profiles of the subtropical and polar jet for January 1–7, 1956, and the variation of the equivalent barotropic level. T 11 (4): 441–451.

TANATAR, I., 1948: Aerologiia: metod sharov-pilotov, nabliudaemykh s odnogo punkta. (Aerology: single station method of pilot balloon observations.) Moscow: Voen.-Izdat. (8.7–12.)

TANCK, H.-J., 1960: Einige Grundzüge des Klimas im Inneren des nordamerikanischen Kontinents (mit besonderer Berücksichtigung der Strecke Montreal–San Francisco). Technischer Bericht, Deutsche Lufthansa, Hamburg, 37 pp.

Tateno, Aerological Observatory, 1954: The relay observation of upper wind over Honjo and Tateno in the winter season 1951, 1952. TAT 5 (3): 199–218. (7.8–55.)

TAYLOR, G. I., 1921: Experiments with rotating fluids. Proc. Roy. Soc. London A 100: 114–121.

— 1924: Experiments with rotating fluids. Proc. 1st Intern. Congress Appl. Mech., Delft pp. 89–96.

TAYLOR, R. C., 1960: Mean monthly meridional cross-sections of temperature from the South Pole to the North Pole near 170° E—a preliminary note. AMO 439–452.

TEICH, M., 1955: Beitrag zum Problem der allgemeinen Zirkulation, insbesondere der mitteltroposphärischen Hochdruckgebiete der nördlichen Nordhemisphäre. DDR, Met. und Hydr. Dienst, Abhandlungen 5 (36). (8.9–170.)

TEISSERENC DE BORT, L., 1887: Étude sur la synthése de la répartition des pressions à la surface du globe. Bureau Centr. Mét. de France, I Mémoires, p. C 1.

TEPPER, M., 1950: A proposed mechanism of squall lines: the pressure jump line. JM 7: 21–29.

— and Staff Members, 1954: Pressure jump lines in Midwestern United States. USWB, Research Paper No. 37, Washington, D.C.

TEWELES, S. JR., 1953: A test of the relation between precipitation and synoptic patterns at 200 and 300 mb. JM 10: 450–456.

— 1954: Jet stream detail with respect to other meteorological factors. AMST 188–192. (6.3–190.)

— 1958: Anomalous warming of the stratosphere over North America in early 1957. MWR 86 (10): 377–396.

— 1959: Structure and circulation of the stratosphere. IGY-Bulletin, National Academy of Sciences, No. 21.

— and F. G. FINGER, 1958: An abrupt change in stratospheric circulation beginning in Mid-January 1958. MWR 86 (1): 23–28.

— — 1960: Reduction of diurnal variations in the reported temperatures and heights of stratospheric constant-pressure surfaces. JM 17 (2): 177–194.

— L. ROTHENBERG, and F. G. FINGER, 1960: The circulation at the 10-mb constant pressure surface over North America and adjacent ocean areas, July 1957 through June 1958. MWR 88 (4): 137–150.

THURONYI, G., 1959: Selective annotated bibliography on propagation of acoustic and explosion waves in the atmosphere. Supplement 1959. AMS, Met. Abstracts and Bibliography, 10 (7): 1072–1098.

TOLEFSON, H. B., 1956: An investigation of vertical wind shear intensities from balloon soundings for application to airplane and missile-response problems. NACA, TN No. 3732. (9.11–88.)

TOLLNER, H., 1954: Die meteorologisch-klimatischen Ursachen der Gletscherschwankungen in den Ostalpen während der letzten zwei Jahrhunderte. Mitt. der Geogr. Ges. 96 (1–4): 31–74.

TRELOAR, H. M., 1948: Extreme winds in high levels. Weather Development and Research Bulletin, Melbourne, 10: 15–18. (4 G–17.)

— 1954: Geostrophic wind approximation in low latitudes. AMMM No. 7: 7–12. (7.2–195.)

TRENKLE, H., 1957: Die zonale Windkomponente im atlantisch-europäischen Sektor in Abhängigkeit von kurzperiodischen Schwankungen der Sonnenaktivität. MR 10 (1): 35–38. (8.7–248.)

TREWARTHA, G. T., 1954: An introduction to climate. New York: McGraw-Hill.

— 1958: Climate as related to the jet stream in the Orient. Erdkunde 12 (3): 205–214.

TRIEGAARDT, D. O., and G. M. E. KRAUS, 1956: Aerological study of polar outbreak in the African sector, Aug. 27–Sept. 1, 1956. Notos 5 (4): 229–234. (9.3–176.)

— — 1957: An example of wave disruption over Southern Africa. Notos 6 (1/2): 6–12. (10.2–201.)

TROWBRIDGE, C. C., 1907: On atmospheric currents at very great altitude. MWR 35: 390–397. (4 F–1.)

TSCHIRHART, G., 1959: Les perturbations atmosphériquès intéressants l'A. E. F. Méridionale. MNM No. 13. (11.6–272.)

TUCKER, G. B., 1957: Evidence of a mean meridional circulation in the atmosphere from surface wind observations. QJRMS 83 (357): 290–302. (8.10–143.)

— 1959: Mean meridional circulation in the atmosphere. QJRMS 85 (365): 209–224 and 86 (368): 277–281 (1960).

— 1960: The atmospheric budget of angular momentum. T 12 (2): 134–144.

TULL, W. J., 1957: Doppler Navigation. N 5 (6): 290–298.

University of California, at Los Angeles, Institute of Geophysics, 1950: Survey of data and theoretical analysis of the upper atmosphere. Contract Cwb 7904, Final Report. (4 F–52.)

University of Chicago, Department of Meteorology, 1947: On the general circulation of the atmosphere in middle latitudes. BAMS 28: 255–280. (4 G–6.)

— 1954: Report on an experiment with forecasting of cyclone development. Contract AF 19 (604)–390, TR No. 4. (6.6–104.)

— 1955: Experiments in forecasting the displacement of troughs and ridges, by the staff members, Weather Forecasting Research Center. C. W. Newton, ed. Contract AF 19 (604)–1293, TR No. 5, July 1955. (9.6–1.)

— Weather Forecasting Research Center 1956: An experiment in forecasting the displacement of 500-mb troughs and ridges. JM 13 (5): 421–432. (8.2–135.)

University of Michigan, Engineering Research Institute, 1955–56: Rocket-grenade experiment for upper atmosphere temperature and winds. Contr. DA-36-039 SC-64659, Project DA-3-17-02-001 etc. (9.3–155.)

U.S. Air Force 1948: Comparative and functional test of the U.S. Weather Bureau 500-gram and standard balloon ML-391/AM 1400-gram. Project No. 34824-5, Report Dec. 9, 1948. (3.7–55.)

— 1954: Comparison of high level aircraft and meteorological wind observations. MacDill Air Force Base, Florida. TN No. 3, Black Sheep Series VI, Sept. 1954.

— 1960: Handbook of Geophysics. Chapter 5.3.4: The structure of the jet stream. New York: Macmillan.

U.S. Air Force, Cambridge Research Center, 1956: Compilations of meteorologically useful data from Project "Moby Dick." July 1956. 10 vol. (8.3–25.)

U.S. Air Weather Service, 1950*a*: Preparation of weather maps and charts. AWS, Manual 105–22. (3.1–55.)

— 1950*b*: Theory and design of a gradient wind scale. AWS, TR 105–69. (3.2–21.)

U.S. Air Weather Service, 1951: High-level isotach analysis. AWS, Manual 105–26. (4 E–220.)

— 1952*a*: Bibliography on the jet stream. AWS Bibliography No. 12, 9 pp. (4 G–117), (6 B–136.)

— 1952*b*: Tropopause analysis and forecasting. U.S. AWS, TR 105–86. (5 D–241.)

— 1954*a*: Comparison of high-level aircraft and meteorological wind observations. TN No. 3, Black Sheep Ser. VI.

— 1954*b*: Mean contours, isotachs and isotherms over the Northern Hemisphere at the 300-, 200- and 100-mb levels. Jan., Feb., July and Aug. 1949. (No. 7 in a series of background reports for AWS Manual 105–50.) AWS TR 105–128. (9.8–9.)

— 1954*c*: Meteorological aspects of pressure pattern flight. AWS Manual 345–1 (rev.). (8.1–91.)

— 1954*d*: Radioactivity fall-out plots. AWS Manual 105–33. (7.4–294.)

— 1955: Winds over 100 knots in the Northern Hemisphere (No. 6 in a series of background reports for AWS Manual 105–50). TR 105–121. (8.9–237.)

— 1956*a*: 4-D analysis and forecasting procedures for optimum flight planning. AWS Manual 105–49. (8.8–82.)

— 1956*b*: Preliminary results of project cloud trail. AWS TR 105–132.

— 1956*c*: Studies of 2-hour and 4-hour upper-wind variabilities over Nevada. TR 105–141. (8.10–200.)

— 1956*d*: The Black Sheep System of forecasting winds for long-range jet aircraft. TR 105–139. (8 C–79.)

U.S. Bureau of Aeronautics (Navy), 1953*a*: Operational research into the detailed structure of the jet stream. Project AROWA, Task 15, TR No. 1. (5.8–111.)

— 1953*b*: Operational research into the detailed structure of the jet stream. Project AROWA (TED-UNL-MA-501.15), Second Quart. Prog. Rep., Jan. 1–April 1 1953. Techn. Rep. No. 2, Task 15, 59 pp. + appendix. (4 G–129, 5.8–111.)

U.S. Federal Civil Defence Administration, 1955: Construction of fallout plots from coded messages provided by the U.S. Weather Bureau. Advisory Bulletin No. 188. (7 E–180.)

U.S. Navy, 1954: Tables of winds and their aiding and retarding effect at 850, 700, 500 and 200 mb. Part I: North Pacific area. Part II: North Atlantic area. NAVAER 50-1c-526, Aerology Branch, Off. Chief Nav. Oper., 275 and 261 pp.

— 1958: The upper atmosphere. Preliminary research report on Task 26. NWRF 26-0958-013.

— 1959*a*: Jet stream probing, 1956–1958. NWRF 15-0159-017.

— 1959*b*: The synoptic stratosphere. NWRF 26-0359-023. (11.6–256.)

— 1960*a*: Upper wind extrapolation from 500-mb data. NWRF 26-0660-034, 28 pp.

— 1960*b*: Supplement to the synoptic stratosphere. NWRF 26-0760-036, 11 pp.

U.S. Office of Naval Operations, 1948–50: A study of the atmosphere between 30,000 and 100,000 feet. Preliminary report and Second, Third and Fourth Report. U.S. Office of Naval Operations NAVAER 50-1 R-224, 224A, 224B, 224C. (6.6–67.)

— 1952: Practical methods of weather analysis and prognoses. U.S. Office of Naval Operations. NA 50 1 P 502. (5 D–216.)

U.S. Weather Bureau, 1952: Normal weather charts for the Northern Hemisphere. TP No. 21.

— 1955: Fallout of radioactive debris. Circular Letter 7–55. (7 E–182.)

— 1956: Upper air fallout data code. USWB. (7 E–193.)

— 1959: 10-mb Synoptic Weather Maps, Three Times Monthly, July 1957 through June 1958, of the IGY Period. USWB.

UWAI, K., 1952: Analysis of a cyclone in middle latitudes near Japan. JMSJ 30 (10): 313–328. (5.3–103.)

VÄISÄLÄ, V., 1928: Beobachtungen über die Anvisierungsgenauigkeit von Pilotballonen. MZ 45: 351–354.

— 1953: A new method of radio direction finding designed especially for the Finnish (Väisälä) radiosonde. I.U.G.G. Association of Met., Brussels 1951, Procès-Verbaux des Séances, Mémoires et Discussion. (7.3–116.)

— 1957: Radiation error of different radiosondes at Payerne 1956. GH 6 (1): 1–6. (9.7–129.)

— and Y. WILSKA, 1957: A graphical method for computing wind values from the Finnish radiotheodolite record. GH 6 (1): 7–12. (9.6–109.)

VÄISÄNEN, A., 1954: Comparison between the geostrophic and gradient wind in a case of westerly jet. GH 4 (4): 203–217. (8.3–232.)

VAN BEMMELEN, 1924: Der intertropische Teil der allgemeinen Zirkulation nach Beobachtungen in Batavia. MZ 41: 133.

VAN DEN DUNGEN, F. H., J. F. COX, and J. VAN MIEGHEM, 1950: Variations in the earth's angular velocity resulting from fluctuations in atmospheric and oceanic circulation. T 2 (4): 319–320. (2.8–63.)

— — — 1952: Les fluctuations saisonnières de la rotation du globe terrestre et la circulation atmosphérique générale. T 4 (1): 1–7. (4.2–105.)

— — — 1956: Seasonal fluctuations in the rate of rotation of the earth. In: BEER, A.: Vistas in astronomy, London 1955–1956. (11.2–185.)

— — — 1959: Sur les irrégularités de la rotation de la Terre. Brussels. Académie Royale de Belgique, Classe des Sciences, Bulletin. Ser. 5, 65 (1): 69–71. (11.4–236.)

VAN DER HAM, C. J., 1954: De Straalstrom. Hemel en Dampkring. 52 (11): 201–210. (6.11–203.)

VAN DER HOVEN, 1957: Power spectrum of horizontal wind speed in the frequency range from 0.0007 to 900 cycles per hour. JM 14: 160–164.

VAN LOON, H., 1955: A note on meridional atmospheric cross sections in the Southern Hemisphere. Notos 4 (2): 127–129. (8.4–103.)

— 1956*a*: Blocking action in the Southern Hemisphere. Pt. 1. Notos 5 (3): 171–175. (9.4–126.)

— 1956*b*: Description of a blocking situation in the central South Atlantic Ocean (April 29–May 11, 1956). Notos 5 (2): 117–119. (8.6–205.)

— 1960: Features of the atmospheric circulation in the South Pacific Ocean during the whaling seasons 1955–1956 and 1956–1957. AMO 274–280.

VAN MIEGHEM, J., 1939: Sur l'existence de l'air tropical froid et de l'effect de foehn dans l'atmosphère libre. Mém. Inst. Roy. Mét. Belg., No. 12, 32 pp. (5 D–105.)

— 1944*a*: Forme intrinsèque du critère d'instabilité dynamique de E. KLEINSCHMIDT. Bull. Acad. Belg. Cl. Sci., ser. 5, 30: 19–33.

— 1944*b*: Relation d'identité entre la stabilité de l'equilibre dynamique de E. KLEINSCHMIDT et la stabilité des oscillations d'inertie de l'atmosphère terrestre. Bull. Acad. Belg. Cl. Sci., ser. 5, 30: 134–143.

— 1945: Interprétations énergétiques du critère d'instabilité de E. KLEINSCHMIDT. Bull. Acad. Belg. Cl. Sci., ser. 5, 31: 345–352.

— 1946: Sur la stabilité du courant géostrophique. LM 9–33.

— 1948: L'instabilité hydrodynamique et les perturbations du courant zonal d'ouest. AMGBA 1 (2): 143–148. (1.4–50.)

— 1950: Sur la circulation transversale associée à un courant atmospherique. T 2: 52–55. (6–37, 4 G–56.)

VAN MIEGHEM, J., 1951: Hydrodynamic instability, CM. (3.8–11.)

— 1952*a*: Seasonal fluctuations of the earth's rotation and the general circulation of the atmosphere. BDWUS No. 35: 24–26. (5.4–102.)

— 1952*b*: Sur les équations du mouvement de l'atmosphere integrées suivant la verticale. Belgium, Inst. Royale Mét., Publications Sér. B. No. 3. (6.4–141.)

— 1952*c*: Großräumige Energieumsetzungen in der Atmosphäre. AM 5 (6): 169–174. (4.6–100.)

— 1955: Note on energy transfer and conversion in large atmospheric disturbances. QJRMS 81 (347): 18–22. (6.5–120.)

— 1956*a*: Vorticity transport in the atmosphere (Summary). IUGG 415–429. (8.10–136.)

— 1956*b*: Réflexions sur le transport et la production du moment et de l'énergie cinetiques dans l'atmosphère et sur l'existence de circulations méridiennes moyennes. BPA 29 (2): 55–82.

— 1956*c*: On the existence of mean meridional circulations. BDW 22: 124–125.

— 1959: Les ballons-sondes plafonnant à un niveau barique constant et les sondes transocéaniques. Brussels, Ciel et Terre, 75 (3/4): 77–90. (11.4–201.)

— 1961: Clear Air Turbulence. An Essay Review. WMO Bulletin 10 (1): 18–21.

— and P. DEFRISE, and J. VAN ISACKER, 1959: On the selective role of the motion systems in the atmospheric general circulation. RMV 230–239.

VAN ROOY, M. P., 1957: Meteorology of the Antarctic. Weather Bur., Dep. of Transport, Pretoria. (Printed: Government Printer, Pretoria.)

VEDERMAN, J., 1954: The life cycles of jet streams and extratropical cyclones. BAMS 35 (6): 239–244. (6.7–174.)

— and B. DUBOFSKY, 1959: An operational technique for the forecasting of flow patterns in the upper troposphere. BAMS 40 (5): 233–239. (11.3–6.)

VENKATESWARLU, V., and Y. H. GANGAL, 1955: Rate of ascent of pilot balloons. IJMG 6 (4): 363–366. (7.9–87.)

VENKITESHWARAN, S. P., 1950*a*: Winds at 10 km and above over India and its neighbourhood. National Institute of Sciences of India, Proc. 16 (1): 19–27. (5.4–167.)

— 1950*b*: Winds at 10 km and above over India and its neighbourhood. India, Met. Dep., Memoirs 28, Part 2: 55–120. (4 F–63.)

— and S. YEGNANARAYANAN, 1951: Radar measurements of upper winds over Poona during the southwest monsoon. IJMG 2 (3): 228–232. (3.7–146.)

VETTIN, F., 1884/85: Experimentelle Darstellung von Luftbewegungen unter dem Einfluß von Temperaturunterschieden und Rotationsimpulsen. MZ 1: 227–230; 1: 271–276; 2: 172–183.

VIALAR, J., 1950: Abaque pour la détermination des vents géostrophiques et du gradient. Journal Scientifique de la Météorologie 2 (8): 131–141. (2.3–14.)

VIAUT, A., 1956: Quelques considérations sur le champ de pression et les perturbations du front polaire austral le sudouest de l'Océan Indien. IUGG 290–301. (8.10–104.)

VÍTEK, V., 1955: Analysa ageostroficke vorticity. (Analysis of ageostrophic vorticity). Meteorologicke Zprávy, Prague, 8 (4): 95–96. (8.3–153.)

VITVITSKII, G. N., 1956: Tsirkuliatsiia vozdukha nad Kitaem. (Atmospheric circulation over China.) ISG (Ser. Geog.) No. 2: 35–44. (10.6–183.)

VOSS, H., 1950: Lassen sich Vertikalbewegungen in der Atmosphäre mit Hilfe der Windmessung durch Funkmeßgeräte (elektrische Windmessung) erfassen? AM 3 (5–6): 175–178. (2.1–125.)

VUORELA, L. A., 1948: Contribution to the aerology of the tropical Atlantic. JM 5: 115–117.

— 1950: Synoptic aspects of tropical regions of the Atlantic Ocean, West Africa and South America. Helsinki Univ., Meteorologian Laitos, Mitteilungen No. 67. (2.4–27.)

VUORELA, L. A., 1953: On the air flow connected with the invasion of upper tropical air over Northwestern Europe. Helsinki, Meteorologian Laitos, Mitteilungen No. 75. (5 D–244.)

— 1954: Über die Luftbewegung im Zusammenhang mit Vorstößen tropischer Luft in höheren Schichten über Nordwesteuropa. MAB 2 (3): 152–172. (8.3–125.)

— 1957*a*: A study of vertical velocity distribution in some jet stream cases over Western Europe. GH 6 (2): 68–90.

— 1957*b*: On the observed zonal and meridional circulations at latitudes 15° N and 30° N in winter. GH 6 (2): 106–120. (9.7–161.)

WAGNER, A., 1931: Zur Aerologie des indischen Monsuns. GBG 30: 196–238.

— 1940: Klimaänderungen und Klimaschwankungen. Braunschweig: Vieweg.

WAHL, E. W., 1953: Changes in the circulation reflected in the occurrence and intensity of weather singularities. GRP 24: 129–141. (6.7–168.)

— 1955: Singularitäten des Wetterablaufes und die allgemeine Zirkulation der Atmosphäre. Was verbirgt sich hinter Begriffen wie: Eisheilige, Schafskälte, Altweibersommer und Weihnachtstauwetter. Umschau, Frankfurt a. M., 55 (18): 545–547. (7.2–251.)

WALLINGTON, C. E., 1959: An introduction to lee waves in the atmosphere. SAR 34 (3): 187–190 and OSTIV Publication V. (11.1–231.)

WALTER, A., 1927: Results of observations on the direction and velocity of the upper air current over South Indian Ocean. GM 39, 32 pp.

WARES, G. W., 1953: Terminology of atmospheric shells. BAMS 34 (5): 221. (8.3–65.)

WARNECKE, G., 1956: Ein Beitrag zur Aerologie der arktischen Stratosphäre. MAB 3 (3).

WARNER, J., and E. G. BOWEN, 1953: A new method of studying the fine structure of air movements in the atmosphere. T 5 (1): 36–41. (5.2–102.)

WASKO, P. E., 1952: The control-line method of constructing prognostic charts BAMS 33 (6): 233–236. (4.6–58.)

WEBER, F., 1959: Monographie der Strahlströme. DFS Forschungsbericht No. 5.

WEBER, S., 1952: Studie über Vertikalgeschwindigkeiten in der hohen Troposphäre innerhalb starker Windfelder. BDWUS 35: 124–132. (3.11–166.)

WEEKS, K., 1954: Reviews of modern meteorology 11: The physical state of the upper atmosphere. QJRMS 80: 2–15.

WEGE, K., 1957: Druck-, Temperatur- und Strömungsverhältnisse über der Nordhalbkugel. MAB 5 (4).

— 1958: Druck- und Temperaturverhältnisse der Stratosphäre über der Nordhalbkugel in den Monaten März, Mai, September, November und Dezember. MAB 7 (1).

— *et al.*, 1958: Mean seasonal conditions of the atmosphere at altitudes of 20 to 30 km and cross sections along selected meridians in the Northern Hemisphere. MAB 6 (4).

WEGENER, A., 1929: Die Entstehung der Kontinente und Ozeane, 4. Aufl. Braunschweig: Vieweg.

WEICKMANN, L., and B. HAURWITZ, 1929: Mechanik und Thermodynamik der Atmosphäre. In: B. GUTENBERG, Lehrbuch der Geophysik, pp. 917–935.

WEICKMANN, L. JR., 1960: Häufigkeitsverteilung und Zugbahnen von Depressionen im mittleren Osten. MR 13 (2): 33–38.

WEISNER, A. G., 1956: Measurement of winds at elevations of 30 to 80 km by the rocket-grenade experiment. JM 13 (1): 30–39. (7.8–185.)

WELLS, H. W., 1958: Upper atmospheric winds, absorption and other special projects in the U.S. program in ionospheric physics. "Geophysics and the IGY," Amer. Geoph. Union, Publ. No. 590, p. 49–54.

WENGER, R., 1917: Die Steiggeschwindigkeit der Gummiballone und die Turbulenz in der Atmosphäre. Annalen der Hydrogr. u. Marit. Meteorologie 45 (4): 121–137. (3 K–8.)

WERNER, J., 1952: Radiosondehöhen und temperaturbedingte Druckdosenkorrektionen im Spiegel gleichzeitiger Radarmessungen. BDWUS 35: 320–322. (3.10–67.)

WEXLER, H., 1950: The great smoke pall—September 24–30, 1950. WW 3 (6): 129–134. (2.3–46.)

— 1951: Spread of the Krakatoa volcanic dust clouds as related to the high-level circulation. BAMS 32 (2): 48–51. (4 E–225.)

— 1953: Radiation balance oı the earth as a factor in climatic change. In: H. SHAPLEY, Climatic Change, pp. 73–105. Harvard Univ. Press.

— 1955: Circulation of the atmosphere. Scientific Amer., N.Y., 193 (3): 114–124. (9.3–174.)

— 1958: A meteorologist looks at the upper atmosphere. In: American Academy of Arts and Sciences: "Atmospheric explorations." Cambridge, M.I.T. pp. 79–100. (11.1–298.)

— 1959: Seasonal and other temperature changes in the Antarctic atmosphere. QJRMS 85 (365): 196–208.

— 1960*a*: Possible causes of climatic fluctuations. In: Dynamics of Climate. Editor: R. L. PFEFFER, pp. 93–95. New York.

— 1960*b*: Seasonal and other temperature changes in the Antarctic atmosphere (Summary). AMO p. 463.

— and S. FRITZ, 1960: Tiros reveals cloud formations. Science, 131 (3415): 1708–1710. 10. Juni, 1960.

— and W. B. MORELAND, 1957: Winds and temperatures in the Arctic stratosphere. Polar Atmosph. Sympos., Pt. 1: 71–84. London: Pergamon.

— — W. S. WEYANT, 1960: A preliminary report on ozone observation at Little America, Antarctica. MWR 88 (2): 43–54.

WEYANT, W. S., 1960: Extrapolation to the 50-mb level from 100-mb data in Antarctica. MWR 88 (7): 251–255.

WHIPPLE, F. J. W., 1935: The propagation of sound to great distances. QJRMS 61 (261): 285–308.

WHITE, R. M., 1949: The role of mountains in the angular momentum balance of the atmosphere. JM 6 (5): 353–355. (1.2–83.)

— 1951: On the energy balance of the atmosphere. TAGU 32 (3): 391–396. (3.6–82.)

— and D. S. COOLEY, 1952: The large-scale vertical eddy stress in the free atmosphere. TAGU 33 (4): 502–506. (4.8–95.)

— — 1956: Kinetic-energy spectrum of meridional motion in the mid-troposphere. JM 13 (1): 67–69. (7.8–124.)

— and G. F. NOLAN, 1960: A preliminary study of the potential to kinetic energy conversion process in the stratosphere. T 12 (2): 145–148.

— and B. SALTZMAN, 1956: On conversions between potential and kinetic energy in the atmosphere. T 8 (3): 357–368. (8.7–168.)

WIDGER, W. K., JR., 1949: A study of the flow of angular momentum in the atmosphere. JM 6 (5): 291–299. (1.2–82.)

— 1952: Survey of available information on the wind fields between the surface and the lower stratosphere. AFS No. 25, 154 pp. (6.1–13), (6 B–140.)

WIIN-NIELSEN, A., 1959*a*: On a graphical method for an approximate determination of the vertical velocity in the mid-troposphere. T 11 (4): 432–440.

— 1959*b*: A study of energy conversion and meridional circulation for the large-scale motion in the atmosphere. MWR 87 (9): 319–332.

WILKINS, E. M., 1949: Relation between speed and latitudinal position of the belt of strongest westerlies and the location of troughs and ridges aloft. U of C, Dep. of Met., Contract N6ori, Task Order 23, Rep. Nov. 1949. (6.4–149.)

WILLETT, H. C., 1944: Descriptive Meteorology. New York: Academic Press. (4 G–5.)

— 1950: The circulation of the upper troposphere and lower stratosphere. Collected papers presented at the Centennial Celebration, Washington, D.C., Sept. 13–17, 1948. American Association for the Advancement of Science, pp. 192–301. (2.5–70.)

— 1953: Atmospheric and oceanic circulation as factors in glacial-interglacial changes of climate. In: H. SHAPLEY, Climatic Change, pp. 51–71.

— *et al.*, 1940: Report on experiment in five-day weather forecasting. MIT and Woods Hole; Papers in Physical Oceanography and Meteorology, 8 (3). (2 A–100.)

WILLIAMS, J. E. D., 1957: Navigational aspects of turboprop operation on the North Atlantic. JINL 10 (1): 31–46. (8.6–71.)

WINSTON, J. S., 1955: Physical aspects of rapid cyclogenesis in the Gulf of Alaska. T 7 (4): 481–500. (7.8–139.)

— 1960: Some new data on the longitudinal dimensions of planetary waves. JM 17 (5): 522–531.

WIPPERMANN, F., 1951: Zur Frage des Einflusses der Land- und Meerverteilung auf die Lage der quasistationären Tröge in einer atmosphärischen Zonalzirkulation. AMGBA 4: 112–121. (3.4–117.)

— 1952: Die Konfiguration mittlerer Höhenströmungsfelder und ihre Ursachen. T 4 (2): 112–117. (4.4–106.)

— 1956: Numerische Untersuchungen zur zeitlichen Änderung der Spektralverteilung kinetischer Energie für eine zweidimensionale, divergenz- und reibungsfreie Strömung. AMGBA 9 (1): 1–18. (7.5–118.)

WÖRNER, H., 1935: Beobachtung leuchtender Nachtwolken. MZ 52: 379. (4 F–14.)

WOLFF, P. M., 1955: Quantitative determination of long waves and their time variations. JM 12 (6): 536–541. (7.5–127.)

— and R. R. DICKSON, 1953: Precipitation and vorticity. U.S. Navy, Bureau of Aeronautics, Project AROWA (TED-UNL-MA-501.13) TR Sept. 1953. (6.3–82.)

WOLLSCHLÄGER, H., 1959: Extreme Druck- und Temperaturabweichungen in der Troposphäre. MAB 8 (1).

WOODBRIDGE, D. D., 1959: Observed winds at high-level. BAMS 40 (11): 549–553.

— and W. C. DAVIS, 1958: Geomagnetic relationships to upper wind systems (a possible solar-weather relationship). U.S. Army Ballistic Missile Agency, Redstone Arsenal. Alabama, DV Technical Note 68–58, July 30. (11.2–91.)

WOOLCOCK, A. F., 1952: Flying the "D value" in Australia. AMMM 2: 16–21. (8.5–108.)

WULF, O. R., and L. DAVIS JR., 1952: On the efficiency of the engine driving the atmospheric circulation. JM 9 (2): 79–82. (3.9–97.)

— and M. W. HODGE, 1950: On the relation between variations of the earth's magnetic field and variations of the large-scale atmospheric circulation. JGR 55 (1): 1–20. (1.7–42.)

WURTELE, M. G., 1956: The vertical velocity pattern created by an isolated mountain. In: OSTIV Publication IV. and SAR 1957 (12).

YAMADA, H., and S. MATSUHASHI, 1951: On the winds aloft analysis by raob. TAT 5 (1): 20–31. (4 F–87.)

— — 1957: Seasonal variation of the jet stream over Japan. TAT 6 (1): 1–7. (9.7–164.)

— and S. NAKAMURA, 1954: Mean condition of wind aloft in winter over Japan. TAT 5 (4): 323–335. (7.2–196.)

YAMADA, H., S. NAKAMURA, S. MATSUHASHI, and K. FURUKAWA, 1954: Mean charts of upper air in winter over Japan. TAT 5 (4): 283–322. (8.4–244.)

YAMAMOTO, T., 1957: Long-term variations of the jet stream. Translation in: Canada, Defence Research Board. Translation 60 J, Feb. 1958. (11.2–187.)

— 1958: On the mechanism of the climatic changes in Japan. GMT 28 (4): 505–515. (10.11–238.)

YEH, T.-CH., 1949: On energy dispersion in the atmosphere. JM 6 (1): 1–16.

— 1950: The circulation of the high troposphere over China in the winter of 1945–46. T 2 (3): 173–183. (4 G–57.)

— 1951: On the maintenance of zonal circulation in the atmosphere. JM 8 (3): 146–150. (4 G–86.)

— 1957*a*: The mean meridional circulation and angular momentum balance in the atmosphere. Scientia Sinica, Peking, 6 (2): 339–346, and AMSP 26 (4): 304–321. (10.1–211.)

— 1957*b*: Maintenance of zonal circulation in the atmosphere. Acta Geophysica Polonia, Warschau 5 (2): 65–73. (9.5–149.)

— 1958: On the mechanism of maintenance of zonal circulation. GH 6 (3–4): 607–620. (11.1–205.)

— J. F. CARSON, and J. J. MARCIANO, 1951: On the relation between the circumpolar westerly current and rainfall over the Hawaiian Islands. MM 1 (3): 47–55. (4 G–87.)

— S.-Y. DAO, and M.-T. LI, 1959: The abrupt change of circulation over the Northern Hemisphere during June and October. RMV 249–267. (11.1–204.)

— and KOO-CHEN-CHAO, 1956: Vliianie Tibetskogo nagor'ia na atmosferniu tsirkuliatsiiu na pogodu Kitaia. (Influence of the Tibetan highland on atmospheric circulation and weather in China.) ISG Ser. Geog. No. 2: 127–138. (10.6–184.)

— and T.-SH. YANG, 1956: The annual variation of the atmospheric angular momentum of the Northern Hemisphere and the mechanism of its transfer. Scientia Sinica, Peking, 5 (3): 561–574. (9.2–193.)

YIN, M. T., 1949: A synoptic-aerologic study of the onset of the summer monsoon over India and Burma. JM 6: 393–400. (5 B–262.)

ZIEREP, J., 1958: Das Leewellenproblem der Meteorologie. Die Naturwissenschaften, Berlin 45 (9): 197–200. (10.7–108.)

ZISTLER, P., 1928: Die Windverhältnisse in der Stratosphäre über München. BPA 14: 65–74. (4 F–7.)

ZOBEL, R. F., 1958: The evaluation of winds at 200 mb from contour charts. MML 87 (1028): 44–49. (10.11–203.)

ZUBIAN, G. D., 1952: O planetarnoi vysotnoi frontal'noi zone. (On the planetary upper air frontal zone.) MG 7: 10–16. (5.1–156.)

— 1956: Planetarnaia frontal'naia zona v nizhnei stratosfere. (Planetary frontal zone in the lower stratosphere.) MG 9: 12–21. (10.10–240.)

— 1957: Issledovanie prostranstvennoi modeli fronta, okhvatyvaiushchei vsiu troposferu i nizhniuiu stratosferu. (Investigations on a spacial frontal model embracing the entire troposphere and the lower stratosphere.) MG No. 5: 3–11. (11.3–15.)

INDEX

Numbers in italics refer to main discussions.